THE PEARSON CUSTOM LIBRARY FOR
CHEMISTRY

Introductory Chemistry
CHM 1025
Miami Dade - Kendall

PEARSON

Cover Art: Courtesy of Photodisc, Age Fotostock America, Inc., and Photo Researchers, and Getty Images.

The information, illustrations, and/or software contained in this book, and regarding the above mentioned programs, are provided "as is," without warranty of any kind, express or implied, including without limitation any warranty concerning the accuracy, adequacy, or completeness of such information. Neither the publisher, the authors, nor the copyright holders shall be responsible for any claims attributable to errors, omissions, or other inaccuracies contained in this book. Nor shall they be liable for direct, indirect, special, incidental, or consequential damages arising out of the use of such information or material.

The authors and publisher believe that the lab experiments described in this publication, when conducted in conformity with the safety precautions described herein and according to the school's laboratory safety procedures, are reasonably safe for the students for whom this manual is directed. Nonetheless, many of the described experiments are accompanied by some degree of risk, including human error, the failure or misuse of laboratory or electrical equipment, mismeasurement, spills of chemicals, and exposure to sharp objects, heat, body fluids, blood or other biologics. The authors and publisher disclaim any liability arising from such risks in connections with any of the experiments contained in this manual. If students have questions or problems with materials, procedures, or instructions on any experiment, they should always ask their instructor for help before proceeding.

This special edition published in cooperation with Pearson Learning Solutions.

Please visit our website at *www.pearsonlearningsolutions.com.*

Attention bookstores: For permission to return unused stock, contact us at *pe-uscustomreturns@pearson.com.*

Pearson Learning Solutions, 501 Boylston Street, Suite 900, Boston, MA 02116
A Pearson Education Company
www.pearsoned.com
V092

ISBN 10: 1-269-29641-8
ISBN 13: 978-1-269-29641-0

Table of Contents

Measurement
and Problem Solving

Global Temperature
(meteorological stations)

Measurement and Problem Solving

"The important thing in science is not so much to obtain new facts as to discover new ways of thinking about them."

SIR WILLIAM LAWRENCE BRAGG (1890–1971)

1 Measuring Global Temperatures

A unit is a standard, agreed-on quantity by which other quantities are measured.

Global warming has become a household term. Average global temperatures affect things from agriculture to weather and ocean levels. The media report that global temperatures are increasing. These reports are based on the work of scientists who—after analyzing records from thousands of temperature-measuring stations around the world—concluded that average global temperatures have risen by 0.6 °C in the last century.

Notice how the scientists reported their results. What if they had reported a temperature increase of simply 0.6 without any *units*? The result would be unclear. Units are extremely important in reporting and working with scientific measurements, and they must always be included. Suppose that the scientists had included additional zeros in their results—for example, 0.60 °C or 0.600 °C—or that they had reported the number their computer displayed after averaging many measurements, something like 0.58759824 °C. Would these convey the same information? Not really. Scientists agree to a standard way of reporting measured quantities in which the number of reported digits reflects the precision in the measurement—more digits, more precision; fewer digits, less precision. Numbers are usually written so that the uncertainty is indicated by the last reported digit. For example, by reporting a temperature increase of 0.6 °C, the scientists mean 0.6 ± 0.1 °C ($\pm$ means plus or minus). The temperature rise could be as much as 0.7 °C or as little as 0.5 °C, but it is not 1.0 °C. The degree of certainty in this particular measurement is critical, influencing political decisions that directly affect people's lives.

◄ The graph in this image displays average global temperatures (relative to the mean) over the past 100 years.

2 Scientific Notation: Writing Large and Small Numbers

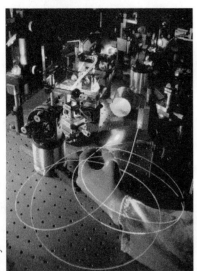

▲ Lasers such as this one can measure time periods as short as 1×10^{-15} s.

Science has constantly pushed the boundaries of the very large and the very small. We can, for example, now measure time periods as short as 0.000000000000001 seconds and distances as great as 14,000,000,000 light-years. Because the many zeros in these numbers are cumbersome to write, scientists use **scientific notation** to write them more compactly. In scientific notation, 0.000000000000001 is 1×10^{-15}, and 14,000,000,000 is 1.4×10^{10}. A number written in scientific notation consists of a **decimal part**, a number that is usually between 1 and 10, and an **exponential part**, 10 raised to an **exponent**, n.

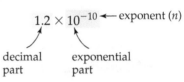

A positive exponent means 1 multiplied by 10 n times.

$$10^0 = 1$$
$$10^1 = 1 \times 10 = 10$$
$$10^2 = 1 \times 10 \times 10 = 100$$
$$10^3 = 1 \times 10 \times 10 \times 10 = 1000$$

A negative exponent $(-n)$ means 1 divided by 10 n times.

$$10^{-1} = \frac{1}{10} = 0.1$$
$$10^{-2} = \frac{1}{10 \times 10} = 0.01$$
$$10^{-3} = \frac{1}{10 \times 10 \times 10} = 0.001$$

To convert a number to scientific notation, move the decimal point (either to the left or to the right, as needed) to obtain a number between 1 and 10 and then multiply that number (the decimal part) by 10 raised to the power that reflects the movement of the decimal point. For example, to write 5983 in scientific notation, move the decimal point to the left three places to get 5.983 (a number between 1 and 10) and then multiply the decimal part by 1000 to compensate for moving the decimal point.

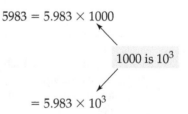

You can do this in one step by counting how many places you move the decimal point to obtain a number between 1 and 10 and then writing the decimal part multiplied by 10 raised to the number of places you moved the decimal point.

$$5983 = 5.983 \times 10^3$$
321

If the decimal point is moved to the left, as in the previous example, the exponent is positive. If the decimal is moved to the right, the exponent is negative.

$$0.00034 = 3.4 \times 10^{-4}$$

To express a number in scientific notation:

1. Move the decimal point to obtain a number between 1 and 10.
2. Write the result from Step 1 multiplied by 10 raised to the number of places you moved the decimal point.
   - The exponent is positive if you moved the decimal point to the left.
   - The exponent is negative if you moved the decimal point to the right.

EXAMPLE 1   Scientific Notation

The 2010 U.S. population was estimated to be 308,255,000 people. Express this number in scientific notation.

To obtain a number between 1 and 10, move the decimal point to the left 8 decimal places; the exponent is 8. Since you move the decimal point to the left, the sign of the exponent is positive.

SOLUTION

$$308,255,000 \text{ people} = 3.08255 \times 10^8 \text{ people}$$

▶**SKILLBUILDER 1 | Scientific Notation**

The total U.S national debt in 2010 was approximately $12,102,000,000,000. Express this number in scientific notation.

Note: The answers to all Skillbuilders appear at the end of the chapter.

▶**FOR MORE PRACTICE**   Example 18; Problems 31, 32.

EXAMPLE 2   Scientific Notation

The radius of a carbon atom is approximately 0.000000000070 m. Express this number in scientific notation.

To obtain a number between 1 and 10, move the decimal point to the right 11 decimal places; therefore, the exponent is 11. Since the decimal point was moved to the right, the sign of the exponent is negative.

SOLUTION

$$0.000000000070 \text{ m} = 7.0 \times 10^{-11} \text{ m}$$

▶**SKILLBUILDER 2 | Scientific Notation**

Express the number 0.000038 in scientific notation.

▶**FOR MORE PRACTICE**   Problems 33, 34.

CONCEPTUAL CHECKPOINT 1

The radius of a dust speck is 4.5×10^{-3} mm. What is the correct value of this number in decimal notation (i.e., express the number without using scientific notation)?

(a) 4500 mm

(b) 0.045 mm

(c) 0.0045 mm

(d) 0.00045 mm

Note: The answers to all Conceptual Checkpoints appear at the end of the chapter.

3 Significant Figures: Writing Numbers to Reflect Precision

▲ Since pennies come in whole numbers, 7 pennies means 7.00000... pennies. This is an exact number and therefore never limits significant figures in calculations.

▲ Our knowledge of the amount of gold in a 10-g gold bar depends on how precisely it was measured.

If we tell someone we have seven pennies, our meaning is clear. Pennies come in whole numbers, and seven pennies means seven whole pennies—it is unlikely that we would have 7.4 pennies. However, if we tell someone that we have a 10-g gold bar, the meaning is *unclear*. Our knowledge of the actual amount of gold in the bar depends on how precisely it was measured, which in turn depends on the scale or balance used to make the measurement. As we just learned, measured quantities are written to reflect the uncertainty in the measurement. If the gold measurement was rough, we could describe the bar as containing "10 g of gold." If a more precise balance was used, we could write the gold content as "10.0 g." We would report an even more precise measurement as "10.00 g."

Scientific numbers are reported so that every digit is certain except the last, which is estimated. For example, suppose a reported measurement is:

$$\textbf{45.87}2$$

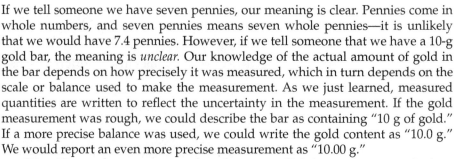

The first four digits are certain; the last digit is estimated.

Suppose that we weigh an object on a balance with marks at every 1 g, and the pointer is between the 1-g mark and the 2-g mark (▼ Figure 1) but much closer to the 1-g mark. To record the measurement, we mentally divide the space between the 1- and 2-g marks into 10 equal spaces and estimate the position of the pointer. In this case, the pointer indicates about 1.2 g. We then write the measurement as 1.2 g, indicating that we are sure of the "1" but have estimated the ".2."

If we measure the same object using a balance with marks every tenth of a gram, we need to write the result with more digits. For example, suppose that on this more precise balance the pointer is between the 1.2-g mark and the 1.3-g mark (▼ Figure 2). We again divide the space between the two marks into 10 equal spaces and estimate the third digit. In the case of the nut shown in Figure 2, we report 1.26 g. Digital balances usually have readouts that report the mass to the correct number of digits.

1.2 g

Balance has marks every one gram

▲ FIGURE 1 **Estimating tenths of a gram** This balance has markings every 1 g, so we estimate to the tenths place. To estimate between markings, mentally divide the space into 10 equal spaces and estimate the last digit. This reading is 1.2 g.

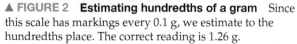

1.26 g

Balance has marks every tenth of a gram

▲ FIGURE 2 **Estimating hundredths of a gram** Since this scale has markings every 0.1 g, we estimate to the hundredths place. The correct reading is 1.26 g.

EXAMPLE 3 Reporting the Right Number of Digits

The bathroom scale in ▼ Figure 3 has markings at every 1 lb. Report the reading to the correct number of digits.

▲ FIGURE 3 **Reading a bathroom scale**

SOLUTION

Since the pointer is between the 147- and 148-lb markings, mentally divide the space between the markings into 10 equal spaces and estimate the next digit. In this case, the result should be reported as:

147.7 lb

What if you estimated a little differently and wrote 147.6 lb? In general, one unit of difference in the last digit is acceptable because the last digit is estimated and different people might estimate it slightly differently. However, if you wrote 147.2 lb, you would clearly be wrong.

▶**SKILLBUILDER 3** | **Reporting the Right Number of Digits**

A thermometer is used to measure the temperature of a backyard hot tub, and the reading is shown in ▼ Figure 4. Write the temperature reading to the correct number of digits.

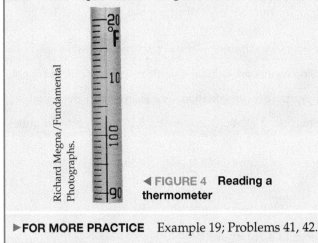

◀ FIGURE 4 **Reading a thermometer**

▶**FOR MORE PRACTICE** Example 19; Problems 41, 42.

COUNTING SIGNIFICANT FIGURES

The non–place-holding digits in a measurement are **significant figures** (or **significant digits**) and, as we have seen, represent the precision of a measured quantity. The greater the number of significant figures, the greater the precision of the measurement. We can determine the number of significant figures in a written number fairly easily; however, if the number contains zeros, we must distinguish between the zeros that are significant and those that simply mark the decimal place. In the number 0.002, for example, the leading zeros simply mark the decimal place; they *do not* add to the precision of the measurement. In the number 0.00200, the trailing zeros *do* add to the precision of the measurement.

To determine the number of significant figures in a number, follow these rules:

1. All nonzero digits are significant.

1.05   0.0110

2. Interior zeros (zeros between two numbers) are significant.

4.0208   50.1

3. Trailing zeros (zeros to the right of a nonzero number) that fall after a decimal point are significant.

5.10   3.00

7

4. Trailing zeros that fall before a decimal point are significant.

50.00   1700.24

5. Leading zeros (zeros to the left of the first nonzero number) are not significant. They only serve to locate the decimal point.

For example, the number 0.0005 has only one significant digit.

6. **Trailing** zeros at the end of a number, but before an *implied* decimal point, are ambiguous and should be avoided by using scientific notation.

For example, it is unclear if the number 350 has two or three significant figures. We can avoid confusion by writing the number as 3.5×10^2 to indicate two significant figures or as 3.50×10^2 to indicate three.

EXACT NUMBERS

Exact numbers have an unlimited number of significant figures. Exact numbers originate from three sources:

* Exact counting of discrete objects. For example, 3 atoms means 3.00000…atoms.
* *Defined quantities*, such as the number of centimeters in 1 m. Because 100 cm is defined as 1 m,

$$100 \, cm = 1 \, m \text{ means } 100.00000 \ldots cm = 1.0000000 \ldots m$$

Note that some conversion factors are defined quantities whereas others are not.

* Integral numbers that are part of an equation. For example, in the equation, $radius = \dfrac{diameter}{2}$, the number 2 is exact and therefore has an unlimited number of significant figures.

EXAMPLE 4   Determining the Number of Significant Figures in a Number

How many significant figures are in each number?

(a) 0.0035

(b) 1.080

(c) 2371

(d) 2.97×10^5

(e) 1 dozen = 12

(f) 100.00

(g) 100,000

	SOLUTION
The 3 and the 5 are significant (rule 1). The leading zeros only mark the decimal place and are not significant (rule 5).	(a) 0.0035 two significant figures
The interior zero is significant (rule 2), and the trailing zero is significant (rule 3). The 1 and the 8 are also significant (rule 1).	(b) 1.080 four significant figures
All digits are significant (rule 1).	(c) 2371 four significant figures
All digits in the decimal part are significant (rule 1).	(d) 2.97×10^5 three significant figures
Defined numbers are exact and therefore have an unlimited number of significant figures.	(e) 1 dozen = 12 unlimited significant figures
The 1 is significant (rule 1), and the trailing zeros before the decimal point are significant (rule 4). The trailing zeros after the decimal point are also significant (rule 3).	(f) 100.00 five significant figures
This number is ambiguous. Write as 1×10^5 to indicate one significant figure or as 1.00000×10^5 to indicate six significant figures.	(g) 100,000 ambiguous

▶**SKILLBUILDER 4** | **Determining the Number of Significant Figures in a Number**

How many significant figures are in each number?

(a) 58.31
(b) 0.00250
(c) 2.7×10^3
(d) $1\,cm = 0.01\,m$
(e) 0.500
(f) 2100

▶**FOR MORE PRACTICE** Example 20; Problems 43, 44, 45, 46, 47, 48.

 CONCEPTUAL CHECKPOINT 2

A researcher reports that the Spirit rover on the surface of Mars recently measured the temperature to be $-25.49\,°F$. What is the actual temperature?

(a) between $-25.490\,°F$ and $-25.499\,°F$
(b) between $-25.48\,°F$ and $-25.50\,°F$
(c) between $-25.4\,°F$ and $-25.5\,°F$
(d) exactly $-25.49\,°F$

4 Significant Figures in Calculations

When we use measured quantities in calculations, the results of the calculation must reflect the precision of the measured quantities. We should not lose or gain precision during mathematical operations.

MULTIPLICATION AND DIVISION

In multiplication or division, the result carries the same number of significant figures as the factor with the fewest significant figures.

For example:

$$\underset{\text{(3 sig. figures)}}{5.02} \times \underset{\text{(5 sig. figures)}}{89.665} \times \underset{\text{(2 sig. figures)}}{0.10} = 45.0118 = \underset{\text{(2 sig. figures)}}{45}$$

The intermediate result (in blue) is rounded to two significant figures to reflect the least precisely known factor (0.10), which has two significant figures.

In division, we follow the same rule.

$$\underset{\text{(4 sig. figures)}}{5.892} \div \underset{\text{(3 sig. figures)}}{6.10} = 0.96590 = \underset{\text{(3 sig. figures)}}{0.966}$$

The intermediate result (in blue) is rounded to three significant figures to reflect the least precisely known factor (6.10), which has three significant figures.

ROUNDING

When we round to the correct number of significant figures:

> we round down if the last (or leftmost) digit dropped is 4 or less;
> we round up if the last (or leftmost) digit dropped is 5 or more.

CHEMISTRY IN THE MEDIA

The COBE Satellite and Very Precise Measurements That Illuminate Our Cosmic Past

Since the earliest times, humans have wondered about the origins of our planet. Science has slowly probed this question and has developed theories for how the universe and the Earth began. The most accepted theory today about the origin of the universe is the Big Bang theory. According to the Big Bang theory, the universe began in a tremendous expansion about 13.7 billion years ago and has been expanding ever since. A measurable prediction of this theory is the presence of a remnant "background radiation" from the expansion of the universe. That remnant is characteristic of the current temperature of the universe. When the Big Bang occurred, the temperature of the universe was very hot and the associated radiation very bright. Today, 13.7 billion years later, the temperature of the universe is very cold and the background radiation very faint.

In the early 1960s, Robert H. Dicke, P. J. E. Peebles, and their coworkers at Princeton University began to build a device to measure this background radiation and thus take a direct look into the cosmological past and provide evidence for the Big Bang theory. At about the same time, quite by accident, Arno Penzias and Robert Wilson of Bell Telephone Laboratories measured excess radio noise on one of their communications satellites. As it turned out, this noise was the background radiation that the Princeton scientists were looking for. The two groups published papers together in 1965 reporting their findings along with the corresponding current temperature of the universe, about 3 degrees above absolute zero, or 3 K. Know that 3 K is an extremely low temperature (460 degrees below zero on the Fahrenheit scale).

In 1989, the Cosmic Background Explorer (COBE) satellite was developed by NASA's Goddard Space Flight Center to measure the background radiation more precisely. The COBE satellite determined that the background radiation corresponded to a universe with a temperature of 2.735 K. (Notice the difference in significant figures from the previous measurement.) It went on to measure tiny fluctuations in the background radiation that amount to temperature differences of 1 part in 100,000. These fluctuations, though small, are an important prediction of the Big Bang theory. Scientists announced that the COBE satellite had produced the strongest evidence yet for the Big Bang theory of the creation of the universe. This is the way that science works. Measurement, and precision in measurement, are important to understanding the world—so important that we dedicate most of this chapter just to the concept of measurement.

CAN YOU ANSWER THIS? *How many significant figures are there in each of the preceding temperature measurements (3 K, 2.735 K)?*

NASA.

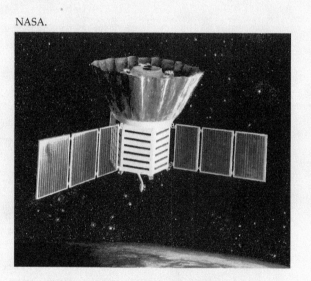

▲ The COBE Satellite, launched in 1989 to measure background radiation. Background radiation is a remnant of the Big Bang—the expansion that is believed to have formed the universe.

Consider rounding each of these numbers to two significant figures.

2.33 rounds to 2.3
2.37 rounds to 2.4
2.34 rounds to 2.3
2.35 rounds to 2.4

We use only the *last (or leftmost) digit being dropped* to decide in which direction to round—we ignore all digits to the right of it. For example, to round 2.349 to two significant figures, only the 4 in the hundredths place (2.349) determines which direction to round—the 9 is irrelevant.

2.349 rounds to 2.3

For calculations involving multiple steps, we round only the final answer—we do not round off between steps. This prevents small rounding errors from affecting the final answer.

EXAMPLE 5 **Significant Figures in Multiplication and Division**

Perform each calculation to the correct number of significant figures.

(a) $1.01 \times 0.12 \times 53.51 \div 96$
(b) $56.55 \times 0.920 \div 34.2585$

Round the intermediate result (in blue) to two significant figures to reflect the two significant figures in the least precisely known quantities (0.12 and 96).	**SOLUTION** **(a)** $1.01 \times 0.12 \times 53.51 \div 96 = 0.067556 = 0.068$
Round the intermediate result (in blue) to three significant figures to reflect the three significant figures in the least precisely known quantity (0.920).	**(b)** $56.55 \times 0.920 \div 34.2585 = 1.51863 = 1.52$

▶**SKILLBUILDER 5 | Significant Figures in Multiplication and Division**

Perform each calculation to the correct number of significant figures.

(a) $1.10 \times 0.512 \times 1.301 \times 0.005 \div 3.4$

(b) $4.562 \times 3.99870 \div 89.5$

▶**FOR MORE PRACTICE** Examples 21, 22; Problems 57, 58, 59, 60.

ADDITION AND SUBTRACTION

In addition or subtraction, the result carries the same number of decimal places as the quantity carrying the fewest decimal places.

For example:

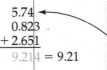

It is sometimes helpful to draw a vertical line directly to the right of the number with the fewest decimal places. The line shows the number of decimal places that should be in the answer.

We round the intermediate answer (in blue) to two decimal places because the quantity with the fewest decimal places (5.74) has two decimal places.

For subtraction, we follow the same rule. For example:

$$\begin{array}{r} 4.8| \\ -3.9|65 \\ \hline 0.8|35 = 0.8 \end{array}$$

We round the intermediate answer (in blue) to one decimal place because the quantity with the fewest decimal places (4.8) has one decimal place. Remember: *For multiplication and division, the quantity with the fewest **significant figures** determines the number of significant figures in the answer. For addition and subtraction, the quantity with the fewest **decimal places** determines the number of decimal places in* *the answer.* In multiplication and division we focus on significant figures, but in addition and subtraction we focus on decimal places. When a problem involves addition and subtraction, the answer may have a different number of significant figures than the initial quantities. For example:

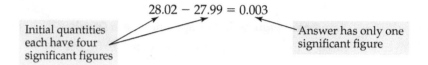

$$28.02 - 27.99 = 0.003$$

Initial quantities each have four significant figures

Answer has only one significant figure

The answer has only one significant figure, even though the initial quantities each had four significant figures.

EXAMPLE 6   Significant Figures in Addition and Subtraction

Perform the calculations to the correct number of significant figures.

(a)
```
     0.987
  +125.1
   −1.22
```

(b)
```
    0.765
   −3.449
   −5.98
```

Round the intermediate answer (in blue) to one decimal place to reflect the quantity with the fewest decimal places (125.1). Notice that 125.1 is not the quantity with the fewest significant figures—it has four while the other quantities only have three—but because it has the fewest decimal places, it determines the number of decimal places in the answer.	**SOLUTION** **(a)** $\quad 0.987$ $\quad\;+125.1$ $\quad\;\;-1.22$ $\quad\;\;124.867 = 124.9$
Round the intermediate answer (in blue) to two decimal places to reflect the quantity with the fewest decimal places (5.98).	**(b)** $\quad 0.765$ $\quad\;-3.449$ $\quad\;-5.98$ $\quad\;-8.664 = -8.66$

▶**SKILLBUILDER 6 | Significant Figures in Addition and Subtraction**

Perform the calculations to the correct number of significant figures.

(a)
```
    2.18
  +5.621
  +1.5870
  −1.8
```

(b)
```
    7.876
   −0.56
  +123.792
```

▶**FOR MORE PRACTICE**   Example 23; Problems 61, 62, 63, 64.

CALCULATIONS INVOLVING BOTH MULTIPLICATION/DIVISION AND ADDITION/SUBTRACTION

In calculations involving both multiplication/division and addition/subtraction, we do the steps in parentheses first; determine the correct number of significant figures in the intermediate answer; then do the remaining steps.

For example:

$$3.489 \times (5.67 - 2.3)$$

We complete the subtraction step first.

$$5.67 - 2.3 = 3.37$$

We use the subtraction rule to determine that the intermediate answer (3.37) has only one significant decimal place. To avoid small errors, it is best not to round at this point; instead, we underline the least significant figure as a reminder.

$$= 3.489 \times 3.\underline{3}7$$

We then do the multiplication step.

$$3.489 \times 3.\underline{3}7 = 11.758 = 12$$

We use the multiplication rule to determine that the intermediate answer (11.758) rounds to two significant figures (12) because it is limited by the two significant figures in $3.\underline{3}7$.

EXAMPLE 7 **Significant Figures in Calculations Involving Both Multiplication/Division and Addition/Subtraction**

Perform the calculations to the correct number of significant figures.

(a) $6.78 \times 5.903 \times (5.489 - 5.01)$
(b) $19.667 - (5.4 \times 0.916)$

	SOLUTION
Do the step in parentheses first. Use the subtraction rule to mark 0.479 to two decimal places since 5.01, the number in the parentheses with the least number of decimal places, has two.	**(a)** $6.78 \times 5.903 \times (5.489 - 5.01)$ $= 6.78 \times 5.903 \times (0.479)$
Then perform the multiplication and round the answer to two significant figures since the number with the least number of significant figures has two.	$= 6.78 \times 5.903 \times 0.4\underline{7}9$ $6.78 \times 5.903 \times 0.4\underline{7}90 = 19.1707$ $= 19$
Do the step in parentheses first. The number with the least number of significant figures within the parentheses (5.4) has two, so mark the answer to two significant figures.	**(b)** $19.667 - (5.4 \times 0.916)$ $= 19.667 - (4.9464)$
Then perform the subtraction and round the answer to one decimal place since the number with the least number of decimal places has one.	$= 19.667 - 4.9\underline{4}64$ $19.667 - 4.9\underline{4}64 = 14.7206$ $= 14.7$

▶**SKILLBUILDER 7** | **Significant Figures in Calculations Involving Both Multiplication/Division and Addition/Subtraction**

Perform each calculation to the correct number of significant figures.

(a) $3.897 \times (782.3 - 451.88)$

(b) $(4.58 \div 1.239) - 0.578$

▶**FOR MORE PRACTICE** Example 24; Problems 65, 66, 67, 68.

✔ **CONCEPTUAL CHECKPOINT 3**

Which calculation would have its result reported to the *greater* number of significant figures?

(a) 3 + (15/12)

(b) (3 + 15)/12

5 The Basic Units of Measurement

By themselves, numbers have limited meaning. Read this sentence: When my son was 7 he walked 3, and when he was 4 he threw his baseball 8 and said his school was 5 away. The sentence is confusing because we don't know what the numbers mean—the **units** are missing. The meaning becomes clear, however, when we add the missing units to the numbers: When my son was 7 *months old* he walked 3 *steps*, and when he was 4 *years old* he threw his baseball 8 *feet* and said his school was 5 *minutes* away. Units make all the difference. In chemistry, units are critical. Never write a number by itself; always use its associated units—otherwise your work will be as confusing as the initial sentence.

The two most common unit systems are the **English system,** used in the United States, and the **metric system,** used in most of the rest of the world. The English system uses units such as inches, yards, and pounds, while the metric system uses centimeters, meters, and kilograms. The most convenient system for science measurements is based on the metric system and is called the **International System** of units or **SI units.** SI units are a set of standard units agreed on by scientists throughout the world.

The abbreviation *SI* comes from the French *le Système International.*

THE STANDARD UNITS

TABLE 1 Important SI Standard Units

Quantity	Unit	Symbol
Length	meter	m
Mass	kilogram	kg
Time	second	s
Temperature	kelvin	K

Table 1 lists the standard units in the SI system. They include the **meter (m)** as the standard unit of length; the **kilogram (kg)** as the standard unit of mass; and the **second (s)** as the standard unit of time. Each of these standard units is precisely defined. The meter is defined as the distance light travels in a certain period of

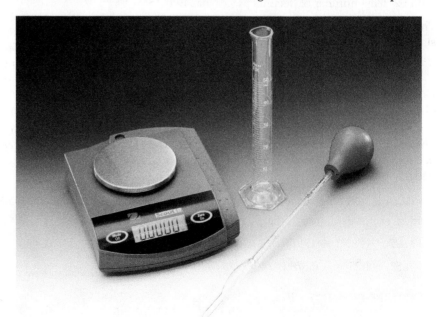

▶ Science uses instruments to make measurements. Every instrument is calibrated in a particular unit without which the measurements would be meaningless.

Richard Megna/Fundamental Photographs.

14

National Institute of Standards and Technology.

Bureau International des Poids et Mesures.

National Institute of Standards and Technology.

▲ FIGURE 5 **The standard of length** The definition of a meter, established by international agreement in 1983, is the distance that light travels in vacuum in 1/299,792,458 s. Question: Why is such a precise standard necessary?

▲ FIGURE 6 **The standard of mass** A duplicate of the international standard kilogram, called kilogram 20, is kept at the National Institute of Standards and Technology near Washington, DC.

▲ FIGURE 7 **The standard of time** The second is defined, using an atomic clock, as the duration of 9,192,631,770 periods of the radiation emitted from a certain transition in a cesium-133 atom.

A nickel (5 cents) has a mass of about 5 grams.

Richard Megna/Fundamental Photographs.

time: 1/299,792,458 s (▲ Figure 5). (The speed of light is $3.0 \times 10^8 \, \text{m/s}$.) The kilogram is defined as the mass of a block of metal kept at the International Bureau of Weights and Measures at Sèvres, France (▲ Figure 6). The second is defined using an atomic standard (▲ Figure 7).

Most people are familiar with the SI standard unit of time, the second. However, if you live in the United States, you may be less familiar with the meter and the kilogram. The meter is slightly longer than a yard (a yard is 36 in. while a meter is 39.37 in.). A 100-yd football field measures only 91.4 m.

The kilogram is a measure of mass, which is different from weight. The **mass** of an object is a measure of the quantity of matter within it, whereas the weight of an object is a measure of the gravitational pull on that matter. Consequently, weight depends on gravity while mass does not. If you were to weigh yourself on Mars, for example, the lower gravity would pull you toward the scale less than Earth's gravity would, resulting in a lower weight. A 150-lb person on Earth weighs only 57 lb on Mars. However, the person's mass, the quantity of matter in his or her body, remains the same. A kilogram of mass is the equivalent of 2.205 lb of weight on Earth, so if we express mass in kilograms, a 150-lb person on Earth has a mass of approximately 68 kg. A second common unit of mass is the gram (g), defined as follows:

$$1000 \, \text{g} = 10^3 \, \text{g} = 1 \, \text{kg}$$

PREFIX MULTIPLIERS

The SI system employs **prefix multipliers** (Table 2) with the standard units. These multipliers change the value of the unit by powers of 10. For example, the kilometer (km) has the prefix *kilo-*, meaning 1000 or 10^3. Therefore:

$$1 \, \text{km} = 1000 \, \text{m} = 10^3 \, \text{m}$$

Similarly, the millisecond (ms) has the prefix *milli-*, meaning 0.001 or 10^{-3}.

$$1 \, \text{ms} = 0.001 \, \text{s} = 10^{-3} \, \text{s}$$

▲ The diameter of a quarter is about 2.4 cm. **Question:** Why would you *not* use meters to make this measurement?

TABLE 2 SI Prefix Multipliers

Prefix	Symbol	Multiplier	
tera-	T	1,000,000,000,000	(10^{12})
giga-	G	1,000,000,000	(10^{9})
mega-	M	1,000,000	(10^{6})
kilo-	k	1,000	(10^{3})
deci-	d	0.1	(10^{-1})
centi-	c	0.01	(10^{-2})
milli-	m	0.001	(10^{-3})
micro-	μ	0.000001	(10^{-6})
nano-	n	0.000000001	(10^{-9})
pico-	p	0.000000000001	(10^{-12})
femto-	f	0.000000000000001	(10^{-15})

The prefix multipliers allow us to express a wide range of measurements in units that are similar in size to the quantity we are measuring. You should choose the prefix multiplier that is most convenient for a particular measurement. For example, to measure the diameter of a quarter, use centimeters because a quarter has a diameter of about 2.4 cm. A centimeter is a common metric unit and is about equivalent to the width of a pinky finger (2.54 cm = 1 in.). The millimeter could also work to express the diameter of the quarter; then the quarter would measure 24 mm. The kilometer, however, would not work as well since, in that unit, the quarter's diameter is 0.000024 km. Pick a unit similar in size to (or smaller than) the quantity you are measuring. Consider expressing the length of a short chemical bond, about 1.2×10^{-10} m. Which prefix multiplier should you use? The most convenient one is probably the picometer (pico = 10^{-12}). Chemical bonds measure about 120 pm.

TABLE 3 Some Common Units and Their Equivalents

Length

1 kilometer (km) = 0.6214 mile (mi)

1 meter (m) = 39.37 inches (in.)
= 1.094 yards (yd)

1 foot (ft) = 30.48 centimeters (cm)

1 inch (in.) = 2.54 centimeters (cm) (exact)

Mass

1 kilogram (kg) = 2.205 pounds (lb)

1 pound (lb) = 453.59 grams (g)

1 ounce (oz) = 28.35 grams (g)

Volume

1 liter (L) = 1000 milliliters (mL)
= 1000 cubic centimeters (cm³)

1 liter (L) = 1.057 quarts (qt)

1 U.S. gallon (gal) = 3.785 liters (L)

CONCEPTUAL CHECKPOINT 4

What would be the most convenient unit to express the dimensions of a polio virus, which is about 2.8×10^{-8} m in diameter?
(a) Mm
(b) mm
(c) μm
(d) nm

DERIVED UNITS

A derived unit is formed from other units. For example, many units of **volume,** a measure of space, are derived units. Any unit of length, when cubed (raised to the third power), becomes a unit of volume. Therefore, cubic meters (m³), cubic centimeters (cm³), and cubic millimeters (mm³) are all units of volume. In these units, a three-bedroom house has a volume of about 630 m³, a can of soda pop has a volume of about 350 cm³, and a rice grain has a volume of about 3 mm³. We also use the **liter (L)** and milliliter (mL) to express volume (although these are not derived units). A gallon is equal to 3.785 L. A milliliter is equivalent to 1 cm³. Table 3 lists some common units and their equivalents.

6 Problem Solving and Unit Conversions

Problem solving is one of the most important skills you will acquire in this course. Not only will this skill help you succeed in chemistry, but it will help you to learn how to think critically, which is important in every area of knowledge. My daughter, a freshman in high school, recently came to me for help on an algebra problem. The statement of the problem went something like this:

> Sam and Sara live 11 miles apart. Sam leaves his house traveling at 6 miles per hour toward Sara's house. Sara leaves her house traveling at 3 miles per hour toward Sam's house. How much time until Sam and Sara meet?

Solving the problem requires setting up the equation $11 - 6t = 3t$. Although my daughter could solve this equation for t quite easily, getting to the equation from the problem statement was another matter—that process requires *critical thinking*. You can't succeed in chemistry—or in life, really—without developing critical thinking skills. Learning how to solve chemical problems will help you develop these kinds of skills.

Although no simple formula applies to every problem, you can learn problem-solving strategies and begin to develop some chemical intuition. Many of the problems you will solve in this course can be thought of as *unit conversion problems*, where you are given one or more quantities and asked to convert them into different units. Other problems require the use of *specific equations* to get to the information you are trying to find. In the sections that follow, we examine strategies to help you solve both of these types of problems. Of course, many problems contain both conversions and equations, requiring the combination of these strategies, and some problems may require an altogether different approach but the basic tools you learn here can be applied to those problems as well.

CONVERTING BETWEEN UNITS

Using units as a guide to solving problems is called dimensional analysis.

Units are critical in calculations. Knowing how to work with and manipulate units in calculations is a very important part of problem solving. In calculations, units help determine correctness. Units should always be included in calculations, and we can think of many calculations as converting from one unit to another. Units are multiplied, divided, and canceled like any other algebraic quantity.

Remember:

1. Always write every number with its associated unit. Never ignore units; they are critical.

2. Always include units in your calculations, dividing them and multiplying them as if they were algebraic quantities. Do not let units magically appear or disappear in calculations. Units must flow logically from beginning to end.

Consider converting 17.6 in. to centimeters. We know from Table 3 that 1 in. = 2.54 cm. To determine how many centimeters are in 17.6 in., we perform the conversion:

$$17.6 \text{ in.} \times \frac{2.54 \text{ cm}}{1 \text{ in.}} = 44.7 \text{ cm}$$

The unit *in.* cancels and we are left with *cm* as our final unit. The quantity $\frac{2.54 \text{ cm}}{1 \text{ in.}}$ is a **conversion factor** between *in.* and *cm*—it is a quotient with *cm* on top and *in.* on bottom.

For most conversion problems, we are given a quantity in some unit and asked to convert the quantity to another unit. These calculations take the form:

information given × conversion factor(s) = information sought

$$\text{given unit} \times \frac{\text{desired unit}}{\text{given unit}} = \text{desired unit}$$

Conversion factors are constructed from any two quantities known to be equivalent. In our example, 2.54 cm = 1 in., so we construct the conversion factor by dividing both sides of the equality by 1 in. and canceling the units.

$$2.54 \text{ cm} = 1 \text{ in.}$$

$$\frac{2.54 \text{ cm}}{1 \text{ in.}} = \frac{1 \text{ in.}}{1 \text{ in.}}$$

$$\frac{2.54 \text{ cm}}{1 \text{ in.}} = 1$$

The quantity $\dfrac{2.54 \text{ cm}}{1 \text{ in.}}$ is equal to 1 and can be used to convert between inches and centimeters.

What if we want to perform the conversion the other way, from centimeters to inches? If we try to use the same conversion factor, the units do not cancel correctly.

$$44.7 \text{ cm} \times \frac{2.54 \text{ cm}}{1 \text{ in.}} = \frac{114 \text{ cm}^2}{\text{in.}}$$

The units in the answer, as well as the value of the answer, are incorrect. The unit cm²/in. is not correct, and, based on our knowledge that centimeters are smaller than inches, we know that 44.7 cm cannot be equivalent to 114 in. In solving problems, always check if the final units are correct, and consider whether or not the magnitude of the answer makes sense. In this case, our mistake was in how we used the conversion factor. We must invert it.

$$44.7 \text{ cm} \times \frac{1 \text{ in.}}{2.54 \text{ cm}} = 17.6 \text{ in.}$$

Conversion factors can be inverted because they are equal to 1 and the inverse of 1 is 1.

$$\frac{1}{1} = 1$$

Therefore,

$$\frac{2.54 \text{ cm}}{1 \text{ in.}} = 1 = \frac{1 \text{ in.}}{2.54 \text{ cm}}$$

We can diagram conversions using a **solution map.** A solution map is a visual outline that shows the strategic route required to solve a problem. For unit conversion, the solution map focuses on units and how to convert from one unit to another. The solution map for converting from inches to centimeters is:

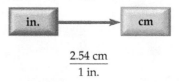

$$\frac{2.54 \text{ cm}}{1 \text{ in.}}$$

The solution map for converting from centimeters to inches is:

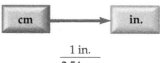

$$\frac{1 \text{ in.}}{2.54 \text{ cm}}$$

Each arrow in a solution map for a unit conversion has an associated conversion factor with the units of the previous step in the denominator and the units of the following step in the numerator. For one-step problems such as these, the solution map is only moderately helpful, but for multistep problems, it becomes a powerful way to develop a problem-solving strategy. In the section that follows, you will learn how to incorporate solution maps into an overall problem-solving strategy.

GENERAL PROBLEM-SOLVING STRATEGY

In this text, we use a standard problem-solving procedure that can be adapted to many of the problems encountered in chemistry and beyond. Solving any problem essentially requires you to assess the information given in the problem and devise a way to get to the information asked for. In other words, you need to

- Identify the starting point (the *given* information).
- Identify the end point (what you must *find*).
- Devise a way to get from the starting point to the end point using what is given as well as what you already know or can look up. You can use a *solution map* to diagram the steps required to get from the starting point to the end point.

In graphic form, we can represent this progression as

$$\textbf{Given} \longrightarrow \textbf{Solution Map} \longrightarrow \textbf{Find}$$

One of the main difficulties beginning students have when trying to solve problems in general chemistry is not knowing where to start. Although no problem-solving procedure is applicable to all problems, the following four-step procedure can be helpful in working through many of the numerical problems you will encounter in this text.

1. **Sort.** Begin by sorting the information in the problem. *Given* information is the basic data provided by the problem—often one or more numbers with their associated units. The given information is the starting point for the problem. *Find* indicates what the problem is asking you to find (the end point of the problem).

2. **Strategize.** This is usually the hardest part of solving a problem. In this step, you must create a solution map—the series of steps that will get you from the given information to the information you are trying to find. You have already seen solution maps for simple unit conversion problems. Each arrow in a solution map represents a computational step. On the left side of the arrow is the quantity (or quantities) you had before the step; on the right side of the arrow is the quantity (or quantities) you will have after the step; and below the arrow is the information you need to get from one to the other—the relationship between the quantities.

   Often such relationships will take the form of conversion factors or equations. These may be given in the problem, in which case you will have written them down under "Given" in Step 1. Usually, however, you will need other information—which may include physical constants, formulas, or conversion factors—to help get you from what you are given to what you must find. You may recall this information from what you have learned or you can look it up in the chapters or tables within the book.

   In some cases, you may get stuck at the strategize step. If you cannot figure out how to get from the given information to the information you are asked to find, you might try working backwards. For example, you may want to look at the units of the quantity you are trying to find and look for conversion factors to get to the units of the given quantity. You may even try a combination of strategies; work forward, backward, or some of both. If you persist, you will develop a strategy to solve the problem.

3. **Solve.** This is the easiest part of solving a problem. Once you set up the problem properly and devise a solution map, you follow the map to solve the problem. Carry out mathematical operations (paying attention to the rules for significant figures in calculations) and cancel units as needed.

4. **Check.** This is the step most often overlooked by beginning students. Experienced problem solvers always ask, Does this answer make physical sense? Are the units correct? Is the number of significant figures correct? When solving multistep problems, errors easily creep into the solution. You can catch most of these errors by simply checking the answer. For example, suppose you are calculating the number of atoms in a gold coin and end up with an answer of 1.1×10^{-6} atoms. Could the gold coin really be composed of one-millionth of one atom?

In Examples 8 and 9, you will find this problem-solving procedure applied to unit conversion problems. The procedure is summarized in the left column, and two examples of applying the procedure are shown in the middle and right columns. This three-column format is used in selected examples in this text. It allows you to see how a particular procedure can be applied to two different problems. Work through one problem first (from top to bottom) and then examine how the same procedure is applied to the other problem. Recognizing the commonalities and differences between problems is a key part of problem solving.

PROBLEM-SOLVING PROCEDURE	EXAMPLE 8 Unit Conversion Convert 7.8 km to miles.	EXAMPLE 9 Unit Conversion Convert 0.825 m to millimeters.
SORT Begin by sorting the information in the problem into *given* and *find*.	GIVEN: 7.8 km FIND: mi	GIVEN: 0.825 m FIND: mm
STRATEGIZE Draw a *solution map* for the problem. Begin with the *given* quantity and symbolize each step with an arrow. Below the arrow, write the conversion factor for that step. The solution map ends at the *find* quantity. (In these examples, the relationships used in the conversions are below the solution map.)	SOLUTION MAP $\boxed{\text{km}} \longrightarrow \boxed{\text{mi}}$ $\dfrac{0.6214 \text{ mi}}{1 \text{ km}}$ RELATIONSHIPS USED $1 \text{ km} = 0.6214 \text{ mi}$ (This conversion factor is from Table 3.)	SOLUTION MAP $\boxed{\text{m}} \longrightarrow \boxed{\text{mm}}$ $\dfrac{1 \text{ mm}}{10^{-3} \text{ m}}$ RELATIONSHIPS USED $1 \text{ mm} = 10^{-3} \text{ m}$ (This conversion factor is from Table 2.)
SOLVE Follow the *solution map* to solve the problem. Begin with the *given* quantity and its units. Multiply by the appropriate conversion factor, canceling units to arrive at the *find* quantity. Round the answer to the correct number of significant figures. (If possible, obtain conversion factors to enough significant figures so that they do not limit the number of significant figures in the answer.)	SOLUTION $7.8 \text{ km} \times \dfrac{0.6214 \text{ mi}}{1 \text{ km}} = 4.84692 \text{ mi}$ $4.84692 \text{ mi} = 4.8 \text{ mi}$ Round the answer to two significant figures, since the quantity given has two significant figures.	SOLUTION $0.825 \text{ m} \times \dfrac{1 \text{ mm}}{10^{-3} \text{ m}} = 825 \text{ mm}$ $825 \text{ mm} = 825 \text{ mm}$ Leave the answer with three significant figures, since the quantity given has three significant figures and the conversion factor is a definition and therefore does not limit the number of significant figures in the answer.

CHECK

Check your answer. Are the units correct? Does the answer make physical sense?

The units, mi, are correct. The magnitude of the answer is reasonable. A mile is longer than a kilometer, so the value in miles should be smaller than the value in kilometers.

▶**SKILLBUILDER 8**
Unit Conversion

Convert 56.0 cm to inches.

▶**FOR MORE PRACTICE** Example 25; Problems 73, 74, 75, 76.

The units, mm, are correct and the magnitude is reasonable. A millimeter is shorter than a meter, so the value in millimeters should be larger than the value in meters.

▶**SKILLBUILDER 9**
Unit Conversion

Convert 5678 m to kilometers.

▶**FOR MORE PRACTICE** Problems 69, 70, 71, 72.

✓ **CONCEPTUAL CHECKPOINT 5**

Which conversion factor would you use to convert a distance in meters to kilometers?

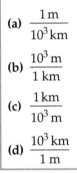

(a) $\dfrac{1\,\text{m}}{10^3\,\text{km}}$

(b) $\dfrac{10^3\,\text{m}}{1\,\text{km}}$

(c) $\dfrac{1\,\text{km}}{10^3\,\text{m}}$

(d) $\dfrac{10^3\,\text{km}}{1\,\text{m}}$

---

7 Solving Multistep Unit Conversion Problems

When solving multistep unit conversion problems, we follow the preceding procedure, but we add more steps to the solution map. Each step in the solution map should have a conversion factor with the units of the previous step in the denominator and the units of the following step in the numerator. For example, suppose we want to convert 194 cm to feet. The solution map begins with cm, and we use the relationship 2.54 cm = 1 in to convert to in. We then use the relationship 12 in. = 1 ft to convert to ft.

SOLUTION MAP

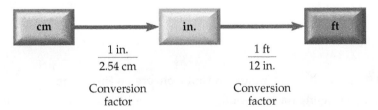

Conversion
factor

Conversion
factor

Once the solution map is complete, we follow it to solve the problem.

SOLUTION

$$194 \text{ cm} \times \frac{1 \text{ in.}}{2.54 \text{ cm}} \times \frac{1 \text{ ft}}{12 \text{ in.}} = 6.3648 \text{ ft}$$

21

Since 1 foot is defined as 12 in., it does not limit significant figures.

We then round to the correct number of significant figures—in this case, three (from 194 cm, which has three significant figures).

$$6.3648 \text{ ft} = 6.36 \text{ ft}$$

Finally, we check the answer. The units of the answer, feet, are the correct ones, and the magnitude seems about right. Since a foot is larger than a centimeter, it is reasonable that the value in feet is smaller than the value in centimeters.

EXAMPLE 10 Solving Multistep Unit Conversion Problems

A recipe for making creamy pasta sauce calls for 0.75 L of cream. Your measuring cup measures only in cups. How many cups of cream should you use? (4 cups = 1 quart)

SORT	**GIVEN:** 0.75 L
Begin by sorting the information in the problem into given and find.	**FIND:** cups

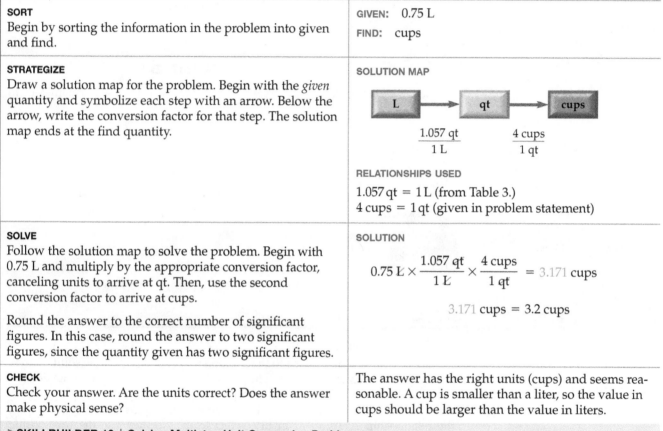

STRATEGIZE	**SOLUTION MAP**
Draw a solution map for the problem. Begin with the *given* quantity and symbolize each step with an arrow. Below the arrow, write the conversion factor for that step. The solution map ends at the find quantity.	**RELATIONSHIPS USED** 1.057 qt = 1 L (from Table 3.) 4 cups = 1 qt (given in problem statement)

SOLVE	**SOLUTION**
Follow the solution map to solve the problem. Begin with 0.75 L and multiply by the appropriate conversion factor, canceling units to arrive at qt. Then, use the second conversion factor to arrive at cups. Round the answer to the correct number of significant figures. In this case, round the answer to two significant figures, since the quantity given has two significant figures.	$$0.75 \text{ L} \times \frac{1.057 \text{ qt}}{1 \text{ L}} \times \frac{4 \text{ cups}}{1 \text{ qt}} = 3.171 \text{ cups}$$ $$3.171 \text{ cups} = 3.2 \text{ cups}$$

CHECK	
Check your answer. Are the units correct? Does the answer make physical sense?	The answer has the right units (cups) and seems reasonable. A cup is smaller than a liter, so the value in cups should be larger than the value in liters.

▶**SKILLBUILDER 10** | **Solving Multistep Unit Conversion Problems**

A recipe calls for 1.2 cups of oil. How many liters of oil is this?

▶**FOR MORE PRACTICE** Problems 85, 86.

EXAMPLE 11 Solving Multistep Unit Conversion Problems

One lap of a running track measures 255 m. To run 10.0 km, how many laps should you run?

SORT	**GIVEN:** 10.0 km
Begin by sorting the information in the problem into given and find. You are given a distance in km and asked to find the distance in laps. You are also given the quantity 255 m per lap, which is a conversion factor between m and laps.	255 m = 1 lap **FIND:** number of laps

STRATEGIZE

Build the solution map beginning with km and ending at laps. Focus on the units.

SOLUTION MAP

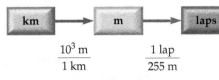

$$\frac{10^3 \text{ m}}{1 \text{ km}} \qquad \frac{1 \text{ lap}}{255 \text{ m}}$$

RELATIONSHIPS USED

$1\,\text{km} = 10^3\,\text{m}$ (from Table 2)
$1\,\text{lap} = 255\,\text{m}$ (given in problem)

SOLVE

Follow the solution map to solve the problem. Begin with 10.0 km and multiply by the appropriate conversion factor, canceling units to arrive at m. Then, use the second conversion factor to arrive at laps. Round the intermediate answer (in blue) to three significant figures because it is limited by the three significant figures in the given quantity, 10.0 km.

SOLUTION

$$10.0\,\cancel{\text{km}} \times \frac{10^3\,\cancel{\text{m}}}{1\,\cancel{\text{km}}} \times \frac{1\,\text{lap}}{255\,\cancel{\text{m}}} = 39.216\,\text{laps} = 39.2\,\text{laps}$$

CHECK

Check your answer. Are the units correct? Does the answer make physical sense?

The units of the answer are correct, and the value of the answer makes sense: If a lap is 255 m, there are about 4 laps to each km (1000 m), so it seems reasonable that you would have to run about 40 laps to cover 10 km.

▶**SKILLBUILDER 11 | Solving Multistep Unit Conversion Problems**

A running track measures 1056 ft per lap. To run 15.0 km, how many laps should you run? (1 mi = 5280 ft)

▶**SKILLBUILDER PLUS 1**

An island is 5.72 nautical mi from the coast. How far is the island in meters? (1 nautical mi = 1.151 mi)

▶**FOR MORE PRACTICE**   Problems 83, 84.

8   Units Raised to a Power

| The unit cm³ is often abbreviated as cc.

When converting quantities with units raised to a power, such as cubic centimeters (cm^3), the conversion factor must also be raised to that power. For example, suppose we want to convert the size of a motorcycle engine reported as 1255 cm³ to cubic inches. We know that

$$2.54\,\text{cm} = 1\,\text{in.}$$

Most tables of conversion factors do not include conversions between cubic units, but we can derive them from the conversion factors for the basic units. We cube both sides of the preceding equality to obtain the proper conversion factor.

| 2.54 cm = 1 in. is an exact conversion factor. After cubing, we retain five significant figures so that the conversion factor does not limit the four significant figures of our original quantity (1255 cm³).

$$(2.54\,\text{cm})^3 = (1\,\text{in.})^3$$
$$(2.54)^3\,\text{cm}^3 = 1^3\,\text{in.}^3$$
$$16.387\,\text{cm}^3 = 1\,\text{in.}^3$$

We can do the same thing in fractional form.

$$\frac{1\,\text{in.}}{2.54\,\text{cm}} = \frac{(1\,\text{in.})^3}{(2.54\,\text{cm})^3} = \frac{1\,\text{in.}^3}{16.387\,\text{cm}^3}$$

We then proceed with the conversion in the usual manner.

CHEMISTRY AND HEALTH

Drug Dosage

The unit of choice in specifying drug dosage is the milligram (mg). Pick up a bottle of aspirin, Tylenol, or any other common drug, and the label tells you the number of milligrams of the active ingredient contained in each tablet, as well as the number of tablets to take per dose. The following table shows the mass of the active ingredient per pill in several common pain relievers, all reported in milligrams. The remainder of each tablet is composed of inactive ingredients such as cellulose (or fiber) and starch.

The recommended adult dose for many of these pain relievers is one or two tablets every 4 to 8 hours (depending on the specific pain reliever). Notice that the extra-strength version of each pain reliever just contains a higher dose of the same compound found in the regular-strength version. For the pain relievers listed, three regular-strength tablets are the equivalent of two extra-strength tablets (and probably cost less).

The dosages given in the table are fairly standard for each drug, regardless of the brand. When you look on your drugstore shelf, you will find many different brands of regular-strength ibuprofen, some sold under the generic name and others sold under their brand names (such as Advil). However, if you look closely at the labels, you will find that they all contain the same thing: 200 mg of the compound ibuprofen. There is no difference in the compound or in the amount of the compound. Yet these pain relievers will most likely all have different prices. Choose the least expensive. Why pay more for the same thing?

CAN YOU ANSWER THIS? *Convert each of the doses in the table to ounces. Why are drug dosages not listed in ounces?*

Drug Mass per Pill for Common Pain Relievers

Pain Reliever	Mass of Active Ingredient per Pill
Aspirin	325 mg
Aspirin, extra strength	500 mg
Ibuprofen (Advil)	200 mg
Ibuprofen, extra strength	300 mg
Acetaminophen (Tylenol)	325 mg
Acetaminophen, extra strength	500 mg

Maxwellartandphoto.com.

SOLUTION MAP

$$\boxed{cm^3} \longrightarrow \boxed{in.^3}$$

$$\frac{1\ in.^3}{16.387\ cm^3}$$

SOLUTION

$$1255\ cm^3 \times \frac{1\ in.^3}{16.387\ cm^3} = 76.5851\ in.^3 = 76.59\ in.^3$$

EXAMPLE 12   Converting Quantities Involving Units Raised to a Power

A circle has an area of 2659 cm². What is its area in square meters?

SORT	**GIVEN:** 2659 cm²
You are given an area in square centimeters and asked to convert the area to square meters.	**FIND:** m²

STRATEGIZE	**SOLUTION MAP**
Build a solution map beginning with cm² and ending with m². Remember that you must square the conversion factor.	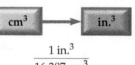

RELATIONSHIPS USED

$1\,cm = 0.01\,m$ (from Table 2)

SOLVE	SOLUTION
Follow the solution map to solve the problem. Square the conversion factor (both the units and the number) as you carry out the calculation.	$2659\,cm^2 \times \dfrac{(0.01\,m)^2}{(1\,cm)^2}$
Round the answer to four significant figures to reflect the four significant figures in the given quantity. The conversion factor is exact and therefore does not limit the number of significant figures.	$= 2659\,cm^2 \times \dfrac{10^{-4}\,m^2}{1\,cm^2}$ $= 0.265900\,m^2$ $= 0.2659\,m^2$

CHECK	
Check your answer. Are the units correct? Does the answer make physical sense?	The units of the answer are correct, and the magnitude makes physical sense. A square meter is much larger than a square centimeter, so the value in square meters should be much smaller than the value in square centimeters.

▶**SKILLBUILDER 12** | **Converting Quantities Involving Units Raised to a Power**

An automobile engine has a displacement (a measure of the size of the engine) of 289.7 in.^{3} What is its displacement in cubic centimeters?

▶**FOR MORE PRACTICE**   Example 26; Problems 87, 88, 89, 90, 91, 92.

EXAMPLE 13   **Solving Multistep Conversion Problems Involving Units Raised to a Power**

The average annual per person crude oil consumption in the United States is 15,615 dm^3. What is this value in cubic inches?

SORT	GIVEN: 15,615 dm^3
You are given a volume in cubic decimeters and asked to convert it to cubic inches.	FIND: in.^{3}

STRATEGIZE	SOLUTION MAP
Build a solution map beginning with dm^3 and ending with in.^{3} Each of the conversion factors must be cubed, since the quantities involve cubic units.	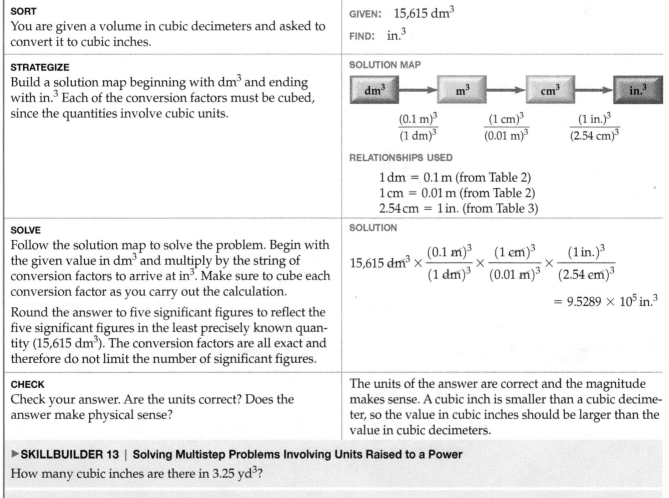 RELATIONSHIPS USED 1 dm = 0.1 m (from Table 2) 1 cm = 0.01 m (from Table 2) 2.54 cm = 1 in. (from Table 3)

SOLVE	SOLUTION
Follow the solution map to solve the problem. Begin with the given value in dm^3 and multiply by the string of conversion factors to arrive at in.^{3}. Make sure to cube each conversion factor as you carry out the calculation.	$15{,}615\,dm^3 \times \dfrac{(0.1\,m)^3}{(1\,dm)^3} \times \dfrac{(1\,cm)^3}{(0.01\,m)^3} \times \dfrac{(1\,in.)^3}{(2.54\,cm)^3}$ $= 9.5289 \times 10^5\,in.^3$
Round the answer to five significant figures to reflect the five significant figures in the least precisely known quantity (15,615 dm^3). The conversion factors are all exact and therefore do not limit the number of significant figures.	

CHECK	
Check your answer. Are the units correct? Does the answer make physical sense?	The units of the answer are correct and the magnitude makes sense. A cubic inch is smaller than a cubic decimeter, so the value in cubic inches should be larger than the value in cubic decimeters.

▶**SKILLBUILDER 13** | **Solving Multistep Problems Involving Units Raised to a Power**

How many cubic inches are there in 3.25 yd^3?

▶**FOR MORE PRACTICE**   Problems 93, 94.

✓ CONCEPTUAL CHECKPOINT 6

You know that there are 3 ft in a yard. How many cubic feet are there in a cubic yard?

(a) 3

(b) 6

(c) 9

(d) 27

9 Density

▲ Top-end bicycle frames are made of titanium because of titanium's low density and high relative strength. Titanium has a density of 4.50 g/cm³, while iron, for example, has a density of 7.86 g/cm³.

TABLE 4 Densities of Some Common Substances

Substance	Density (g/cm³)
Charcoal, oak	0.57
Ethanol	0.789
Ice	0.92
Water	1.0
Glass	2.6
Aluminum	2.7
Titanium	4.50
Iron	7.86
Copper	8.96
Lead	11.4
Gold	19.3
Platinum	21.4

❙ Remember that cubic centimeters and
❙ milliliters are equivalent units.

Why do some people pay more than $3000 for a bicycle made of titanium? A steel frame would be just as strong for a fraction of the cost. The difference between the two bikes is their mass—the titanium bike is lighter. For a given volume of metal, titanium has less mass than steel. We describe this property by saying that titanium is *less dense* than steel. The **density** of a substance is the ratio of its mass to its volume.

$$\text{Density} = \frac{\text{Mass}}{\text{Volume}} \quad \text{or} \quad d = \frac{m}{V}$$

Density is a fundamental property of substances that differs from one substance to another. The units of density are those of mass divided by those of volume, most conveniently expressed in grams per cubic centimeter (g/cm³) or grams per milliliter (g/mL). See Table 4 for a list of the densities of some common substances. Aluminum is among the least dense structural metals with a density of 2.70 g/cm³, while platinum is among the densest with a density of 21.4 g/cm³. Titanium has a density of 4.50 g/cm³.

CALCULATING DENSITY

We calculate the density of a substance by dividing the mass of a given amount of the substance by its volume. For example, a sample of liquid has a volume of 22.5 mL and a mass of 27.2 g. To find its density, we use the equation $d = m/V$.

$$d = \frac{m}{V} = \frac{27.2 \text{ g}}{22.5 \text{ mL}} = 1.21 \text{ g/mL}$$

We can use a solution map for solving problems involving equations, but the solution map will take a slightly different form than for pure conversion problems. In a problem involving an equation, the solution map shows how the *equation* takes you from the *given* quantities to the *find* quantity. The solution map for this problem is:

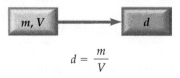

$$d = \frac{m}{V}$$

The solution map illustrates how the values of m and V, when substituted into the equation $d = \frac{m}{V}$ give the desired result, d.

EXAMPLE 14 Calculating Density

A jeweler offers to sell a ring to a woman and tells her that it is made of platinum. Noting that the ring felt a little light, the woman decides to perform a test to determine the ring's density. She places the ring on a balance and finds that it has a mass of 5.84 g. She also finds that the ring *displaces* 0.556 cm^3 of water. Is the ring made of platinum? The density of platinum is 21.4 g/cm^3. (The displacement of water is a common way to measure the volume of irregularly shaped objects. To say that an object *displaces* 0.556 cm^3 of water means that when the object is submerged in a container of water filled to the brim, 0.556 cm^3 of water overflows. Therefore, the volume of the object is 0.556 cm^3.)

SORT You are given the mass and volume of the ring and asked to find the density.	**GIVEN:** $m = 5.84$ g $\qquad\qquad V = 0.556$ cm^3 **FIND:** density in g/cm^3
STRATEGIZE If the ring is platinum, its density should match that of platinum. Build a solution map that represents how you get from the given quantities (mass and volume) to the find quantity (density). Unlike in conversion problems, where you write a conversion factor beneath the arrow, here you write the equation for density beneath the arrow.	**SOLUTION MAP** $$d = \frac{m}{V}$$ **RELATIONSHIPS USED** $$d = \frac{m}{V} \quad \text{(equation for density)}$$
SOLVE Follow the solution map. Substitute the given values into the density equation and compute the density. Round the answer to three significant figures to reflect the three significant figures in the given quantities.	**SOLUTION** $$d = \frac{m}{V} = \frac{5.84 \text{ g}}{0.556 \text{ cm}^3} = 10.5 \text{ g/cm}^3$$ The density of the ring is much too low to be platinum; therefore the ring is a fake.
CHECK Check your answer. Are the units correct? Does the answer make physical sense?	The units of the answer are correct, and the magnitude seems reasonable to be an actual density. As you can see from Table 4, the densities of liquids and solids range from below 1 g/cm^3 to just over 20 g/cm^3.

▶**SKILLBUILDER 14 | Calculating Density**

The woman takes the ring back to the jewelry shop, where she is met with endless apologies. They accidentally had made the ring out of silver rather than platinum. They give her a new ring that they promise is platinum. This time when she checks the density, she finds the mass of the ring to be 9.67 g and its volume to be 0.452 cm^3. Is this ring genuine?

▶**FOR MORE PRACTICE** Example 27; Problems 95, 96, 97, 98, 99, 100.

DENSITY AS A CONVERSION FACTOR

We can use the density of a substance as a conversion factor between the mass of the substance and its volume. For example, suppose we need 68.4 g of a liquid with a density of 1.32 g/cm^3 and want to measure the correct amount with a graduated cylinder (a piece of laboratory glassware used to measure volume). How much volume should we measure?

We start with the mass of the liquid and use the density as a conversion factor to convert mass to volume. However, we must use the inverted density expression 1 cm^3/1.32 g because we want g, the unit we are converting from, to be on the bottom (in the denominator) and cm^3, the unit we are converting to, on the top (in the numerator). Our solution map takes this form:

Cholesterol is fatty substance found in animal-derived foods such as beef, eggs, fish, poultry, and milk products. Cholesterol is used by the body for several purposes. However, excessive amounts in the blood—which can be caused by both genetic factors and diet—may result in the deposition of cholesterol in arterial walls, leading to a condition called atherosclerosis, or blocking of the arteries. These blockages are dangerous because they inhibit blood flow to important organs, causing heart attacks and strokes. The risk of stroke and heart attack increases with increasing blood cholesterol levels (Table 5). Cholesterol is carried in the bloodstream by a class of substances known as lipoproteins. Lipoproteins are often separated and classified according to their density.

The main carriers of blood cholesterol are low-density lipoproteins (LDLs). LDLs, also called bad cholesterol, have a density of 1.04 g/cm^3. They are bad because they tend to deposit cholesterol on arterial walls, increasing the risk of stroke and heart attack. Cholesterol is also carried by high-density lipoproteins (HDLs). HDLs, also called good cholesterol, have a density of 1.13 g/cm^3. HDLs transport cholesterol to the liver for processing and excretion and therefore have a tendency to reduce cholesterol on arterial walls. Too low a level of HDLs (below 35 mg/100 mL) is considered a risk factor for heart disease. Exercise, along with a diet low in saturated fats, is believed to raise HDL levels in the blood while lowering LDL levels.

CAN YOU ANSWER THIS? *What mass of low-density lipoprotein is contained in a cylinder that is 1.25 cm long and 0.50 cm in diameter? (The volume of a cylinder, V, is given by $V = \pi r^2 \ell$, where r is the radius of the cylinder and ℓ is its length.)*

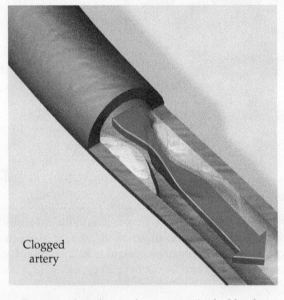

Clogged artery

▲ Too many low-density lipoproteins in the blood can lead to the blocking of arteries.

TABLE 5 Risk of Stroke and Heart Attack vs. Blood Cholesterol Level

Risk Level	Total Blood Cholesterol (mg/100 mL)	LDL (mg/100 mL)
low	< 200	< 130
borderline	200–239	130–159
high	240+	160+

SOLUTION MAP

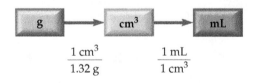

$$\frac{1 \text{ cm}^3}{1.32 \text{ g}} \qquad \frac{1 \text{ mL}}{1 \text{ cm}^3}$$

SOLUTION

$$68.4 \text{ g} \times \frac{1 \text{ cm}^3}{1.32 \text{ g}} \times \frac{1 \text{ mL}}{1 \text{ cm}^3} = 51.8 \text{ mL}$$

We must measure 51.8 mL to obtain 68.4 g of the liquid.

EXAMPLE 15 Density as a Conversion Factor

The gasoline in an automobile gas tank has a mass of 60.0 kg and a density of 0.752 g/cm^3. What is its volume in cm^3?

SORT You are given the mass in kilograms and asked to find the volume in cubic centimeters. Density is the conversion factor between mass and volume.	**GIVEN:** 60.0 kg Density = 0.752 g/cm^3 **FIND:** volume in cm^3
STRATEGIZE Build the solution map starting with kg and ending with cm^3. Use the density (inverted) to convert from g to cm^3.	**SOLUTION MAP** $$\boxed{kg} \longrightarrow \boxed{g} \longrightarrow \boxed{cm^3}$$ $\qquad \dfrac{1000\ g}{1\ kg} \qquad \dfrac{1\ cm^3}{0.752\ g}$ **RELATIONSHIPS USED** $\quad$ 0.752 g/cm^3 (given in problem) $\quad$ 1000 g = 1 kg (from Table 2)
SOLVE Follow the solution map to solve the problem. Round the answer to three significant figures to reflect the three significant figures in the given quantities.	**SOLUTION** $60.0\ \cancel{kg} \times \dfrac{1000\ \cancel{kg}}{1\ \cancel{kg}} \times \dfrac{1\ cm^3}{0.752\ \cancel{g}} = 7.98 \times 10^4\ cm^3$
CHECK Check your answer. Are the units correct? Does the answer make physical sense?	The units of the answer are those of volume, so they are correct. The magnitude seems reasonable because the density is somewhat less than 1 g/cm^3; therefore the volume of 60.0 kg should be somewhat more than 60.0×10^3 cm^3.

▶**SKILLBUILDER 15 | Density as a Conversion Factor**

A drop of acetone (nail polish remover) has a mass of 35 mg and a density of 0.788 g/cm^3. What is its volume in cubic centimeters?

▶**SKILLBUILDER PLUS 2**

A steel cylinder has a volume of 246 cm^3 and a density of 7.93 g/cm^3. What is its mass in kilograms?

▶**FOR MORE PRACTICE** Example 28; Problems 101, 102.

10 Numerical Problem-Solving Overview

In this chapter, you have seen a few examples of how to solve numerical problems. In Section 6, we developed a procedure to solve simple unit conversion problems. We then learned how to modify that procedure to work with multistep unit conversion problems and problems involving an equation. We will now summarize and generalize these procedures and apply them to two additional examples. As we did in Section 6, we provide the general procedure for solving numerical problems in the left column and the application of the procedure to two examples in the center and right columns.

SOLVING NUMERICAL PROBLEMS	**EXAMPLE 16** **Unit Conversion** A 23.5-kg sample of ethanol is needed for a large-scale reaction. What volume in liters of ethanol should be used? The density of ethanol is 0.789 g/cm³.	**EXAMPLE 17** **Unit Conversion with Equation** A 55.9-kg person displaces 57.2 L of water when submerged in a water tank. What is the density of the person in grams per cubic centimeter?
SORT • Scan the problem for one or more numbers and their associated units. This number (or numbers) is (are) the starting point(s) of the calculation. Write them down as given. • Scan the problem to determine what you are asked to find. Sometimes the units of this quantity are implied; other times they are specified. Write down the quantity and/or units you are asked to find.	GIVEN: 23.5 kg ethanol $\quad$ density $= 0.789\,\text{g/cm}^3$ FIND: volume in L	GIVEN: $m = 55.9\,\text{kg}$ $\quad\quad V = 57.2\,\text{L}$ FIND: density in g/cm^3
STRATEGIZE • For problems involving only conversions, focus on units. The solution map shows how to get from the units in the given quantity to the units in the quantity you are asked to find. • For problems involving equations, focus on the equation. The solution map shows how the equation takes you from the given quantity (or quantities) to the quantity you are asked to find. • Some problems may involve both unit conversions and equations, in which case the solution map employs both of the above points.	SOLUTION MAP $\boxed{\text{kg}} \rightarrow \boxed{\text{g}} \rightarrow \boxed{\text{cm}^3} \rightarrow \boxed{\text{mL}} \rightarrow \boxed{\text{L}}$ $\dfrac{1000\,\text{g}}{1\,\text{kg}} \quad \dfrac{1\,\text{cm}^3}{0.789\,\text{g}} \quad \dfrac{1\,\text{mL}}{1\,\text{cm}^3} \quad \dfrac{1\,\text{L}}{1000\,\text{mL}}$ RELATIONSHIPS USED $0.789\,\text{g/cm}^3$ (given in problem) $1000\,\text{g} = 1\,\text{kg}$ (Table 2) $1000\,\text{mL} = 1\,\text{L}$ (Table 2) $1\,\text{mL} = 1\,\text{cm}^3$ (Table 3)	SOLUTION MAP $\boxed{m, V} \rightarrow \boxed{d}$ $d = \dfrac{m}{V}$ RELATIONSHIPS USED $d = \dfrac{m}{V}$ (definition of density)
SOLVE • For problems involving only conversions, begin with the given quantity and its units. Multiply by the appropriate conversion factor(s), canceling units, to arrive at the quantity you are asked to find.	SOLUTION $23.5\,\text{kg} \times \dfrac{1000\,\text{g}}{1\,\text{kg}} \times \dfrac{1\,\text{cm}^3}{0.789\,\text{g}} \times$ $\dfrac{1\,\text{mL}}{1\,\text{cm}^3} \times \dfrac{1\,\text{L}}{1000\,\text{mL}} = 29.7845\,\text{L}$ $29.7845\,\text{L} = 29.8\,\text{L}$	The equation is already solved for the find quantity. Convert mass from kilograms to grams. $m = 55.9\,\text{kg} \times \dfrac{1000\,\text{g}}{1\,\text{kg}}$ $= 5.59 \times 10^4\,\text{g}$

· For problems involving equations, solve the equation to arrive at the quantity you are asked to find. (Use algebra to rearrange the equation so that the quantity you are asked to find is isolated on one side.) Gather each of the quantities that must go into the equation in the correct units. (Convert to the correct units using additional solution maps if necessary.) Finally, substitute the numerical values and their units into the equation and compute the answer.

· Round the answer to the correct number of significant figures. Use the significant-figure rules from Sections 3 and 4.

Convert volume from liters to cubic centimeters.

$$V = 57.2 \, \cancel{L} \times \frac{1000 \, \cancel{mL}}{1 \, \cancel{L}} \times \frac{1 \, cm^3}{1 \, \cancel{mL}}$$

$$= 57.2 \times 10^3 \, cm^3$$

Compute density.

$$d = \frac{m}{V} = \frac{55.9 \times 10^3}{57.2 \times 10^3 \, cm^3}$$

$$= 0.9772727 \, \frac{g}{cm^3}$$

$$= 0.977 \, \frac{g}{cm^3}$$

CHECK

· Does the magnitude of the answer make physical sense? Are the units correct?

The units are correct (L) and the magnitude is reasonable. Since the density is less than 1 g/cm^3, the computed volume (29.8 L) should be greater than the mass (23.5 kg).

The units are correct. Since the mass in kilograms and the volume in liters were very close to each other in magnitude, it makes sense that the density is close to 1 g/cm^3.

▶**SKILLBUILDER 16**

Unit Conversion

A pure gold metal bar displaces 0.82 L of water. What is its mass in kilograms? (The density of gold is 19.3 g/cm^3.)

▶**SKILLBUILDER 17**

Unit Conversion with Equation

A gold-colored pebble is found in a stream. Its mass is 23.2 mg, and its volume is 1.20 mm^3. What is its density in grams per cubic centimeter? Is it gold? (The density of gold = 19.3 g/cm^3.)

▶**FOR MORE PRACTICE** Problems 103, 109, 110, 111, 112.

▶**FOR MORE PRACTICE** Problems 104, 105, 106.

CHAPTER IN REVIEW

CHEMICAL PRINCIPLES

Uncertainty: Scientists report measured quantities so that the number of digits reflects the certainty in the measurement. Write measured quantities so that every digit is certain except the last, which is estimated.

RELEVANCE

Uncertainty: Measurement is a hallmark of science, and the precision of a measurement must be communicated with the measurement so that others know how reliable the measurement is. When you write or manipulate measured quantities, you must show and retain the precision with which the original measurement was made.

Units: Measured quantities usually have units associated with them. The SI unit for length is the meter; for mass, the kilogram; and for time, the second. Prefix multipliers such as *kilo-* or *milli-* are often used in combination with these basic units. The SI units of volume are units of length raised to the third power; liters or milliliters are often used as well.

Units: The units in a measured quantity communicate what the quantity actually is. Without an agreed-on system of units, scientists could not communicate their measurements. Units are also important in calculations, and the tracking of units throughout a calculation is essential.

Density: The density of a substance is its mass divided by its volume, $d = m/V$, and is usually reported in units of grams per cubic centimeter or grams per milliliter. Density is a fundamental property of all substances and generally differs from one substance to another.

Density: The density of substances is an important consideration in choosing materials from which to make things. Airplanes, for example, are made of low-density materials, while bridges are made of higher-density materials. Density is important as a conversion factor between mass and volume and vice versa.

CHEMICAL SKILLS

EXAMPLES

Scientific Notation (Section 2)

To express a number in scientific notation:

- Move the decimal point to obtain a number between 1 and 10.

- Write the decimal part multiplied by 10 raised to the number of places you moved the decimal point.

- The exponent is positive if you moved the decimal point to the left and negative if you moved the decimal point to the right.

EXAMPLE 18   Scientific Notation

Express the number 45,000,000 in scientific notation.

45,000,000

7 6 5 4 3 2 1

4.5×10^7

Reporting Measured Quantities to the Right Number of Digits (Section 3)

Report measured quantities so that every digit is certain except the last, which is estimated.

EXAMPLE 19   Reporting Measured Quantities to the Right Number of Digits

Record the volume of liquid in the graduated cylinder to the correct number of digits. Laboratory glassware is calibrated (and should therefore be read) from the bottom of the meniscus (see figure).

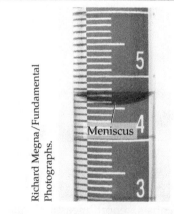

Richard Megna/Fundamental Photographs.

Meniscus

Since the graduated cylinder has markings every 0.1 mL, the measurement should be recorded to the nearest 0.01 mL. In this case, that is 4.57 mL.

Counting Significant Digits (Section 3)

The following digits should always be counted as significant:

- nonzero digits

- interior zeros

- trailing zeros after a decimal point

- trailing zeros before a decimal point but after a nonzero number

The following digits should never be counted as significant:

- zeros to the left of the first nonzero number

The following digits are ambiguous and should be avoided by using scientific notation:

- zeros at the end of a number, but before a decimal point

EXAMPLE 20   Counting Significant Digits

How many significant figures are in the following numbers?

1.0050	five significant figures
0.00870	three significant figures
100.085	six significant digits
5400	It is not possible to tell in its current form.

In order for us to know, the number needs to be written as 5.4×10^3, 5.40×10^3, or 5.400×10^3, depending on the number of significant figures intended.

Rounding (Section 4)

When rounding numbers to the correct number of significant figures, round down if the last digit dropped is 4 or less; round up if the last digit dropped is 5 or more.

EXAMPLE 21   Rounding

Round 6.442 and 6.456 to two significant figures each.

6.442 rounds to 6.4
6.456 rounds to 6.5

Significant Figures in Multiplication and Division (Section 4)

The result of a multiplication or division should carry the same number of significant figures as the factor with the least number of significant figures.

EXAMPLE 22   Significant Figures in Multiplication and Division

Perform the following calculation and report the answer to the correct number of significant figures.

$$8.54 \times 3.589 \div 4.2$$
$$= 7.2976$$
$$= 7.3$$

Round the final result to two significant figures to reflect the two significant figures in the factor with the least number of significant figures (4.2).

Significant Figures in Addition and Subtraction (Section 4)

The result of an addition or subtraction should carry the same number of decimal places as the quantity carrying the least number of decimal places.

EXAMPLE 23   Significant Figures in Addition and Subtraction

Perform the following operation and report the answer to the correct number of significant figures.

$$3.098$$
$$0.67$$
$$\underline{-0.9452}$$
$$2.8228 = 2.82$$

Round the final result to two decimal places to reflect the two decimal places in the quantity with the least number of decimal places (0.67).

Significant Figures in Calculations Involving Both Addition/Subtraction and Multiplication/Division (Section 4)

In calculations involving both addition/subtraction and multiplication/division, do the steps in parentheses first, keeping track of how many significant figures are in the answer by underlining the least significant figure, then proceeding with the remaining steps. Do not round off until the very end.

EXAMPLE 24 Significant Figures in Calculations Involving Both Addition/Subtraction and Multiplication/Division

Perform the following operation and report the answer to the correct number of significant figures.

$$8.16 \times (5.4323 - 5.411)$$
$$= 8.16 \times 0.021\underline{3}$$
$$= 0.1738 = 0.17$$

Unit Conversion (Sections 6, 7)

Solve unit conversion problems by following these steps.

1. **Sort** Write down the given quantity and its units and the quantity you are asked to find and its units.

2. **Strategize** Draw a solution map showing how to get from the given quantity to the quantity you are asked to find.

EXAMPLE 25 Unit Conversion

Convert 108 ft to meters.

GIVEN: 108 ft

FIND: m

SOLUTION MAP

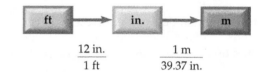

$$\frac{12 \text{ in.}}{1 \text{ ft}} \qquad \frac{1 \text{ m}}{39.37 \text{ in.}}$$

RELATIONSHIPS USED

$$1 \text{ m} = 39.37 \text{ in.} \quad \text{(Table 3)}$$
$$1 \text{ ft} = 12 \text{ in.} \quad \text{(by definition)}$$

3. **Solve** Follow the solution map. Starting with the given quantity and its units, multiply by the appropriate conversion factor(s), canceling units, to arrive at the quantity to find in the desired units. Round the final answer to the correct number of significant figures.

SOLUTION

$$108 \text{ ft} \times \frac{12 \text{ in.}}{1 \text{ ft}} \times \frac{1 \text{ m}}{39.37 \text{ in.}}$$
$$= 32.918 \text{ m}$$
$$= 32.9 \text{ m}$$

4. **Check** Are the units correct? Does the answer make physical sense?

The answer has the right units (meters), and it makes sense; since a meter is longer than a foot, the number of meters should be less than the number of feet.

Unit Conversion Involving Units Raised to a Power (Section 8)

When working problems involving units raised to a power, raise the conversion factors to the same power.

1. **Sort** Write down the given quantity and its units and the quantity you are asked to find and its units.

2. **Strategize** Draw a solution map showing how to get from the given quantity to the quantity you are asked to find. Since the units are squared, you must square the conversion factor.

EXAMPLE 26 Unit Conversion Involving Units Raised to a Power

How many square meters are in 1.0 km²?

GIVEN: 1.0 km^2

FIND: m^2

SOLUTION MAP

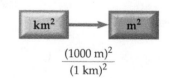

$$\frac{(1000 \text{ m})^2}{(1 \text{ km})^2}$$

RELATIONSHIPS USED

$$1 \text{ km} = 1000 \text{ m} \quad \text{(Table 2)}$$

3. **Solve** Follow the solution map. Starting with the given quantity and its units, multiply by the appropriate conversion factor(s), canceling units, to arrive at the quantity you are asked to find in the desired units. Don't forget to square the conversion factor for squared units.

4. **Check** Are the units correct? Does the answer make physical sense?

SOLUTION

$$1.0 \, km^2 \times \frac{(1000 \, m)^2}{(1 \, km)^2}$$

$$= 1.0 \, km^2 \times \frac{1 \times 10^6 \, m^2}{1 \, km^2}$$

$$= 1.0 \times 10^6 \, m^2$$

The units are correct. The answer makes physical sense; a square meter is much smaller than a square kilometer, so the number of square meters should be much larger than the number of square kilometers.

Calculating Density (Section 10)

The density of an object or substance is its mass divided by its volume.

$$d = \frac{m}{V}$$

1. **Sort** Write down the given quantity and its units and the quantity you are asked to find and its units.

EXAMPLE 27 Calculating Density

An object has a mass of 23.4 g and displaces 5.7 mL of water. Determine its density in grams per milliliter.

GIVEN:

$$m = 23.4 \, g$$

$$V = 5.7 \, mL$$

FIND: density in g/mL

2. **Strategize** Draw a solution map showing how to get from the given quantity to the quantity you are asked to find. Use the definition of density as the equation that takes you from the mass and the volume to the density.

SOLUTION MAP

$$\boxed{m, V} \longrightarrow \boxed{d}$$

$$d = \frac{m}{V}$$

RELATIONSHIPS USED

$$d = \frac{m}{V} \text{ (definition of density)}$$

3. **Solve** Substitute the correct values into the equation for density.

SOLUTION

$$d = \frac{m}{V}$$

$$= \frac{23.4 \, g}{5.7 \, mL}$$

$$= 4.11 \, g/mL$$

$$= 4.1 \, g/mL$$

4. **Check** Are the units correct? Does the answer make physical sense?

The units (g/mL) are units of density. The answer is in the range of values for the densities of liquids and solids (see Table 4).

Density as a Conversion Factor (Section 10)

Density can be used as a conversion factor from mass to volume or from volume to mass. To convert between volume and mass, use density directly. To convert between mass and volume, invert the density.

1. **Sort** Write down the given quantity and its units and the quantity you are asked to find and its units.

2. **Strategize** Draw a solution map showing how to get from the given quantity to the quantity you are asked to find. Use the inverse of the density to convert from g to mL.

3. **Solve** Begin with given quantity and multiply by the appropriate conversion factors to arrive at the quantity you are asked to find. Round to the correct number of significant figures.

4. **Check** Are the units correct? Does the answer make physical sense?

EXAMPLE 28   Density as a Conversion Factor

What is the volume in liters of 321 g of a liquid with a density of 0.84 g/mL?

GIVEN: 321 g

FIND: volume in L

SOLUTION MAP

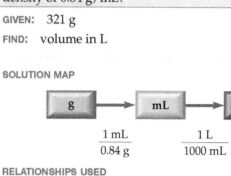

$$\frac{1\ mL}{0.84\ g} \qquad \frac{1\ L}{1000\ mL}$$

RELATIONSHIPS USED

0.84 g/mL (given in the problem)
1 L = 1000 mL (Table 2)

SOLUTION

$$321\ g \times \frac{1\ mL}{0.84\ g} \times \frac{1\ L}{1000\ mL}$$

$$= 0.382\ L = 0.38\ L$$

The answer is in the correct units. The magnitude seems right because the density is slightly less than 1; therefore the volume (382 mL) should be slightly greater than the mass (321 g).

KEY TERMS

conversion factor **[Section 6]**
decimal part **[Section 2]**
density **[Section 9]**
English system **[Section 5]**
exponent **[Section 2]**
exponential part **[Section 2]**

International System
   [Section 5]
kilogram (kg) **[Section 5]**
liter (L) **[Section 5]**
mass **[Section 5]**
meter (m) **[Section 5]**

metric system **[Section 5]**
prefix multipliers **[Section 5]**
scientific notation **[Section 2]**
second (s) **[Section 5]**
SI units **[Section 5]**

significant figures
   (digits) **[Section 3]**
solution map **[Section 6]**
units **[Section 5]**
volume **[Section 5]**

EXERCISES

QUESTIONS

Answers to all questions numbered in blue appear in the Answers section at the end of the chapter.

1. Why is it important to report units with scientific measurements?

2. Why are the number of digits reported in scientific measurements important?

3. Why is scientific notation useful?

4. If a measured quantity is written correctly, which digits are certain? Which are uncertain?

5. Explain when zeros count as significant digits and when they do not.

6. How many significant digits are there in exact numbers? What kinds of numbers are exact?

7. What limits the number of significant digits in a calculation involving only multiplication and division?

8. What limits the number of significant digits in a calculation involving only addition and subtraction?

9. How are significant figures determined in calculations involving both addition/subtraction and multiplication/division?

10. What are the rules for rounding numbers?

11. What are the basic SI units of length, mass, and time?

12. List the common units of volume.

13. Suppose you are trying to measure the diameter of a Frisbee. What unit and prefix multiplier should you use?

14. What is the difference between mass and weight?

15. Obtain a metric ruler and measure these objects to the correct number of significant figures.
    (a) quarter (diameter)
    (b) dime (diameter)
    (c) notebook paper (width)
    (d) this book (width)
16. Obtain a stopwatch and measure each time to the correct number of significant figures.
    (a) time between your heartbeats
    (b) time it takes you to do the next problem
    (c) time between your breaths
17. Explain why units are important in calculations.
18. How are units treated in a calculation?
19. What is a conversion factor?
20. Why is the fundamental value of a quantity not changed when the quantity is multiplied by a conversion factor?
21. Write the conversion factor that converts a measurement in inches to feet. How would the conversion factor change for converting a measurement in feet to inches?
22. Write conversion factors for each:
    (a) miles to kilometers
    (b) kilometers to miles

(c) gallons to liters
(d) liters to gallons
23. This book outlines a four-step problem-solving strategy. Describe each step and its significance.
    (a) Sort
    (b) Strategize
    (c) Solve
    (d) Check
24. Experienced problem solvers always consider both the value and units of their answer to a problem. Why?
25. Draw a solution map to convert a measurement in grams to pounds.
26. Draw a solution map to convert a measurement in milliliters to gallons.
27. Draw a solution map to convert a measurement in meters to feet.
28. Draw a solution map to convert a measurement in ounces to grams. (1 lb = 16 oz)
29. What is density? Explain why density can work as a conversion factor. Between what quantities does it convert?
30. Explain how you would calculate the density of a substance. Include a solution map in your explanation.

PROBLEMS

Note: The exercises in the Problems section are paired, and the answers to the odd-numbered exercises (numbered in blue) appear in the Answers section at the end of the chapter.

SCIENTIFIC NOTATION

31. Express each number in scientific notation.
    (a) 36,756,000 (population of California)
    (b) 1,288,000 (population of Hawaii)
    (c) 19,490,000 (population of New York)
    (d) 532,000 (population of Wyoming)

32. Express each number in scientific notation.
    (a) 6,796,000,000 (population of the world)
    (b) 1,338,000,000 (population of China)
    (c) 11,451,000 (population of Cuba)
    (d) 4,203,000 (population of Ireland)

33. Express each number in scientific notation.
    (a) 0.00000000007461 m (length of a hydrogen–hydrogen chemical bond)
    (b) 0.0000158 mi (number of miles in an inch)
    (c) 0.000000632 m (wavelength of red light)
    (d) 0.000015 m (diameter of a human hair)

34. Express each number in scientific notation.
    (a) 0.000000001 s (time it takes light to travel 1 ft)
    (b) 0.143 s (time it takes light to travel around the world)
    (c) 0.000000000001 s (time it takes a chemical bond to undergo one vibration)
    (d) 0.000001 m (approximate size of a dust particle)

35. Express each number in decimal notation (i.e., express the number without using scientific notation).
    (a) 6.022×10^{23} (number of carbon atoms in 12.01 g of carbon)
    (b) 1.6×10^{-19} C (charge of a proton in coulombs)
    (c) 2.99×10^{8} m/s (speed of light)
    (d) 3.44×10^{2} m/s (speed of sound)

36. Express each number in decimal notation (i.e., express the number without using scientific notation).
    (a) 450×10^{-19} m (wavelength of blue light)
    (b) 13.7×10^{9} years (approximate age of the universe)
    (c) 5×10^{9} years (approximate age of Earth)
    (d) 4.7×10^{1} years (approximate age of this author)

37. Express each number in decimal notation (i.e., express the number without using scientific notation).
    (a) 3.22×10^{7}
    (b) 7.2×10^{-3}
    (c) 1.18×10^{11}
    (d) 9.43×10^{-6}

38. Express each number in decimal notation. (i.e., express the number without using scientific notation)
    (a) 1.30×10^{6}
    (b) 1.1×10^{-4}
    (c) 1.9×10^{2}
    (d) 7.41×10^{-10}

39. Complete the table.

Decimal Notation	Scientific Notation
2,000,000,000	———
———	1.211×10^9
0.000874	———
———	3.2×10^{11}

40. Complete the table.

Decimal Notation	Scientific Notation
———	4.2×10^{-3}
315,171,000	———
———	1.8×10^{-11}
1,232,000	———

SIGNIFICANT FIGURES

41. Read each instrument to the correct number of significant figures. Laboratory glassware should always be read from the bottom of the *meniscus* (the curved surface at the top of the liquid column).

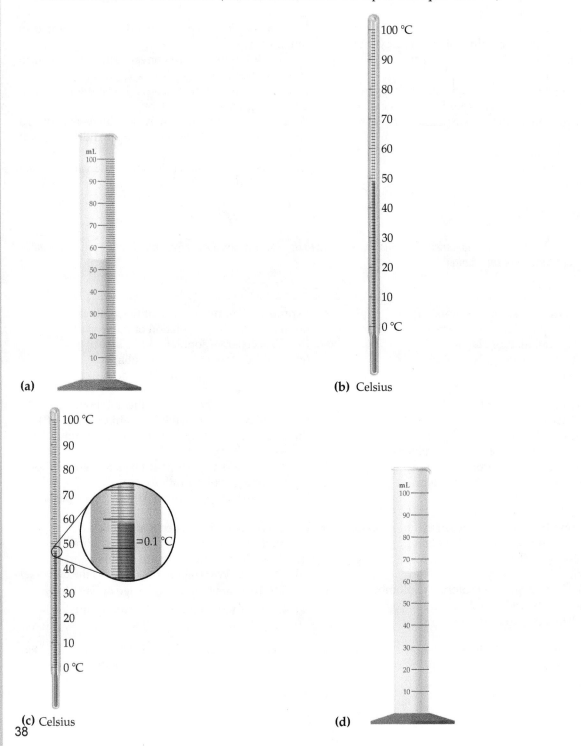

(a)

(b) Celsius

(c) Celsius

(d)

42. Read each instrument to the correct number of significant figures. Laboratory glassware should always be read from the bottom of the meniscus (the curved surface at the top of the liquid column).

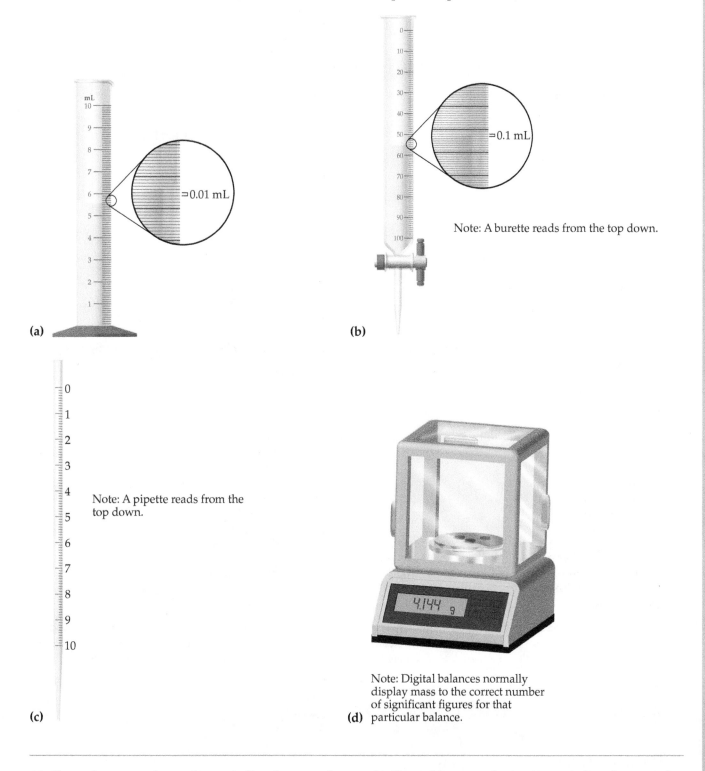

Note: A burette reads from the top down.

Note: A pipette reads from the top down.

Note: Digital balances normally display mass to the correct number of significant figures for that particular balance.

(a)   (b)   (c)   (d)

---

43. For each measured quantity, underline the zeros that are significant and draw an X through the zeros that are not.
   (a) 0.005050 m
   (b) 0.0000000000000060 s
   (c) 220,103 kg
   (d) 0.00108 in.

44. For each measured quantity, underline the zeros that are significant and draw an X through the zeros that are not.
   (a) 0.00010320 s
   (b) 1,322,600,324 kg
   (c) 0.0001240 in.
   (d) 0.02061 m

45. How many significant figures are in each measured quantity?
  (a) 0.001125 m
  (b) 0.1125 m
  (c) 1.12500×10^4 m
  (d) 11205 m

46. How many significant figures are in each measured quantity?
  (a) 13001 kg
  (b) 13111 kg
  (c) 1.30×10^4 kg
  (d) 0.00013 kg

47. Determine whether each of the entries in the table is correct. Correct the entries that are wrong.

Quantity	Significant Figures
(a) 895675 m	6
(b) 0.000869 kg	6
(c) 0.5672100 s	5
(d) 6.022×10^{23} atoms	4

48. Determine whether each of the entries in the table is correct. Correct the entries that are wrong.

Quantity	Significant Figures
(a) 24 days	2
(b) 5.6×10^{-12} s	3
(c) 3.14 m	3
(d) 0.00383 g	5

ROUNDING

49. Round each number to four significant figures.
  (a) 255.98612
  (b) 0.0004893222
  (c) 2.900856×10^{-4}
  (d) 2,231,479

50. Round each number to three significant figures.
  (a) 10,776.522
  (b) 4.999902×10^6
  (c) 1.3499999995
  (d) 0.0000344988

51. Round each number to two significant figures.
  (a) 2.34
  (b) 2.35
  (c) 2.349
  (d) 2.359

52. Round each number to three significant figures.
  (a) 65.74
  (b) 65.749
  (c) 65.75
  (d) 65.750

53. Each number was supposed to be rounded to three significant figures. Find the ones that were incorrectly rounded and correct them.
  (a) 42.3492 to 42.4
  (b) 56.9971 to 57.0
  (c) 231.904 to 232
  (d) 0.04555 to 0.046

54. Each number was supposed to be rounded to two significant figures. Find the ones that were incorrectly rounded and correct them.
  (a) 1.249×10^3 to 1.3×10^3
  (b) 3.999×10^2 to 40
  (c) 56.21 to 56.2
  (d) 0.009964 to 0.010

55. Round the number on the left to the number of significant figures indicated as shown by the example in the first row. (Use scientific notation as needed to avoid ambiguity.)

Number	Rounded to 4 Significant Figures	Rounded to 2 Significant Figures	Rounded to 1 Significant Figure
1.45815	1.458	1.5	1
8.32466			
84.57225			
132.5512			

56. Round the number on the left to the number of significant figures indicated as shown by the example in the first row. (Use scientific notation as needed to avoid ambiguity.)

Number	Rounded to 4 Significant Figures	Rounded to 2 Significant Figures	Rounded to 1 Significant Figure
94.52118	94.52	95	9×10^1
105.4545			
0.455981			
0.009999991			

SIGNIFICANT FIGURES IN CALCULATIONS

57. Perform each calculation to the correct number of significant figures.
  (a) $4.5 \times 0.03060 \times 0.391$
  (b) $5.55 \div 8.97$
  (c) $(7.890 \times 10^{12}) \div (6.7 \times 10^4)$
  (d) $67.8 \times 9.8 \div 100.04$

58. Perform each calculation to the correct number of significant figures.
  (a) $89.3 \times 77.0 \times 0.08$
  (b) $(5.01 \times 10^5) \div (7.8 \times 10^2)$
  (c) $4.005 \times 74 \times 0.007$
  (d) $453 \div 2.031$

59. Determine whether the answer to each calculation has the correct number of significant figures. If not, correct it.
    (a) $34.00 \times 567 \div 4.564 = 4.2239 \times 10^3$
    (b) $79.3 \div 0.004 \times 35.4 = 7 \times 10^5$
    (c) $89.763 \div 22.4581 = 3.997$
    (d) $(4.32 \times 10^{12}) \div (3.1 \times 10^{-4}) = 1.4 \times 10^{16}$

60. Determine whether the answer to each calculation has the correct number of significant figures. If not, correct it.
    (a) $45.3254 \times 89.00205 = 4034.05$
    (b) $0.00740 \times 45.0901 = 0.334$
    (c) $49857 \div 904875 = 0.05510$
    (d) $0.009090 \times 6007.2 = 54.605$

61. Perform each calculation to the correct number of significant figures.
    (a) $87.6 + 9.888 + 2.3 + 10.77$
    (b) $43.7 - 2.341$
    (c) $89.6 + 98.33 - 4.674$
    (d) $6.99 - 5.772$

62. Perform each calculation to the correct number of significant figures.
    (a) $1459.3 + 9.77 + 4.32$
    (b) $0.004 + 0.09879$
    (c) $432 + 7.3 - 28.523$
    (d) $2.4 + 1.777$

63. Determine whether the answer to each calculation has the correct number of significant figures. If not, correct it.
    (a) $(3.8 \times 10^5) - (8.45 \times 10^5) = -4.7 \times 10^5$
    (b) $0.00456 + 1.0936 = 1.10$
    (c) $8475.45 - 34.899 = 8440.55$
    (d) $908.87 - 905.34095 = 3.5291$

64. Determine whether the answer to each calculation has the correct number of significant figures. If not, correct it.
    (a) $78.9 + 890.43 - 23 = 9.5 \times 10^2$
    (b) $9354 - 3489.56 + 34.3 = 5898.74$
    (c) $0.00407 + 0.0943 = 0.0984$
    (d) $0.00896 - 0.007 = 0.00196$

65. Perform each calculation to the correct number of significant figures.
    (a) $(78.4 - 44.889) \div 0.0087$
    (b) $(34.6784 \times 5.38) + 445.56$
    (c) $(78.7 \times 10^5 \div 88.529) + 356.99$
    (d) $(892 \div 986.7) + 5.44$

66. Perform each calculation to the correct number of significant figures.
    (a) $(1.7 \times 10^6 \div 2.63 \times 10^5) + 7.33$
    (b) $(568.99 - 232.1) \div 5.3$
    (c) $(9443 + 45 - 9.9) \times 8.1 \times 10^6$
    (d) $(3.14 \times 2.4367) - 2.34$

67. Determine whether the answer to each calculation has the correct number of significant figures. If not, correct it.
    (a) $(78.56 - 9.44) \times 45.6 = 3152$
    (b) $(8.9 \times 10^5 \div 2.348 \times 10^2) + 121 = 3.9 \times 10^3$
    (c) $(45.8 \div 3.2) - 12.3 = 2$
    (d) $(4.5 \times 10^3 - 1.53 \times 10^3) \div 34.5 = 86$

68. Determine whether the answer to each calculation has the correct number of significant figures. If not, correct it.
    (a) $(908.4 - 3.4) \div 3.52 \times 10^4 = 0.026$
    (b) $(1206.7 - 0.904) \times 89 = 1.07 \times 10^5$
    (c) $(876.90 + 98.1) \div 56.998 = 17.11$
    (d) $(455 \div 407859) + 1.00098 = 1.00210$

UNIT CONVERSION

69. Perform each conversion within the metric system.
    (a) 3.55 kg to grams
    (b) 8944 mm to meters
    (c) 4598 mg to kilograms
    (d) 0.0187 L to milliliters

70. Perform each conversion within the metric system.
    (a) 155.5 cm to meters
    (b) 2491.6 g to kilograms
    (c) 248 cm to millimeters
    (d) 6781 mL to liters

71. Perform each conversion within the metric system.
    (a) 5.88 dL to liters
    (b) 3.41×10^{-5} g to micrograms
    (c) 1.01×10^{-8} s to nanoseconds
    (d) 2.19 pm to meters

72. Perform each conversion within the metric system.
    (a) 1.08 Mm to kilometers
    (b) 4.88 fs to picoseconds
    (c) 7.39×10^{11} m to gigameters
    (d) 1.15×10^{-10} m to picometers

73. Perform each conversion between the English and metric systems.
    (a) 22.5 in. to centimeters
    (b) 126 ft to meters
    (c) 825 yd to kilometers
    (d) 2.4 in. to millimeters

74. Perform each conversion between the English and metric systems.
    (a) 78.3 in. to centimeters
    (b) 445 yd to meters
    (c) 336 ft to centimeters
    (d) 45.3 in. to millimeters

75. Perform each conversion between the metric and English systems.
   (a) 40.0 cm to inches
   (b) 27.8 m to feet
   (c) 10.0 km to miles
   (d) 3845 kg to pounds

76. Perform each conversion between the metric and English systems.
   (a) 254 cm to inches
   (b) 89 mm to inches
   (c) 7.5 L to quarts
   (d) 122 kg to pounds

77. Complete the table:

m	km	Mm	Gm	Tm
5.08×10^8 m	___	508 Mm	___	___
___	___	27,976 Mm	___	
___	___		___	1.77 Tm
___	1.5×10^5 km	___	___	___
___	___	___	423 Gm	___

78. Complete the table:

s	ms	μs	ns	ps
1.31×10^{-4} s	___	131 μs	___	___
___	___	___	___	12.6 ps
___	___	___	155 ns	___
___	1.99×10^{-3} ms	___	___	___
___	___	$8.66 \times 10^{-5}\,\mu$s	___	___

79. Convert 2.255×10^{10} g to each unit:
   (a) kg
   (b) Mg
   (c) mg
   (d) metric tons (1 metric ton = 1000 kg)

80. Convert 1.88×10^{-6} g to each unit.
   (a) mg
   (b) cg
   (c) ng
   (d) μg

81. A student loses 3.3 lb in one month. How many grams did he lose?

82. A student gains 1.9 lb in two weeks. How many grams did he gain?

83. A runner wants to run 10.0 km. She knows that her running pace is 7.5 mi/h. How many minutes must she run? *Hint:* Use 7.5 mi/h as a conversion factor between distance and time.

84. A cyclist rides at an average speed of 24 mi/h. If she wants to bike 195 km, how long (in hours) must she ride?

85. A recipe calls for 5.0 qt of milk. What is this quantity in cubic centimeters?

86. A gas can holds 2.0 gal of gasoline. What is this quantity in cubic centimeters?

UNITS RAISED TO A POWER

87. Fill in the blanks.
   (a) 1.0 km^2 = _____ m^2
   (b) 1.0 cm^3 = _____ m^3
   (c) 1.0 mm^3 = _____ m^3

88. Fill in the blanks.
   (a) 1.0 ft^2 = _____ in.^{2}
   (b) 1.0 yd^2 = _____ ft^2
   (c) 1.0 m^2 = _____ yd^2

89. The hydrogen atom has a volume of approximately 6.2×10^{-31} m^3. What is this volume in each unit?
   (a) cubic picometers
   (b) cubic nanometers
   (c) cubic angstroms (1 angstrom = 10^{-10} m)

90. Earth has a surface area of 197 million square miles. What is its area in each unit?
   (a) square kilometers
   (b) square megameters
   (c) square decimeters

91. A modest-sized house has an area of 215 m^2. What is its area in each unit?
   (a) km^2
   (b) dm^2
   (c) cm^2

92. A classroom has a volume of 285 m^3. What is its volume in each unit?
   (a) km^3
   (b) dm^3
   (c) cm^3

93. Total U.S. farmland occupies 954 million acres. How many square miles is this?

(1 acre = 43,560 ft^2; 1 mi = 5280 ft)

94. The average U.S. farm occupies 435 acres. How many square miles is this?

(1 acre = 43,560 ft^2; 1 mi = 5280 ft)

DENSITY

95. A sample of an unknown metal has a mass of 35.4 g and a volume of 3.11 cm^3. Calculate its density and identify the metal by comparison to Table 4.

96. A new penny has a mass of 2.49 g and a volume of 0.349 cm^3. Is the penny pure copper?

97. Glycerol is a syrupy liquid often used in cosmetics and soaps. A 2.50-L sample of pure glycerol has a mass of 3.15×10^3 g. What is the density of glycerol in grams per cubic centimeter?

98. An aluminum engine block has a volume of 4.77 L and a mass of 12.88 kg. What is the density of the aluminum in grams per cubic centimeter?

99. A supposedly gold tooth crown is tested to determine its density. It displaces 10.7 mL of water and has a mass of 206 g. Could the crown be made of gold?

100. A vase is said to be solid platinum. It displaces 18.65 mL of water and has a mass of 157 g. Could the vase be solid platinum?

101. Ethylene glycol (antifreeze) has a density of 1.11 g/cm^3.
    (a) What is the mass in grams of 387 mL of this liquid?
    (b) What is the volume in liters of 3.46 kg of this liquid?

102. Acetone (fingernail-polish remover) has a density of 0.7857 g/cm^3.
    (a) What is the mass in grams of 17.56 mL of acetone?
    (b) What is the volume in milliliters of 7.22 g of acetone?

CUMULATIVE PROBLEMS

103. A thief uses a bag of sand to replace a gold statue that sits on a weight-sensitive, alarmed pedestal. The bag of sand and the statue have exactly the same volume, 1.75 L. (Assume that the mass of the bag is negligible.)
    (a) Calculate the mass of each object. (density of gold = 19.3 g/cm^3; density of sand = 3.00 g/cm^3)
    (b) Did the thief set off the alarm? Explain.

104. One of the particles that composes an atom is the proton. A proton has a radius of approximately 1.0×10^{-13} cm and a mass of 1.7×10^{-24} g. Determine the density of a proton.

$$\left(\text{volume of a sphere} = -\frac{4}{3}\,\pi r^3; \pi = 3.14 \right)$$

105. A block of metal has a volume of 13.4 in.^{3} and weighs 5.14 lb. What is its density in grams per cubic centimeter?

106. A log is either oak or pine. It displaces 2.7 gal of water and weighs 19.8 lb. Is the log oak or pine? (density of oak = 0.9 g/cm^3; density of pine = 0.4 g/cm^3)

107. The density of aluminum is 2.7 g/cm^3. What is its density in kilograms per cubic meter?

108. The density of platinum is 21.4 g/cm^3. What is its density in pounds per cubic inch?

109. A typical backyard swimming pool holds 150 yd^3 of water. What is the mass in pounds of the water?

110. An iceberg has a volume of 8975 ft^3. What is the mass in kilograms of the iceberg?

111. The mass of fuel in an airplane must be carefully accounted for before takeoff. If a 747 contains 155,211 L of fuel, what is the mass of the fuel in kilograms? Assume the density of the fuel to be 0.768 g/cm^3.

112. A backpacker carries 2.5 L of white gas as fuel for her stove. How many pounds does the fuel add to her load? Assume the density of white gas to be 0.79 g/cm^3.

113. Honda produces a hybrid electric car called the Honda Insight. The Insight has both a gasoline-powered engine and an electric motor and has an EPA gas mileage rating of 43 miles per gallon on the highway. What is the Insight's rating in kilometers per liter?

114. You rent a car in Germany with a gas mileage rating of 12.8 km/L. What is its rating in miles per gallon?

115. A car has a mileage rating of 38 miles per gallon of gasoline. How many miles can the car travel on 76.5 liters of gasoline?

116. A hybrid SUV consumes fuel at a rate of 12.8 km/L. How many miles can the car travel on 22.5 gallons of gasoline?

117. Block A of an unknown metal has a volume of 125 cm^3. Block B of a different metal has a volume of 145 cm^3. If block A has a greater mass than block B, what can be said of the relative densities of the two metals? (Assume that both blocks are solid.)

118. Block A of an unknown metal has a volume of 125 cm^3. Block B of a different metal has a volume of 105 cm^3. If block A has a greater mass than block B, what can be said of the relative densities of the two metals? (Assume that both blocks are solid.)

119. The masses and volumes of two cylinders are measured. The mass of cylinder 1 is 1.35 times the mass of cylinder 2. The volume of cylinder 1 is 0.792 times the volume of cylinder 2. If the density of cylinder 1 is 3.85 g/cm^3, what is the density of cylinder 2?

120. A bag contains a mixture of copper and lead BBs. The average density of the BBs is 9.87 g/cm^3. Assuming that the copper and lead are pure, determine the relative amounts of each kind of BB.

HIGHLIGHT PROBLEMS

121. In 1999, NASA lost a $94 million orbiter because one group of engineers used metric units in their calculations while another group used English units. Consequently, the orbiter descended too far into the Martian atmosphere and burned up. Suppose that the orbiter was to have established orbit at 155 km and that one group of engineers specified this distance as 1.55×10^5 m. Suppose further that a second group of engineers programmed the orbiter to go to 1.55×10^5 ft. What was the difference in kilometers between the two altitudes? How low did the probe go?

122. A NASA satellite showed that in 2009 the ozone hole over Antarctica had a maximum surface area of 24.1 million km^2. The largest ozone hole on record occurred in 2006 and had a surface area of 29.6 million km^2. Calculate the difference in diameter (in meters) between the ozone hole in 2009 and in 2006.

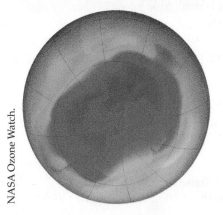

NASA Ozone Watch.

▲ A layer of ozone gas (a form of oxygen) in the upper atmosphere protects Earth from harmful ultraviolet radiation in sunlight. Human-made chemicals react with the ozone and deplete it, especially over the Antarctic at certain times of the year (the so-called ozone hole). The region of low ozone concentration in 2006 (represented here by the dark purple color) was the largest on record.

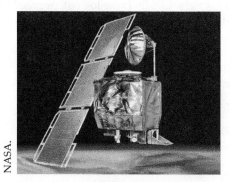

NASA.

▲ The $94 million Mars Climate Orbiter was lost in the Martian atmosphere in 1999 because two groups of engineers failed to communicate to each other the units that they used in their calculations.

123. In 1999, scientists discovered a new class of black holes with masses 100 to 10,000 times the mass of our sun, but occupying less space than our moon. Suppose that one of these black holes has a mass of 1×10^3 suns and a radius equal to one-half the radius of our moon. What is its density in grams per cubic centimeter? The mass of the sun is 2.0×10^{30} kg, and the radius of the moon is

2.16×10^3 mi. $\left(\text{Volume of a sphere} = \dfrac{4}{3}\pi r^3.\right)$

124. A titanium bicycle frame contains the same amount of titanium as a titanium cube measuring 6.8 cm on a side. Use the density of titanium to calculate the mass in kilograms of titanium in the frame. What would be the mass of a similar frame composed of iron?

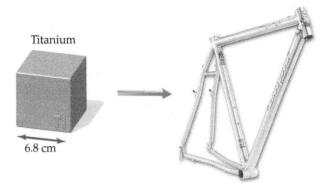

Titanium

6.8 cm

▲ A titanium bicycle frame contains the same amount of titanium as a titanium cube measuring 6.8 cm on a side.

►ANSWERS TO SKILLBUILDER EXERCISES

Skillbuilder 1	$\$1.2102 \times 10^{13}$
Skillbuilder 2	3.8×10^{-5}
Skillbuilder 3	103.4 °F

Skillbuilder 4
  (a) four significant figures
  (b) three significant figures
  (c) two significant figures
  (d) unlimited significant figures
  (e) three significant figures
  (f) ambiguous

Skillbuilder 5
  (a) 0.001 or 1×10^{-3}
  (b) 0.204

Skillbuilder 6
  (a) 7.6
  (b) 131.11

Skillbuilder 7
  (a) 1288
  (b) 3.12

Skillbuilder 8	22.0 in.
Skillbuilder 9	5.678 km
Skillbuilder 10	0.28 L
Skillbuilder 11	46.6 laps
Skillbuilder Plus 1	1.06×10^4 m
Skillbuilder 12	4747 cm^3
Skillbuilder 13	1.52×10^5 in.^{3}
Skillbuilder 14	Yes, the density is 21.4 g/cm^3 and matches that of platinum.
Skillbuilder 15	4.4×10^{-2} cm^3
Skillbuilder Plus 2	1.95 kg
Skillbuilder 16	16 kg
Skillbuilder 17	$d = 19.3$ g/cm^3; yes, the density is consistent with that of gold.

►ANSWERS TO CONCEPTUAL CHECKPOINTS

1 (c) Multiplying by 10^{-3} is equivalent to moving the decimal point three places to the left.
2 (b) The last digit is considered to be uncertain by ±1.
3 (b) The result of the calculation in **(a)** would be reported as 4; the result of the calculation in **(b)** would be reported as 1.5.

4 (d) The diameter would be expressed as 28 nm.
5 (c) Kilometers must appear in the numerator and meters in the denominator, and the conversion factor in **(d)** is incorrect (10^3 km ≠ 1 m).
6 (d) $(3 \text{ ft}) \times (3 \text{ ft}) \times (3 \text{ ft}) = 27 \text{ ft}^3$

ANSWERS TO ODD-NUMBERED EXERCISES

QUESTIONS

1. Without units, the results are unclear and it is hard to keep track of what each separate measurement entails.

3. Often scientists work with very large or very small numbers that contain a lot of zeros. Scientific notation allows these numbers to be written more compactly, and the information is more organized.

5. Zeros count as significant digits when they are interior zeros (zeros between two numbers) and when they are trailing zeros (zeros after a decimal point). Zeros are **not** significant digits when they are leading zeros, which are zeros to the left of the first nonzero number.

7. For calculations involving only multiplication and division, the result carries the same number of significant figures as the factor with the fewest significant figures.

9. In calculations involving both multiplication/division and addition/subtraction, do the steps in parentheses first; determine the correct number of significant figures in the intermediate answer; then do the remaining steps.

11. The basic SI unit of length is the meter. The kilogram is the SI unit of mass. Lastly, the second is the SI unit of time.

13. For measuring a Frisbee, the unit would be the meter and the prefix multiplier would be *centi-*. The final measurement would be in centimeters.

15. **a.** 2.42 cm   **b.** 1.79 cm
   c. 21.58 cm   **d.** 21.85 cm

17. Units act as a guide in the calculation and are able to show if the calculation is off track. The units must be followed in the calculation, so that the answer is correctly written and understood.

19. A conversion factor is a quantity used to relate two separate units. They are constructed from any two quantities known to be equivalent.

21. The conversion factor is $\dfrac{1\ \text{ft}}{12\ \text{in.}}$. For a feet-to-inches conversion, the conversion factor must be inverted $\left(\dfrac{12\ \text{in.}}{1\ \text{ft}}\right)$.

23. **a.** Sort the information into the **given** information (the starting point for the problem) and the **find** information (the end point).

   b. Create a solution map to get from the given information to the information you are trying to find. This will likely include conversion factors or equations.

   c. Follow the solution map to solve the problem. Carry out mathematical operations and cancel units as needed.

   d. Ask, does this answer make physical sense? Are the units correct? Is the number of significant figures correct?

25. The solution map for converting grams to pounds is:

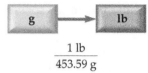

$$\frac{1\ \text{lb}}{453.59\ \text{g}}$$

27. The solution map for converting meters to feet is:

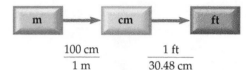

$$\frac{100\ \text{cm}}{1\ \text{m}} \qquad \frac{1\ \text{ft}}{30.48\ \text{cm}}$$

29. The density of a substance is the ratio of its mass to its volume. Density is a fundamental property of materials and differs from one substance to another. Density can be used to relate two separate units, thus working as a conversion factor. Density is a conversion factor between mass and volume.

PROBLEMS

31. **a.** 3.6756×10^7 **b.** 1.288×10^6
   c. 1.949×10^7 **d.** 5.32×10^5

33. **a.** $7.461 \times 10^{-11}\,\text{m}$ **b.** $1.58 \times 10^{-5}\,\text{mi}$
   c. $6.32 \times 10^{-7}\,\text{m}$ **d.** $1.5 \times 10^{-5}\,\text{m}$

35. **a.** 602,200,000,000,000,000,000,000
   b. 0.00000000000000000000016 C
   c. 299,000,000 m/s
   d. 344 m/s

37. **a.** 32,000,000   **b.** 0.0072
   c. 118,000,000,000   **d.** 0.00000943

39. 2,000,000,000 2×10^9
   1,211,000,000 1.211×10^9
   0.000874 8.74×10^{-4}
   320,000,000,000 3.2×10^{11}

41. **a.** 54.9 mL   **b.** 48.7 °C
   c. 46.83 °C   **d.** 64 mL

43. **a.** 0.005050   **b.** 0.00000000000000000060
   c. 220,103   **d.** 0.00108

45. **a.** 4   **b.** 4
   c. 6   **d.** 5

47. **a.** correct   **b.** 3
   c. 7   **d.** correct

49. **a.** 256.0   **b.** 0.0004893
   c. 2.901×10^{-4} **d.** 2.231×10^{-6}

51. **a.** 2.3   **b.** 2.4
     c. 2.3   **d.** 2.4

53. **a.** 42.3   **b.** correct
     c. correct   **d.** 0.0456

55.

8.32466	8.325	8.3	8
84.57225	84.57	85	8×10^1
132.5512	132.6	1.3×10^2	1×10^2

57. **a.** 0.054   **b.** 0.619
     c. 1.2×10^8 **d.** 6.6

59. **a.** 4.22×10^3 **b.** correct
     c. 3.9969   **d.** correct

61. **a.** 110.6   **b.** 41.4
     c. 183.3   **d.** 1.22

63. **a.** correct   **b.** 1.0982
     c. correct   **d.** 3.53

65. **a.** 3.9×10^3 **b.** 632
     c. 8.93×10^4 **d.** 6.34

67. **a.** 3.15×10^3 **b.** correct
     c. correct   **d.** correct

69. **a.** $3.55 \times 10^3 \, \text{g}$ **b.** 8.944 m
     c. $4.598 \times 10^{-3} \, \text{kg}$ **d.** 18.7 mL

71. **a.** 0.588 L   **b.** 34.1 μg
     c. 10.1 ns   **d.** $2.19 \times 10^{-12} \, \text{m}$

73. **a.** 57.2 cm   **b.** 38.4 m
     c. 0.754 km   **d.** 61 mm

75. **a.** 15.7 in   **b.** 91.2 ft
     c. 6.21 mi   **d.** 8478 lb

77.

$5.08 \times 10^8 \, \text{m}$	$5.08 \times 10^5 \, \text{km}$	508 Mm
$5.08 \times 10^{-1} \, \text{Gm}$	$5.08 \times 10^{-4} \, \text{Tm}$	
$2.7976 \times 10^{10} \, \text{m}$	$2.7976 \times 10^7 \, \text{km}$	27,976 Mm
$2.7976 \times 10^1 \, \text{Gm}$	$2.7976 \times 10^{-2} \, \text{Tm}$	
$1.77 \times 10^{12} \, \text{m}$	$1.77 \times 10^9 \, \text{km}$	$1.77 \times 10^6 \, \text{Mm}$
$1.77 \times 10^3 \, \text{Gm}$	1.77 Tm	
$1.5 \times 10^8 \, \text{m}$	$1.5 \times 10^5 \, \text{km}$	$1.5 \times 10^2 \, \text{Mm}$
0.15 Gm	$1.5 \times 10^{-4} \, \text{Tm}$	
$4.23 \times 10^{11} \, \text{m}$	$4.23 \times 10^8 \, \text{km}$	$4.23 \times 10^5 \, \text{Mm}$
423 Gm	0.423 Tm	

79. **a.** $2.255 \times 10^7 \, \text{kg}$ **b.** $2.255 \times 10^4 \, \text{Mg}$
     c. $2.255 \times 10^{13} \, \text{mg}$ **d.** 2.255×10^4 metric tons

81. $1.5 \times 10^3 \, \text{g}$

83. $5.0 \times 10^1 \, \text{min}$

85. $4.7 \times 10^3 \, \text{cm}^3$

87. **a.** $1.0 \times 10^6 \, \text{m}^2$ **b.** $1.0 \times 10^{-6} \, \text{m}^3$
     c. $1.0 \times 10^{-9} \, \text{m}^3$

89. **a.** $6.2 \times 10^5 \, \text{pm}^3$ **b.** $6.2 \times 10^{-4} \, \text{nm}^3$
     c. $6.2 \times 10^{-1} \, \text{Å}^3$

91. **a.** $2.15 \times 10^{-4} \, \text{km}^2$ **b.** $2.15 \times 10^4 \, \text{dm}^2$
     c. $2.15 \times 10^6 \, \text{cm}^2$

93. $1.49 \times 10^6 \, \text{mi}^2$

95. $11.4 \, \text{g/cm}^3$, lead

97. $1.26 \, \text{g/cm}^3$

99. Yes, the density of the crown is $19.3 \, \text{g/cm}^3$.

101. **a.** $4.30 \times 10^2 \, \text{g}$ **b.** 3.12 L

103. **a.** $3.38 \times 10^4 \, \text{g}$ (gold); $5.25 \times 10^3 \, \text{g}$ (sand)
     b. Yes, the mass of the bag of sand is different from the mass of the gold vase; thus, the weight-sensitive pedestal will sound the alarm.

105. $10.6 \, \text{g/cm}^3$

107. $2.7 \times 10^3 \, \dfrac{\text{kg}}{\text{m}^3}$

109. $2.5 \times 10^5 \, \text{lbs}$

111. $1.19 \times 10^5 \, \text{kg}$

113. 18 km/L

115. 768 mi

117. Metal A is denser than metal B.

119. $2.26 \, \text{g/cm}^3$

121. 108 km; 47.2 km

123. $9.1 \times 10^{10} \, \text{g/cm}^3$

Matter and Energy

From Chapter 3 of *Introductory Chemistry*, Fourth Edition, Nivaldo J. Tro. Copyright © 2011 by Pearson Education, Inc. Published by Pearson Prentice Hall. All rights reserved.

Matter and Energy

"Thus, the task is, not so much to see what no one has yet seen; but to think what nobody has yet thought, about that which everybody sees."

ERWIN SCHRÖDINGER (1887–1961)

1   In Your Room

◀ Everything that you can see in this room is made of matter. As students of chemistry, we are interested in how the differences between different kinds of matter are related to the differences between the molecules and atoms that compose the matter. The molecular structures shown here are water molecules on the left and carbon atoms in graphite on the right.

Look around the room you are in—what do you see? You might see your desk, your bed, or a glass of water. Maybe you have a window and can see trees, grass, or mountains. You can certainly see this book and possibly the table it sits on. What are these things made of? They are all made of *matter*, which we will define more carefully shortly. For now, know that all you see is matter—your desk, your bed, the glass of water, the trees, the mountains, and this book. Some of what you don't see is matter as well. For example, you are constantly breathing air, which is also matter, into and out of your lungs. You feel the matter in air when you feel wind on your skin. Virtually everything is made of matter.

Think about the differences between different kinds of matter. Air is different from water, and water is different from wood. One of our first tasks as we learn about matter is to identify the similarities and differences among different kinds of matter. How are sugar and salt similar? How are air and water different? Why are they different? Why is a mixture of sugar and water similar to a mixture of salt and water but different from a mixture of sand and water? As students of chemistry, we are particularly interested in the similarities and differences between various kinds of matter and how these reflect the similarities and differences between their component atoms and molecules. We strive to understand the connection between the macroscopic world and the molecular one.

2 What Is Matter?

Matter is defined as anything that occupies space and has mass. Some types of matter—such as steel, water, wood, and plastic—are easily visible to our eyes. Other types of matter—such as air or microscopic dust—are impossible to see without magnification. Matter may sometimes appear smooth and continuous, but actually it is not. Matter is ultimately composed of **atoms**, submicroscopic particles that are the fundamental building blocks of matter (▼ Figure 1a). In many cases, these atoms are bonded together to form **molecules**, two or more atoms joined to one another in specific geometric arrangements (Figure 1b). Recent advances in microscopy have allowed us to image the atoms (▼ Figure 2) and molecules (▼ Figure 3) that compose matter, sometimes with stunning clarity.

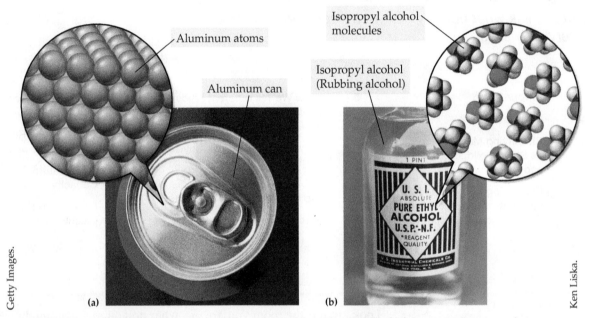

▲ **FIGURE 1**   **Atoms and molecules**   All matter is ultimately composed of atoms. **(a)** In some substances, such as aluminum, the atoms exist as independent particles. **(b)** In other substances, such as rubbing alcohol, several atoms bond together in well-defined structures called molecules.

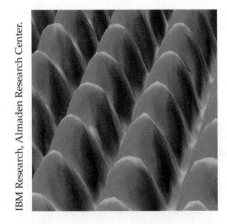

▲ **FIGURE 2**   **Scanning tunneling microscope image of nickel atoms**   A scanning tunneling microscope (STM) creates an image by scanning a surface with a tip of atomic dimensions. It can distinguish individual atoms, seen as blue bumps, in this image. (*Source:* Reprint Courtesy of International Business Machines Corporation, copyright © International Business Machines Corporation.)

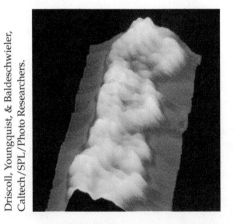

▲ **FIGURE 3**   **Scanning tunneling microscope image of a DNA molecule**   DNA is the hereditary material that encodes the operating instructions for most cells in living organisms. In this image, the DNA molecule is yellow, and the double-stranded structure of DNA is discernible.

3 Classifying Matter According to Its State: Solid, Liquid, and Gas

The common **states of matter** are **solid**, **liquid**, and **gas** (▼ Figure 4). In solid matter, atoms or molecules pack close to each other in fixed locations. Although neighboring atoms or molecules in a solid may vibrate or oscillate, they do not move around each other, giving solids their familiar fixed volume and rigid shape.

▶ **FIGURE 4 Three states of matter** Water exists as ice (solid), water (liquid), and steam (gas). In ice, the water molecules are closely spaced and, although they vibrate about a fixed point, they do not generally move relative to one another. In liquid water, the water molecules are also closely spaced but are free to move around and past each other. In steam, water molecules are separated by large distances and do not interact significantly with one another.

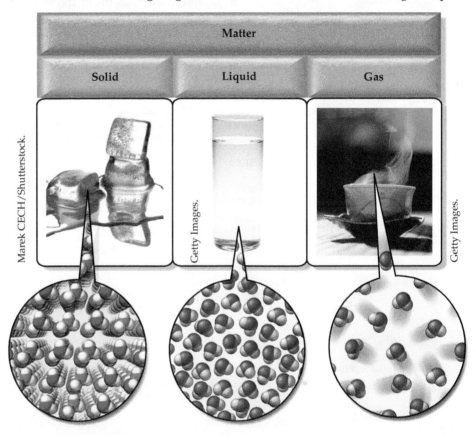

Marek CECH/Shutterstock.

Getty Images.

Getty Images.

Ice, diamond, quartz, and iron are examples of solid matter. Solid matter may be **crystalline**, in which case its atoms or molecules arrange in geometric patterns with long-range, repeating order (◀ Figure 5a), or it may be **amorphous**, in which case its atoms or molecules do not have long-range order (Figure 5b). Examples of *crystalline* solids include salt (▼ Figure 6) and diamond; the well-ordered, geometric shapes of salt and diamond crystals reflect the well-ordered geometric arrangement of their atoms. Examples of *amorphous* solids include glass, rubber, and plastic.

(a) Crystalline solid

(b) Amorphous solid

▲ **FIGURE 5 Types of solid matter** (a) In a crystalline solid, atoms or molecules occupy specific positions to create a well-ordered, three-dimensional structure. (b) In an amorphous solid, atoms do not have any long-range order.

Natural History Museum, London/Alamy.

▲ **FIGURE 6 Salt: a crystalline solid** Sodium chloride is an example of a crystalline solid. The well-ordered, cubic shape of salt crystals is due to the well-ordered, cubic arrangement of its atoms.

In liquid matter, atoms or molecules are close to each other (about as close as molecules in a solid) but are free to move around and by each other. Like solids, liquids have a fixed volume because their atoms or molecules are in close contact. Unlike solids, however, liquids assume the shape of their container because the atoms or molecules are free to move relative to one another. Water, gasoline, alcohol, and mercury are all examples of liquid matter.

In gaseous matter, atoms or molecules are separated by large distances and are free to move relative to one another. Since the atoms or molecules that compose gases are not in contact with one another, gases are **compressible** (◄ Figure 7). When you inflate a bicycle tire, for example, you push more atoms and molecules into the same space, compressing them and making the tire harder. Gases always assume the shape and volume of their containers. Oxygen, helium, and carbon dioxide are all good examples of gases. Table 1 summarizes the properties of solids, liquids, and gases.

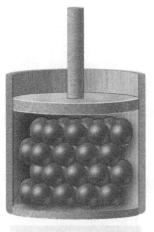

Solid—not compressible

TABLE 1 Properties of Liquids, Solids, and Gases

State	Atomic/Molecular Motion	Atomic/Molecular Spacing	Shape	Volume	Compressibility
Solid	Oscillation/ vibration about fixed point	Close together	Definite	Definite	Incompressible
Liquid	Free to move relative to one another	Close together	Indefinite	Definite	Incompressible
Gas	Free to move relative to one another	Far apart	Indefinite	Indefinite	Compressible

Gas—compressible

◄ FIGURE 7 **Gases are compressible** Since the atoms or molecules that compose gases are not in contact with one another, gases can be compressed.

4 Classifying Matter According to Its Composition: Elements, Compounds, and Mixtures

In addition to classifying matter according to its state, we can classify it according to its composition (▶ Figure 8). Matter may be either a **pure substance**, composed of only one type of atom or molecule, or a **mixture**, composed of two or more different types of atoms or molecules combined in variable proportions.

Pure substances are composed of only one type of atom or molecule. Helium and water are both pure substances. The atoms that compose helium are all helium atoms, and the molecules that compose water are all water molecules—no other atoms or molecules are mixed in.

Pure substances can themselves be divided into two types: elements and compounds. Copper is an example of an **element**, a substance that cannot be broken down into simpler substances. The graphite in pencils is also an element—carbon. No chemical transformation can decompose graphite into simpler substances; it is pure carbon. All known elements are listed in the periodic table.

A pure substance can also be a **compound**, a substance composed of two or more elements in fixed definite proportions. Compounds are more common than pure elements because most elements are chemically reactive and combine with other elements to form compounds. Water, table salt, and sugar are examples of compounds; they can all be decomposed into simpler substances. If you heat sugar on a pan over a flame, you decompose it into several substances including carbon

A compound is composed of different atoms that are chemically united (bonded). A mixture is composed of different substances that are not chemically united, but simply mixed together.

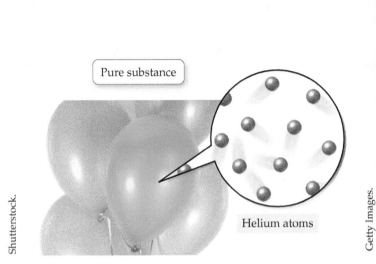

Pure substance

Helium atoms

▲ Helium is a pure substance composed only of helium atoms.

Shutterstock.

Pure substance

Water molecules

▲ Water is a pure substance composed only of water molecules.

Getty Images.

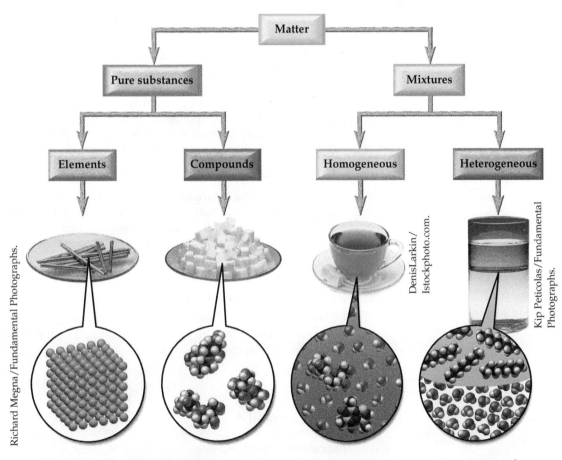

Richard Megna/Fundamental Photographs.

DenisLarkin/Istockphoto.com.

Kip Peticolas/Fundamental Photographs.

▲ FIGURE 8 **Classification of matter** Matter may be a pure substance or a mixture. A pure substance may be either an element (such as copper) or a compound (such as sugar), and a mixture may be either homogeneous (such as sweetened tea) or heterogeneous (such as hydrocarbon and water).

(an element) and gaseous water (a different compound). The black substance left on your pan after burning contains the carbon; the water escapes into the air as steam.

The majority of matter that we encounter is in the form of mixtures. Apple juice, a flame, salad dressing, and soil are all examples of mixtures; they each contain several substances mixed together in proportions that vary from one sample to another. Other common mixtures include air, seawater, and brass. Air is a mixture composed primarily of nitrogen and oxygen gas, seawater is a mixture composed primarily of salt and water, and brass is a mixture composed of copper and zinc. Each of these mixtures can have different proportions of its constituent components. For example, metallurgists vary the relative amounts of copper and zinc in brass to tailor the metal's properties to its intended use—the higher the zinc content relative to the copper content, the more brittle the brass.

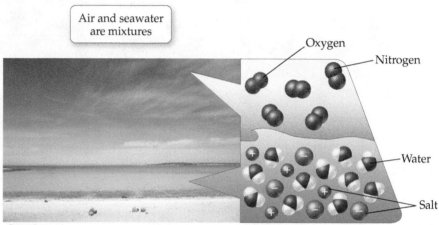

Air and seawater are mixtures

Oxygen

Nitrogen

Water

Salt

Getty Images.

▶ Air and seawater are examples of mixtures. Air contains primarily nitrogen and oxygen. Seawater contains primarily salt and water.

Mixtures can be classified according to how uniformly the substances within them mix. In a **heterogeneous mixture**, such as oil and water, the composition varies from one region to another. In a **homogeneous mixture**, such as salt water or sweetened tea, the composition is the same throughout. Homogeneous mixtures have uniform compositions because the atoms or molecules that compose them mix uniformly. Remember that the properties of matter are determined by the atoms or molecules that compose it.

To summarize, as shown in Figure 8:

- Matter may be a pure substance, or it may be a mixture.
- A pure substance may be either an element or a compound.
- A mixture may be either homogeneous or heterogeneous.
- Mixtures may be composed of two or more elements, two or more compounds, or a combination of both.

EXAMPLE 1   Classifying Matter

Classify each type of matter as a pure substance or a mixture. If it is a pure substance, classify it as an element or a compound; if it is a mixture, classify it as homogeneous or heterogeneous.

(a) a lead weight
(b) seawater
(c) distilled water
(d) Italian salad dressing

SOLUTION

Begin by examining an alphabetical listing of pure elements. If the substance appears in that table, it is a pure substance and an element. If it is not in the table but is a pure substance, then it is a compound.

If the substance is not a pure substance, then it is a mixture. Refer to your everyday experience with each mixture to determine if it is homogeneous or heterogeneous.

(a) Lead is listed in the table of elements. It is a pure substance and an element.
(b) Seawater is composed of several substances, including salt and water; it is a mixture. It has a uniform composition, so it is a homogeneous mixture.
(c) Distilled water is not listed in the table of elements, but it is a pure substance (water); therefore, it is a compound.
(d) Italian salad dressing contains a number of substances and is therefore a mixture. It usually separates into at least two distinct regions with different composition and is therefore a heterogeneous mixture.

▶SKILLBUILDER 1 | Classifying Matter

Classify each type of matter as a pure substance or a mixture. If it is a pure substance, classify it as an element or a compound. If it is a mixture, classify it as homogeneous or heterogeneous.

(a) mercury in a thermometer
(b) exhaled air
(c) minestrone soup
(d) sugar

▶FOR MORE PRACTICE   Example 12; Problems 31, 32, 33, 34, 35, 36.

Note: The answers to all Skillbuilders appear at the end of the chapter.

5   How We Tell Different Kinds of Matter Apart: Physical and Chemical Properties

The characteristics that distinguish one substance from another are called **properties**. Different substances have unique properties that characterize them and distinguish them from other substances. For example, we can distinguish water from alcohol based on their different smells, or we can distinguish gold from silver based on their different colors.

In chemistry, we categorize properties into two different types: physical and chemical. A **physical property** is one that a substance displays without changing its composition. A **chemical property** is one that a substance displays only through changing its composition. For example, the characteristic odor of gasoline is a physical property—gasoline does not change its composition when it exhibits its odor. On the other hand, the flammability of gasoline is a chemical property—gasoline does change its composition when it burns.

The atomic or molecular composition of a substance does not change when the substance displays its physical properties. For example, the boiling point of water—a physical property—is 100 °C. When water boils, it changes from a liquid to a gas, but the gas is still water (◀ Figure 9).

istockphoto.com.

◀ FIGURE 9   **A physical property**   The boiling point of water is a physical property, and boiling is a physical change. When water boils, it turns into a gas, but the water molecules are the same in both the liquid water and the gaseous steam.

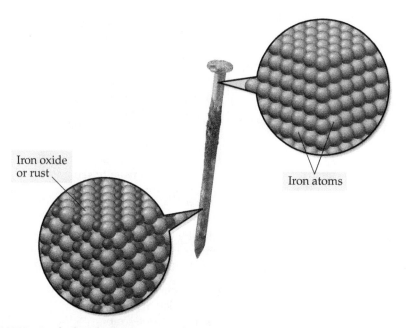

▲ FIGURE 10 **A chemical property** The susceptibility of iron to rusting is a chemical property, and rusting is a chemical change. When iron rusts, it turns from iron to iron oxide.

On the other hand, the susceptibility of iron to rust is a chemical property—iron must change into iron oxide to display this property (▲ Figure 10). Physical properties include odor, taste, color, appearance, melting point, boiling point, and density. Chemical properties include corrosiveness, flammability, acidity, and toxicity.

EXAMPLE 2   Physical and Chemical Properties

Determine whether each property is physical or chemical.

(a) the tendency of copper to turn green when exposed to air
(b) the tendency of automobile paint to dull over time
(c) the tendency of gasoline to evaporate quickly when spilled
(d) the low mass (for a given volume) of aluminum relative to other metals

SOLUTION

(a) Copper turns green because it reacts with gases in air to form compounds; this is a chemical property.
(b) Automobile paint dulls over time because it can fade (decompose) due to sunlight or it can react with oxygen in air. In either case, this is a chemical property.
(c) Gasoline evaporates quickly because it has a low boiling point; this is a physical property.
(d) Aluminum's low mass (for a given volume) relative to other metals is due to its low density; this is a physical property.

▶**SKILLBUILDER 2 | Physical and Chemical Properties**

Determine whether each property is physical or chemical.

(a) the explosiveness of hydrogen gas
(b) the bronze color of copper
(c) the shiny appearance of silver
(d) the ability of dry ice to sublime (change from solid directly to vapor)

▶**FOR MORE PRACTICE**   Example 13; Problems 37, 38, 39, 40.

6 How Matter Changes: Physical and Chemical Changes

Every day, we witness changes in matter: Ice melts, iron rusts, and fruit ripens, for example. What happens to the atoms and molecules that make up these substances during the change? The answer depends on the kind of change. In a **physical change**, matter changes its appearance but not its composition. For example, when ice melts, it looks different—water looks different from ice—but its composition is the same. Solid ice and liquid water are both composed of water molecules, so melting is a physical change. Similarly, when glass shatters, it looks different, but its composition remains the same—it is still glass. Again, this is a physical change. On the other hand, in a **chemical change**, matter *does* change its composition. For example, copper turns green upon continued exposure to air because it reacts with gases in air to form new compounds. This is a chemical change. Matter undergoes a chemical change when it undergoes a **chemical reaction**. In a chemical reaction, the substances present before the chemical change are called **reactants**, and the substances present after the change are called **products**:

$$\text{Reactants} \xrightarrow[\text{Change}]{\text{Chemical}} \text{Products}$$

The differences between physical and chemical changes are not always apparent. Only chemical examination of the substances before and after the change can verify whether the change is physical or chemical. For many cases, however, we can identify chemical and physical changes based on what we know about the changes. Changes in state, such as melting or boiling, or changes that involve merely appearance, such as those produced by cutting or crushing, are always physical changes. Changes involving chemical reactions—often evidenced by heat exchange or color changes—are always chemical changes.

The main difference between chemical and physical changes is related to the changes at the molecular and atomic level. In physical changes, the atoms that compose the matter *do not* change their fundamental associations, even though the matter may change its appearance. In chemical changes, atoms do change their fundamental associations, resulting in matter with a new identity. *A physical change results in a different form of the same substance, while a chemical change results in a completely new substance.*

Consider physical and chemical changes in liquid butane, the substance used to fuel butane lighters. In many lighters, you can see the liquid butane through the plastic case of the lighter. If you push the fuel button on the lighter without turning the flint, some of the liquid butane *vaporizes* (changes from liquid to gas). If you listen carefully you can usually hear hissing as the gaseous butane leaks out (◀ Figure 11). Since the liquid butane and the gaseous butane are both composed of butane molecules, the change is physical. On the other hand, if you push the button *and* turn the flint to create a spark, a chemical change occurs. The butane molecules react with oxygen molecules in air to form new molecules, carbon dioxide and water (◀ Figure 12). The change is chemical because the molecular composition changes upon burning.

> State changes—transformations from one state of matter (such as solid or liquid) to another—are always physical changes.

▼ **FIGURE 11** **Vaporization: a physical change** If you push the button on a lighter without turning the flint, some of the liquid butane vaporizes to gaseous butane. Since the liquid butane and the gaseous butane are both composed of butane molecules, this is a physical change.

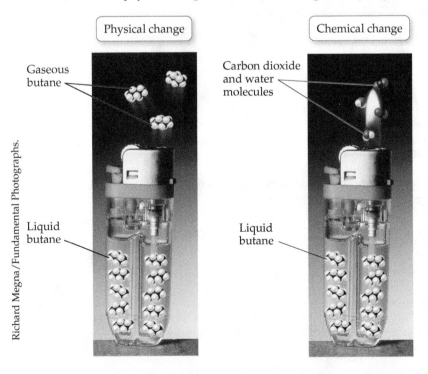

Physical change

Gaseous butane

Liquid butane

Chemical change

Carbon dioxide and water molecules

Liquid butane

Richard Megna/Fundamental Photographs.

◀ **FIGURE 12** **Burning: a chemical change** If you push the button *and* turn the flint to create a spark, you produce a flame. The butane molecules react with oxygen molecules in air to form new molecules, carbon dioxide and water. This is a chemical change.

EXAMPLE 3 Physical and Chemical Changes

Determine whether each change is physical or chemical.

(a) the rusting of iron
(b) the evaporation of fingernail-polish remover (acetone) from the skin
(c) the burning of coal
(d) the fading of a carpet upon repeated exposure to sunlight

SOLUTION

(a) Iron rusts because it reacts with oxygen in air to form iron oxide; therefore, this is a chemical change.
(b) When fingernail-polish remover (acetone) evaporates, it changes from liquid to gas, but it remains acetone; therefore, this is a physical change.
(c) Coal burns because it reacts with oxygen in air to form carbon dioxide; this is a chemical change.
(d) A carpet fades on repeated exposure to sunlight because the molecules that give the carpet its color are decomposed by sunlight; this is a chemical change.

▶**SKILLBUILDER 3 | Physical and Chemical Changes**

Determine whether each change is physical or chemical.

(a) copper metal forming a blue solution when it is dropped into colorless nitric acid
(b) a train flattening a penny placed on a railroad track
(c) ice melting into liquid water
(d) a match igniting a firework

▶**FOR MORE PRACTICE** Example 14; Problems 41, 42, 43, 44.

✔ CONCEPTUAL CHECKPOINT 1

In this figure liquid water is being vaporized into steam.

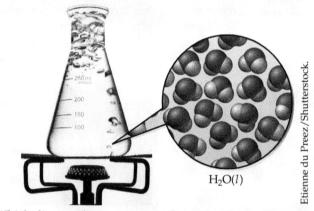

$H_2O(l)$

Etienne du Preez/Shutterstock.

Which diagram best represents the molecules in the steam?

(a)　　　　　　(b)　　　　　　(c)

Note: The answers to all Conceptual Checkpoints appear at the end of the chapter.

► FIGURE 13 **Separating a mixture of two liquids by distillation** The liquid with the lower boiling point vaporizes first. The vapors are collected and cooled (with cold water) until they condense back into liquid form.

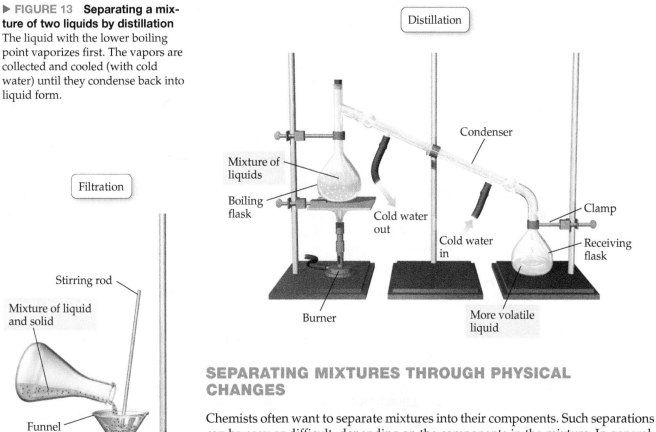

Filtration

Distillation

Stirring rod

Mixture of liquid and solid

Funnel

Filter paper traps solid

Liquid component of mixture

Mixture of liquids

Boiling flask

Condenser

Cold water out

Cold water in

Clamp

Receiving flask

Burner

More volatile liquid

▲ FIGURE 14 **Separating a solid from a liquid by filtration**

SEPARATING MIXTURES THROUGH PHYSICAL CHANGES

Chemists often want to separate mixtures into their components. Such separations can be easy or difficult, depending on the components in the mixture. In general, mixtures are separable because the different components have different properties. Various techniques that exploit these differences can be used to achieve separation. For example, oil and water are immiscible (do not mix) and have different densities. For this reason, oil floats on top of water and can be separated from water by **decanting**—carefully pouring off—the oil into another container. Mixtures of miscible liquids can usually be separated by **distillation**, a process in which the mixture is heated to boil off the more **volatile**—the more easily vaporizable—liquid. The volatile liquid is then recondensed in a condenser and collected in a separate flask (▲ Figure 13). If a mixture is composed of a solid and a liquid, the two can be separated by **filtration**, in which the mixture is poured through filter paper usually held in a funnel (◄ Figure 14).

7 Conservation of Mass: There Is No New Matter

As we have seen, our planet, our air, and even our own bodies are composed of matter. Physical and chemical changes do not destroy matter, nor do they create new matter. Recall that Antoine Lavoisier, by studying combustion, established the law of conservation of mass, which states:

This law is a slight oversimplification. In nuclear reactions, significant changes in mass can occur. In chemical reactions, however, the changes are so minute that they can be ignored.

Matter is neither created nor destroyed in a chemical reaction.

During physical and chemical changes, the total amount of matter remains constant even though it may not initially appear that it has. When we burn butane in a lighter, for example, the butane slowly disappears. Where does it go? It combines with oxygen to form carbon dioxide and water that travel into the surrounding air. The mass of the carbon dioxide and water that form, however, exactly equals the mass of the butane and oxygen that combined.

Suppose that we burn 58 g of butane in a lighter. It will react with 208 g of oxygen to form 176 g of carbon dioxide and 90 g of water.

$$\underbrace{\begin{array}{c} \text{Butane} + \text{Oxygen} \\ 58\,\text{g} + 208\,\text{g} \end{array}}_{266\,\text{g}} \longrightarrow \underbrace{\begin{array}{c} \text{Carbon Dioxide} + \text{Water} \\ 176\,\text{g} + 90\,\text{g} \end{array}}_{266\,\text{g}}$$

The sum of the masses of the butane and oxygen, 266 g, is equal to the sum of the masses of the carbon dioxide and water, which is also 266 g. In this chemical reaction, as in all chemical reactions, matter is conserved.

EXAMPLE 4 Conservation of Mass

A chemist forms 16.6 g of potassium iodide by combining 3.9 g of potassium with 12.7 g of iodine. Show that these results are consistent with the law of conservation of mass.

SOLUTION

The sum of the masses of the potassium and iodine is:

$$3.9\,\text{g} + 12.7\,\text{g} = 16.6\,\text{g}$$

The sum of the masses of potassium and iodine equals the mass of the product, potassium iodide. The results are consistent with the law of conservation of mass.

▶**SKILLBUILDER 4** | Conservation of Mass

Suppose 12 g of natural gas combines with 48 g of oxygen in a flame. The chemical change produces 33 g of carbon dioxide. How many grams of water form?

▶**FOR MORE PRACTICE** Example 15; Problems 45, 46, 47, 48, 49, 50.

✔ CONCEPTUAL CHECKPOINT 2

Consider a drop of water that is put into a flask, sealed with a cap, and heated until the droplet vaporizes. Is the mass of the container and water different after heating?

8 Energy

JLGutierrez/istockphoto.com.

▲ Water behind a dam contains potential energy.

Matter is one of the two major components of our universe. The other major component is **energy**, *the capacity to do work*. **Work** is defined as the result of a force acting on a distance. For example, if you push this book across your desk, you have done work. You may at first think that chemistry is concerned only with matter, but the behavior of matter is driven in large part by energy, so understanding energy is critical to understanding chemistry. Like matter, energy is conserved. The **law of conservation of energy** states that *energy is neither created nor destroyed*. The total amount of energy is constant; energy can be changed from one form to another or transferred from one object to another, but it cannot be created out of nothing, and it does not vanish into nothing.

Virtually all samples of matter have energy. The total energy of a sample of matter is the sum of its **kinetic energy**, the energy associated with its motion, and its **potential energy**, the energy associated with its position or composition. For example, a moving billiard ball contains *kinetic energy* because it is *moving* at some speed across the billiard table. Water behind a dam contains *potential energy* because it is held at a high *position* in the Earth's gravitational field by the dam.

CHEMISTRY IN THE ENVIRONMENT
Getting Energy out of Nothing?

The law of conservation of energy has significant implications for energy use. The best we can do with energy is break even (and even that is not really possible); we can't continually draw energy from a device without putting energy into it. A device that supposedly produces energy without the need for energy input is sometimes called a *perpetual motion machine* (▼ Figure 15) and, according to the law of conservation of energy, cannot exist. Occasionally, the media report or speculate on the discovery of a system that appears to produce more energy than it consumes. For example, I once heard a radio talk show on the subject of energy and gasoline costs. The reporter suggested that we simply design an electric car that recharges itself while being

◀ FIGURE 15 A proposed perpetual motion machine The rolling balls supposedly keep the wheel perpetually spinning. Question: Can you explain why this would not work?

driven. The battery in the electric car would charge during operation in the same way that the battery in a conventional car recharges, except the electric car would run with energy from the battery. Although people have dreamed of machines such as this for decades, such ideas violate the law of conservation of energy because they produce energy without any energy input. In the case of the perpetually moving electric car, the fault lies in the idea that driving the electric car can recharge the battery—it can't.

The battery in a conventional car recharges because energy from gasoline combustion is converted into electrical energy that then charges the battery. The electric car needs energy to move forward, and the battery will eventually discharge as it provides that energy. Hybrid cars (electric and gasoline-powered) such as the Toyota Prius can capture some limited energy from braking and use that energy to recharge the battery. However, they could never run indefinitely without the addition of fuel. Our society has a continual need for energy, and as our current energy resources dwindle, new energy sources will be required. Unfortunately, those sources must also follow the law of conservation of energy—energy must be conserved.

CAN YOU ANSWER THIS? *A friend asks you to invest in a new flashlight he invented that never needs batteries. What questions should you ask before writing a check?*

When the water flows through the dam from a higher position to a lower position, it can turn a turbine and produce electrical energy. **Electrical energy** is the energy associated with the flow of electrical charge. **Thermal energy** is the energy associated with the random motions of atoms and molecules in matter. The hotter an object, the more thermal energy it contains.

Chemical systems contain **chemical energy**, a form of potential energy associated with the positions of the particles that compose the chemical system. For example, the molecules that compose gasoline contain a substantial amount of chemical energy. They are a bit like the water behind a dam. Burning the gasoline is analogous to releasing the water from the dam. The chemical energy present in the gasoline is released upon burning. When we drive a car, we use that chemical energy to move the car forward. When we heat a home, we use chemical energy stored in natural gas to produce heat and warm the air in the house.

UNITS OF ENERGY

Several different energy units are in common use. The SI unit of energy is the joule (J), named after the English scientist James Joule (1818–1889), who demonstrated that energy could be converted from one type to another as long as the total energy was conserved. A second unit of energy is the **calorie (cal)**, the amount of energy required to raise the temperature of 1 g of water by 1 °C. A calorie is a larger unit than a joule: 1 cal = 4.184 J. A related energy unit is the nutritional or *capital C* **Calorie (Cal)**, equivalent to 1000 *little c* calories. Electricity bills usually come in yet another energy unit, the **kilowatt-hour (kWh)**. The average cost of residential electricity in the United States is about $0.12 per kilowatt-hour. Table 2 lists various energy units and their conversion factors. Table 3 shows the amount of energy required for various processes in each of these units.

TABLE 2 Energy Conversion Factors

1 calorie (cal)	=	4.184 joules (J)
1 Calorie (Cal)	=	1000 calories (cal)
1 kilowatt-hour (kWh)	=	3.60×10^6 joules (J)

TABLE 3 Energy Use in Various Units

Unit	Energy Required to Raise Temperature of 1 g of Water by 1 °C	Energy Required to Light 100-W Bulb for 1 Hour	Total Energy Used by Average U.S. Citizen in 1 Day
joule (J)	4.18	3.6×10^5	9.0×10^8
calorie (cal)	1.00	8.60×10^4	2.2×10^8
Calorie (Cal)	0.00100	86.0	2.2×10^5
kilowatt-hour (kWh)	1.16×10^{-6}	0.100	2.50×10^2

EXAMPLE 5 Conversion of Energy Units

A candy bar contains 225 Cal of nutritional energy. How many joules does it contain?

SORT Begin by sorting the information in the problem. Here you are *given* energy in Calories and asked to *find* energy in joules.	**GIVEN:** 225 Cal **FIND:** J
STRATEGIZE Draw a solution map. Begin with Cal, convert to cal, and then convert to J.	**SOLUTION MAP** 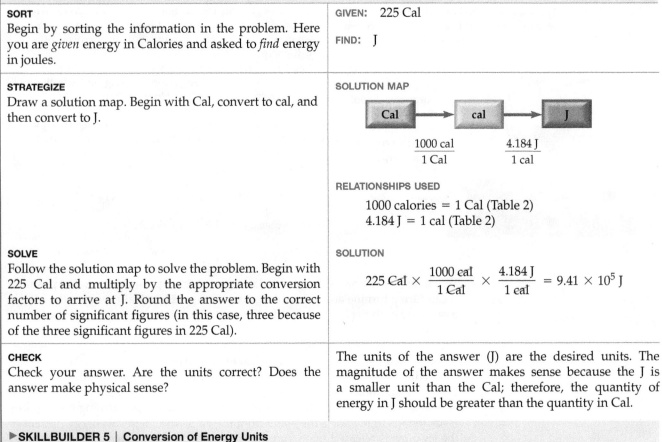 **RELATIONSHIPS USED** 1000 calories = 1 Cal (Table 2) 4.184 J = 1 cal (Table 2)
SOLVE Follow the solution map to solve the problem. Begin with 225 Cal and multiply by the appropriate conversion factors to arrive at J. Round the answer to the correct number of significant figures (in this case, three because of the three significant figures in 225 Cal).	**SOLUTION** $225 \, \text{Cal} \times \dfrac{1000 \, \text{cal}}{1 \, \text{Cal}} \times \dfrac{4.184 \, \text{J}}{1 \, \text{cal}} = 9.41 \times 10^5 \, \text{J}$
CHECK Check your answer. Are the units correct? Does the answer make physical sense?	The units of the answer (J) are the desired units. The magnitude of the answer makes sense because the J is a smaller unit than the Cal; therefore, the quantity of energy in J should be greater than the quantity in Cal.

▶**SKILLBUILDER 5 | Conversion of Energy Units**

The complete combustion of a small wooden match produces approximately 512 cal of heat. How many kilojoules are produced?

▶**SKILLBUILDER PLUS 1**

Convert 2.75×10^4 kJ to calories.

▶**FOR MORE PRACTICE**   Example 16; Problems 51, 52, 53, 54, 55, 56, 57, 58.

CONCEPTUAL CHECKPOINT 3

Suppose a salesperson wants to make an appliance seem as efficient as possible. In which units would the yearly energy consumption of the appliance have the lowest numerical value and therefore seem most efficient?

(a) J

(b) cal

(c) Cal

(d) kWh

9 Energy and Chemical and Physical Change

When discussing energy transfer, we often define the object of our study (such as a flask in which a chemical reaction is occurring) as the *system*. The system then exchanges energy with its *surroundings*. In other words, we view energy changes as an exchange of energy between the system and the surroundings.

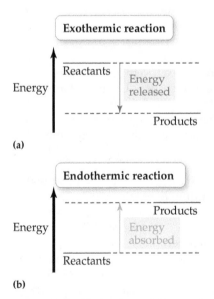

(a)

(b)

▲ FIGURE 16 **Exothermic and endothermic reactions** (a) In an exothermic reaction, energy is released. (b) In an endothermic reaction, energy is absorbed.

The physical and chemical changes that we discussed in Section 6 are usually accompanied by energy changes. For example, when water evaporates from your skin (a physical change), the water molecules absorb energy, cooling your skin. When you burn natural gas on the stove (a chemical change), energy is released, heating the food you are cooking.

The release of energy during a chemical reaction is analogous to the release of energy that occurs when you drop a weight to the ground. When you lift a weight, you raise its potential energy; when you drop it, the potential energy is released. *Systems with high potential energy—like the raised weight—have a tendency to change in a way that lowers their potential energy.* For this reason, objects or systems with high potential energy tend to be *unstable*. A weight lifted several meters from the ground is unstable because it contains a significant amount of localized potential energy. Unless restrained, the weight will fall, lowering its potential energy.

Some chemical substances are like the raised weight just described. For example, the molecules that compose TNT (trinitrotoluene) have a relatively high potential energy—energy is concentrated in them just as energy is concentrated in the raised weight. TNT molecules therefore tend to undergo rapid chemical changes that lower their potential energy, which is why TNT is explosive. Chemical reactions that *release* energy, like the explosion of TNT, are said to be **exothermic**.

Some chemical reactions behave in just the opposite way—they *absorb* energy from their surroundings as they occur. Such reactions are said to be **endothermic**. The use of a chemical cold pack is a good example of an endothermic reaction. When a barrier separating the reactants in a chemical cold pack is broken, the substances mix, react, and absorb heat from the surroundings. The surroundings—possibly including your bruised ankle—get colder.

We can represent the energy changes that occur during a chemical reaction with an energy diagram, as shown in ◀ Figure 16. In an exothermic reaction (Figure 16a), the reactants have greater energy than the products, and energy is released as the reaction occurs. In an endothermic reaction (Figure 16b), the products have more energy than the reactants, and energy is absorbed as the reaction occurs.

If a particular reaction or process is exothermic, then the reverse process must be endothermic. For example, the evaporation of water from your skin is endothermic (and therefore cools you off), but the condensation of water onto your skin is exothermic (which is why steam burns can be so painful and dangerous).

EXAMPLE 6 Exothermic and Endothermic Processes

Identify each change as exothermic or endothermic.

(a) wood burning in a fire
(b) ice melting

SOLUTION

(a) When wood burns, it emits heat into the surroundings. Therefore, the process is exothermic.

(b) When ice melts, it absorbs heat from the surroundings. For example, when ice melts in a glass of water, it cools the water as the melting ice absorbs heat from the water. Therefore, the process is endothermic.

▶ **SKILLBUILDER 6** | **Exothermic and Endothermic Processes**

Identify each change as exothermic or endothermic.

(a) water freezing into ice
(b) natural gas burning

▶ **FOR MORE PRACTICE** Problems 61, 62, 63, 64.

10 Temperature: Random Motion of Molecules and Atoms

The atoms and molecules that compose matter are in constant random motion—they contain *thermal energy*. The **temperature** of a substance is a measure of its thermal energy. The hotter an object, the greater the random motion of the atoms and molecules that compose it, and the higher its temperature. We must be careful to not confuse *temperature* with *heat*. **Heat**, which has units of energy, is the *transfer* or *exchange* of thermal energy caused by a temperature difference. For example, when a cold ice cube is dropped into a warm cup of water, heat is transferred from the water to the ice, resulting in the cooling of the water. Temperature, by contrast, is a *measure* of the thermal energy of matter (not the exchange of thermal energy).

Three different temperature scales are in common use. The most familiar in the United States is the **Fahrenheit (°F) scale**. On the Fahrenheit scale, water freezes at 32 °F and boils at 212 °F. Room temperature is approximately 72 °F. The Fahrenheit scale was initially set up by assigning 0 °F to the freezing point of a concentrated saltwater solution and 96 °F to normal body temperature (although body temperature is now known to be 98.6 °F).

The scale used by scientists is the **Celsius (°C) scale**. On this scale, water freezes at 0 °C and boils at 100 °C. Room temperature is approximately 22 °C.

The Fahrenheit and Celsius scales differ in both the size of their respective degrees and the temperature each calls "zero" (▶ Figure 17). Both the Fahrenheit and Celsius scales contain negative temperatures. A third temperature scale, called the **Kelvin (K) scale**, avoids negative temperatures by assigning 0 K to the coldest temperature possible, absolute zero. Absolute zero (-273.15 °C or -459.7 °F) is the temperature at which molecular motion virtually stops. There is no lower temperature. The kelvin degree, or kelvin (K), is the same size as the Celsius degree—the only difference is the temperature that each scale designates as zero.

We can convert between these temperature scales using the following formulas.

The degree symbol is used with the Celsius and Fahrenheit scales, but not with the Kelvin scale.

$$K = °C + 273.15$$

$$°C = \frac{(°F - 32)}{1.8}$$

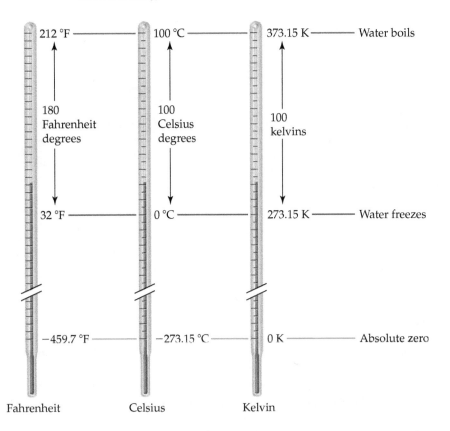

▶ FIGURE 17 **Comparison of the Fahrenheit, Celsius, and Kelvin temperature scales** The Fahrenheit degree is five-ninths the size of a Celsius degree. The Celsius degree and the kelvin degree are the same size.

For example, suppose we want to convert 212 K to Celsius. Following the procedure for solving numerical problems, we first sort the information in the problem statement:

GIVEN: 212 K

FIND: °C

In a solution map involving a formula, the formula establishes the relationship between the variables. However, the formula under the arrow is not necessarily solved for the correct variable until later, as is the case here.

SOLUTION MAP
We then strategize by building a solution map.

$$K \longrightarrow °C$$

$$K = °C + 273.15$$

RELATIONSHIPS USED
K = °C + 273.15 (This equation relates the *given* quantity (K) to the *find* quantity (°C) and is given in this section.)

SOLUTION
Finally, we follow the solution map to solve the problem. The equation below the arrow shows the relationship between K and °C, but it is not solved for the correct variable. Before using the equation, we must solve it for °C.

$$K = °C + 273.15$$

$$°C = K - 273.15$$

We can now substitute the given value for K and compute the answer to the correct number of significant figures.

$$°C = 212 - 273.15$$

$$= -61 °C$$

EXAMPLE 7   Converting between Celsius and Kelvin Temperature Scales

Convert −25 °C to kelvins.

SORT	
You are given a temperature in degrees Celsius and asked to find the value of the temperature in kelvins.	GIVEN: −25 °C FIND: K

STRATEGIZE	
Draw a solution map. Use the equation that relates the temperature in kelvins to the temperature in Celsius to convert from the given quantity to the quantity you are asked to find.	SOLUTION MAP °C ⟶ K $$K = °C + 273.15$$ RELATIONSHIPS USED $$K = °C + 273.15 \text{ (presented in this section)}$$

SOLVE	
Follow the solution map to solve the problem by substituting the correct value for °C and calculating the answer to the correct number of significant figures.	SOLUTION $$K = °C + 273.15$$ $$K = -25°C + 273.15 = 248\,K$$

CHECK	
Check your answer. Are the units correct? Does the answer make physical sense?	The units (K) are correct. The answer makes sense because the value in kelvins should be a more positive number than the value in degrees Celsius.

▶**SKILLBUILDER 7 | Converting between Celsius and Kelvin Temperature Scales**

Convert 358 K to Celsius.

▶**FOR MORE PRACTICE**   Example 17; Problems 65c, 66d.

EXAMPLE 8   Converting between Fahrenheit and Celsius Temperature Scales

Convert 55 °F to Celsius.

SORT	
You are given a temperature in degrees Fahrenheit and asked to find the value of the temperature in degrees Celsius.	GIVEN: 55 °F FIND: °C

STRATEGIZE	
Draw the solution map. Use the equation that shows the relationship between the given quantity (°F) and the find quantity (°C).	SOLUTION MAP °F ⟶ °C $$°C = \frac{(°F - 32)}{1.8}$$ RELATIONSHIPS USED $$°C = \frac{(°F - 32)}{1.8} \text{ (presented in this section)}$$

SOLVE	
Substitute the given value into the equation and calculate the answer to the correct number of significant figures.	SOLUTION $$°C = \frac{(°F - 32)}{1.8}$$ $$°C = \frac{(55 - 32)}{1.8} = 12.778\,°C = 13\,°C$$

<table>
<tr><td>CHECK
Check your answer. Are the units correct? Does the answer make physical sense?</td><td>The units (°C) are correct. The value of the answer (13 °C) is smaller than the value in degrees Fahrenheit. For positive temperatures, the value of a temperature in degrees Celsius will always be smaller than the value in degrees Fahrenheit because the Fahrenheit degree is smaller than the Celsius degree and the Fahrenheit scale is offset by 32 degrees (see Figure 17).</td></tr>
</table>

▶**SKILLBUILDER 8** | **Converting between Fahrenheit and Celsius Temperature Scales**

Convert 139 °C to Fahrenheit.

▶**FOR MORE PRACTICE**   Example 18; Problems 65a, 66a, c.

EXAMPLE 9   Converting between Fahrenheit and Kelvin Temperature Scales

Convert 310 K to Fahrenheit.

<table>
<tr><td>SORT
You are given a temperature in kelvins and asked to find the value of the temperature in degrees Fahrenheit.</td><td>GIVEN: 310 K

FIND: °F</td></tr>
<tr><td>STRATEGIZE
Build the solution map, which requires two steps: one to convert kelvins to degrees Celsius and one to convert degrees Celsius to degrees Fahrenheit.</td><td>SOLUTION MAP

$$\boxed{K} \longrightarrow \boxed{°C} \longrightarrow \boxed{°F}$$
$$K = °C + 273.15 \qquad °C = \frac{(°F - 32)}{1.8}$$

RELATIONSHIPS USED
$$K = °C + 273.15 \quad \text{(presented in this section)}$$
$$°C = \frac{(°F - 32)}{1.8} \text{ (presented in this section)}$$</td></tr>
<tr><td>SOLVE
Solve the first equation for °C and substitute the given quantity in K to convert it to °C.

Solve the second equation for °F. Substitute the value of the temperature in °C (from the previous step) to convert it to °F and round the answer to the correct number of significant figures.</td><td>SOLUTION
$$K = °C + 273.15$$
$$°C = K - 273.15$$
$$°C = 310 - 273.15 = 37 \, °C$$

$$°C = \frac{(°F - 32)}{1.8}$$
$$1.8 \, °C = (°F - 32)$$
$$°F = 1.8 \, °C + 32$$
$$°F = 1.8(37) + 32 = 98.6 \, °F = 99 \, °F$$</td></tr>
<tr><td>CHECK
Check your answer. Are the units correct? Does the answer make physical sense?</td><td>The units (°F) are correct. The magnitude of the answer is a bit trickier to judge. In this temperature range, a temperature in Fahrenheit should indeed be smaller than the temperature in kelvins. However, because the Fahrenheit degree is smaller, temperatures in Fahrenheit become larger than temperatures in kelvins above 575 °F.</td></tr>
</table>

▶**SKILLBUILDER 9** | **Converting between Fahrenheit and Kelvin Temperature Scales**

Convert −321 °F to kelvins.

▶**FOR MORE PRACTICE**   Problems 65b, d, 66b.

Which temperature is identical on both the Celsius and the Fahrenheit scale?

(a) 100°

(b) 32°

(c) 0°

(d) −40°

11 Temperature Changes: Heat Capacity

TABLE 4 Specific Heat Capacities of Some Common Substances

Substance	Specific Heat Capacity (J/g °C)
Lead	0.128
Gold	0.128
Silver	0.235
Copper	0.385
Iron	0.449
Aluminum	0.903
Ethanol	2.42
Water	4.184

▲ San Francisco enjoys cool weather even in summer months because of the high heat capacity of the surrounding ocean.

All substances change temperature when they are heated, but how much they change for a given amount of heat varies significantly from one substance to another. For example, if you put a steel skillet on a flame, its temperature rises rapidly. However, if you put some water in the skillet, the temperature increases more slowly. Why? One reason is that when you add water, the same amount of heat energy must warm more matter, so the temperature rise is slower. The second and more interesting reason is that water is more resistant to temperature change than steel because water has a higher *heat capacity*. The **heat capacity** of a substance is the quantity of heat (usually in joules) required to change the temperature of a given amount of the substance by 1 °C. When the amount of the substance is expressed in grams, the heat capacity is called the **specific heat capacity** (or simply the **specific heat**) and has units of joules per gram per degree Celsius (J/g °C). Table 4 lists the values of the specific heat capacity for several substances.

Notice that water has the highest specific heat capacity on the list—changing its temperature requires a lot of heat. If you have traveled from an inland geographical region to a coastal one and have felt the drop in temperature, you have experienced the effects of water's high specific heat capacity. On a summer day in California, for example, the temperature difference between Sacramento (an inland city) and San Francisco (a coastal city) can be 30 °F; San Francisco enjoys a cool 68 °F, while Sacramento bakes at near 100 °F. Yet the intensity of sunlight falling on these two cities is the same. Why the large temperature difference? The difference between the two locations is due to the presence of the Pacific Ocean, which practically surrounds San Francisco. Water, with its high heat capacity, absorbs much of the sun's heat without undergoing a large increase in temperature, keeping San Francisco cool. The land surrounding Sacramento, on the other hand, with its low heat capacity, cannot absorb a lot of heat without a large increase in temperature—it has a lower *capacity* to absorb heat without a large temperature increase.

Similarly, only two U.S. states have never recorded a temperature above 100 °F. One of them is obvious: Alaska. It is too far north to get that hot. The other one, however, may come as a surprise. It is Hawaii. The water that surrounds America's only island state moderates the temperature, preventing Hawaii from ever getting too hot.

If you want to heat a metal plate to as high a temperature as possible for a given energy input, you should make the plate out of:

(a) copper

(b) iron

(c) aluminum

(d) it would make no difference

EVERYDAY CHEMISTRY
Coolers, Camping, and the Heat Capacity of Water

Have you ever loaded a cooler with ice and then added room-temperature drinks? If you have, you know that the ice quickly melts. In contrast, if you load your cooler with chilled drinks, the ice lasts for hours. Why the difference? The answer is related to the high heat capacity of the water within the drinks. As we just learned, water must absorb a lot of heat to raise its temperature, and it must also release a lot of heat to lower its temperature. When the warm drinks are placed into the ice, they release heat, which then melts the ice. The chilled drinks, on the other hand, are already cold, so they do not release much heat. It is always better to load your cooler with chilled drinks—that way, the ice will last the rest of the day.

CAN YOU ANSWER THIS? *Suppose you are cold-weather camping and decide to heat some objects to bring into your sleeping bag for added warmth. You place a large water jug and a rock of equal mass close to the fire. Over time, both the rock and the water jug warm to about 38 °C (100 °F). If you could bring only one into your sleeping bag, which one should you bring to keep you the warmest? Why?*

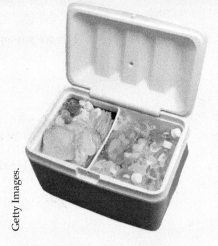

Getty Images.

▲ The ice in a cooler loaded with cold drinks lasts much longer than the ice in a cooler loaded with warm drinks.
Question: Can you explain why?

12 Energy and Heat Capacity Calculations

When a substance absorbs heat (which we represent with the symbol q), its temperature change (which we represent as ΔT) is in direct proportion to the amount of heat absorbed.

$$\xrightarrow{\ q\ } \text{System} \atop \Delta T$$

In other words, the more heat absorbed, the greater the temperature change. The specific heat capacity of the substance can be used to *quantify* the relationship between the amount of heat added to a given amount of the substance and the corresponding temperature increase. The equation that relates these quantities is:

$$\text{Heat} = \text{Mass} \times \text{Specific Heat Capacity} \times \text{Temperature Change}$$

$$q = m \times C \times \Delta T$$

where q is the amount of heat in joules, m is the mass of the substance in grams, C is the specific heat capacity in joules per gram per degree Celsius, and ΔT is the temperature change in Celsius. The symbol Δ means *the change in*, so ΔT means *the change in temperature*. For example, suppose you are making a cup of tea and

ΔT in °C is equal to ΔT in K but is not equal to ΔT in °F.

71

want to know how much heat energy will warm 235 g of water (about 8 oz) from 25 °C to 100.0 °C (boiling). We begin by sorting the information in the problem.

GIVEN: 235 g water (m)
25 °C initial temperature (T_i)
100.0 °C final temperature (T_f)

FIND: amount of heat needed (q)

SOLUTION MAP
Then we strategize by building a solution map.

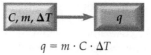

$$q = m \cdot C \cdot \Delta T$$

In addition to m and ΔT, the equation requires C, the specific heat capacity of water. The next step is to gather all of the required quantities for the equation (C, m, and ΔT) in the correct units. These are:

$$C = 4.18 \, \text{J/g} \, °C$$

$$m = 235 \, \text{g}$$

The other required quantity is ΔT. The change in temperature is the difference between the final temperature (T_f) and the initial temperature (T_i).

$$\Delta T = T_f - T_i$$
$$= 100.0 \, °C - 25 \, °C = 75 \, °C$$

SOLUTION
Finally, we solve the problem. Substitute the correct values into the equation and calculate the answer to the correct number of significant figures.

$$q = m \cdot C \cdot \Delta T$$

$$= 235 \, \cancel{g} \times 4.18 \times \frac{J}{\cancel{g} \, \cancel{°C}} \times 75 \, \cancel{°C}$$

$$= 7.367 \times 10^4 \, J = 7.4 \times 10^4 \, J$$

It is critical that you substitute each of the correct variables into the equation in the correct units and cancel units as you compute the answer. If, during this process, you learn that one of your variables is not in the correct units, convert it to the correct units. Notice that the sign of q is positive (+) if the substance is increasing in temperature (heat entering the substance) and negative (−) if the substance is decreasing in temperature (heat leaving the substance).

EXAMPLE 10 Relating Heat Energy to Temperature Changes

Gallium is a solid metal at room temperature but melts at 29.9 °C. If you hold gallium in your hand, it melts from your body heat. How much heat must 2.5 g of gallium absorb from your hand to raise its temperature from 25.0 °C to 29.9 °C? The specific heat capacity of gallium is 0.372 J/g °C.

SORT You are given the mass of gallium, its initial and final temperatures, and its specific heat capacity, and are asked to find the amount of heat absorbed.	**GIVEN:** 2.5 g gallium (m) $T_i = 25.0\,°C$ $T_f = 29.9\,°C$ $C = 0.372\,J/g\,°C$ **FIND:** q
STRATEGIZE The equation that relates the *given* and *find* quantities is the specific heat capacity equation. The solution map indicates that this equation takes you from the *given* quantities to the quantity you are asked to *find*.	**SOLUTION MAP** $\boxed{C, m, \Delta T} \longrightarrow \boxed{q}$ $q = m \cdot C \cdot \Delta T$ **RELATIONSHIPS USED** $q = m \cdot C \cdot \Delta T$ (presented in this section)
SOLVE Before solving the problem, you must gather the necessary quantities—C, m, and ΔT—in the correct units. Substitute C, m, and ΔT into the equation, canceling units, and calculate the answer to the correct number of significant figures.	**SOLUTION** $C = 0.372\,J/g\,°C$ $m = 2.5\,g$ $\Delta T = T_f - T_i$ $\qquad = 29.9\,°C - 25.0\,°C$ $\qquad = 4.9\,°C$ $q = m \cdot C \cdot \Delta T$ $\quad = 2.5\,\cancel{g} \times 0.372\,\dfrac{J}{\cancel{g}\,\cancel{°C}} \times 4.9\,\cancel{°C} = 4.557\,J = 4.6\,J*$
CHECK Check your answer. Are the units correct? Does the answer make physical sense?	The units (J) are correct. The magnitude of the answer makes sense because it takes almost 1 J to heat the 2.5 g sample of the metal by 1 °C; therefore, it should take about 5 J to heat the sample by 5 °C.

▶**SKILLBUILDER 10 | Relating Heat Energy to Temperature Changes**

You find a copper penny (pre-1982) in the snow and pick it up. How much heat is absorbed by the penny as it warms from the temperature of the snow, −5.0 °C, to the temperature of your body, 37.0 °C? Assume the penny is pure copper and has a mass of 3.10 g. You can find the heat capacity of copper in Table 4.

▶**SKILLBUILDER PLUS 2 |**

The temperature of a lead fishing weight rises from 26 °C to 38 °C as it absorbs 11.3 J of heat. What is the mass of the fishing weight in grams?

▶**FOR MORE PRACTICE** Example 19; Problems 75, 76, 77, 78.

---

* This is the amount of heat required to raise the temperature to the melting point. Actually melting the gallium requires additional heat.

EXAMPLE 11 Relating Heat Capacity to Temperature Changes

A chemistry student finds a shiny rock that she suspects is gold. She weighs the rock on a balance and obtains the mass, 14.3 g. She then finds that the temperature of the rock rises from 25 °C to 52 °C upon absorption of 174 J of heat. Find the heat capacity of the rock and determine whether the value is consistent with the heat capacity of gold.

SORT You are given the mass of the "gold" rock, the amount of heat absorbed, and the initial and final temperature. You are asked to find the heat capacity.	**GIVEN:** 14.3 g 174 J of heat absorbed $T_i = 25\ °C$ $T_f = 52\ °C$ **FIND:** C
STRATEGIZE The solution map shows how the heat capacity equation relates the given and find quantities.	**SOLUTION MAP** $m, q, \Delta T \longrightarrow C$ $q = m \cdot C \cdot \Delta T$ **RELATIONSHIPS USED** $q = m \cdot C \cdot \Delta T$ (presented in this section)
SOLVE First, gather the necessary quantities—m, q, and ΔT—in the correct units. Then solve the equation for C and substitute the correct variables into the equation. Finally, calculate the answer to the right number of significant figures.	**SOLUTION** $m = 14.3\ g$ $q = 174\ J$ $\Delta T = 52\ °C - 25\ °C = 27\ °C$ $q = m \cdot C \cdot \Delta T$ $C = \dfrac{q}{m \cdot \Delta T}$ $C = \dfrac{174\ J}{14.3\ g \times 27\ °C}$ $= 0.4507\ \dfrac{J}{g\ °C} = 0.45\ \dfrac{J}{g\ °C}$ By comparing the calculated value of the specific heat capacity (0.45 J/g °C) with the specific heat capacity of gold from Table 4 (0.128 J/g °C), we conclude that the rock could not be pure gold.
CHECK Check your answer. Are the units correct? Does the answer make physical sense?	The units of the answer are those of specific heat capacity, so they are correct. The magnitude of the answer falls in the range of specific heat capacities given in Table 4. A value of heat capacity that falls far outside this range would immediately be suspect.

▶**SKILLBUILDER 11 | Relating Heat Capacity to Temperature Changes**

A 328-g sample of water absorbs 5.78×10^3 J of heat. Calculate the change in temperature for the water. If the water is initially at 25.0 °C, what is its final temperature?

▶**FOR MORE PRACTICE** Problems 85, 86, 87, 88.

CONCEPTUAL CHECKPOINT 6

The heat capacity of substance A is twice that of substance B. If samples of equal mass of both substances absorb the same amount of heat, which substance undergoes the largest change in temperature?

CHAPTER IN REVIEW

CHEMICAL PRINCIPLES

Matter: Matter is anything that occupies space and has mass. It is composed of atoms, which are often bonded together as molecules. Matter can exist as a solid, a liquid, or a gas. Solid matter can be either amorphous or crystalline.

Classification of Matter: Matter can be classified according to its composition. Pure matter is composed of only one type of substance; that substance may be an element (a substance that cannot be decomposed into simpler substances), or it may be a compound (a substance composed of two or more elements in fixed definite proportions). Mixtures are composed of two or more different substances the proportions of which may vary from one sample to the next. Mixtures can be either homogeneous, having the same composition throughout, or heterogeneous, having a composition that varies from region to region.

Properties and Changes of Matter: The properties of matter can be divided into two types: physical and chemical. The physical properties of matter do not involve a change in composition. The chemical properties of matter involve a change in composition. The changes in matter can be divided into physical and chemical. In a physical change, the appearance of matter may change, but its composition does not. In a chemical change, the composition of matter changes.

Conservation of Mass: Whether the changes in matter are chemical or physical, matter is always conserved. In a chemical change, the masses of the matter undergoing the chemical change must equal the sum of the masses of matter resulting from the chemical change.

Energy: Besides matter, energy is the other major component of our universe. Like matter, energy is conserved—it can be neither created nor destroyed. Energy exists in various different types, and these can be converted from one to another. Some common units of energy are the joule (J), the calorie (cal), the nutritional Calorie (Cal), and the kilowatt-hour (kWh). Chemical reactions that emit energy are said to be exothermic; those that absorb energy are said to be endothermic.

Temperature: The temperature of matter is related to the random motions of the molecules and atoms that compose it—the greater the motion, the higher the temperature. Temperature is commonly measured on three scales: Fahrenheit (°F), Celsius (°C), and Kelvin (K).

RELEVANCE

Matter: Everything is made of matter—you, me, the chair you sit on, and the air we breathe. The physical universe basically contains only two things: matter and energy. We begin our study of chemistry by defining and classifying these two building blocks of the universe.

Classification of Matter: Since ancient times, humans have tried to understand matter and harness it for their purposes. The earliest humans shaped matter into tools and used the transformation of matter—especially fire—to keep warm and to cook food. To manipulate matter, we must understand it. Fundamental to this understanding is the connection between the properties of matter and the molecules and atoms that compose it.

Properties and Changes of Matter: The physical and chemical properties of matter make the world around us the way it is. For example, a physical property of water is its boiling point at sea level—100 °C. The physical properties of water—and all matter—are determined by the atoms and molecules that compose it. If water molecules were different—even slightly different—water would boil at a different temperature. Imagine a world where water boiled at room temperature.

Conservation of Mass: The conservation of matter is relevant to, for example, pollution. We often think that humans create pollution, but, actually, we are powerless to create anything. Matter cannot be created. So, pollution is simply misplaced matter—matter that has been put into places where it does not belong.

Energy: Our society's energy sources will not last forever because as we burn fossil fuels—our primary energy source—we convert chemical energy, stored in molecules, to kinetic and thermal energy. The kinetic and thermal energy is not readily available to be used again. Consequently, our energy resources are dwindling, and the conservation of energy implies that we will not be able simply to create new energy—it must come from somewhere. All of the chemical reactions that we use for energy are exothermic.

Temperature: The temperature of matter and its measurement are relevant to many everyday phenomena. Humans are understandibly interested in the weather, and air temperature is a fundamental part of weather. We use body temperature as one measure of human health and global temperature as one measure of the planet's health.

Heat Capacity: The temperature change that a sample of matter undergoes upon absorption of a given amount of heat is related to the heat capacity of the substance composing the matter. Water has one of the highest heat capacities, meaning that it is most resistant to rapid temperature changes.

Heat Capacity: The heat capacity of water explains why it is cooler in coastal areas, which are near large bodies of high-heat-capacity water, than in inland areas, which are surrounded by low-heat-capacity land. It also explains why it takes longer to cool a refrigerator filled with liquids than an empty one.

CHEMICAL SKILLS

EXAMPLES

Classifying Matter (Sections 3, 4)

Begin by examining as alphabetical listing of elements. If the substance is listed in that table, it is a pure substance and an element.

If the substance is not listed in that table, refer to your everyday experience with the substance to determine whether it is a pure substance. If it is a pure substance not listed in the table, then it is a compound.

If it is not a pure substance, then it is a mixture. Refer to your everyday experience with the mixture to determine whether it has uniform composition throughout (homogeneous) or nonuniform composition (heterogeneous).

EXAMPLE 12   Classifying Matter

Classify each type of matter as a pure substance or a mixture. If it is a pure substance, classify it as an element or compound. If it is a mixture, classify it as homogeneous or heterogeneous.

(a) pure silver
(b) swimming-pool water
(c) dry ice (solid carbon dioxide)
(d) blueberry muffin

SOLUTION

(a) Pure element; silver appears in the element table.
(b) Homogeneous mixture; pool water contains at least water and chlorine, and it is uniform throughout.
(c) Compound; dry ice is a pure substance (carbon dioxide), but it is not listed in the table.
(d) Heterogeneous mixture; a blueberry muffin is a mixture of several things and has nonuniform composition.

Physical and Chemical Properties (Section 5)

To distinguish between physical and chemical properties, consider whether the substance changes composition while displaying the property. If it *does not* change composition, the property is physical; if it *does*, the property is chemical.

EXAMPLE 13   Physical and Chemical Properties

Determine whether each property is physical or chemical.

(a) the tendency for platinum jewelry to scratch easily
(b) the ability of sulfuric acid to burn the skin
(c) the ability of hydrogen peroxide to bleach hair
(d) the density of lead relative to other metals

SOLUTION

(a) Physical; scratched platinum is still platinum.
(b) Chemical; the acid chemically reacts with the skin to produce the burn.
(c) Chemical; the hydrogen peroxide chemically reacts with hair to bleach it.
(d) Physical; the heaviness can be felt without changing the lead into anything else.

Physical and Chemical Changes (Section 6)

To distinguish between physical and chemical changes, consider whether the substance changes composition during the change. If it *does not* change composition, the change is physical; if it *does*, the change is chemical.

EXAMPLE 14   Physical and Chemical Changes

Determine whether each change is physical or chemical.

(a) the explosion of gunpowder in the barrel of a gun
(b) the melting of gold in a furnace
(c) the bubbling that occurs upon mixing baking soda and vinegar
(d) the bubbling that occurs when water boils

SOLUTION

(a) Chemical; the gunpowder reacts with oxygen during the explosion.
(b) Physical; the liquid gold is still gold.
(c) Chemical; the bubbling is a result of a chemical reaction between the two substances to form new substances, one of which is carbon dioxide released as bubbles.
(d) Physical; the bubbling is due to liquid water turning into gaseous water, but it is still water.

Conservation of Mass (Section 7)

The sum of the masses of the substances involved in a chemical change must be the same before and after the change.

EXAMPLE 15 Conservation of Mass

An automobile runs for 10 minutes and burns 47 g of gasoline. The gasoline combined with oxygen from air and formed 132 g of carbon dioxide and 34 g of water. How much oxygen was consumed in the process?

SOLUTION

The total mass after the chemical change is:

$$132 \text{ g} + 34 \text{ g} = 166 \text{ g}$$

The total mass before the change must also be 166 g.

$$47 \text{ g} + \text{oxygen} = 166 \text{ g}$$

So, the mass of oxygen consumed is the total mass (166 g) minus the mass of gasoline (47 g).

$$\text{grams of oxygen} = 166 \text{ g} - 47 \text{ g} = 119 \text{ g}$$

Conversion of Energy Units (Section 8)

Solve unit conversion problems using problem-solving strategies.

EXAMPLE 16 Conversion of Energy Units

Convert 1.7×10^3 kWh (the amount of energy used by the average U.S. citizen in one week) into calories.

SORT
You are given an amount of energy in kilowatt-hours and asked to find the amount in calories.

GIVEN: 1.7×10^3 kWh

FIND: cal

STRATEGIZE
Draw a solution map. Begin with kilowatt-hours and determine the conversion factors to get to calories.

SOLUTION MAP

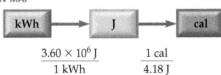

$$\frac{3.60 \times 10^6 \text{ J}}{1 \text{ kWh}} \qquad \frac{1 \text{ cal}}{4.18 \text{ J}}$$

RELATIONSHIPS USED

$$1 \text{ kWh} = 3.60 \times 10^6 \text{ J (Table 2)}$$
$$1 \text{ cal} = 4.18 \text{ J (Table 2)}$$

SOLVE
Follow the solution map to solve the problem. Begin with the given quantity and multiply by the conversion factors to arrive at calories. Round the answer to the correct number of significant figures.

SOLUTION

$$1.7 \times 10^3 \text{ kWh} \times \frac{3.60 \times 10^6 \text{ J}}{1 \text{ kWh}} \times \frac{1 \text{ cal}}{4.18 \text{ J}}$$
$$= 1.464 \times 10^9 \text{ cal}$$

$$1.464 \times 10^9 \text{ cal} = 1.5 \times 10^9 \text{ cal}$$

CHECK
Are the units correct? Does the answer make physical sense?

The unit of the answer, cal, is correct. The magnitude of the answer makes sense since cal is a smaller unit than kWh; therefore, the value in cal should be larger than the value in kWh.

Converting between Celsius and Kelvin Temperature Scales (Section 10)

Solve temperature conversion problems. Take the steps appropriate for equations.

SORT

You are given the temperature in kelvins and asked to convert it to degrees Celsius.

STRATEGIZE

Draw a solution map. Use the equation that relates the *given* quantity to the *find* quantity.

SOLVE

Solve the equation for the *find* quantity (°C) and substitute the temperature in K into the equation. Calculate the answer to the correct number of significant figures.

CHECK

Are the units correct? Does the answer make physical sense?

EXAMPLE 17 Converting between Celsius and Kelvin Temperature Scales

Convert 257 K to Celsius.

GIVEN: 257 K

FIND: °C

SOLUTION MAP

$$K = °C + 273.15$$

RELATIONSHIPS USED

$$K = °C + 273.15 \text{ (Section 10)}$$

SOLUTION

$$K = °C + 273.15$$
$$°C = K - 273.15$$
$$°C = 257 - 273.15 = -16\,°C$$

The answer has the correct unit, and its magnitude seems correct (see Figure 17).

Converting between Fahrenheit and Celsius Temperature Scales (Section 10)

Solve temperature conversion problems. Take the steps appropriate for equations.

SORT

You are given the temperature in degrees Celsius and asked to convert it to degrees Fahrenheit.

STRATEGIZE

Draw a solution map. Use the equation that relates the *given* quantity to the *find* quantity.

SOLVE

Solve the equation for the *find* quantity (°F) and substitute the temperature in °C into the equation. Calculate the answer to the correct number of significant figures.

CHECK

Are the units correct? Does the answer make physical sense?

EXAMPLE 18 Converting between Fahrenheit and Celsius Temperature Scales

Convert 62.0 °C to Fahrenheit.

GIVEN: 62.0 °C

FIND: °F

SOLUTION MAP

$$°C = \frac{(°F - 32)}{1.8}$$

RELATIONSHIPS USED

$$°C = \frac{(°F - 32)}{1.8}$$

SOLUTION

$$°C = \frac{(°F - 32)}{1.8}$$

$$1.8\,(°C) = °F - 32$$

$$°F = 1.8\,(°C) + 32$$

$$°F = 1.8\,(62.0) + 32 = 143.60\,°F = 144\,°F$$

The answer is in the correct units, and its magnitude seems correct (see Figure 17).

Energy, Temperature Change, and Heat Capacity Calculations (Sections 11, 12)

Solve heat capacity problems. Take the steps appropriate for equations.

SORT

You are given the volume of water and the amount of heat absorbed. You are asked to find the change in temperature.

STRATEGIZE

The solution map shows how the heat capacity equation relates the *given* and *find* quantities.

SOLVE

First, gather the necessary quantities—m, q, and ΔT—in the correct units. The value for q must be converted from kJ to J.

You must convert the value for m from milliliters to grams; use the density of water, 1.0 g/mL, to convert milliliters to grams.

Look up the heat capacity for water in Table 4.

Then solve the equation for ΔT and substitute the correct variables into the equation. Finally, calculate the answer to the right number of significant figures.

CHECK

Check your answer. Are the units correct? Does the answer make physical sense?

EXAMPLE 19 Energy, Temperature Change, and Heat Capacity Calculations

What is the temperature change in 355 mL of water upon absorption of 34 kJ of heat?

GIVEN: 355 mL water
34 kJ of heat

FIND: ΔT

SOLUTION MAP

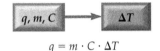

$$q = m \cdot C \cdot \Delta T$$

RELATIONSHIPS USED

$$q = m \cdot C \cdot \Delta T$$

SOLUTION

$$q = 34 \text{ kj} \times \frac{1000 \text{ J}}{1 \text{ kj}} = 3.4 \times 10^4 \text{ J}$$

$$m = 355 \text{ mL} \times \frac{1.0 \text{ g}}{1 \text{ mL}} = 355 \text{ g}$$

$$C = 4.18 \text{ J/g}\,^{\circ}\text{C}$$

$$q = m \cdot C \cdot \Delta T$$

$$\Delta T = \frac{q}{mC}$$

$$\Delta T = \frac{3.4 \times 10^4 \text{ J}}{355 \text{ g} \times 4.18 \text{ J/g}\,^{\circ}\text{C}}$$

$$= 22.91\,^{\circ}\text{C} = 23\,^{\circ}\text{C}$$

The answer has the correct units, and the magnitude seems correct. If the magnitude of the answer were a huge number—3×10^6, for example—we would go back and look for a mistake. Above 100 °C, water boils, so such a large answer would be unlikely.

KEY TERMS

amorphous [**Section 3**]
atoms [**Section 2**]
calorie (cal) [**Section 8**]
Calorie (Cal) [**Section 8**]
Celsius (°C) scale [**Section 10**]
chemical change [**Section 6**]
chemical energy [**Section 8**]
chemical property
   [**Section 5**]
chemical reaction [**Section 7**]

compound [**Section 4**]
compressible [**Section 3**]
crystalline [**Section 3**]
decanting [**Section 6**]
distillation [**Section 6**]
electrical energy [**Section 8**]
element [**Section 4**]
endothermic [**Section 9**]
energy [**Section 8**]
exothermic [**Section 9**]

Fahrenheit (°F)
   scale [**Section 10**]
filtration [**Section 6**]
gas [**Section 3**]
heat [**Section 10**]
heat capacity [**Section 11**]
heterogeneous
   mixture [**Section 4**]
homogeneous mixture
   [**Section 4**]

Kelvin (K) scale [**Section 10**]
kilowatt-hour (kWh)
   [**Section 8**]
kinetic energy [**Section 8**]
law of conservation of
   energy [**Section 8**]
liquid [**Section 3**]
matter [**Section 2**]
mixture [**Section 4**]

molecule [**Section 2**]
physical change [**Section 6**]
physical property [**Section 5**]
potential energy [**Section 8**]

product [**Section 7**]
property [**Section 5**]
pure substance [**Section 4**]
reactant [**Section 7**]

solid [**Section 3**]
specific heat capacity
    (specific heat) [**Section 11**]
state of matter [**Section 3**]

temperature [**Section 10**]
thermal energy [**Section 8**]
volatile [**Section 6**]
work [**Section 8**]

EXERCISES

QUESTIONS

Answers to all odd-numbered questions (numbered in blue) appear in the Answers section at the end of the chapter.

1. Define matter and list some examples.
2. What is matter composed of?
3. What are the three states of matter?
4. What are the properties of a solid?
5. What is the difference between a crystalline solid and an amorphous solid?
6. What are the properties of a liquid?
7. What are the properties of a gas?
8. Why are gases compressible?
9. What is a mixture?
10. What is the difference between a homogeneous mixture and a heterogeneous mixture?
11. What is a pure substance?
12. What is an element? A compound?
13. What is the difference between a mixture and a compound?
14. What is the definition of a physical property? What is the definition of a chemical property?
15. What is the difference between a physical change and a chemical change?
16. What is the law of conservation of mass?
17. What is the definition of energy?
18. What is the law of conservation of energy?
19. Expain the difference between kinetic energy and potential energy.
20. What is chemical energy? List some examples of common substances that contain chemical energy.

21. What are three common units for energy?
22. What is an exothermic reaction? Which has greater energy in an exothermic reaction, the reactants or the products?
23. What is an endothermic reaction? Which has greater energy in an endothermic reaction, the reactants or the products?
24. List three common units for measuring temperature.
25. Explain the difference between heat and temperature.
26. How do the three temperature scales differ?
27. What is heat capacity?
28. Why are coastal geographic regions normally cooler in the summer than inland geographic regions?
29. The following equation can be used to convert Fahrenheit temperature to Celsius temperature.

$$°C = \frac{(°F - 32)}{1.8}$$

Use algebra to change the equation to convert Celsius temperature to Fahrenheit temperature.

30. The following equation can be used to convert Celsius temperature to Kelvin temperature.

$$K = °C + 273$$

Use algebra to change the equation to convert Kelvin temperature to Celsius temperature.

PROBLEMS

Note: The exercises in the Problems section are paired, and the answers to the odd-numbered exercises (numbered in blue) appear in the Answers section at the end of the chapter.

CLASSIFYING MATTER

31. Classify each pure substance as an element or a compound.
    (a) aluminum
    (b) sulfur
    (c) methane
    (d) acetone

32. Classify each pure substance as an element or a compound.
    (a) carbon
    (b) baking soda (sodium bicarbonate)
    (c) nickel
    (d) gold

33. Classify each mixture as homogeneous or heterogeneous.
    (a) coffee
    (b) chocolate sundae
    (c) apple juice
    (d) gasoline

34. Classify each mixture as homogeneous or heterogeneous.
    (a) baby oil
    (b) chocolate chip cookie
    (c) water and gasoline
    (d) wine

35. Classify each substance as a pure substance or a mixture. If it is a pure substance, classify it as an element or a compound. If it is a mixture, classify it as homogeneous or heterogeneous.
    (a) helium gas
    (b) clean air
    (c) rocky road ice cream
    (d) concrete

36. Classify each substance as a pure substance or a mixture. If it is a pure substance, classify it as an element or a compound. If it is a mixture, classify it as homogeneous or heterogeneous.
    (a) urine
    (b) pure water
    (c) Snickers™ bar
    (d) soil

PHYSICAL AND CHEMICAL PROPERTIES AND PHYSICAL AND CHEMICAL CHANGES

37. Classify each property as physical or chemical.
    (a) the tendency of silver to tarnish
    (b) the shine of chrome
    (c) the color of gold
    (d) the flammability of propane gas

38. Classify each property as physical or chemical.
    (a) the boiling point of ethyl alcohol
    (b) the temperature at which dry ice sublimes
    (c) the flammability of ethyl alcohol
    (d) the smell of perfume

39. The following list contains several properties of ethylene (a ripening agent for bananas). Which are physical properties, and which are chemical?
    • colorless
    • odorless
    • flammable
    • gas at room temperature
    • 1 L has a mass of 1.260 g under standard conditions
    • mixes with acetone
    • polymerizes to form polyethylene

40. The following list contains several properties of ozone (a pollutant in the lower atmosphere but part of a protective shield against UV light in the upper atmosphere). Which are physical, and which are chemical?
    • bluish color
    • pungent odor
    • very reactive
    • decomposes on exposure to ultraviolet light
    • gas at room temperature

41. Determine whether each change is physical or chemical.
    (a) A balloon filled with hydrogen gas explodes upon contact with a spark.
    (b) The liquid propane in a barbecue evaporates away because the user left the valve open.
    (c) The liquid propane in a barbecue ignites upon contact with a spark.
    (d) Copper metal turns green on exposure to air and water.

42. Determine whether each change is physical or chemical.
    (a) Sugar dissolves in hot water.
    (b) Sugar burns in a pot.
    (c) A metal surface becomes dull because of continued abrasion.
    (d) A metal surface becomes dull on exposure to air.

43. A block of aluminum is (a) ground into aluminum powder and then (b) ignited. It then emits flames and smoke. Classify (a) and (b) as chemical or physical changes.

44. Several pieces of graphite from a mechanical pencil are (a) broken into tiny pieces. Then the pile of graphite is (b) ignited with a hot flame. Classify (a) and (b) as chemical or physical changes.

THE CONSERVATION OF MASS

45. An automobile gasoline tank holds 42 kg of gasoline. When the gasoline burns, 168 kg of oxygen are consumed and carbon dioxide and water are produced. What is the total combined mass of carbon dioxide and water that is produced?

46. In the explosion of a hydrogen-filled balloon, 0.50 g of hydrogen reacted with 4.0 g of oxygen. How many grams of water vapor are formed? (Water vapor is the only product.)

47. Are these data sets on chemical changes consistent with the law of conservation of mass?

(a) A 7.5-g sample of hydrogen gas completely reacts with 60.0 g of oxygen gas to form 67.5 g of water.

(b) A 60.5-g sample of gasoline completely reacts with 243 g of oxygen to form 206 g of carbon dioxide and 88 g of water.

48. Are these data sets on chemical changes consistent with the law of conservation of mass?

(a) A 12.8-g sample of sodium completely reacts with 19.6 g of chlorine to form 32.4 g of sodium chloride.

(b) An 8-g sample of natural gas completely reacts with 32 g of oxygen gas to form 17 g of carbon dioxide and 16 g of water.

49. In a butane lighter, 9.7 g of butane combine with 34.7 g of oxygen to form 29.3 g carbon dioxide and how many grams of water?

50. A 56-g sample of iron reacts with 24 g of oxygen to form how many grams of iron oxide?

CONVERSION OF ENERGY UNITS

51. Perform each conversion.

(a) 588 cal to joules

(b) 17.4 J to Calories

(c) 134 kJ to Calories

(d) 56.2 Cal to joules

52. Perform each conversion.

(a) 45.6 J to calories

(b) 355 cal to joules

(c) 43.8 kJ to calories

(d) 215 cal to kilojoules

53. Perform each conversion.

(a) 25 kWh to joules

(b) 249 cal to Calories

(c) 113 cal to kilowatt-hours

(d) 44 kJ to calories

54. Perform each conversion.

(a) 345 Cal to kilowatt-hours

(b) 23 J to calories

(c) 5.7×10^3 J to kilojoules

(d) 326 kJ to joules

55. Complete the table:

J	cal	Cal	kWh
225 J	_____	5.38×10^{-2} Cal	_____
_____	8.21×10^5 cal	_____	_____
_____	_____	_____	295 kWh
_____	_____	155 Cal	_____

56. Complete the table:

J	cal	Cal	kWh
7.88×10^6 J	1.88×10^6 cal	_____	_____
_____	_____	1154 Cal	_____
_____	88.4 cal	_____	_____
_____	_____	_____	125 kWh

57. An energy bill indicates that a customer used 1027 kWh in July. How many joules did the customer use?

58. A television uses 32 kWh of energy per year. How many joules does it use?

59. An adult eats food whose nutritional energy totals approximately 2.2×10^3 Cal per day. The adult burns 2.0×10^3 Cal per day. How much excess nutritional energy, in kilojoules, does the adult consume per day? If 1 lb of fat is stored by the body for each 14.6×10^3 kJ of excess nutritional energy consumed, how long will it take this person to gain 1 lb?

60. How many joules of nutritional energy are in a bag of chips whose label reads 245 Cal? If 1 lb of fat is stored by the body for each 14.6×10^3 kJ of excess nutritional energy consumed, how many bags of chips contain enough nutritional energy to result in 1 lb of body fat?

ENERGY AND CHEMICAL AND PHYSICAL CHANGE

61. A common type of handwarmer contains iron powder that reacts with oxygen to form an oxide of iron. As soon as the handwarmer is exposed to air, the reaction begins and heat is emitted. Is the reaction between the iron and oxygen exothermic or endothermic? Draw an energy diagram showing the relative energies of the reactants and products in the reaction.

62. In a chemical cold pack, two substances are kept separate by a divider. When the divider is broken, the substances mix and absorb heat from the surroundings. The chemical cold pack feels cold. Is the reaction exothermic or endothermic? Draw an energy diagram showing the relative energies of the reactants and products in the reaction.

63. Determine whether each process is exothermic or endothermic.

(a) gasoline burning in a car

(b) isopropyl alcohol evaporating from skin

(c) water condensing as dew during the night

64. Determine whether each process is exothermic or endothermic.

(a) dry ice subliming (changing from a solid directly to a gas)

(b) the wax in a candle burning

(c) a match burning

CONVERTING BETWEEN TEMPERATURE SCALES

65. Perform each temperature conversion.

(a) 212 °F to Celsius (temperature of boiling water)

(b) 77 K to Fahrenheit (temperature of liquid nitrogen)

(c) 25 °C to Kelvin (room temperature)

(d) 98.6 °F to Kelvin (body temperature)

66. Perform each temperature conversion.

(a) 102 °F to Celsius

(b) 0 K to Fahrenheit

(c) −48 °C to Fahrenheit

(d) 273 K to Celsius

67. The coldest temperature ever measured in the United States was −80 °F on January 23, 1971, in Prospect Creek, Alaska. Convert that temperature to degrees Celsius and Kelvin. (Assume that −80 °F is accurate to two significant figures.)

68. The warmest temperature ever measured in the United States was 134 °F on July 10, 1913, in Death Valley, California. Convert that temperature to degrees Celsius and Kelvin.

69. Vodka will not freeze in the freezer because it contains a high percentage of ethanol. The freezing point of pure ethanol is −114 °C. Convert that temperature to degrees Fahrenheit and Kelvin.

70. Liquid helium boils at 4.2 K. Convert this temperature to degrees Fahrenheit and Celsius.

71. The temperature in the South Pole during the Antarctic winter is so cold that planes cannot land or take off, effectively leaving the inhabitants of the South Pole isolated for the winter. The average daily temperature at the South Pole in July is −59.7 °C. Convert this temperature to degrees Fahrenheit.

72. The coldest temperature ever recorded in Iowa was −47 °F on February 3, 1998. Convert this temperature to Kelvin and degrees Celsius.

73. Complete the table.

Kelvin	Fahrenheit	Celsius
0.0 K	_____	−273.0 °C
_____	82.5 °F	_____
_____	_____	8.5 °C

74. Complete the table.

Kelvin	Fahrenheit	Celsius
273.0 K	_____	0.0 °C
_____	−40.0 °F	_____
385 K	_____	_____

ENERGY, HEAT CAPACITY, AND TEMPERATURE CHANGES

75. Calculate the amount of heat required to raise the temperature of a 65-g sample of water from 32 °C to 65 °C.

76. Calculate the amount of heat required to raise the temperature of a 22-g sample of water from 7 °C to 18 °C.

77. Calculate the amount of heat required to heat a 45-kg sample of ethanol from 11.0 °C to 19.0 °C.

78. Calculate the amount of heat required to heat a 3.5-kg gold bar from 21 °C to 67 °C.

79. If 89 J of heat are added to a pure gold coin with a mass of 12 g, what is its temperature change?

80. If 57 J of heat are added to an aluminum can with a mass of 17.1 g, what is its temperature change?

81. An iron nail with a mass of 12 g absorbs 15 J of heat. If the nail was initially at 28 °C, what is its final temperature?

82. A 45-kg sample of water absorbs 345 kJ of heat. If the water was initially at 22.1 °C, what is its final temperature?

83. Calculate the temperature change that occurs when 248 cal of heat are added to 24 g of water.

84. A lead fishing weight with a mass of 57 g absorbs 146 cal of heat. If its initial temperature is 47 °C, what is its final temperature?

85. An unknown metal with a mass of 28 g absorbs 58 J of heat. Its temperature rises from 31.1 °C to 39.9 °C. Calculate the heat capacity of the metal and identify it referring to Table 4.

86. An unknown metal is suspected to be gold. When 2.8 J of heat are added to 5.6 g of the metal, its temperature rises by 3.9 °C. Are these data consistent with the metal being gold?

87. When 56 J of heat are added to 11 g of a liquid, its temperature rises from 10.4 °C to 12.7 °C. What is the heat capacity of the liquid?

88. When 47.5 J of heat are added to 13.2 g of a liquid, its temperature rises by 1.72 °C. What is the heat capacity of the liquid?

89. Two identical coolers are packed for a picnic. Each cooler is packed with eighteen 12-oz soft drinks and 3 lb of ice. However, the drinks that went into cooler A were refrigerated for several hours before they were packed in the cooler, while the drinks that went into cooler B were at room temperature. When the two coolers are opened three hours later, most of the ice in cooler A is still ice, while nearly all of the ice in cooler B has melted. Explain.

90. A 100-g block of iron metal and 100 g of water are each warmed to 75 °C and placed into two identical insulated containers. Two hours later, the two containers are opened and the temperature of each substance is measured. The iron metal has cooled to 38 °C while the water has cooled only to 69 °C. Explain.

CUMULATIVE PROBLEMS

91. Calculate the final temperature of 245 mL of water initially at 32 °C upon absorption of 17 kJ of heat.

92. Calculate the final temperature of 32 mL of ethanol initially at 11 °C upon absorption of 562 J of heat. (density of ethanol = 0.789 g/mL)

93. A pure gold ring with a volume of 1.57 cm³ is initially at 11.4 °C. When it is put on, it warms to 29.5 °C. How much heat did the ring absorb? (density of gold = 19.3 g/cm³)

94. A block of aluminum with a volume of 98.5 cm³ absorbs 67.4 J of heat. If its initial temperature was 32.5 °C, what is its final temperature? (density of aluminum = 2.70 g/cm³)

95. How much heat in kilojoules is required to heat 56 L of water from 85 °F to 212 °F?

96. How much heat in joules is required to heat a 43-g sample of aluminum from 72 °F to 145 °F?

97. What is the temperature change in Celsius when 29.5 L of water absorbs 2.3 kWh of heat?

98. If 1.45 L of water is initially at 25.0 °C, what will its temperature be after absorption of 9.4×10^{-2} kWh of heat?

99. A water heater contains 55 gal of water. How many kilowatt-hours of energy are necessary to heat the water in the water heater by 25 °C?

100. A room contains 48 kg of air. How many kilowatt-hours of energy are necessary to heat the air in the house from 7 °C to 28 °C? The heat capacity of air is 1.03 J/g °C.

101. A backpacker wants to carry enough fuel to heat 2.5 kg of water from 25 °C to 100.0 °C. If the fuel he carries produces 36 kJ of heat per gram when it burns, how much fuel should he carry? (For the sake of simplicity, assume that the transfer of heat is 100% efficient.)

102. A cook wants to heat 1.35 kg of water from 32.0 °C to 100.0 °C. If he uses the combustion of natural gas (which is exothermic) to heat the water, how much natural gas will he need to burn? Natural gas produces 49.3 kJ of heat per gram. (For the sake of simplicity, assume that the transfer of heat is 100% efficient.)

103. Evaporating sweat cools the body because evaporation is endothermic and absorbs 2.44 kJ per gram of water evaporated. Estimate the mass of water that must evaporate from the skin to cool a body by 0.50 °C, if the mass of the body is 95 kg and its heat capacity is 4.0 J/g °C. (Assume that the heat transfer is 100% efficient.)

104. When ice melts, it absorbs 0.33 kJ per gram. How much ice is required to cool a 12.0-oz drink from 75 °F to 35 °F, if the heat capacity of the drink is 4.18 J/g °C (Assume that the heat transfer is 100% efficient.)

105. A 15.7-g aluminum block is warmed to 53.2 °C and plunged into an insulated beaker containing 32.5 g of water initially at 24.5 °C. The aluminum and the water are allowed to come to thermal equilibrium. Assuming that no heat is lost, what is the final temperature of the water and aluminum?

106. 25.0 mL of ethanol (density = 0.789 g/mL) initially at 7.0 °C is mixed with 35.0 mL of water (density = 1.0 g/mL) initially at 25.3 °C in an insulated beaker. Assuming that no heat is lost, what is the final temperature of the mixture?

107. The wattage of an appliance indicates the average power consumption in watts (W), where $1\,W = 1\,J/s$. What is the difference in the number of kJ of energy consumed per month between a refrigeration unit that consumes 625 W and one that consumes 855 W? If electricity costs $0.15 per kWh, what is the monthly cost difference to operate the two refrigerators? (Assume 30.0 days in one month and 24.0 hours per day.)

108. A portable electric water heater transfers 255 watts (W) of power to 5.5 L of water, where $1\,W = 1\,J/s$. How much time (in minutes) will it take for the water heater to heat the 5.5 L of water from 25 °C to 42 °C? (Assume that the water has a density of 1.0 g/mL.)

109. What temperature is the same whether it is expressed in the Celsius or Fahrenheit scale?

110. What temperature on the Celsius scale is equal to twice its value when expressed on the Fahrenheit scale?

HIGHLIGHT PROBLEMS

111. Classify each molecular picture as a pure substance or a mixture.

112. Classify each molecular picture as a pure substance or a mixture. If it is a pure substance, classify it as an element or a compound. If it is a mixture, classify it as homogeneous or heterogeneous.

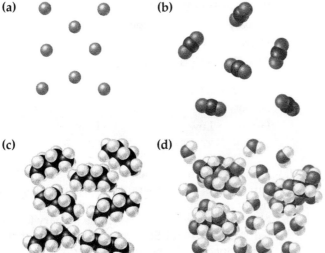

(a)

(b)

(c)

(d)

(a)

(b)

(c)

(d)

113. This molecular drawing shows images of acetone molecules before and after a change. Was the change chemical or physical?

114. This molecular drawing shows images of methane molecules and oxygen molecules before and after a change. Was the change chemical or physical?

---

115. A major event affecting global climate is the El Niño/La Niña cycle. In this cycle, equatorial Pacific Ocean waters warm by several degrees Celsius above normal (El Niño) and then cool by several degrees Celsius below normal (La Niña). This cycle affects weather not only in North and South America, but also in places as far away as Africa. Why does a seemingly small change in ocean temperature have such a large impact on weather?

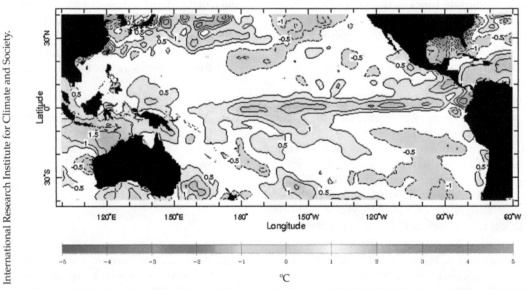

International Research Institute for Climate and Society.

▲ Temperature anomaly plot of the world's oceans for January 17–23, 2010. The large red-orange section in the middle of the map indicates the El Niño effect, a warming of the Pacific Ocean along the equator.

---

116. Global warming refers to the rise in average global temperature due to the increased concentration of certain gases, called greenhouse gases, in our atmosphere. Earth's oceans, because of their high heat capacity, absorb heat and therefore act to slow down global warming. How much heat would be required to warm Earth's oceans by 1.0 °C? Assume that the volume of water in Earth's oceans is $137 \times 10^7 \text{ km}^3$ and that the density of seawater is 1.03 g/cm^3. Also assume that the heat capacity of seawater is the same as that of water.

◄ Earth's oceans moderate temperatures by absorbing heat during warm periods.

117. Examine the data for the maximum and minimum average temperatures of San Francisco and Sacramento in the summer and in the winter.

San Francisco (Coastal City)

January		August	
High	Low	High	Low
57.4 °F	43.8 °F	64.4 °F	54.5 °F

Sacramento (Inland City)

January		August	
High	Low	High	Low
53.2 °F	37.7 °F	91.5 °F	57.7 °F

(a) Notice the difference between the August high in San Francisco and Sacramento. Why is it much hotter in the summer in Sacramento?

(b) Notice the difference between the January low in San Francisco and Sacramento. How might the heat capacity of the ocean contribute to this difference?

►ANSWERS TO SKILLBUILDER EXERCISES

Skillbuilder 1
 (a) pure substance, element
 (b) mixture, homogeneous
 (c) mixture, heterogeneous
 (d) pure substance, compound

Skillbuilder 2
 (a) chemical
 (b) physical
 (c) physical
 (d) physical

Skillbuilder 3
 (a) chemical
 (b) physical
 (c) physical
 (d) chemical

Skillbuilder 4   27 g

Skillbuilder 5   2.14 kJ

Skillbuilder Plus 1 6.57×10^6 cal

Skillbuilder 6
 (a) exothermic
 (b) exothermic

Skillbuilder 7   85 °C

Skillbuilder 8   282 °F

Skillbuilder 9   77 K

Skillbuilder 10   50.1 J

Skillbuilder Plus 2   7.4 g

Skillbuilder 11 $\Delta T = 4.21\ °C; T_f = 29.2\ °C$

►ANSWERS TO CONCEPTUAL CHECKPOINTS

1 (a) Vaporization is a physical change, so the water molecules are the same before and after the boiling.

2 No In the vaporization, the liquid water becomes gaseous, but its mass does not change. Like chemical changes, physical changes also follow the law of conservation of mass.

3 (d) kWh is the largest of the four units listed, so the numerical value of the yearly energy consumption is lowest if expressed in kWh.

4 (d) You can confirm this by substituting each of the Fahrenheit temperatures into the equation in Section 10 and solving for the Celsius temperature.

5 (a) Because copper has the lowest specific heat capacity of the three metals, it experiences the greatest temperature change for a given energy input.

6 Substance B will undergo a greater change in temperature because it has the lower heat capacity. A substance with a lower heat capacity is less resistant to temperature changes.

ANSWERS TO ODD-NUMBERED EXERCISES

QUESTIONS

1. Matter is defined as anything that occupies space and possesses mass. It can be thought of as the physical material that makes up the universe.

3. The three states of matter are solid, liquid, and gas.

5. In a crystalline solid, the atoms/molecules are arranged in geometric patterns with repeating order. In amorphous solids, the atoms/molecules do not have long-range order.

7. The atoms/molecules in gases are not in contact with each other and are free to move relative to one another. The spacing between separate atoms/molecules is very far apart. A gas has no fixed volume or shape; rather, it assumes both the shape and the volume of the container it occupies.

9. A mixture is two or more pure substances combined in variable proportions.

11. Pure substances are those composed of only one type of atom or molecule.

13. A mixture is formed when two or more pure substances are mixed together; however, a new substance is not formed. A compound is formed when two or more elements are bonded together and form a new substance.

15. In a physical change, the composition of the substance does not change, even though its appearance might change. However, in a chemical change, the substance undergoes a change in its composition.

17. Energy is defined as the capacity to do work.

19. Kinetic energy is the energy associated with the motion of an object. Potential energy is the energy associated with the position or composition of an object.

21. Three common units for energy are joules, calories, and kilowatt-hour.

23. An endothermic reaction is one that absorbs energy from the surroundings. The products have more energy than the reactants in an endothermic reaction.

25. Heat is the transfer of thermal energy caused by a temperature difference, whereas temperature is a measure of the thermal energy of matter.

27. Heat capacity is the quantity of heat energy required to change the temperature of a given amount of the substance by 1 °C.

29. $°F = \dfrac{9}{5}(°C) + 32$

PROBLEMS

31. **a.** element **b.** element
c. compound **d.** compound

33. **a.** homogeneous **b.** heterogeneous
c. homogeneous **d.** homogeneous

35. **a.** pure substance-element
b. mixture-homogeneous
c. mixture-heterogeneous
d. mixture-heterogeneous

37. **a.** chemical **b.** physical
c. physical **d.** chemical

39. physical–colorless; odorless; gas at room temperature; one liter has a mass of 1.260 g under standard conditions; mixes with acetone; chemical–flammable; polymerizes to form polyethylene

41. **a.** chemical **b.** physical
c. chemical **d.** chemical

43. **a.** physical **b.** chemical

45. 2.10×10^2 kg

47. **a.** Yes **b.** No

49. 15.1 g of water

51. **a.** 2.46×10^3 J **b.** 4.16×10^{-3} Cal
c. 32.0 Cal **d.** 2.35×10^5 J

53. **a.** 9.0×10^7 J **b.** 0.249 Cal
c. 1.31×10^{-4} kWh **d.** 1.1×10^4 cal

55.

J	cal	Cal	kWh
225	53.8	5.38×10^{-2}	6.25×10^{-5}
3.44×10^6	8.21×10^5	8.21×10^2	9.54×10^{-1}
1.06×10^9	2.54×10^8	2.54×10^5	295
6.49×10^5	1.55×10^5	155	1.80×10^{-1}

57. 3.697×10^9 J

59. 8×10^2 kJ; 17 days

61. Exothermic.

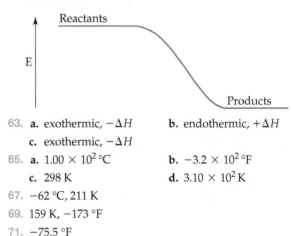

63. **a.** exothermic, $-\Delta H$ **b.** endothermic, $+\Delta H$
c. exothermic, $-\Delta H$

65. **a.** 1.00×10^2 °C **b.** -3.2×10^2 °F
c. 298 K **d.** 3.10×10^2 K

67. -62 °C, 211 K

69. 159 K, -173 °F

71. -75.5 °F

73.
0.0 K	−459.4 °F	−273.0 °C
301 K	82.5 °F	28.1 °C
282 K	47 °F	8.5 °C

75. 9.0×10^3 J

77. 8.7×10^5 J

79. 58 °C

81. 31 °C

83. 1.0×10^1 °C

85. 0.24 J/g°C; silver

87. 2.2 J/g°C

89. When warm drinks are placed into the ice, they release heat, which then melts the ice. The prechilled drinks, on the other hand, are already cold, so they do not release much heat.

91. 49 °C

93. 70.2 J

95. 1.7×10^4 kJ

97. 67 °C

99. 6.0 kWh

101. 22 g of fuel

103. 78 g

105. 27.2 °C

107. 5.96×10^5 kJ; $25

109. −40°

111. **a.** pure substance **b.** pure substance
 c. pure substance **d.** mixture

113. physical change

115. Small temperature changes in the ocean have a great impact on global weather because of the high heat capacity of water.

117. **a.** Sacramento is farther inland than San Francisco, so Sacramento is not as close to the ocean. The ocean water has a high heat capacity and will be able to keep San Francisco cooler in the hot days of summer. However, Sacramento is away from the ocean in a valley, so it will experience high temperatures in the summer.

b. San Francisco is located right next to the ocean, so the high heat capacity of the seawater keeps the temperature in the city from dropping. In the winter, the ocean actually helps to keep the city warmer, compared to an inland city like Sacramento.

Atoms and Elements

From Chapter 4 of *Introductory Chemistry*, Fourth Edition, Nivaldo J. Tro. Copyright © 2011 by Pearson Education, Inc. Published by Pearson Prentice Hall. All rights reserved.

Atoms and Elements

"Nothing exists except atoms and empty space; everything else is opinion."

DEMOCRITUS (460–370 B.C.)

1 Experiencing Atoms at Tiburon

Many atoms exist not as free particles but as groups of atoms bound together to form molecules. Nevertheless, all matter is ultimately made of atoms.

◄ Seaside rocks are typically composed of silicates, compounds of silicon and oxygen atoms. Seaside air, like all air, contains nitrogen and oxygen molecules, and it may also contain substances called amines. The amine shown here is triethylamine, which is emitted by decaying fish. Triethylamine is one of the compounds responsible for the fishy smell of the seaside.

My wife and I recently enjoyed a visit to the northern California seaside town of Tiburon. Tiburon sits next to San Francisco Bay with views of the water, the city of San Francisco, and the surrounding mountains. As we walked along a waterside path, I could feel the wind as it blew over the bay. I could hear the water splashing on the shore, and I could smell the sea air. What was the cause of these sensations? The answer is simple—atoms.

Since all matter is made of atoms, atoms are at the foundation of our sensations. The atom is the fundamental building block of everything you hear, feel, see, and experience. When you feel wind on your skin, you are feeling atoms. When you hear sounds, you are in a sense hearing atoms. When you touch a shoreside rock, you are touching atoms, and when you smell sea air, you are smelling atoms. You eat atoms, you breathe atoms, and you excrete atoms. Atoms are the building blocks of matter; they are the basic units from which nature builds. They are all around us and compose everything, including our own bodies.

Atoms are incredibly small. A single pebble from the shoreline contains more atoms than you could ever count. The number of atoms in a single pebble far exceeds the number of pebbles on the bottom of San Francisco Bay. To get an idea of how small atoms are, imagine this: If every atom within a small pebble were the size of the pebble itself, the pebble would be larger than Mount Everest (► Figure 1). Atoms are small—yet they compose everything.

The key to connecting the microscopic world with the macroscopic world is the atom. Atoms compose matter; their properties determine matter's properties. An **atom** is the smallest identifiable unit of an element. Recall that an *element* is a substance that cannot be broken down into simpler substances.

▲ **FIGURE 1** **The size of the atom** If every atom within a pebble were the size of the pebble itself, then the pebble would be larger than Mount Everest.

The exact number of naturally occurring elements is controversial because some elements previously considered only synthetic may actually occur in nature in very small quantities.

There are about 91 different elements in nature, and consequently about 91 different kinds of atoms. In addition, scientists have succeeded in making about 20 synthetic elements (not found in nature). In this chapter, we examine atoms: what they are made of, how they differ from one another, and how they are structured. We also examine the elements that atoms compose and some of the properties of those elements.

2 Indivisible: The Atomic Theory

▲ Diogenes and Democritus, as imagined by a medieval artist. Democritus is the first person on record to have postulated that matter was composed of atoms.

If we simply look at matter, even under a microscope, it is not obvious that matter is composed of tiny particles. In fact, it appears to be just the opposite. If we divide a sample of matter into smaller and smaller pieces, it seems that we could divide it forever. From our perspective, matter seems continuous. The first people recorded as thinking otherwise were Leucippus (fifth century B.C., exact dates unknown) and Democritus (460–370 B.C.). These Greek philosophers theorized that matter was ultimately composed of small, indivisible particles. Democritus suggested that if you divided matter into smaller and smaller pieces, you would eventually end up with tiny, indestructible particles called *atomos*, or "atoms," meaning "indivisible."

The ideas of Leucippus and Democritus were not widely accepted, and it was not until 1808—over 2000 years later—that John Dalton formalized a theory of atoms that gained broad acceptance. Dalton's atomic theory has three parts:

1. Each element is composed of tiny indestructible particles called atoms.
2. All atoms of a given element have the same mass and other properties that distinguish them from the atoms of other elements.
3. Atoms combine in simple, whole-number ratios to form compounds.

Today, the evidence for the atomic theory is overwhelming. Recent advances in microscopy have allowed scientists not only to image individual atoms but also to pick them up and move them (▶ Figure 2). Matter is indeed composed of atoms.

EVERYDAY CHEMISTRY

Atoms and Humans

All matter is composed of atoms. What does that mean? What does it imply? It means that everything before you is composed of tiny particles too small to see. It means that even you and I are composed of these same particles. We acquired those particles from the food we have eaten over the years. The average carbon atom in our own bodies has been used by 20 other living organisms before we get to it and will be used by other organisms when we are done with it. In fact, it is likely that at this moment, your body contains over 1 trillion carbon atoms that were at one time part of your chemistry professor.*

The idea that all matter is composed of atoms has far-reaching implications. It implies that our bodies, our hearts, and even our brains are composed of atoms acting according to the laws of chemistry and physics. Some people view this as a devaluation of human life. We have always wanted to distinguish ourselves from everything else, and the idea that we are made of the same basic particles as all other matter takes something away from that distinction . . . or does it?

CAN YOU ANSWER THIS?   *Do you find the idea that you are made of atoms disturbing? Why or why not?*

*This calculation assumes that all of the carbon atoms metabolized by your professor over the last 40 years have been uniformly distributed into atmospheric carbon dioxide and subsequently incorporated into plants that you eat.

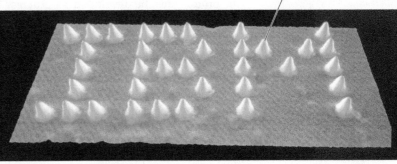

Xenon atoms

▶ FIGURE 2   **Writing with atoms**
Scientists at IBM used a special microscope, called a scanning tunneling microscope (STM), to move xenon atoms to form the letters I, B, and M. The cone shape of these atoms is due to the peculiarities of the instrumentation. Atoms are, in general, spherical in shape.

IBM Communications Media Relations.

3   The Nuclear Atom

By the end of the nineteenth century, scientists were convinced that matter was composed of atoms, the permanent, indestructible building blocks from which all substances are constructed. However, an English physicist named J. J. Thomson (1856–1940) complicated the picture by discovering an even smaller and more fundamental particle called the **electron**. Thomson discovered that electrons are negatively charged, that they are much smaller and lighter than atoms, and that they are uniformly present in many different kinds of substances. The indestructible building block called the atom could apparently be "chipped."

The discovery of negatively charged particles within atoms raised the question of a balancing positive charge. Atoms were known to be charge-neutral, so it was believed that they must contain positive charge that balanced the negative charge of electrons. But how did the positive and negative charges within the atom fit together? Were atoms just a jumble of even more fundamental particles? Were they solid spheres, or did they have some internal structure? Thomson proposed that the negatively charged electrons were small particles held within a positively charged sphere. This model, the most popular of the time, became

> Electric charge is more fully defined in Section 4. For now, think of it as an inherent property of electrons that causes them to interact with other charged particles.

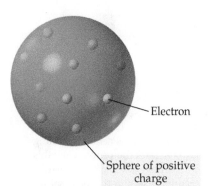

▲ FIGURE 3 **Plum pudding model of the atom** In the model suggested by J. J. Thomson, negatively charged electrons (yellow) were held in a sphere of positive charge (red).

known as the plum pudding model (plum pudding is an English dessert) (◄ Figure 3). The picture suggested by Thomson was—to those of us not familiar with plum pudding—like a blueberry muffin, where the blueberries are the electrons and the muffin is the positively charged sphere.

In 1909, Ernest Rutherford (1871–1937), who had worked under Thomson and adhered to his plum pudding model, performed an experiment in an attempt to confirm it. His experiment instead proved it wrong. In his experiment, Rutherford directed tiny, positively charged particles—called alpha-particles—at an ultrathin sheet of gold foil (▼ Figure 4). Alpha-particles are about 7000 times more massive than electrons and carry a positive charge. These particles were to act as probes of the gold atoms' structure. If the gold atoms were indeed like blueberry muffins or plum pudding—with their mass and charge spread throughout the entire volume of the atom—these speeding probes should pass right through the gold foil with minimum deflection. Rutherford's results were not as he expected. A majority of the particles did pass directly through the foil, but some particles were deflected, and some (1 in 20,000) even bounced back. The results puzzled Rutherford, who found them "about as credible as if you had fired a 15-inch shell at a piece of tissue paper and it came back and hit you." What must the structure of the atom be in order to explain this odd behavior?

Rutherford created a new model to explain his results (► Figure 5). He concluded that matter must not be as uniform as it appears. It must contain large regions of empty space dotted with small regions of very dense matter. In order to explain the deflections he observed, the mass and positive charge of an atom must all be concentrated in a space much smaller than the size of the atom itself. Based on this idea, he developed the **nuclear theory of the atom**, which has three basic parts:

1. Most of the atom's mass and all of its positive charge are contained in a small core called the *nucleus*.
2. Most of the volume of the atom is empty space through which the tiny, negatively charged electrons are dispersed.
3. There are as many negatively charged electrons outside the nucleus as there are positively charged particles (*protons*) inside the nucleus, so that the atom is electrically neutral.

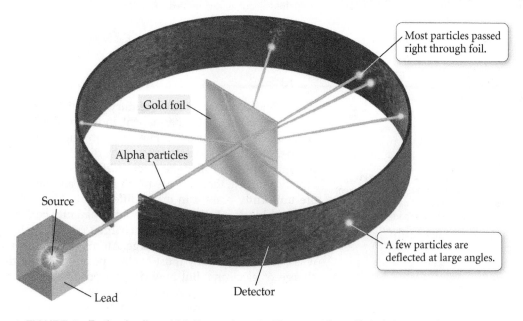

▲ FIGURE 4 **Rutherford's gold foil experiment** Tiny particles called alpha-particles were directed at a thin sheet of gold foil. Most of the particles passed directly through the foil. A few, however, were deflected—some of them at sharp angles.

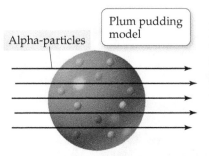

(a) Rutherford's expected result

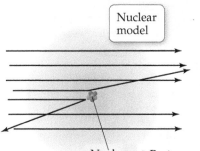

(b) Rutherford's actual result

◄ **FIGURE 5** **Discovery of the atomic nucleus** **(a)** Expected result of Rutherford's gold foil experiment. If the plum pudding model were correct, the alpha-particles would pass right through the gold foil with minimal deflection. **(b)** Actual result of Rutherford's gold foil experiment. A small number of alpha-particles were deflected or bounced back. The only way to explain the deflections was to suggest that most of the mass and all of the positive charge of an atom must be concentrated in a space much smaller than the size of the atom itself—the nucleus. The nucleus itself is composed of positively charged particles (protons) and neutral particles (neutrons).

Later work by Rutherford and others demonstrated that the atom's **nucleus** contains both positively charged **protons** and neutral particles called **neutrons**. The dense nucleus makes up more than 99.9% of the mass of the atom, but occupies only a small fraction of its volume. The electrons are distributed through a much larger region, but don't have much mass (▼ Figure 6). For now, you can think of these electrons like the water droplets that make up a cloud—they are dispersed throughout a large volume but weigh almost nothing.

Rutherford's nuclear theory was a success and is still valid today. The revolutionary part of this theory is the idea that matter—at its core—is much less uniform than it appears. If the nucleus of the atom were the size of this dot ·, the average electron would be about 10 m away. Yet the dot would contain almost the entire mass of the atom. Imagine what matter would be like if atomic structure broke down. What if matter were composed of atomic nuclei piled on top of each other like marbles? Such matter would be incredibly dense; a single grain of sand composed of solid atomic nuclei would have a mass of 5 million kg (or a weight of about 10 million lb). Astronomers believe that black holes and neutron stars are composed of this kind of incredibly dense matter.

▶ **FIGURE 6** **The nuclear atom** In this model, 99.9% of the atom's mass is concentrated in a small, dense nucleus that contains protons and neutrons. The rest of the volume of the atom is mostly empty space occupied by negatively charged electrons. The number of electrons outside the nucleus is equal to the number of protons inside the nucleus. In this image, the nucleus is greatly enlarged and the electrons are portrayed as particles.

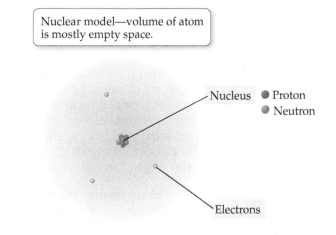

Nuclear model—volume of atom is mostly empty space.

4 The Properties of Protons, Neutrons, and Electrons

Maxwellartandphoto.com.

Protons and neutrons have very similar masses. In SI units, the mass of the proton is 1.67262×10^{-27} kg, and the mass of the neutron is a close 1.67493×10^{-27} kg. A more common unit to express these masses, however, is the **atomic mass unit (amu)**, defined as one-twelfth of the mass of a carbon atom containing six protons and six neutrons. In this unit, a proton has a mass of 1.0073 amu and a neutron has a mass of 1.0087 amu. Electrons, by contrast, have an almost negligible mass of 0.00091×10^{-27} kg, or approximately 0.00055 amu.

◄ If a proton had the mass of a baseball, an electron would have the mass of a rice grain. The proton is nearly 2000 times as massive as an electron.

EVERYDAY CHEMISTRY

Solid Matter?

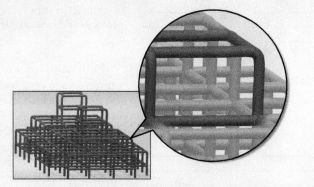

If matter really is mostly empty space as Rutherford suggested, then why does it appear so solid? Why can I tap my knuckles on the table and feel a solid thump? Matter appears solid because the variation in the density is on such a small scale that our eyes can't see it. Imagine a jungle gym 100 stories high and the size of a football field. It is mostly empty space. Yet if you viewed it from an airplane, it would appear as a solid mass. Matter is similar. When you tap your knuckles on the table, it is much like one giant jungle gym (your finger) crashing into another (the table). Even though they are both primarily empty space, one does not fall into the other.

CAN YOU ANSWER THIS? *Use the jungle gym analogy to explain why most of Rutherford's alpha-particles went right through the gold foil and why a few bounced back. Remember that his gold foil was extremely thin.*

▲ Matter appears solid and uniform because the variation in density is on a scale too small for our eyes to see. Just as this scaffolding appears solid at a distance, so matter appears solid to us.

The proton and the electron both have electrical **charge**. The proton's charge is 1+ and the electron's charge is 1−. The charges of the proton and the electron are equal in magnitude but opposite in sign, so that when the two particles are paired, the charges exactly cancel. The neutron has no charge.

What is electrical charge? Electrical charge is a fundamental property of protons and electrons, just as mass is a fundamental property of matter. Most matter is charge-neutral because protons and electrons occur together and their charges cancel. However, you may have experienced excess electrical charge when brushing your hair on a dry day. The brushing action results in the accumulation of electrical charge on the hair strands, which then repel each other, causing your hair to stand on end.

We can summarize the nature of electrical charge as follows (◄ Figure 7)

- Electrical charge is a fundamental property of protons and electrons.
- Positive and negative electrical charges attract each other.
- Positive–positive and negative–negative charges repel each other.
- Positive and negative charges cancel each other so that a proton and an electron, when paired, are charge-neutral.

Note that matter is usually charge-neutral due to the canceling effect of protons and electrons. When matter does acquire charge imbalances, these imbalances usually equalize quickly, often in dramatic ways. For example, the shock you receive when touching a doorknob during dry weather is the equalization of a charge imbalance that developed as you walked across the carpet. Lightning is an equalization of charge imbalances that develop during electrical storms.

If you had a sample of matter—even a tiny sample, such as a sand grain—that was composed of only protons or only electrons, the forces around that matter would be extraordinary, and the matter would be unstable. Fortunately, matter is not that way—protons and electrons exist together, canceling each other's charge and making matter charge-neutral. Table 1 summarizes the properties of protons, neutrons, and electrons.

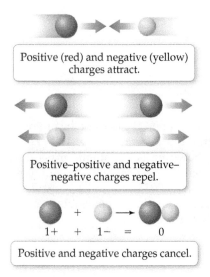

Positive (red) and negative (yellow) charges attract.

Positive–positive and negative–negative charges repel.

1+ + 1− = 0

Positive and negative charges cancel.

▲ FIGURE 7 **The properties of electrical charge**

▶ Matter is normally charge-neutral, having equal numbers of positive and negative charges that exactly cancel. When the charge balance of matter is disturbed, as in an electrical storm, it quickly rebalances, often in dramatic ways such as lightning.

TABLE 1 Subatomic Particles

	Mass (kg)	Mass (amu)	Charge
proton	1.67262×10^{-27}	1.0073	$1+$
neutron	1.67493×10^{-27}	1.0087	0
electron	0.00091×10^{-27}	0.00055	$1-$

✔ CONCEPTUAL CHECKPOINT 1

An atom composed of which of these particles would have a mass of approximately 12 amu and be charge-neutral?

(a) 6 protons and 6 electrons

(b) 3 protons, 3 neutrons, and 6 electrons

(c) 6 protons, 6 neutrons, and 6 electrons

(d) 12 neutrons and 12 electrons

5 Elements: Defined by Their Numbers of Protons

We have seen that atoms are composed of protons, neutrons, and electrons. However, it is the number of protons in the nucleus of an atom that identifies it as a particular element. For example, atoms with 2 protons in their nucleus are helium atoms, atoms with 13 protons in their nucleus are aluminum atoms, and atoms with 92 protons in their nucleus are uranium atoms. The number of protons in an atom's nucleus defines the element (▼ Figure 8). Every aluminum atom has

▼ FIGURE 8 **The number of protons in the nucleus defines the element**

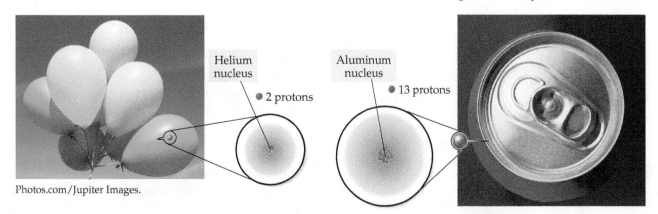

Helium nucleus
● 2 protons

Aluminum nucleus
● 13 protons

Photos.com/Jupiter Images.

Getty Images.

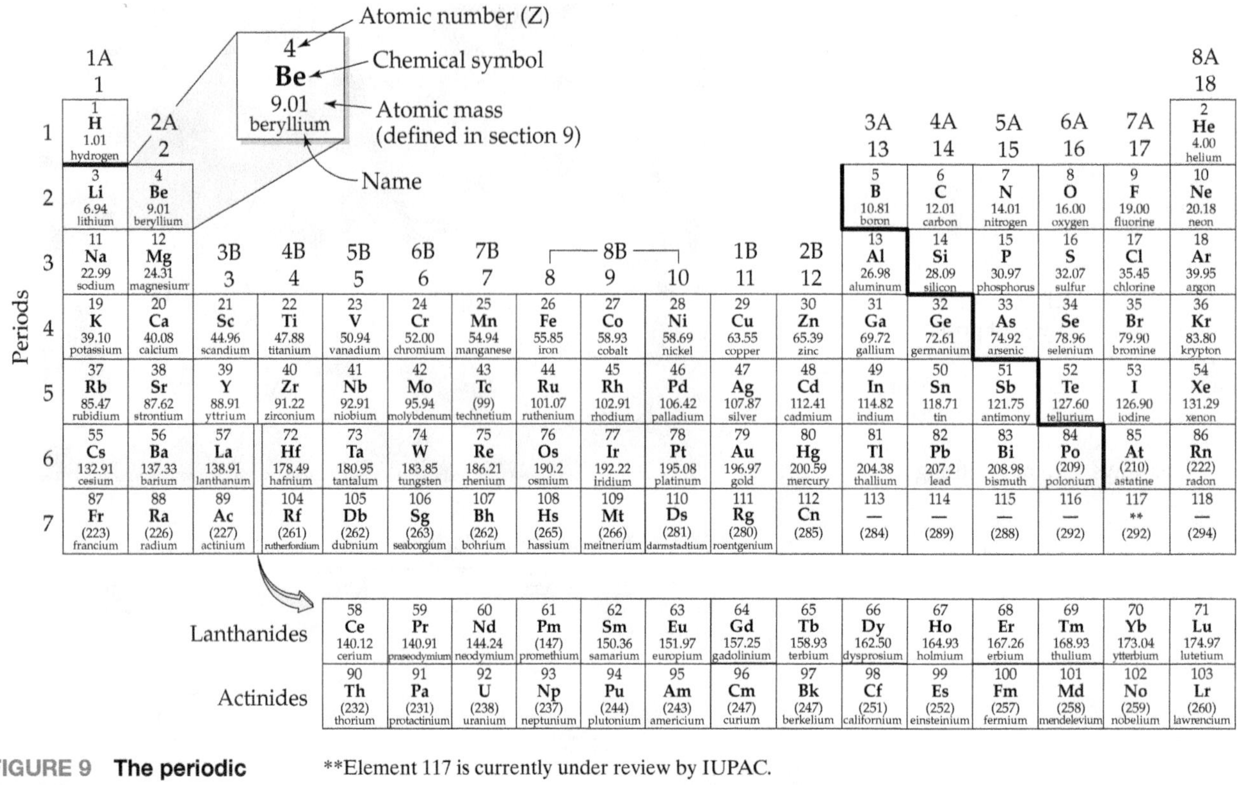

▲ FIGURE 9 **The periodic table of the elements**

**Element 117 is currently under review by IUPAC.

13 protons in its nucleus; if it had a different number of protons, it would be a different element. The number of protons in the nucleus of an atom is its **atomic number** and is given the symbol **Z**.

The periodic table of the elements (▲ Figure 9) lists all known elements according to their atomic numbers. Each element is represented by a unique **chemical symbol**, a one- or two-letter abbreviation for the element that appears directly below its atomic number on the periodic table. The chemical symbol for helium is He; for aluminum, Al; and for uranium, U. The chemical symbol and the atomic number always go together. If the atomic number is 13, the chemical symbol must be Al. If the atomic number is 92, the chemical symbol must be U. This is just another way of saying that the number of protons defines the element.

Most chemical symbols are based on the English name of the element. For example, the symbol for carbon is C; for silicon, Si; and for bromine, Br. Some elements, however, have symbols based on their Latin names. For example, the symbol for potassium is K, from the Latin *kalium*, and the symbol for sodium is Na, from the Latin *natrium*. Additional elements with symbols based on their Greek or Latin names include the following:

lead	Pb	*plumbum*
mercury	Hg	*hydrargyrum*
iron	Fe	*ferrum*
silver	Ag	*argentum*
tin	Sn	*stannum*
copper	Cu	*cuprum*

Early scientists often gave newly discovered elements names that reflected their properties. For example, *argon* originates from the Greek word *argos*, meaning "inactive," referring to argon's chemical inertness (it does not react with other elements). *Bromine* originates from the Greek word *bromos*, meaning "stench," referring to bromine's strong odor. Other elements were named after countries.

For example, polonium was named after Poland, francium after France, and americium after the United States of America. Still other elements were named after scientists. Curium was named after Marie Curie, and mendelevium after Dmitri Mendeleev. Every element's name, symbol, and atomic number are included in the periodic table.

▲ The name *bromine* originates from the Greek word *bromos*, meaning "stench." Bromine vapor, seen as the red-brown gas in this photograph, has a strong odor.

Curium
96
Cm
(247)

▲ Curium is named after Marie Curie, a chemist who helped discover radioactivity and also discovered two new elements. Curie won two Nobel Prizes for her work.

EXAMPLE 1 Atomic Number, Atomic Symbol, and Element Name

Find the atomic symbol and atomic number for each element.

(a) silicon
(b) potassium
(c) gold
(d) antimony

SOLUTION

As you become familiar with the periodic table, you will be able to quickly locate elements on it. For now, it might be easier to find them in an alphabetical listing, but you should also find their position in the periodic table.

Element	Symbol	Atomic Number
silicon	Si	14
potassium	K	19
gold	Au	79
antimony	Sb	51

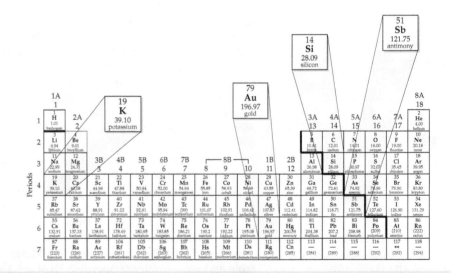

► **SKILLBUILDER 1** | Atomic Number, Atomic Symbol, and Element Name

Find the name and atomic number for each element.

(a) Na
(b) Ni
(c) P
(d) Ta

► **FOR MORE PRACTICE** Problems 41, 42, 45, 46, 47, 48, 49, 50.

6 Looking for Patterns: The Periodic Law and the Periodic Table

▲ Dmitri Mendeleev, a Russian chemistry professor who proposed the periodic law and arranged early versions of the periodic table, shown on a Russian postage stamp.

Stamp from the private collection of Professor C. M. Lang, photography by Gary J. Shulfer, University of Wisconsin, Stevens Point. "Russia: #3607 (1969)"; Scott Standard Postage Stamp Catalogue, Scott Pub. Co., Sidney, Ohio.

> *Periodic* means "recurring regularly." The properties of the elements, when listed in order of increasing relative mass, formed a *repeating pattern*.

The organization of the periodic table has its origins in the work of Dmitri Mendeleev (1834–1907), a nineteenth-century Russian chemistry professor. In his time, about 65 different elements had been discovered. Through the work of a number of chemists, much was known about each of these elements, including their relative masses, chemical activity, and some of their physical properties. However, there was no systematic way of organizing them.

1	2	3	4	5	6	7	8	9	10	11	12	13	14	15	16	17	18	19	20
H	He	Li	Be	B	C	N	O	F	Ne	Na	Mg	Al	Si	P	S	Cl	Ar	K	Ca

▲ **FIGURE 10** **Recurring properties** The elements shown are listed in order of increasing atomic number (Mendeleev used relative mass, which is similar). The color of each element represents its properties. Notice that the properties (colors) of these elements form a repeating pattern.

In 1869, Mendeleev noticed that certain groups of elements had similar properties. He found that if he listed the elements in order of increasing relative mass, those similar properties recurred in a regular pattern (▲ Figure 10). Mendeleev summarized these observations in the **periodic law**:

> When the elements are arranged in order of increasing relative mass, certain sets of properties recur periodically.

Mendeleev organized all the known elements in a table in which relative mass increased from left to right and elements with similar properties were aligned in the same vertical columns (◄ Figure 11). Since many elements had not yet been discovered, Mendeleev's table contained some gaps, which allowed him to predict the existence of yet-undiscovered elements. For example, Mendeleev predicted the existence of an element he called *eka-silicon*, which fell below silicon on the table and between gallium and arsenic. In 1886, eka-silicon was discovered by German chemist Clemens Winkler (1838–1904) and was found to have almost exactly the properties that Mendeleev had anticipated. Winkler named the element germanium, after his home country.

Mendeleev's original listing has evolved into the modern **periodic table**. In the modern table, elements are listed in order of increasing atomic number rather than increasing relative mass. The modern periodic table also contains more elements than Mendeleev's original table because many more have been discovered since his time.

Mendeleev's periodic law was based on observation. Like all scientific laws, the periodic law summarized many observations but did not give the underlying reason for the observation—only theories do that. For now, we accept the periodic law as it is, but later we will examine a powerful theory that explains the law and gives the underlying reasons for it.

The elements in the periodic table can be broadly classified as metals, nonmetals, and metalloids (► Figure 12). **Metals** occupy the left side of the periodic table and have similar properties: They are good conductors of heat and electricity; they can be pounded into flat sheets (malleability); they can be drawn into wires (ductility); they are often shiny; and they tend to lose electrons when they undergo chemical changes. Good examples of metals are iron, magnesium, chromium, and sodium.

Nonmetals occupy the upper right side of the periodic table. The dividing line between metals and nonmetals is the zigzag diagonal line running from boron to astatine (see Figure 12). Nonmetals have more varied properties—some are solids at room temperature, others are gases—but as a whole they tend to be poor conductors of heat and electricity, and they all tend to gain electrons when they undergo chemical changes. Good examples of nonmetals are oxygen, nitrogen, chlorine, and iodine.

1							2
H							He

3	4	5	6	7	8	9	10
Li	Be	B	C	N	O	F	Ne
11	12	13	14	15	16	17	18
Na	Mg	Al	Si	P	S	Cl	Ar
19	20						
K	Ca						

▲ **FIGURE 11** **Making a periodic table** If we place the elements from Figure 10 in a table, we can arrange them in rows so that similar properties align in the same vertical columns. This is similar to Mendeleev's first periodic table.

	1A 1																		8A 18

Metals

Nonmetals

Metalloids

	1A 1	2A 2	3B 3	4B 4	5B 5	6B 6	7B 7	8B 8	8B 9	8B 10	1B 11	2B 12	3A 13	4A 14	5A 15	6A 16	7A 17	8A 18
1	1 H																	2 He
2	3 Li	4 Be											5 B	6 C	7 N	8 O	9 F	10 Ne
3	11 Na	12 Mg											13 Al	14 Si	15 P	16 S	17 Cl	18 Ar
4	19 K	20 Ca	21 Sc	22 Ti	23 V	24 Cr	25 Mn	26 Fe	27 Co	28 Ni	29 Cu	30 Zn	31 Ga	32 Ge	33 As	34 Se	35 Br	36 Kr
5	37 Rb	38 Sr	39 Y	40 Zr	41 Nb	42 Mo	43 Tc	44 Ru	45 Rh	46 Pd	47 Ag	48 Cd	49 In	50 Sn	51 Sb	52 Te	53 I	54 Xe
6	55 Cs	56 Ba	57 La	72 Hf	73 Ta	74 W	75 Re	76 Os	77 Ir	78 Pt	79 Au	80 Hg	81 Tl	82 Pb	83 Bi	84 Po	85 At	86 Rn
7	87 Fr	88 Ra	89 Ac	104 Rf	105 Db	106 Sg	107 Bh	108 Hs	109 Mt	110 Ds	111 Rg	112 Cn	113	114	115	116	117 **	118

Lanthanides	58 Ce	59 Pr	60 Nd	61 Pm	62 Sm	63 Eu	64 Gd	65 Tb	66 Dy	67 Ho	68 Er	69 Tm	70 Yb	71 Lu
Actinides	90 Th	91 Pa	92 U	93 Np	94 Pu	95 Am	96 Cm	97 Bk	98 Cf	99 Es	100 Fm	101 Md	102 No	103 Lr

▲ **FIGURE 12 Metals, nonmetals, and metalloids**
The elements in the periodic table can be broadly classified as metals, nonmetals, and metalloids.

▲ Silicon is a metalloid used extensively in the computer and electronics industries.

Corbis RF.

Most of the elements that lie along the zigzag diagonal line dividing metals and nonmetals are called **metalloids**, or semimetals, and display mixed properties. Metalloids are also called **semiconductors** because of their intermediate electrical conductivity, which can be changed and controlled. This property makes semiconductors useful in the manufacture of the electronic devices that are central to computers, cell phones, and many other modern gadgets. Silicon, arsenic, and germanium are good examples of metalloids.

EXAMPLE 2   Classifying Elements as Metals, Nonmetals, or Metalloids

Classify each element as a metal, nonmetal, or metalloid.

(a) Ba
(b) I
(c) O
(d) Te

SOLUTION

(a) Barium is on the left side of the periodic table; it is a metal.
(b) Iodine is on the right side of the periodic table; it is a nonmetal.
(c) Oxygen is on the right side of the periodic table; it is a nonmetal.
(d) Tellurium is in the middle-right section of the periodic table, along the line that divides the metals from the nonmetals; it is a metalloid.

▶**SKILLBUILDER 2 | Classifying Elements as Metals, Nonmetals, or Metalloids**

Classify each element as a metal, nonmetal, or metalloid.

(a) S
(b) Cl
(c) Ti
(d) Sb

▶**FOR MORE PRACTICE**   Problems: 51, 52, 53, 54.

▶ FIGURE 13 Main-group and transition elements The periodic table can be broadly divided into main-group elements, whose properties can generally be predicted based on their position, and transition elements, whose properties tend to be less predictable based on their position.

Main-group elements			Transition elements										Main-group elements					

Group number

Periods	1A																	8A
1	1 H	2A											3A	4A	5A	6A	7A	2 He
2	3 Li	4 Be											5 B	6 C	7 N	8 O	9 F	10 Ne
3	11 Na	12 Mg	3B	4B	5B	6B	7B		8B		1B	2B	13 Al	14 Si	15 P	16 S	17 Cl	18 Ar
4	19 K	20 Ca	21 Sc	22 Ti	23 V	24 Cr	25 Mn	26 Fe	27 Co	28 Ni	29 Cu	30 Zn	31 Ga	32 Ge	33 As	34 Se	35 Br	36 Kr
5	37 Rb	38 Sr	39 Y	40 Zr	41 Nb	42 Mo	43 Tc	44 Ru	45 Rh	46 Pd	47 Ag	48 Cd	49 In	50 Sn	51 Sb	52 Te	53 I	54 Xe
6	55 Cs	56 Ba	57 La	72 Hf	73 Ta	74 W	75 Re	76 Os	77 Ir	78 Pt	79 Au	80 Hg	81 Tl	82 Pb	83 Bi	84 Po	85 At	86 Rn
7	87 Fr	88 Ra	89 Ac	104 Rf	105 Db	106 Sg	107 Bh	108 Hs	109 Mt	110 Ds	111 Rg	112 Cn	113	114	115	116	117 **	118

The noble gases are inert (or unreactive) compared to other elements. However, some noble gases, especially the heavier ones, will form a limited number of compounds with other elements under special conditions.

The periodic table can also be broadly divided into **main-group elements**, whose properties tend to be more predictable based on their position in the periodic table, and **transition elements** or **transition metals**, whose properties are less easily predictable based simply on their position in the periodic table (▲ Figure 13). Main-group elements are in columns labeled with a number and the letter A. Transition elements are in columns labeled with a number and the letter B. A competing numbering system does not use letters, but only the numbers 1–18.

Each column within the periodic table is called a **family** or **group** of elements. The elements within a family of main-group elements usually have similar properties, and some have a group name. For example, the Group 8A elements, called the **noble gases**, are chemically inert gases. The most familiar noble gas is probably helium, used to fill balloons. Helium, like the other noble gases, is chemically stable—it won't combine with other elements to form compounds—and is therefore safe to put into balloons. Other noble gases include neon, often used in neon signs; argon, which makes up a small percentage of our atmosphere; krypton; and xenon. The Group 1A elements, called the **alkali metals**, are all very reactive metals. A marble-sized piece of sodium can explode when dropped into water. Other alkali metals include lithium, potassium, and rubidium. The Group 2A elements, called the **alkaline earth metals**, are also fairly reactive, although not quite as reactive as the alkali metals. Calcium, for example, reacts fairly vigorously when

Noble gases

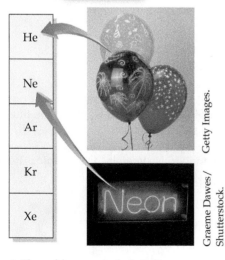

He
Ne
Ar
Kr
Xe

▲ The noble gases include helium (used in balloons), neon (used in neon signs), argon, krypton, and xenon.

Graeme Dawes / Shutterstock.

Getty Images.

Alkali metals ↓
Alkaline earth metals ↓

Noble gases ↓
Halogens ↓

	1A																	8A
	1 H	2A				Group numbers							3A	4A	5A	6A	7A	2 He
	3 Li	4 Be											5 B	6 C	7 N	8 O	9 F	10 Ne
	11 Na	12 Mg				Transition metals							13 Al	14 Si	15 P	16 S	17 Cl	18 Ar
	19 K	20 Ca	21 Sc	22 Ti	23 V	24 Cr	25 Mn	26 Fe	27 Co	28 Ni	29 Cu	30 Zn	31 Ga	32 Ge	33 As	34 Se	35 Br	36 Kr
	37 Rb	38 Sr	39 Y	40 Zr	41 Nb	42 Mo	43 Tc	44 Ru	45 Rh	46 Pd	47 Ag	48 Cd	49 In	50 Sn	51 Sb	52 Te	53 I	54 Xe
	55 Cs	56 Ba	57 La	72 Hf	73 Ta	74 W	75 Re	76 Os	77 Ir	78 Pt	79 Au	80 Hg	81 Tl	82 Pb	83 Bi	84 Po	85 At	86 Rn
	87 Fr	88 Ra	89 Ac	104 Rf	105 Db	106 Sg	107 Bh	108 Hs	109 Mt	110 Ds	111 Rg	112 Cn	113	114	115	116	117 **	118

Lanthanides	58 Ce	59 Pr	60 Nd	61 Pm	62 Sm	63 Eu	64 Gd	65 Tb	66 Dy	67 Ho	68 Er	69 Tm	70 Yb	71 Lu
Actinides	90 Th	91 Pa	92 U	93 Np	94 Pu	95 Am	96 Cm	97 Bk	98 Cf	99 Es	100 Fm	101 Md	102 No	103 Lr

▲ The periodic table with Groups 1A, 2A, 7A, and 8A highlighted.

dropped into water but will not explode as readily as sodium. Other alkaline earth metals are magnesium, a common low-density structural metal; strontium; and barium. The Group 7A elements, called the **halogens**, are very reactive nonmetals. Chlorine, a greenish-yellow gas with a pungent odor is probably the most familiar halogen. Because of its reactivity, chlorine is often used as a sterilizing and disinfecting agent (because it reacts with and kills bacteria and other microscopic organisms). Other halogens include bromine, a red-brown liquid that easily evaporates into a gas; iodine, a purple solid; and fluorine, a pale yellow gas.

EXAMPLE 3   Groups and Families of Elements

To which group or family of elements does each element belong?

(a) Mg
(b) N
(c) K
(d) Br

SOLUTION

(a) Mg is in Group 2A; it is an alkaline earth metal.
(b) N is in Group 5A.
(c) K is in Group 1A; it is an alkali metal.
(d) Br is in Group 7A; it is a halogen.

▶**SKILLBUILDER 3 | Groups and Families of Elements**

To which group or family of elements does each element belong?

(a) Li
(b) B
(c) I
(d) Ar

▶**FOR MORE PRACTICE**   Problems 57, 58, 59, 60, 61, 62, 63, 64.

Alkali metals

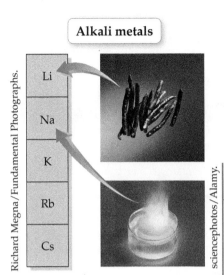

Richard Megna/Fundamental Photographs.

▲ The alkali metals include lithium (shown in the first photo), sodium (shown in the second photo reacting with water), potassium, rubidium, and cesium.

sciencephotos/Alamy.

Charles D. Winters/Photo Researchers.

Alkaline earth metals

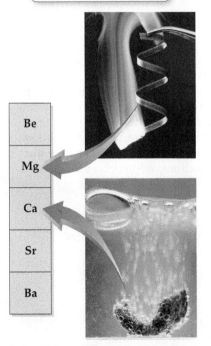

◀ The alkaline earth metals include beryllium, magnesium (shown burning in the first photo), calcium (shown reacting with water in the second photo), strontium, and barium.

Richard Megna/Fundamental Photographs.

Halogens

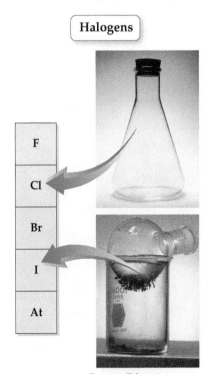

▶ The halogens include fluorine, chlorine (shown in the first photo), bromine, iodine (shown in the second photo), and astatine.

Pearson Education.   105

✔ **CONCEPTUAL CHECKPOINT 2**

Which statement can NEVER be true?

(a) An element can be both a transition element and a metal.

(b) An element can be both a transition element and a metalloid.

(c) An element can be both a metalloid and a halogen.

(d) An element can be both a main-group element and a halogen.

7 Ions: Losing and Gaining Electrons

The charge of an ion is shown in the upper right corner of the symbol.

In chemical reactions, atoms often lose or gain electrons to form charged particles called **ions**. For example, neutral lithium (Li) atoms contain 3 protons and 3 electrons; however, in reactions, lithium atoms lose one electron (e^-) to form Li^+ ions.

$$Li \longrightarrow Li^+ + e^-$$

The Li^+ *ion* contains 3 protons but only 2 electrons, resulting in a net charge of 1+. Ion charges are usually written with the magnitude of the charge first followed by the sign of the charge. For example, a positive two charge is written as 2+, and a negative two charge is written as 2−. The charge of an ion depends on how many electrons were gained or lost and is given by the formula:

$$\text{Ion charge} = \text{number of protons} - \text{number of electrons}$$

$$= \#p^+ - \#e^-$$

where p^+ stands for *proton* and e^- stands for *electron*.

For the Li^+ ion with 3 protons and 2 electrons the charge is:

$$\text{Ion Charge} = 3 - 2 = 1+$$

Neutral fluorine (F) atoms contain 9 protons and 9 electrons; however, in chemical reactions fluorine atoms gain 1 electron to form F^- ions:

$$F + e^- \longrightarrow F^-$$

The F^- *ion* contains 9 protons and 10 electrons, resulting in a 1− charge.

$$\text{Ion charge} = 9 - 10$$

$$= 1-$$

Positively charged ions, such as Li^+, are **cations**, and negatively charged ions, such as F^-, are **anions**. Ions behave very differently than the atoms from which they are formed. Neutral sodium atoms, for example, are extremely reactive, interacting violently with most things they contact. Sodium cations (Na^+), on the other hand, are relatively inert—we eat them all the time in sodium chloride (table salt). In nature, cations and anions always occur together so that, again, matter is charge-neutral. For example, in table salt, the sodium cation occurs together with the chloride anion (Cl^-).

EXAMPLE 4 **Determining Ion Charge from Numbers of Protons and Electrons**

Determine the charge of each ion.

(a) a magnesium ion with 10 electrons
(b) a sulfur ion with 18 electrons
(c) an iron ion with 23 electrons

SOLUTION

To determine the charge of each ion, use the ion charge equation.

$$\text{Ion charge} = \#p - \#e^-$$

The number of electrons is given in the problem. The number of protons is obtained from the element's atomic number in the periodic table.

(a) magnesium with atomic number 12

$$\text{Ion charge} = 12 - 10 = 2+ (Mg^{2+})$$

(b) sulfur with atomic number 16

$$\text{Ion charge} = 16 - 18 = 2- (S^{2-})$$

(c) iron with atomic number 26

$$\text{Ion charge} = 26 - 23 = 3+ (Fe^{3+})$$

▶**SKILLBUILDER 4 | Determining Ion Charge from Numbers of Protons and Electrons**

Determine the charge of each ion.

(a) a nickel ion with 26 electrons
(b) a bromine ion with 36 electrons
(c) a phosphorus ion with 18 electrons

▶**FOR MORE PRACTICE**   Example 10; Problems 73, 74.

EXAMPLE 5   Determining the Number of Protons and Electrons in an Ion

Find the number of protons and electrons in the Ca^{2+} ion.

From the periodic table, find that the atomic number for calcium is 20, so calcium has 20 protons. The number of electrons can be found using the ion charge equation.	**SOLUTION** $$\text{Ion charge} = \#p - \#e^-$$ $$2+ = 20 - \#e^-$$ $$\#e^- = 20 - 2 = 18$$ Therefore the number of electrons is 18. The Ca^{2+} ion has 20 protons and 18 electrons.

▶**SKILLBUILDER 5 | Determining the Number of Protons and Electrons in an Ion**

Find the number of protons and electrons in the S^{2-} ion.

▶**FOR MORE PRACTICE**   Example 11; Problems 75, 76.

IONS AND THE PERIODIC TABLE

For many main-group elements, we can use the periodic table to predict how many electrons tend to be lost or gained when an atom of that particular element ionizes. The number associated with the letter A above each *main-group* column in the periodic table—1 through 8—gives the number of *valence electrons* for the elements in that column. For now, think of valence electrons as the outermost electrons in an atom. Since oxygen is in column 6A, we can deduce that it has 6 valence

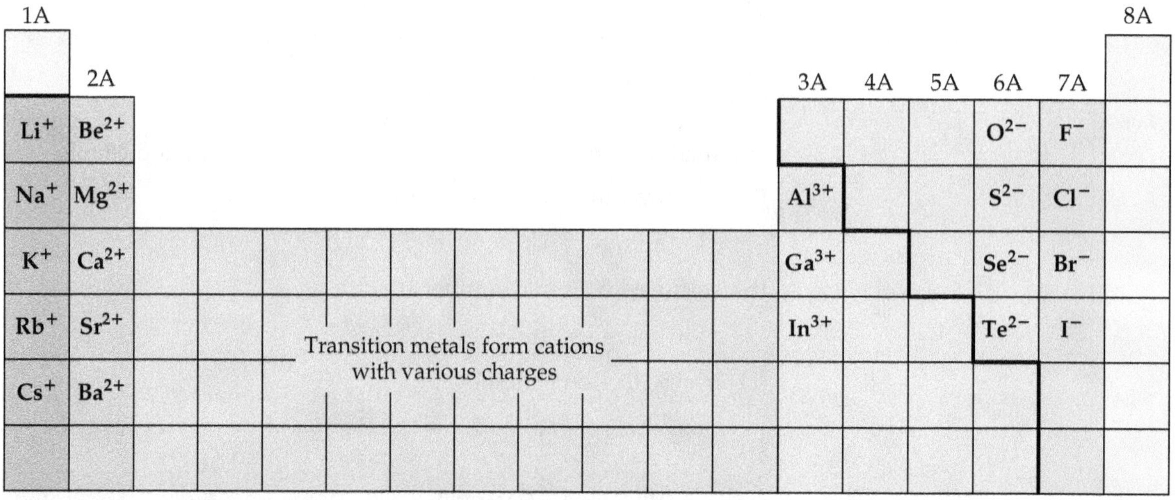

▲ FIGURE 14   **Elements that form predictable ions**

electrons; since magnesium is in column 2A, it has 2 valence electrons, and so on. An important exception to this rule is helium—it is in column 8A, but has only 2 valence electrons. Valence electrons are particularly important because, it is these electrons that take part in chemical bonding.

The key to predicting the charge acquired by a particular element when it ionizes is its position in the periodic table relative to the noble gases:

Main-group elements tend to form ions that have the same number of valence electrons as the nearest noble gas.

For example, the closest noble gas to oxygen is neon. When oxygen ionizes, it *acquires* two additional electrons for a total of 8 valence electrons—the same number as neon. When determining the closest noble gas, we can move either forward or backward on the periodic table. For example, the closest noble gas to magnesium is also neon, even though neon (atomic number 10) falls before magnesium (atomic number 12) in the periodic table. Therefore magnesium *loses* its 2 valence electrons to attain the same number of valence electrons as neon.

In accordance with this principle, the alkali metals (Group 1A) tend to lose 1 electron and therefore form 1+ ions, while the alkaline earth metals (Group 2A) tend to lose 2 electrons and therefore form 2+ ions. The halogens (Group 7A) tend to gain 1 electron and therefore form 1− ions. The groups in the periodic table that form predictable ions are shown in ▲ Figure 14. Be familiar with these groups and the ions they form.

EXAMPLE 6   Charge of Ions from Position in Periodic Table

Based on their position in the periodic table, what ions do barium and iodine tend to form?

SOLUTION

Since barium is in Group 2A, it tends to form a cation with a 2+ charge (Ba^{2+}). Since iodine is in Group 7A, it tends to form an anion with a 1− charge (I^-).

►**SKILLBUILDER 6** | **Charge of Ions from Position in Periodic Table**

Based on their position in the periodic table, what ions do potassium and selenium tend to form?

►**FOR MORE PRACTICE**   Problems 79, 80.

✔ CONCEPTUAL CHECKPOINT 3

Which of these pairs of ions have the same total number of electrons?

(a) Na^+ and Mg^{2+}

(b) F^- and Cl^-

(c) O^- and O^{2-}

(d) Ga^{3+} and Fe^{3+}

8 Isotopes: When the Number of Neutrons Varies

All atoms of a given element have the same number of protons; however, they do not necessarily have the same number of neutrons. Since neutrons and protons have nearly the same mass (approximately 1 amu), and since the number of neutrons in the atoms of a given element can vary, all atoms of a given element *do not* have the same mass (contrary to what John Dalton originally proposed in his atomic theory). For example, all neon atoms in nature contain 10 protons, but they may have 10, 11, or 12 neutrons (▼ Figure 15). All three types of neon atoms exist, and each has a slightly different mass. Atoms with the same number of protons but different numbers of neutrons are called **isotopes**. Some elements, such as beryllium (Be) and aluminum (Al), have only one naturally occurring isotope, while other elements, such as neon (Ne) and chlorine (Cl), have two or more.

There are a few exceptions to this rule, such as boron, but they are beyond our scope in this text.

For a given element, the relative amounts of each different isotope in a naturally occurring sample of that element is always the same. For example, in any natural sample of neon atoms, 90.48% of them are the isotope with 10 neutrons, 0.27% are the isotope with 11 neutrons, and 9.25% are the isotope with 12 neutrons as summarized in Table 2. This means that out of 10,000 neon atoms, 9048 have

TABLE 2 Neon Isotopes

Symbol	Number of Protons	Number of Neutrons	A (Mass Number)	Percent Natural Abundance
Ne-20 or $^{20}_{10}Ne$	10	10	20	90.48%
Ne-21 or $^{21}_{10}Ne$	10	11	21	0.27%
Ne-22 or $^{22}_{10}Ne$	10	12	22	9.25%

▶ FIGURE 15 **Isotopes of neon** Naturally occurring neon contains three different isotopes, Ne-20 (with 10 neutrons), Ne-21 (with 11 neutrons), and Ne-22 (with 12 neutrons).

Getty Images.

● Ne-21
● Ne-22
● Ne-20

Percent means "per hundred." 90.48% means that 90.48 atoms out of 100 are the isotope with 10 neutrons.

10 neutrons, 27 have 11 neutrons, and 925 have 12 neutrons. These percentages are referred to as the **percent natural abundance** of the isotopes. The preceding numbers are for neon only; all elements have their own unique percent natural abundance of isotopes.

The sum of the number of neutrons and protons in an atom is its **mass number** and is given the symbol **A**.

$$A = \text{Number of protons} + \text{Number of neutrons}$$

For neon, which has 10 protons, the mass numbers of the three different naturally occurring isotopes are 20, 21, and 22, corresponding to 10, 11, and 12 neutrons, respectively.

Isotopes are often symbolized in the following way:

Mass number
Atomic number
$$^{A}_{Z}X$$
Chemical symbol

where X is the chemical symbol, A is the mass number, and Z is the atomic number.

For example, the symbols for the neon isotopes are:

$$^{20}_{10}\text{Ne} \quad ^{21}_{10}\text{Ne} \quad ^{22}_{10}\text{Ne}$$

Notice that the chemical symbol, Ne, and the atomic number, 10, are redundant: If the atomic number is 10, the symbol must be Ne, and vice versa. The mass numbers, however, are different, reflecting the different number of neutrons in each isotope.

A second common notation for isotopes is the chemical symbol (or chemical name) followed by a hyphen and the mass number of the isotope.

$$X - A$$
Chemical symbol or name
Mass number

In this notation, the neon isotopes are:

Ne-20	neon-20
Ne-21	neon-21
Ne-22	neon-22

Notice that all isotopes of a given element have the same number of protons (otherwise they would be a different element). Notice also that the mass number is the *sum* of the number of protons and the number of neutrons. The number of neutrons in an isotope is the difference between the mass number and the atomic number.

In general, mass number increases with increasing atomic number.

EXAMPLE 7   Atomic Numbers, Mass Numbers, and Isotope Symbols

What are the atomic number (Z), mass number (A), and symbols of the carbon isotope with 7 neutrons?

SOLUTION

Find that the atomic number (Z) of carbon is 6 (from the periodic table). This tells you that carbon atoms have 6 protons. The mass number (A) for the isotope with 7 neutrons is the sum of the number of protons and the number of neutrons.

$$A = 6 + 7 = 13$$

So, Z = 6, A = 13, and the symbols for the isotope are C-13 and $^{13}_{6}\text{C}$.

▶**SKILLBUILDER 7** │ **Atomic Numbers, Mass Numbers, and Isotope Symbols**

What are the atomic number, mass number, and symbols for the chlorine isotope with 18 neutrons?

▶**FOR MORE PRACTICE**   Example 12; Problems: 85, 87, 89, 90.

EXAMPLE 8   **Numbers of Protons and Neutrons from Isotope Symbols**

How many protons and neutrons are in the chromium isotope $^{52}_{24}\text{Cr}$?

The number of protons is equal to Z (lower left number).	**SOLUTION** $\#\text{p}^+ = Z = 24$
The number of neutrons is equal to A (upper left number) −Z (lower left number).	$\begin{aligned} \#\text{n} &= A - Z \\ &= 52 - 24 \\ &= 28 \end{aligned}$

▶**SKILLBUILDER 8** │ **Numbers of Protons and Neutrons from Isotope Symbols**

How many protons and neutrons are in the potassium isotope $^{39}_{19}\text{K}$?

▶**FOR MORE PRACTICE**   Example 13; Problems 91, 92.

 CONCEPTUAL CHECKPOINT 4

If an atom with a mass number of 27 has 14 neutrons, it is an isotope of which element?

(a) silicon

(b) aluminum

(c) cobalt

(d) niobium

 CONCEPTUAL CHECKPOINT 5

Throughout this book, we represent atoms as spheres. For example, a carbon atom is represented by a black sphere as shown here. In light of the nuclear theory of the atom, would C-12 and C-13 look different in this representation of atoms? Why or why not?

Carbon

9 Atomic Mass: The Average Mass of an Element's Atoms

An important part of Dalton's atomic theory was that all atoms of a given element have the same mass. But as we just learned, the atoms of a given element may have different masses (because of isotopes). So Dalton was not completely correct. We can, however, calculate an average mass—called the **atomic mass**—for each

CHEMISTRY IN THE ENVIRONMENT

Radioactive Isotopes at Hanford, Washington

Nuclei of the isotopes of a given element are not all equally stable. For example, naturally occurring lead is composed primarily of Pb-206, Pb-207, and Pb-208. Other isotopes of lead also exist, but their nuclei are unstable. Scientists can make some of these other isotopes, such as Pb-185, in the laboratory. However, within seconds Pb-185 atoms emit a few energetic subatomic particles from their nuclei and change into different isotopes of different elements (which are themselves unstable). These emitted subatomic particles are called **nuclear radiation**, and the isotopes that emit them are termed **radioactive**. Nuclear radiation, always associated with unstable nuclei, can be harmful to humans and other living organisms because the energetic particles interact with and damage biological molecules. Some isotopes, such as Pb-185, emit significant amounts of radiation only for a very short time. Others, however, remain radioactive for a long time—in some cases millions or even billions of years.

The nuclear power and nuclear weapons industries produce by-products containing unstable isotopes of several different elements. Many of these isotopes emit nuclear radiation for a long time, and their disposal is an environmental problem. For example, in Hanford, Washington, which for 50 years produced fuel for nuclear weapons, 177 underground storage tanks contain 55 million gallons of highly radioactive nuclear waste. Certain radioactive isotopes within that waste will produce nuclear radiation for the foreseeable future. Unfortunately, some of the underground storage tanks are aging, and leaks have allowed some of the waste to seep into the environment. While the danger from short-term external exposure to this waste is minimal, ingestion of the waste through contamination of drinking water or food supplies would pose significant health risks. Consequently, Hanford is now the site of the largest environmental cleanup project in U.S. history. The U.S. government expects the project to take more than 20 years and cost about $10 billion.

Radioactive isotopes are not always harmful, however, and many have beneficial uses. For example, technetium-99 (Tc-99) is often given to patients to diagnose disease. The radiation emitted by Tc-99 helps doctors image internal organs or detect infection.

CAN YOU ANSWER THIS? *Give the number of neutrons in each of the following isotopes: Pb-206, Pb-207, Pb-208, Pb-185, Tc-99.*

◀ Storage tanks at Hanford, Washington, contain 55 million gallons of high-level nuclear waste. Each tank pictured here holds 1 million gallons.

U.S. Department of Energy.

element. The atomic mass of each element is listed in the periodic table directly beneath the element's symbol; it represents the average mass of the atoms that compose that element. For example, the periodic table lists the atomic mass of chlorine as 35.45 amu. Naturally occurring chlorine consists of 75.77% chlorine-35 (mass 34.97 amu) and 24.23% chlorine-37 (mass 36.97 amu). Its atomic mass is:

Some books call this *average atomic mass* or atomic weight instead of simply *atomic mass*.

$$\text{Atomic mass} = (0.7577 \times 34.97 \text{ amu}) + (0.2423 \times 36.97 \text{ amu})$$
$$= 35.45 \text{ amu}$$

Notice that the atomic mass of chlorine is closer to 35 than 37 because naturally occurring chlorine contains more chlorine-35 atoms than chlorine-37 atoms. Notice also that when percentages are used in these calculations, they must always be converted to their decimal value. To convert a percentage to its decimal value, divide by 100. For example:

$$75.77\% = 75.77/100 = 0.7577$$
$$24.33\% = 24.23/100 = 0.2423$$

In general, atomic mass is calculated according to the following equation:

$$
\begin{aligned}
\text{Atomic mass} = {} & (\text{Fraction of isotope 1} \times \text{Mass of isotope 1}) + \\
& (\text{Fraction of isotope 2} \times \text{Mass of isotope 2}) + \\
& (\text{Fraction of isotope 3} \times \text{Mass of isotope 3}) + \ldots
\end{aligned}
$$

where the fractions of each isotope are the percent natural abundances converted to their decimal values. Atomic mass is useful because it allows us to assign a characteristic mass to each element and it allows us to quantify the number of atoms in a sample of that element.

EXAMPLE 9   Calculating Atomic Mass

Gallium has two naturally occurring isotopes: Ga-69 with mass 68.9256 amu and a natural abundance of 60.11%, and Ga-71 with mass 70.9247 amu and a natural abundance of 39.89%. Calculate the atomic mass of gallium.

Convert the percent natural abundances into decimal form by dividing by 100.	**SOLUTION** $$\text{Fraction Ga-69} = \frac{60.11}{100} = 0.6011$$ $$\text{Fraction Ga-71} = \frac{39.89}{100} = 0.3989$$
Use the fractional abundances and the atomic masses of the isotopes to compute the atomic mass according to the atomic mass definition given earlier.	$$\text{Atomic mass} = (0.6011 \times 68.9256 \text{ amu}) + (0.3989 \times 70.9247 \text{ amu})$$ $$= 41.4321 \text{ amu} + 28.2919 \text{ amu}$$ $$= 69.7231 = 69.72 \text{ amu}$$

▶**SKILLBUILDER 9 | Calculating Atomic Mass**

Magnesium has three naturally occurring isotopes with masses of 23.99, 24.99, and 25.98 amu and natural abundances of 78.99%, 10.00%, and 11.01%. Calculate the atomic mass of magnesium.

▶**FOR MORE PRACTICE**   Example 14; Problems 95, 96.

✔ CONCEPTUAL CHECKPOINT 6

A fictitious element is composed of isotopes A and B with masses of 61.9887 and 64.9846 amu, respectively. The atomic mass of the element is 64.52. What can you conclude about the natural abundances of the two isotopes?

(a) The natural abundance of isotope A must be greater than the natural abundance of isotope B.

(b) The natural abundance of isotope B must be greater than the natural abundance of isotope A.

(c) The natural abundances of both isotopes must be about equal.

(d) Nothing can be concluded about the natural abundances of the two isotopes from the given information.

CHAPTER IN REVIEW

CHEMICAL PRINCIPLES

RELEVANCE

The Atomic Theory: Democritus and Leucippus, ancient Greek philosophers, were the first to assert that matter is ultimately composed of small, indestructible particles. It was not until 2000 years later, however, that John Dalton introduced a formal atomic theory stating that matter is composed of atoms; atoms of a given element have unique properties that distinguish them from atoms of other elements; and atoms combine in simple, whole-number ratios to form compounds.

The Atomic Theory: The concept of atoms is important because it explains the physical world. You and everything you see are made of atoms. To understand the physical world, we must begin by understanding atoms. Atoms are the key concept—they determine the properties of matter.

Discovery of the Atom's Nucleus: Rutherford's gold foil experiment probed atomic structure, and his results led to the nuclear model of the atom, which, with minor modifications to accommodate neutrons, is still valid today. In this model, the atom is composed of protons and neutrons—which compose most of the atom's mass and are grouped together in a dense nucleus—and electrons, which compose most of the atom's volume. Protons and neutrons have similar masses (1 amu), while electrons have a much smaller mass (0.00055 amu).

Discovery of the Atom's Nucleus: We can understand why this is relevant by asking, what if it were otherwise? What if matter were *not* mostly empty space? While we cannot know for certain, it seems probable that such matter would not form the diversity of substances required for life—and then, of course, we would not be around to ask the question.

Charge: Protons and electrons both have electrical charge; the charge of the proton is +1 and the charge of the electron is −1. The neutron has no charge. When protons and electrons combine in atoms, their charges cancel.

Charge: Electrical charge is relevant to much of our modern world. Many of the machines and computers we depend on are powered by electricity, which is the movement of electrical charge.

The Periodic Table: The periodic table tabulates all known elements in order of increasing atomic number. The periodic table is arranged so that similar elements are grouped in columns. Columns of elements in the periodic table have similar properties and are called groups or families. Elements on the left side of the periodic table are metals and tend to lose electrons in their chemical changes. Elements on the upper right side of the periodic table are nonmetals and tend to gain electrons in their chemical changes. Elements between the two are called metalloids.

The Periodic Table: The periodic table helps us organize the elements in ways that allow us to predict their properties. Helium, for example, is not toxic in small amounts because it is an inert gas—it does not react with anything. The gases in the column below it on the periodic table are also inert gases and form a family or group of elements called the noble gases. By tabulating the elements and grouping similar ones together, we begin to understand their properties.

Atomic Number: The characteristic that defines an element is the number of protons in the nuclei of its atoms; this number is called the atomic number (Z).

Atomic Number: Elements are the fundamental building blocks from which all compounds are made.

Ions: When an atom gains or loses electrons, it becomes an ion. Positively charged ions are called cations, and negatively charged ions are called anions. Cations and anions occur together so that matter is ordinarily charge-neutral.

Ions: Ions occur in many compounds, such as sodium chloride.

Isotopes: While all atoms of a given element have the same number of protons, they do not necessarily have the same number of neutrons. Atoms of the same element with different numbers of neutrons are called isotopes. Isotopes are characterized by their mass number (A), the sum of the number of protons and the number of neutrons in their nucleus.

Each naturally occurring sample of an element has the same percent natural abundance of each isotope. These percentages, together with the mass of each isotope, are used to compute the atomic mass of the element, a weighted average of the masses of the individual isotopes.

Isotopes: Isotopes are relevant because they influence tabulated atomic masses. To understand these masses, we must understand the presence and abundance of isotopes. In nuclear processes—processes in which the nuclei of atoms actually change—the presence of different isotopes becomes even more important.

Some isotopes are not stable—they lose subatomic particles and are transformed into other elements. The emission of subatomic particles by unstable nuclei is called radioactive decay. In many situations, such as in diagnosing and treating certain diseases, nuclear radiation is extremely useful. In other situations, such as in the disposal of radioactive waste, it can pose environmental problems.

CHEMICAL SKILLS

EXAMPLES

Determining Ion Charge from Numbers of Protons and Electrons (Section 7)

- From the periodic table or from the alphabetical list of elements, find the atomic number of the element; this number is equal to the number of protons.

- Use the ion charge equation to compute charge.

  Ion charge $= \#p^+ - \#e^-$

EXAMPLE 10 Determining Ion Charge from Numbers of Protons and Electrons

Determine the charge of a selenium ion with 36 electrons.

SOLUTION
Selenium is atomic number 34; therefore, it has 34 protons.

  Ion charge $= 34 - 36 = 2-$

Determining the Number of Protons and Electrons in an Ion (Section 7)

- From the periodic table or from the alphabetical list of elements, find the atomic number of the element; this number is equal to the number of protons.

- Use the ion charge equation and substitute in the known values.

  Ion charge $= \#p^+ - \#e^-$

- Solve the equation for the number of electrons.

EXAMPLE 11 Determining the Number of Protons and Electrons in an Ion

Find the number of protons and electrons in the O^{2-} ion.

SOLUTION
The atomic number of O is 8; therefore, it has 8 protons.

  Ion charge $= \#p^+ - \#e^-$

  $2- = 8 - \#e^-$

  $\#e^- = 8 + 2 = 10$

The ion has 8 protons and 10 electrons.

Determining Atomic Numbers, Mass Numbers, and Isotope Symbols for an Isotope (Section 8)

- From the periodic table or from the alphabetical list of elements, find the atomic number of the element.

- The mass number (A) is equal to the atomic number plus the number of neutrons.

- Write the symbol for the isotope by writing the symbol for the element with the mass number in the upper left corner and the atomic number in the lower left corner.

- The other symbol for the isotope is simply the chemical symbol followed by a hyphen and the mass number.

EXAMPLE 12 Determining Atomic Numbers, Mass Numbers, and Isotope Symbols for an Isotope

What are the atomic number (Z), mass number (A), and symbols for the iron isotope with 30 neutrons?

SOLUTION
The atomic number of iron is 26.

  $A = 26 + 30 = 56$

The mass number is 56.

  $^{56}_{26}\text{Fe}$

  Fe-56

Number of Protons and Neutrons from Isotope Symbols (Section 8)

- The number of protons is equal to Z (lower left number).

- The number of neutrons is equal to

    A (upper left number) − Z (lower left number.)

EXAMPLE 13   Number of Protons and Neutrons from Isotope Symbols

How many protons and neutrons are in $^{62}_{28}Ni$?

SOLUTION

28 protons

$$\#n = 62 - 28 = 34 \text{ neutrons}$$

Calculating Atomic Mass from Percent Natural Abundances and Isotopic Masses (Section 9)

- Convert the natural abundances from percent to decimal values by dividing by 100.

- Find the atomic mass by multiplying the fractions of each isotope by their respective masses and adding.

- Round to the correct number of significant figures.

- Check your work.

EXAMPLE 14   Calculating Atomic Mass from Percent Natural Abundances and Isotopic Masses

Copper has two naturally occurring isotopes: Cu-63 with mass 62.9395 amu and a natural abundance of 69.17%, and Cu-65 with mass 64.9278 amu and a natural abundance of 30.83%. Calculate the atomic mass of copper.

SOLUTION

$$\text{Fraction Cu-63} = \frac{69.17}{100} = 0.6917$$

$$\text{Fraction Cu-65} = \frac{30.83}{100} = 0.3083$$

$$\begin{aligned}
\text{Atomic mass} &= (0.6917 \times 62.9395 \text{ amu}) \\
&= 43.5353 \text{ amu} + 20.0107 \text{ amu} \\
&= 63.5460 \text{ amu} \\
&= 63.55 \text{ amu}
\end{aligned}$$

KEY TERMS

alkali metals [**Section 6**]
alkaline earth metals
    [**Section 6**]
anions [**Section 7**]
atom [**Section 1**]
atomic mass [**Section 9**]
atomic mass unit (amu)
    [**Section 4**]
atomic number (Z)
    [**Section 5**]
cation [**Section 7**]

charge [**Section 4**]
chemical symbol
    [**Section 5**]
electron [**Section 3**]
family (of elements)
    [**Section 6**]
group (of elements)
    [**Section 6**]
halogens [**Section 6**]
ion [**Section 7**]
isotope [**Section 8**]

main-group elements
    [**Section 6**]
mass number (A) [**Section 8**]
metalloids [**Section 6**]
metals [**Section 6**]
neutron [**Section 3**]
noble gases [**Section 6**]
nonmetals [**Section 6**]
nuclear radiation [**Section 9**]
nuclear theory of the
    atom [**Section 3**]
nucleus [**Section 3**]

percent natural
    abundance [**Section 8**]
periodic law [**Section 6**]
periodic table [**Section 6**]
proton [**Section 3**]
radioactive [**Section 9**]
semiconductor [**Section 6**]
transition elements
    [**Section 6**]
transition metals
    [**Section 6**]

EXERCISES

QUESTIONS

1. What did Democritus contribute to our modern understanding of matter?

2. What are three main ideas in Dalton's atomic theory?

3. Describe Rutherford's gold foil experiment and the results of that experiment. How did these results contradict the plum pudding model of the atom?

4. What are the main ideas in the nuclear theory of the atom?

5. List the three subatomic particles and their properties.

6. What is electrical charge?

7. Is matter usually charge-neutral? How would matter be different if it were not charge-neutral?

8. What does the atomic number of an element specify?

9. What is a chemical symbol?

10. List some examples of how elements got their names.

11. What was Dmitri Mendeleev's main contribution to our modern understanding of chemistry?
12. What is the main idea in the periodic law?
13. How is the periodic table organized?
14. What are the properties of metals? Where are metals found on the periodic table?
15. What are the properties of nonmetals? Where are nonmetals found on the periodic table?
16. Where on the periodic table are metalloids found?
17. What is a family or group of elements?
18. Locate each group of elements on the periodic table and list its group number.
    (a) alkali metals
    (b) alkaline earth metals
    (c) halogens
    (d) noble gases

19. What is an ion?
20. What is an anion? What is a cation?
21. Locate each group on the periodic table and list the charge of the ions it tends to form.
    (a) Group 1A
    (b) Group 2A
    (c) Group 3A
    (d) Group 6A
    (e) Group 7A
22. What are isotopes?
23. What is the percent natural abundance of isotopes?
24. What is the mass number of an isotope?
25. What notations are commonly used to specify isotopes? What do each of the numbers in these symbols mean?
26. What is the atomic mass of an element?

PROBLEMS

ATOMIC AND NUCLEAR THEORY

27. Which statements are *inconsistent* with Dalton's atomic theory as it was originally stated? Why?
    (a) All carbon atoms are identical.
    (b) Helium atoms can be split into two hydrogen atoms.
    (c) An oxygen atom combines with 1.5 hydrogen atoms to form water molecules.
    (d) Two oxygen atoms combine with a carbon atom to form carbon dioxide molecules.

28. Which statements are *consistent* with Dalton's atomic theory as it was originally stated? Why?
    (a) Calcium and titanium atoms have the same mass.
    (b) Neon and argon atoms are the same.
    (c) All cobalt atoms are identical.
    (d) Sodium and chlorine atoms combine in a 1:1 ratio to form sodium chloride.

29. Which statements are *inconsistent* with Rutherford's nuclear theory as it was originally stated? Why?
    (a) Helium atoms have two protons in the nucleus and two electrons outside the nucleus.
    (b) Most of the volume of hydrogen atoms is due to the nucleus.
    (c) Aluminum atoms have 13 protons in the nucleus and 22 electrons outside the nucleus.
    (d) The majority of the mass of nitrogen atoms is due to their 7 electrons.

30. Which statements are *consistent* with Rutherford's nuclear theory as it was originally stated? Why?
    (a) Atomic nuclei are small compared to the size of atoms.
    (b) The volume of an atom is mostly empty space.
    (c) Neutral potassium atoms contain more protons than electrons.
    (d) Neutral potassium atoms contain more neutrons than protons.

31. If atoms are mostly empty space, and atoms compose all ordinary matter, then why does solid matter seem to have no space within it?

32. Rutherford's experiment suggested that matter was not as uniform as it appears. What part of his experimental results implied this idea? Explain.

PROTONS, NEUTRONS, AND ELECTRONS

33. Which statements about electrons are true?
    (a) Electrons repel each other.
    (b) Electrons are attracted to protons.
    (c) Some electrons have a charge of 1− and some have no charge.
    (d) Electrons are much lighter than neutrons.

34. Which statements about electrons are false?
    (a) Most atoms have more electrons than protons.
    (b) Electrons have a charge of 1−.
    (c) If an atom has an equal number of protons and electrons, it will be charge-neutral.
    (d) Electrons experience an attraction to protons.

35. Which statements about protons are true?

    (a) Protons have twice the mass of neutrons.

    (b) Protons have the same magnitude of charge as electrons but are opposite in sign.

    (c) Most atoms have more protons than electrons.

    (d) Protons have a charge of 1+.

36. Which statements about protons are false?

    (a) Protons have about the same mass as neutrons.

    (b) Protons have about the same mass as electrons.

    (c) Some atoms don't have any protons.

    (d) Protons have the same magnitude of charge as neutrons, but are opposite in sign.

37. How many electrons would it take to equal the mass of a proton?

38. A helium nucleus has two protons and two neutrons. How many electrons would it take to equal the mass of a helium nucleus?

39. What mass of electrons would be required to just neutralize the charge of 1.0 g of protons?

40. What mass of protons would be required to just neutralize the charge of 1.0 g of electrons?

ELEMENTS, SYMBOLS, AND NAMES

41. Find the atomic number (Z) for each element.

    (a) Fr

    (b) Kr

    (c) Pa

    (d) Ge

    (e) Al

42. Find the atomic number (Z) for each element.

    (a) Si

    (b) W

    (c) Ni

    (d) Rn

    (e) Sr

43. How many protons are in the nucleus of an atom of each element?

    (a) Ar

    (b) Sn

    (c) Xe

    (d) O

    (e) Tl

44. How many protons are in the nucleus of an atom of each element?

    (a) Ti

    (b) Li

    (c) U

    (d) Br

    (e) F

45. List the symbol and atomic number corresponding to each element.

    (a) carbon

    (b) nitrogen

    (c) sodium

    (d) potassium

    (e) copper

46. List the symbol and atomic number corresponding to each element.

    (a) boron

    (b) neon

    (c) silver

    (d) mercury

    (e) curium

47. List the name and the atomic number corresponding to the symbol for each element.

    (a) Mn

    (b) Ag

    (c) Au

    (d) Pb

    (e) S

48. List the name and the atomic number corresponding to the symbol for each element.

    (a) Y

    (b) N

    (c) Ne

    (d) K

    (e) Mo

49. Fill in the blanks to complete the table.

Element Name	Element Symbol	Atomic Number
____	Au	79
Tin	____	____
____	As	____
Copper	____	29
____	Fe	____
____	____	80

50. Fill in the blanks to complete the table.

Element Name	Element Symbol	Atomic Number
____	Al	13
Iodine	____	____
____	Sb	____
Sodium	____	____
____	Rn	86
____	____	82

THE PERIODIC TABLE

51. Classify each element as a metal, nonmetal, or metalloid.
(a) Sr
(b) Mg
(c) F
(d) N
(e) As

52. Classify each element as a metal, nonmetal, or metalloid.
(a) Na
(b) Ge
(c) Si
(d) Br
(e) Ag

53. Which elements would you expect to lose electrons in chemical changes?
(a) potassium
(b) sulfur
(c) fluorine
(d) barium
(e) copper

54. Which elements would you expect to gain electrons in chemical changes?
(a) nitrogen
(b) iodine
(c) tungsten
(d) strontium
(e) gold

55. Which elements are main-group elements?
(a) Te
(b) K
(c) V
(d) Re
(e) Ag

56. Which elements are *not* main-group elements?
(a) Al
(b) Br
(c) Mo
(d) Cs
(e) Pb

57. Which elements are alkaline earth metals?
(a) sodium
(b) aluminum
(c) calcium
(d) barium
(e) lithium

58. Which elements are alkaline earth metals?
(a) rubidium
(b) tungsten
(c) magnesium
(d) cesium
(e) beryllium

59. Which elements are alkali metals?
(a) barium
(b) sodium
(c) gold
(d) tin
(e) rubidium

60. Which elements are alkali metals?
(a) scandium
(b) iron
(c) potassium
(d) lithium
(e) cobalt

61. Classify each element as a halogen, a noble gas, or neither.
    (a) Cl
    (b) Kr
    (c) F
    (d) Ga
    (e) He

62. Classify each element as a halogen, a noble gas, or neither.
    (a) Ne
    (b) Br
    (c) S
    (d) Xe
    (e) I

63. To what group number does each element belong?
    (a) oxygen
    (b) aluminum
    (c) silicon
    (d) tin
    (e) phosphorus

64. To what group number does each element belong?
    (a) germanium
    (b) nitrogen
    (c) sulfur
    (d) carbon
    (e) boron

65. Which element do you expect to be most like sulfur? Why?
    (a) nitrogen
    (b) oxygen
    (c) fluorine
    (d) lithium
    (e) potassium

66. Which element do you expect to be most like magnesium? Why?
    (a) potassium
    (b) silver
    (c) bromine
    (d) calcium
    (e) lead

67. Which pair of elements do you expect to be most similar? Why?
    (a) Si and P
    (b) Cl and F
    (c) Na and Mg
    (d) Mo and Sn
    (e) N and Ni

68. Which pair of elements do you expect to be most similar? Why?
    (a) Ti and Ga
    (b) N and O
    (c) Li and Na
    (d) Ar and Br
    (e) Ge and Ga

69. Fill in the blanks to complete the table.

Chemical Symbol	Group Number	Group Name	Metal or Nonmetal
K	____	____	metal
Br	____	halogens	____
Sr	____	____	____
He	8A	____	____
Ar	____	____	____

70. Fill in the blanks to complete the table.

Chemical Symbol	Group Number	Group Name	Metal or Nonmetal
Cl	7A	____	____
Ca	____	____	metal
Xe	____	____	nonmetal
Na	____	alkali metal	____
F	____	____	____

IONS

71. Complete each ionization equation.
    (a) $Na \longrightarrow Na^+ + \underline{\quad}$
    (b) $O + 2e^- \longrightarrow \underline{\quad}$
    (c) $Ca \longrightarrow Ca^{2+} + \underline{\quad}$
    (d) $Cl + e^- \longrightarrow \underline{\quad}$

72. Complete each ionization equation.
    (a) $Mg \longrightarrow \underline{\quad} + 2e^-$
    (b) $Ba \longrightarrow Ba^{2+} + \underline{\quad}$
    (c) $I + e^- \longrightarrow \underline{\quad}$
    (d) $Al \longrightarrow \underline{\quad} + 3e^-$

73. Determine the charge of each ion.
    (a) oxygen ion with 10 electrons
    (b) aluminum ion with 10 electrons
    (c) titanium ion with 18 electrons
    (d) iodine ion with 54 electrons

74. Determine the charge of each ion.
    (a) tungsten ion with 68 electrons
    (b) tellurium ion with 54 electrons
    (c) nitrogen ion with 10 electrons
    (d) barium ion with 54 electrons

75. Determine the number of protons and electrons in each ion.
    (a) Na^+
    (b) Ba^{2+}
    (c) O^{2+}
    (d) Co^{3+}

76. Determine the number of protons and electrons in each ion.
    (a) Al^{3+}
    (b) S^{2-}
    (c) I^-
    (d) Ag^+

77. Determine whether each statement is true or false. If false, correct it.
    (a) The Ti^{2+} ion contains 22 protons and 24 electrons.
    (b) The I^- ion contains 53 protons and 54 electrons.
    (c) The Mg^{2+} ion contains 14 protons and 12 electrons.
    (d) The O^{2-} ion contains 8 protons and 10 electrons.

78. Determine whether each statement is true or false. If false, correct it.
    (a) The Fe^+ ion contains 29 protons and 26 electrons.
    (b) The Cs^+ ion contains 55 protons and 56 electrons.
    (c) The Se^{2-} ion contains 32 protons and 34 electrons.
    (d) The Li^+ ion contains 3 protons and 2 electrons.

79. Predict the ion formed by each element:
    (a) Rb
    (b) K
    (c) Al
    (d) O

80. Predict the ion formed by each element:
    (a) F
    (b) N
    (c) Mg
    (d) Na

81. Predict how many electrons will most likely be gained or lost by each element:
    (a) Ga
    (b) Li
    (c) Br
    (d) S

82. Predict how many electrons will most likely be gained or lost by each element:
    (a) I
    (b) Ba
    (c) Cs
    (d) Se

83. Fill in the blanks to complete the table.

Symbol	Ion Commonly Formed	Number of Electrons in Ion	Number of Protons in Ion
Te	____	54	____
In	____	____	49
Sr	Sr^{2+}	____	____
____	Mg^{2+}	____	12
Cl	____	____	____

84. Fill in the blanks to complete the table.

Symbol	Ion Commonly Formed	Number of Electrons in Ion	Number of Protons in Ion
F	____	____	9
____	Be^{2+}	2	____
Br	____	36	____
Al	____	____	13
O	____	____	____

ISOTOPES

85. What are the atomic number and mass number for each isotope?

    (a) the hydrogen isotope with 2 neutrons

    (b) the chromium isotope with 28 neutrons

    (c) the calcium isotope with 22 neutrons

    (d) the tantalum isotope with 109 neutrons

86. How many neutrons are in an atom with each set of atomic numbers and mass numbers?

    (a) $Z = 28$, $A = 59$

    (b) $Z = 92$, $A = 235$

    (c) $Z = 21$, $A = 46$

    (d) $Z = 18$, $A = 42$

87. Write isotopic symbols of the form $_Z^A X$ for each isotope.

    (a) the oxygen isotope with 8 neutrons

    (b) the fluorine isotope with 10 neutrons

    (c) the sodium isotope with 12 neutrons

    (d) the aluminum isotope with 14 neutrons

88. Write isotopic symbols of the form X-A (for example, C-13) for each isotope.

    (a) the iodine isotope with 74 neutrons

    (b) the phosphorus isotope with 16 neutrons

    (c) the uranium isotope with 234 neutrons

    (d) the argon isotope with 22 neutrons

89. Write the symbol for each isotope in the form $_Z^A X$.

    (a) cobalt-60

    (b) neon-22

    (c) iodine-131

    (d) plutonium-244

90. Write the symbol for each isotope in the form $_Z^A X$.

    (a) U-235

    (b) V-52

    (c) P-32

    (d) Xe-144

91. Determine the number of protons and neutrons in each isotope:

    (a) $_{11}^{23}\text{Na}$

    (b) $_{28}^{266}\text{Ra}$

    (c) $_{82}^{208}\text{Pb}$

    (d) $_{7}^{14}\text{N}$

92. Determine the number of protons and neutrons in each isotope:

    (a) $_{15}^{33}\text{P}$

    (b) $_{19}^{40}\text{K}$

    (c) $_{86}^{222}\text{Rn}$

    (d) $_{43}^{99}\text{Tc}$

93. Carbon-14, present within living organisms and substances derived from living organisms, is often used to establish the age of fossils and artifacts. Determine the number of protons and neutrons in a carbon-14 isotope and write its symbol in the form $_Z^A X$.

94. Plutonium-239 is used in nuclear bombs. Determine the number of protons and neutrons in plutonium-239 and write its symbol in the form $_Z^A X$.

ATOMIC MASS

95. Rubidium has two naturally occurring isotopes: Rb-85 with mass 84.9118 amu and a natural abundance of 72.17%, and Rb-87 with mass 86.9092 amu and a natural abundance of 27.83%. Calculate the atomic mass of rubidium.

96. Silicon has three naturally occurring isotopes: Si-28 with mass 27.9769 amu and a natural abundance of 92.21%, Si-29 with mass 28.9765 amu and a natural abundance of 4.69%, and Si-30 with mass 29.9737 amu and a natural abundance of 3.10%. Calculate the atomic mass of silicon.

97. Bromine has two naturally occurring isotopes (Br-79 and Br-81) and an atomic mass of 79.904 amu.

    (a) If the natural abundance of Br-79 is 50.69%, what is the natural abundance of Br-81?

    (b) If the mass of Br-81 is 80.9163 amu, what is the mass of Br-79?

98. Silver has two naturally occurring isotopes (Ag-107 and Ag-109).

    (a) Use the periodic table to find the atomic mass of silver.

    (b) If the natural abundance of Ag-107 is 51.84%, what is the natural abundance of Ag-109?

    (c) If the mass of Ag-107 is 106.905 amu, what is the mass of Ag-109?

99. An element has two naturally occurring isotopes. Isotope 1 has a mass of 120.9038 amu and a relative abundance of 57.4%, and isotope 2 has a mass of 122.9042 amu and a relative abundance of 42.6%. Find the atomic mass of this element and, referring to the periodic table, identify it.

100. Copper has two naturally occurring isotopes. Cu-63 has a mass of 62.939 amu and relative abundance of 69.17%. Use the atomic weight of copper to determine the mass of the other copper isotope.

CUMULATIVE PROBLEMS

101. Electrical charge is sometimes reported in coulombs (C). On this scale, 1 electron has a charge of -1.6×10^{-19} C. Suppose your body acquires -125 mC (millicoulombs) of charge on a dry day. How many excess electrons has it acquired? (*Hint:* Use the charge of an electron in coulombs as a conversion factor between charge and electrons.)

102. How many excess protons are in a positively charged object with a charge of $+398$ mC (millicoulombs)? The charge of 1 proton is $+1.6 \times 10^{-19}$ C.

103. The hydrogen atom contains 1 proton and 1 electron. The radius of the proton is approximately 1.0 fm (femtometers), and the radius of the hydrogen atom is approximately 53 pm (picometers). Calculate the volume of the nucleus and the volume of the atom for hydrogen. What percentage of the hydrogen atom's volume is occupied by the nucleus?

104. Carbon-12 contains 6 protons and 6 neutrons. The radius of the nucleus is approximately 2.7 fm, and the radius of the atom is approximately 70 pm. Calculate the volume of the nucleus and the volume of the atom. What percentage of the carbon atom's volume is occupied by the nucleus?

105. Prepare a table such as Table 2 for the four different isotopes of Sr that have the following natural abundances and masses.

Sr-84	0.56%	83.9134 amu
Sr-86	9.86%	85.9093 amu
Sr-87	7.00%	86.9089 amu
Sr-88	82.58%	87.9056 amu

Use your table and the preceding atomic masses to calculate the atomic mass of strontium.

106. Determine the number of protons and neutrons in each isotope of chromium and use the following natural abundances and masses to calculate its atomic mass.

Cr-50	4.345%	49.9460 amu
Cr-52	83.79%	51.9405 amu
Cr-53	9.50%	52.9407 amu
Cr-54	2.365%	53.9389 amu

107. Fill in the blanks to complete the table.

Symbol	Z	A	Number of Protons	Number of Electrons	Number of Neutrons	Charge
Zn^+	___	___	___	___	34	1+
___	25	55	___	22	___	___
___	___	___	15	15	16	___
O^{2-}	___	16	___	___	___	2−
___	___	___	16	18	18	___

108. Fill in the blanks to complete the table.

Symbol	Z	A	Number of Protons	Number of Electrons	Number of Neutrons	Charge
Mg^{2+}	___	25	___	___	13	2+
___	22	48	___	18	___	___
___	16	___	___	___	16	2−
Ga^{3+}	___	71	___	___	___	___
___	___	___	82	80	125	___

109. Europium has two naturally occurring isotopes: Eu-151 with a mass of 150.9198 amu and a natural abundance of 47.8%, and Eu-153. Use the atomic mass of europium to find the mass and natural abundance of Eu-153.

110. Rhenium has two naturally occurring isotopes: Re-185 with a natural abundance of 37.40%, and Re-187 with a natural abundance of 62.60%. The sum of the masses of the two isotopes is 371.9087 amu. Find the masses of the individual isotopes.

111. Recall the difference between observations, laws, and theories. Provide two examples of theories from this chapter and explain why they are theories.

112. Recall the difference between observations, laws, and theories. Provide one example of a law from this chapter and explain why it is a law.

113. The atomic mass of fluorine is 19.00 amu, and all fluorine atoms in a naturally occurring sample of fluorine have this mass. The atomic mass of chlorine is 35.45 amu, but no chlorine atoms in a naturally occurring sample of chlorine have this mass. Explain the difference.

114. The atomic mass of germanium is 72.61 amu. Is it likely that any individual germanium atoms have a mass of 72.61 amu?

115. Copper has only two naturally occurring isotopes, Cu-63 and Cu-65. The mass of Cu-63 is 62.9396 amu, and the mass of Cu-65 is 64.9278 amu. Use the atomic mass of copper to determine the relative abundance of each isotope in a naturally occurring sample.

116. Gallium has only two naturally occurring isotopes, Ga-69 and Ga-71. The mass of Ga-69 is 68.9256 amu, and the mass of Ga-71 is 70.9247 amu. Use the atomic mass of gallium to determine the relative abundance of each isotope in a naturally occurring sample.

HIGHLIGHT PROBLEMS

117. The figure is a representation of 50 atoms of a fictitious element with the symbol Nt and atomic number 120. Nt has three isotopes represented by the following colors: Nt-304 (red), Nt-305 (blue), and Nt-306 (green).

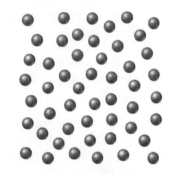

(a) Assuming that the figure is statistically representative of naturally occurring Nt, what is the percent natural abundance of each Nt isotope?

(b) Use the following masses of each isotope to calculate the atomic mass of Nt. Then draw a box for the element similar to the boxes for each element shown in the periodic table. Make sure your box includes the atomic number, symbol, and atomic mass. (Assume that the percentages from part (a) are correct to four significant figures.)

Nt-304	303.956 amu
Nt-305	304.962 amu
Nt-306	305.978 amu

118. Neutron stars are believed to be composed of solid nuclear matter, primarily neutrons.

(a) If the radius of a neutron is 1.0×10^{-13} cm, calculate its density in g/cm^3.

(volume of a sphere $= \frac{4}{3}\pi r^3$)

(b) Assuming that a neutron star has the same density as a neutron, calculate the mass in kilograms of a small piece of a neutron star the size of a spherical pebble with a radius of 0.10 mm.

▶ANSWERS TO SKILLBUILDER EXERCISES

Skillbuilder 1
(a) sodium, 11
(b) nickel, 28
(c) phosphorus, 15
(d) tantalum, 73

Skillbuilder 2
(a) nonmetal
(b) nonmetal
(c) metal
(d) metalloid

Skillbuilder 3
(a) alkali metal, group 1A
(b) group 3A
(c) halogen, group 7A
(d) noble gas, group 8A

Skillbuilder 4
(a) 2+
(b) 1−
(c) 3−

Skillbuilder 5   16 protons, 18 electrons

Skillbuilder 6 K^+ and Se^{2-}

Skillbuilder 7   Z = 17, A= 35, Cl-35, and $^{35}_{17}Cl$

Skillbuilder 8   19 protons, 20 neutrons

Skillbuilder 9   24.31 amu

▶ANSWERS TO CONCEPTUAL CHECKPOINTS

1 **(c)** The mass in amu is approximately equal to the number of protons plus the number of neutrons. In order to be charge-neutral, the number of protons must equal the number of electrons.

2 **(b)** All of the metalloids are main-group elements (see Figures 12 and 13).

3 **(a)** Both of these ions have 10 electrons.

4 **(b)** This atom must have (27 − 14) = 13 protons; the element with an atomic number of 13 is Al.

5 The isotopes C-12 and C-13 would not look different in this representation of atoms because the only difference between the two isotopes is that C-13 has an extra neutron in the nucleus. The illustration represents the whole atom and does not attempt to illustrate its nucleus. Since the nucleus of an atom is miniscule compared to the size of the atom itself, the extra neutron would not affect the size of the atom.

6 **(b)** The natural abundance of isotope B must be greater than the natural abundance of isotope A because the atomic mass is closer to the mass of isotope B than to the mass of isotope A.

ANSWERS TO ODD-NUMBERED EXERCISES

QUESTIONS

1. Democritus theorized that matter was ultimately composed of small, indivisible particles called atoms. Upon dividing matter, one would find tiny, indestructible atoms.

3. Rutherford's gold foil experiment involved sending positively charged alpha-particles through a thin sheet of gold foil and detecting if there was any deflection of the particles. He found that most passed straight through, yet some particles showed some deflection. This result contradicts the plum-pudding model of the atom because the plum-pudding model does not explain the deflection of the alpha-particles.

5.

Particle	Mass (kg)	Mass (amu)	Charge
Proton	1.67262×10^{-27}	1	+1
Neutron	1.67493×10^{-27}	1	0
Electron	0.00091×10^{-27}	0.00055	−1

7. Matter is usually charge-neutral due to protons and electrons having opposite charges. If matter were not charge neutral, many unnatural things would occur, such as objects repelling or attracting each other.

9. A chemical symbol is a unique one- or two-letter abbreviation for an element. It is listed below the atomic number for that element on the periodic table.

11. Mendeleev noticed that many patterns were evident when elements were organized by increasing mass; from this observation he formulated the periodic law. He also organized the elements based on this law and created the basis for the periodic table being used today.

13. The periodic table is organized by listing the elements in order of increasing atomic number.

15. Nonmetals have varied properties (solid, liquid, or gas at room temperature); however, as a whole they tend to be poor conductors of heat and electricity, and they all tend to gain electrons when they undergo chemical changes. They are located toward the upper right side of the periodic table.

17. Each column within the main group elements in the periodic table is labeled as a family or group of elements. The elements within a group usually have similar chemical properties.

19. An ion is an atom or group of atoms that has lost or gained electrons and has become charged.

21. **a.** ion charge = +1   **b.** ion charge = +2
    c. ion charge = +3   **d.** ion charge = −2
    e. ion charge = −1

23. The percent natural abundance of isotopes is the relative amount of each different isotope in a naturally occurring sample of a given element.

25. Isotopes are noted in this manner: $_Z^A X$. X represents the chemical symbol, A represents the mass number, and Z represents the atomic number.

PROBLEMS

27. **a.** Correct.
    b. False; different elements contain different types of atoms according to Dalton.
    c. False; one cannot have 1.5 hydrogen atoms; combinations must be in simple, whole-number ratios.
    d. Correct.

29. **a.** Correct.
    b. False; most of the volume of the atom is empty space occupied by tiny, negatively charged electrons.
    c. False, the number of negatively charged particles outside the nucleus equals the number of positively charged particles inside the nucleus.
    d. False, the majority of the mass of an atom is found in the nucleus.

31. Solid matter seems to have no empty space within it because electromagnetic forces hold the atoms in a tight arrangement and the variation in density is too small to perceive with our eyes.

33. a, b, d

35. b, d

37. approximately 1.8×10^3 electrons

39. 5.4×10^{-4} g

41. **a.** 87   **b.** 36
    c. 91   **d.** 32
    e. 13

43. **a.** 18   **b.** 50
    c. 54   **d.** 8
    e. 81

45. **a.** C, 6   **b.** N, 7
    c. Na, 11   **d.** K, 19
    e. Cu, 29

47. **a.** manganese, 25   **b.** silver, 47
    c. gold, 79   **d.** lead, 82
    e. sulfur, 16

49.

Element Name	Element Symbol	Atomic Number
Gold	Au	79
Tin	Sn	50
Arsenic	As	33
Copper	Cu	29
Iron	Fe	26
Mercury	Hg	80

51. **a.** metal   **b.** metal

    c. nonmetal   **d.** nonmetal

    e. metalloid

53. a, d, e

55. a, b

57. c, d

59. b, e

61. **a.** halogen   **b.** noble gas

    c. halogen   **d.** neither

    e. noble gas

63. **a.** 6A   **b.** 3A

    c. 4A   **d.** 4A

    e. 5A

65. b, oxygen; it is in the same group or family.

67. b, chlorine and fluorine; they are in the same family or group.

69.

Chemical Symbol	Group Number	Group Name	Metal or Nonmetal
K	1A	Alkali Metals	Metals
Br	7A	Halogens	Nonmetal
Sr	2A	Alkaline Earth	Metal
He	8A	Noble Gas	Nonmetal
Ar	8A	Noble Gas	Nonmetal

71. **a.** e^- **b.** O^{2-}

    c. $2e^-$ **d.** Cl^-

73. **a.** 2−   **b.** 3+

    c. 4+   **d.** 1−

75. **a.** 11 protons, 10 electrons

    b. 56 protons, 54 electrons

    c. 8 protons, 10 electrons

    d. 27 protons, 24 electrons

77. **a.** False; Ti^{2+} has 22 protons and 20 electrons.

    b. True

    c. False; Mg^{2+} has 12 protons and 10 electrons

    d. True

79. **a.** Rb^+ **b.** K^+

    c. Al^{3+} **d.** O^{2-}

81. **a.** 3 electrons lost   **b.** 1 electron lost

    c. 1 electron gained   **d.** 2 electrons gained

83.

Symbol	Ion Commonly Formed	Number of Electrons in Ion	Number of Protons in Ion
Te	Te^{2-}	54	52
In	In^{3+}	46	49
Sr	Sr^{2+}	36	38
Mg	Mg^{2+}	10	12
Cl	Cl^-	18	17

85. **a.** Z = 1, A = 3   **b.** Z = 24, A = 52

    c. Z = 20, A = 42   **d.** Z = 73, A = 182

87. **a.** $^{16}_{8}O$ **b.** $^{19}_{9}F$

    c. $^{23}_{11}Na$ **d.** $^{27}_{13}Al$

89. **a.** $^{60}_{27}Co$ **b.** $^{22}_{10}Ne$

    c. $^{131}_{53}I$ **d.** $^{244}_{94}Pu$

91. **a.** 11 protons, 12 neutrons

    b. 88 protons, 178 neutrons

    c. 82 protons, 126 neutrons

    d. 7 protons, 7 neutrons

93. 6 protons, 8 neutrons, $^{14}_{6}C$

95. 85.47 amu

97. **a.** 49.31%   **b.** 78.91 amu

99. 121.8 amu, Sb

101. 7.8×10^{17} electrons

103. $4.2 \times 10^{-45} m^3$; $6.2 \times 10^{-31} m^3$; 6.7×10^{-13} %

105.

Number Symbol	Number of Protons	Number of Neutrons	A (Mass Number)	Natural Abundance
Sr-84 or $^{84}_{38}Sr$	38	46	84	0.56%
Sr-86 or $^{86}_{38}Sr$	38	48	86	9.86%
Sr-87 or $^{87}_{38}Sr$	38	49	87	7.00%
Sr-88 or $^{88}_{38}Sr$	38	50	88	82.58%

Atomic mass of Sr = 87.62 amu

Symbol	Z	A	Number of Protons	Number of Electrons	Number of Neutrons	Charge
Zn^+	30	64	30	29	34	1+
Mn^{3+}	25	55	25	22	30	3+
P	15	31	15	15	16	0
O^{2-}	8	16	8	10	8	2−
S^{2-}	16	34	16	18	18	2−

107.

109. 153 amu, 52.2%

111. The atomic theory and nuclear model of the atom are both theories because they attempt to provide a broader understanding and model behavior of chemical systems.

113. Atomic mass is measured as the mean value of masses of all isotopes in a sample. In the case of fluorine, only the 19.00 amu isotope is naturally occurring. In the case of chlorine, about 76% of naturally occurring atoms are 35 amu, and 24% are 37 amu.

115. 69.3% Cu-63, 30.7% Cu-65

117. **a.** Nt − 304 = 72%; Nt − 305 = 4%; Nt − 306 = 24%

    b.

120
Nt
304.5

Molecules and Compounds

From Chapter 5 of *Introductory Chemistry*, Fourth Edition, Nivaldo J. Tro. Copyright © 2011 by Pearson Education, Inc. Published by Pearson Prentice Hall. All rights reserved.

Molecules and Compounds

*"Almost all aspects of life are engineered at the molecular level,
and without understanding molecules, we can only have a very
sketchy understanding of life itself."*

FRANCIS HARRY COMPTON CRICK (1916–2004)

1   Sugar and Salt

Sodium, a shiny metal (▼ Figure 1) that dulls almost instantly upon exposure to air, is extremely reactive and poisonous. If you were to consume any appreciable amount of elemental sodium, you would need immediate medical help. Chlorine, a pale yellow gas (▼ Figure 2), is equally reactive and poisonous. Yet the compound formed from these two elements, sodium chloride, is the relatively harmless flavor enhancer that we call table salt (► Figure 3). When elements combine to form compounds, their properties completely change.

◄ Ordinary table sugar is a compound called sucrose. A sucrose molecule, such as the one shown here, contains carbon, hydrogen, and oxygen atoms. The properties of sucrose are, however, very different from those of carbon (also shown in the form of graphite), hydrogen, and oxygen. The properties of a compound are, in general, different from the properties of the elements that compose it.

Pearson Education/PH College.

▲ FIGURE 1   **Elemental sodium**
Sodium is an extremely reactive metal that dulls almost instantly upon exposure to air.

Charles D. Winters/Photo Researchers.

▲ FIGURE 2   **Elemental chlorine**
Chlorine is a yellow gas with a pungent odor. It is highly reactive and poisonous.

▲ FIGURE 3 **Sodium chloride**
The compound formed by sodium and chlorine is table salt.

Diane Diederich/Istockphoto.com.

Consider ordinary sugar. Sugar is a compound composed of carbon, hydrogen, and oxygen. Each of these elements has its own unique properties. Carbon is most familiar to us as the graphite found in pencils or as the diamonds in jewelry. Hydrogen is an extremely flammable gas used as a fuel for the space shuttle, and oxygen is one of the gases that compose air. When these three elements combine to form sugar, however, a sweet, white, crystalline solid results.

Recall how protons, neutrons, and electrons combine to form different elements, each with its own properties and its own chemistry, each different from the other. In this chapter, we learn how these elements combine with each other to form different compounds, each with its own properties and its own chemistry, each different from all the others and different from the elements that compose it. This is the great wonder of nature: how from such simplicity—protons, neutrons, and electrons—we get such great complexity. It is exactly this complexity that makes life possible. Life could not exist with just 91 different elements if they did not combine to form compounds. It takes compounds in all of their diversity to make living organisms.

2 Compounds Display Constant Composition

Although some of the substances we encounter in everyday life are elements, most are not—they are compounds. Free atoms are rare in nature. A compound is different from a mixture of elements. In a compound, the elements combine in fixed, definite proportions, whereas in a mixture, they can have any proportions whatsoever. Consider the difference between a mixture of hydrogen and oxygen gas (▼ Figure 4) and the compound water (▼ Figure 5). A mixture of hydrogen and oxygen gas can contain any propor-

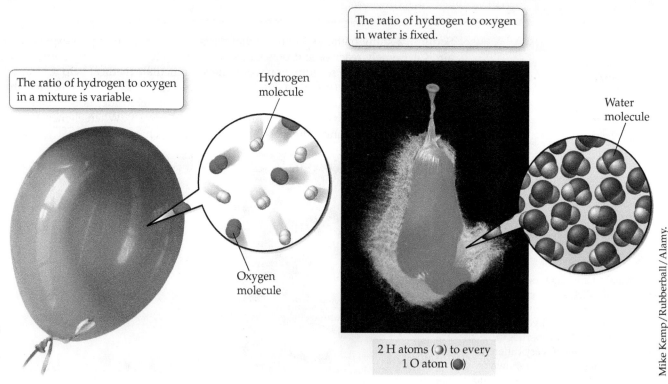

The ratio of hydrogen to oxygen in a mixture is variable.

The ratio of hydrogen to oxygen in water is fixed.

Hydrogen molecule

Oxygen molecule

Water molecule

2 H atoms (◗) to every 1 O atom (●)

Getty Images.

Mike Kemp/Rubberball/Alamy.

▲ FIGURE 4 **A mixture** This balloon is filled with a mixture of hydrogen and oxygen gas. The relative amounts of hydrogen and oxygen are variable. We could easily add either more hydrogen or more oxygen to the balloon.

▲ FIGURE 5 **A chemical compound** This balloon is filled with water, composed of molecules that have a fixed ratio of hydrogen to oxygen. (*Source:* JoLynn E. Funk.)

tions of hydrogen and oxygen. Water, on the other hand, is composed of water molecules that consist of two hydrogen atoms bonded to one oxygen atom. Consequently, water has a definite proportion of hydrogen to oxygen.

The first chemist to formally state the idea that elements combine in fixed proportions to form compounds was Joseph Proust (1754–1826) in the **law of constant composition**, which states:

> All samples of a given compound have the same proportions of their constituent elements.

For example, if we decompose an 18.0 g sample of water, we would get 16.0 g of oxygen and 2.0 g of hydrogen, or an oxygen-to-hydrogen mass ratio of

$$\text{Mass ratio} = \frac{16.0 \text{ g O}}{2.0 \text{ g H}} = 8.0 \quad \text{or} \quad 8.0{:}1$$

This is true of any sample of pure water, no matter what its origin. The law of constant composition applies not only to water, but to every compound. If we decomposed a 17.0 g sample of ammonia, a compound composed of nitrogen and hydrogen, we would get 14.0 g of nitrogen and 3.0 g of hydrogen, or a nitrogen-to–hydrogen mass ratio of

Even though atoms combine in whole-number ratios, their mass ratios are not necessarily whole numbers.

$$\text{Mass ratio} = \frac{14.0 \text{ g N}}{3.0 \text{ g H}} = 4.7 \quad \text{or} \quad 4.7{:}1$$

Again, this ratio is the same for every sample of ammonia—the composition of each compound is constant.

EXAMPLE 1 Constant Composition of Compounds

Two samples of carbon dioxide, obtained from different sources, are decomposed into their constituent elements. One sample produces 4.8 g of oxygen and 1.8 g of carbon, and the other sample produces 17.1 g of oxygen and 6.4 g of carbon. Show that these results are consistent with the law of constant composition.

Compute the mass ratio of one element to the other by dividing the larger mass by the smaller one. For the first sample:	**SOLUTION** $$\frac{\text{Mass oxygen}}{\text{Mass carbon}} = \frac{4.8 \text{ g}}{1.8 \text{ g}} = 2.7$$
For the second sample:	$$\frac{\text{Mass oxygen}}{\text{Mass carbon}} = \frac{17.1 \text{ g}}{6.4 \text{ g}} = 2.7$$

Since the ratios are the same for the two samples, these results are consistent with the law of constant composition.

▶ **SKILLBUILDER 1 | Constant Composition of Compounds**

Two samples of carbon monoxide, obtained from different sources, are decomposed into their constituent elements. One sample produces 4.3 g of oxygen and 3.2 g of carbon, and the other sample produces 7.5 g of oxygen and 4.6 g of carbon. Are these results consistent with the law of constant composition?

▶ **FOR MORE PRACTICE**   Example 16; Problems 25, 26.

3 Chemical Formulas: How to Represent Compounds

Compounds have constant composition with respect to mass (as we learned in the previous section) because they are composed of atoms in fixed ratios.

We represent a compound with a **chemical formula**, which indicates the elements present in the compound and the relative number of atoms of each. For example, H_2O is the chemical formula for water; it indicates that water consists of hydrogen and oxygen atoms in a 2:1 ratio. The formula contains the symbol for each element, accompanied by a subscript indicating the number of atoms of that element. By convention, a subscript of 1 is omitted.

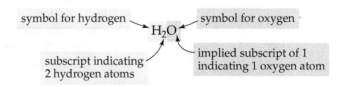

Other common chemical formulas include NaCl for table salt, indicating sodium and chlorine atoms in a 1:1 ratio; CO_2 for carbon dioxide, indicating carbon and oxygen atoms in a 1:2 ratio; and $C_{12}H_{22}O_{11}$ for table sugar (sucrose), indicating carbon, hydrogen, and oxygen atoms in a 12:22:11 ratio. The subscripts in a chemical formula are part of the compound's definition—if they change, the formula no longer specifies the same compound. For example, CO is the chemical formula for carbon monoxide, an air pollutant with adverse health effects on humans. When inhaled, carbon monoxide interferes with the blood's ability to carry oxygen, which can be fatal. CO is the primary substance responsible for the deaths of people who inhale too much automobile exhaust. If you change the subscript of the O in CO from 1 to 2, however, you get the formula for a totally different compound. CO_2 is the chemical formula for carbon dioxide, the relatively harmless product of combustion and human respiration. We breathe small amounts of CO_2 all the time with no harmful effects. So, remember that:

> The subscripts in a chemical formula represent the relative numbers of each type of atom in a chemical compound; they never change for a given compound.

Chemical formulas normally list the most metallic elements first. Therefore, the formula for table salt is NaCl, not ClNa. In compounds that do not include a metal, the more metal-like element is listed first. Recall that metals are found on the left side of the periodic table and nonmetals on the upper right side. Among nonmetals, those to the left in the periodic table are more metal-like than those to the right and are normally listed first. Therefore, we write CO_2 and NO, not O_2C and ON. Within a single column in the periodic table, elements toward the bottom are more metal-like than elements toward the top. So, we write SO_2, not O_2S. The specific order for listing nonmetal elements in a chemical formula is shown in Table 1.

CO CO_2

There are a few historical exceptions to the practice in which the most metallic element is listed first, such as the hydroxide ion, which is written as OH^-.

TABLE 1   Order of Listing Nonmetal Elements in a Chemical Formula

C	P	N	H	S	I	Br	Cl	O	F

Elements on the left are generally listed before elements on the right.

EXAMPLE 2   Writing Chemical Formulas

Write a chemical formula for each compound.

(a) the compound containing two aluminum atoms to every three oxygen atoms
(b) the compound containing three oxygen atoms to every sulfur atom
(c) the compound containing four chlorine atoms to every carbon atom

	SOLUTION
Since aluminum is the metal, it is listed first.	(a) Al_2O_3
Since sulfur is below oxygen on the periodic table and since it occurs before oxygen in Table 1, it is listed first.	(b) SO_3
Since carbon is to the left of chlorine on the periodic table and since it occurs before chlorine in Table 1, it is listed first.	(c) CCl_4

▶SKILLBUILDER 2 | Writing Chemical Formulas

Write a chemical formula for each compound.

(a) the compound containing two silver atoms to every sulfur atom
(b) the compound containing two nitrogen atoms to every oxygen atom
(c) the compound containing two oxygen atoms to every titanium atom

▶FOR MORE PRACTICE Example 17; Problems 31, 32, 33, 34.

Some chemical formulas contain groups of atoms that act as a unit. When several groups of the same kind are present, their formula is set off in parentheses with a subscript to indicate the number of that group. Many of these groups of atoms have a charge associated with them and are called **polyatomic ions**. For example, NO_3^- is a polyatomic ion with a 1− charge. Polyatomic ions are described in more detail in Section 7.

To determine the total number of each type of atom in a compound containing a group within parentheses, multiply the subscript outside the parentheses by the subscript for each atom inside the parentheses. For example, $Mg(NO_3)_2$ indicates a compound containing one magnesium atom (present as the Mg^{2+} ion) and two NO_3^- groups.

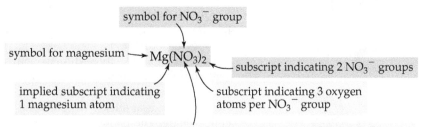

Therefore, the preceding formula has the following numbers of each type of atom.

Mg: 1 Mg
N: $1 \times 2 = 2\,N$ (implied 1 inside parentheses times 2 outside parentheses)
O: $3 \times 2 = 6\,O$ (3 inside parentheses times 2 outside parentheses)

EXAMPLE 3   Total Number of Each Type of Atom in a Chemical Formula

Determine the number of each type of atom in $Mg_3(PO_4)_2$.

SOLUTION

Mg: There are three Mg atoms (present as Mg^{2+} ions), as indicated by the subscript 3.
P: There are two P atoms. We determine this by multiplying the subscript outside the parentheses (2) by the subscript for P inside the parentheses, which is 1 (implied).
O: There are eight O atoms. We determine this by multiplying the subscript outside the parentheses (2) by the subscript for O inside the parentheses (4).

▶SKILLBUILDER 3 | Total Number of Each Type of Atom in a Chemical Formula

Determine the number of each type of atom in K_2SO_4.

▶SKILLBUILDER PLUS 1

Determine the number of each type of atom in $Al_2(SO_4)_3$.

▶FOR MORE PRACTICE Example 18; Problems 35, 36, 37, 38.

CONCEPTUAL CHECKPOINT 1

Which formula represents the greatest total number of atoms?

(a) $Al(C_2H_3O_2)_3$

(b) $Al_2(Cr_2O_7)_3$

(c) $Pb(HSO_4)_4$

(d) $Pb_3(PO_4)_4$

(e) $(NH_4)_3PO_4$

TYPES OF CHEMICAL FORMULAS

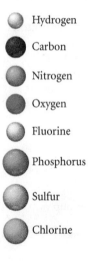

Hydrogen

Carbon

Nitrogen

Oxygen

Fluorine

Phosphorus

Sulfur

Chlorine

We can categorize chemical formulas as three different types: empirical, molecular, and structural. An **empirical formula** gives the simplest whole-number ratio of atoms of each element in a compound. A **molecular formula** gives the *actual* number of atoms of each element in a molecule of the compound. For example, the molecular formula for hydrogen peroxide is H_2O_2, and its empirical formula is HO. The molecular formula is always a whole number multiple of the empirical formula. For many compounds, the molecular and empirical formula are the same. For example, the empirical and molecular formula for water is H_2O because water molecules contain two hydrogen atoms and one oxygen atom; no simpler whole number ratio can express the relative number of hydrogen atoms to oxygen atoms.

A **structural** formula uses lines to represent chemical bonds and shows how the atoms in a molecule are connected to each other. The structural formula for hydrogen peroxide is H—O—O—H. In addition to formulas, we also use **molecular models**—three-dimensional representations of molecules—to represent compounds. In this text, we use two types of molecular models: ball-and-stick and space-filling. In **ball-and-stick models**, we represent atoms as balls and chemical bonds as sticks. The balls and sticks are connected to represent the molecule's shape. The balls are color coded, and each element is assigned a color as shown in the margin.

In **space-filling models**, atoms fill the space between each other to more closely represent our best idea for how a molecule might appear if we could scale it to a visible size. Consider the following ways to represent a molecule of methane, the main component of natural gas:

CH_4

$$H—\overset{\overset{\textstyle H}{|}}{\underset{\underset{\textstyle H}{|}}{C}}—H$$

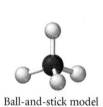

Molecular formula   Structural formula   Ball-and-stick model   Space-filling model

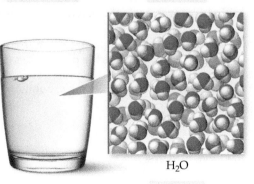

Macroscopic

Molecular

H_2O

Symbolic

The molecular formula of methane indicates that methane has one carbon atom and four hydrogen atoms. The structural formula shows how the atoms are connected: Each hydrogen atom is bonded to the central carbon atom. The ball-and-stick model and the space-filling model illustrate the *geometry* of the molecule: how the atoms are arranged in three dimensions.

Throughout this text, you have seen and will continue to see images that show the connection between the *macroscopic world* (what we see), the *atomic and molecular world* (the particles that compose matter), and the *symbolic way* that chemists represent the atomic and molecular world. For example, at left is a representation of water using this kind of image.

The main goal of these images is to help you visualize the main theme of this book: *the connection between the world around us and the world of atoms and molecules.*

4 A Molecular View of Elements and Compounds

Pure substances could be categorized as either elements or compounds. We can further subcategorize elements and compounds according to the basic units that compose them (▼ Figure 6). Pure substances may be elements, or they may be compounds. Elements may be either atomic or molecular. Compounds may be either molecular or ionic.

▶ FIGURE 6 **A molecular view of elements and compounds**

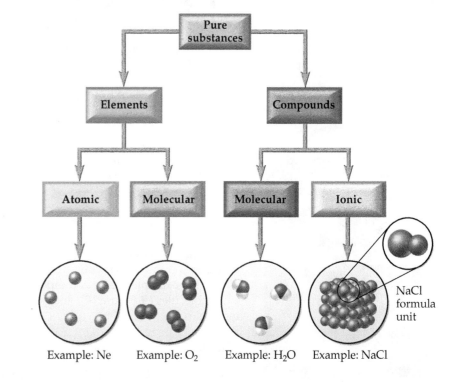

Example: Ne   Example: O_2 Example: H_2O Example: NaCl

Harry Taylor/Dorling Kindersly Media Library.

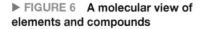

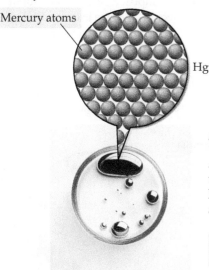

Hg

▲ FIGURE 7 **An atomic element** The basic units that compose mercury, an atomic element and a metal, are single mercury atoms.

A few molecular elements, such as S_8 and P_4, are composed of molecules containing several atoms.

ATOMIC ELEMENTS

Atomic elements are those that exist in nature with single atoms as their basic units. Most elements fall into this category. For example, helium is composed of helium atoms, copper is composed of copper atoms, and mercury of mercury atoms (◀ Figure 7).

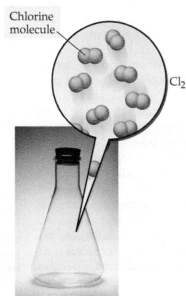

Cl_2

Chlorine molecule

MOLECULAR ELEMENTS

Molecular elements do not normally exist in nature with single atoms as their basic units. Instead, these elements exist as *diatomic molecules*—two atoms of that element bonded together—as their basic units. For example, hydrogen is composed of H_2 molecules, oxygen is composed of O_2 molecules, and chlorine of Cl_2 molecules (◀ Figure 8). Elements that exist as diatomic molecules are shown in Table 2 and ▶ Figure 9.

◀ FIGURE 8 **A molecular element** The basic units that compose chlorine, a molecular element, are diatomic chlorine molecules, each composed of two chlorine atoms.

Charles D. Winters/Photo Researchers.

TABLE 2 Elements That Occur as Diatomic Molecules

Name of Element	Formula of Basic Unit
hydrogen	H_2
nitrogen	N_2
oxygen	O_2
fluorine	F_2
chlorine	Cl_2
bromine	Br_2
iodine	I_2

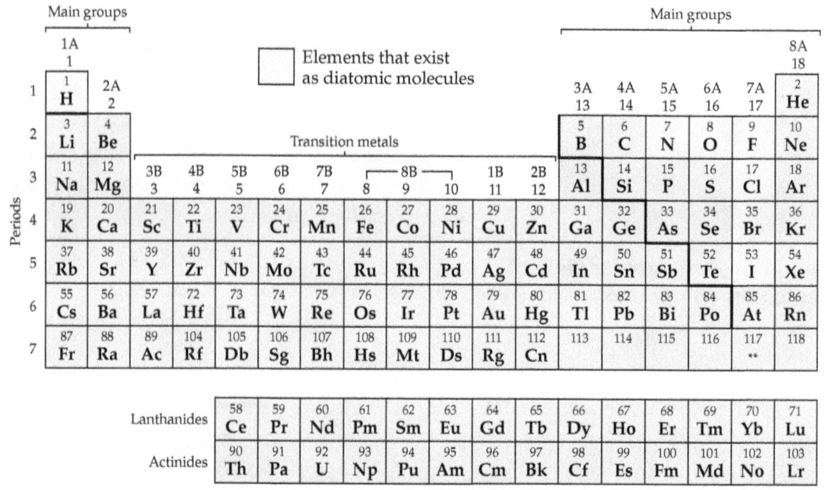

Carbon dioxide molecule

CO_2

Ken Karp/Omni-Photo Communication.

▲ **FIGURE 10 A molecular compound** The basic units that compose dry ice, a molecular compound, are CO_2 molecules.

▲ **FIGURE 9 Elements that form diatomic molecules** Elements that normally exist as diatomic molecules are highlighted in yellow on this periodic table. Note that they are all nonmetals, and include four of the halogens.

MOLECULAR COMPOUNDS

Molecular compounds are compounds formed from two or more nonmetals. The basic units of molecular compounds are molecules composed of the constituent atoms. For example, water is composed of H_2O molecules, dry ice is composed of CO_2 molecules (◄ Figure 10), and acetone (finger nail–polish remover) of C_3H_6O molecules.

IONIC COMPOUNDS

Ionic compounds contain one or more cations paired with one or more anions. In most cases, the cations are metals and the anions are nonmetals. When a metal, which has a tendency to lose electrons, combines with a nonmetal, which has a tendency to gain electrons, one or more electrons transfer from the metal to the nonmetal, creating positive and negative ions that are then attracted to each other. You can assume that a compound composed of a metal and a nonmetal is ionic. The basic unit of ionic compounds is the **formula unit**, the smallest electrically neutral collection of ions. Formula units are different from molecules in that they do not exist as discrete entities, but rather as part of a larger lattice. For example, salt (NaCl) is composed of Na^+ and Cl^- ions in a 1:1 ratio. In table salt, Na^+ and Cl^- ions exist in an alternating three-dimensional array (► Figure 11). However, any one Na^+ ion does not pair with one specific Cl^- ion. Sometimes chemists refer to formula units as molecules, but this is not strictly correct since ionic compounds do not contain distinct molecules.

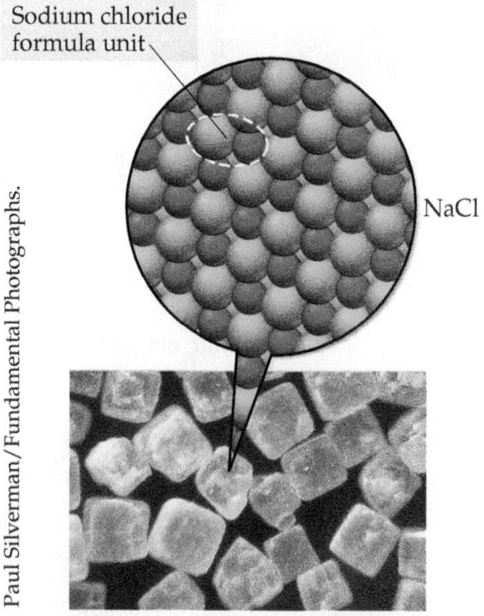

Sodium chloride formula unit

NaCl

Paul Silverman/Fundamental Photographs.

▲ **FIGURE 11 An ionic compound** The basic units that compose table salt, an ionic compound, are NaCl formula units. Unlike molecular compounds, ionic compounds do not contain individual molecules but rather sodium and chloride ions in an alternating three-dimensional array.

EXAMPLE 4   Classifying Substances as Atomic Elements, Molecular Elements, Molecular Compounds, or Ionic Compounds

Classify each substance as an atomic element, molecular element, molecular compound, or ionic compound.

(a) krypton
(b) $CoCl_2$
(c) nitrogen
(d) SO_2
(e) KNO_3

SOLUTION

(a) Krypton is an element that is not listed as diatomic in Table 2; therefore, it is an atomic element.

(b) $CoCl_2$ is a compound composed of a metal (left side of periodic table) and nonmetal (right side of the periodic table); therefore, it is an ionic compound.

(c) Nitrogen is an element that is listed as diatomic in Table 2; therefore, it is a molecular element.

(d) SO_2 is a compound composed of two nonmetals; therefore, it is a molecular compound.

(e) KNO_3 is a compound composed of a metal and two nonmetals; therefore, it is an ionic compound.

▶**SKILLBUILDER 4 | Classifying Substances as Atomic Elements, Molecular Elements, Molecular Compounds, or Ionic Compounds**

Classify each substance as an atomic element, molecular element, molecular compound, or ionic compound.

(a) chlorine
(b) NO
(c) Au
(d) Na_2O
(e) $CrCl_3$

▶**FOR MORE PRACTICE**   Example 19, Example 20; Problems 43, 44, 45, 46.

(a)

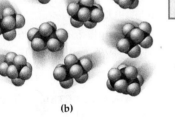

(b)

✓ **CONCEPTUAL CHECKPOINT 2**

Which of the figures at left (in the margin) represents a molecular compound?

5 Writing Formulas for Ionic Compounds

Review the elements that form ions with a predictable charge.

Since ionic compounds must be charge-neutral, and since many elements form only one type of ion with a predictable charge, we can determine the formulas for many ionic compounds based on their constituent elements. For example, the formula for the ionic compound composed of sodium and chlorine must be NaCl and not anything else because in compounds Na always forms 1+ cations and Cl always forms 1− anions. In order for the compound to be charge-neutral, it must contain one Na^+ cation to every Cl^- anion. The formula for the ionic compound composed of magnesium and chlorine, however, must be $MgCl_2$, because Mg always forms 2+ cations and Cl always forms 1− anions. In order for the compound to be charge-neutral, it must contain one Mg^{2+} cation to every two Cl^- anions. In general:

- Ionic compounds always contain positive and negative ions.
- In the chemical formula, the sum of the charges of the positive ions (cations) must always equal the sum of the charges of the negative ions (anions).

To write the formula for an ionic compound, follow the procedure in the left column of the following table. Two examples of how to apply the procedure are provided in the center and right columns.

Writing Formulas for Ionic Compounds	EXAMPLE 5 Write a formula for the ionic compound that forms from aluminum and oxygen.	EXAMPLE 6 Write a formula for the ionic compound that forms from magnesium and oxygen.
1. Write the symbol for the metal and its charge followed by the symbol of the nonmetal and its charge. For many elements, you can determine these charges from their group number in the periodic table.	SOLUTION Al^{3+} O^{2-}	SOLUTION Mg^{2+} O^{2-}
2. Make the magnitude of the charge on each ion (without the sign) become the subscript for the other ion.	Al^{3+} O^{2-} Al_2O_3	Mg^{2+} O^{2-} Mg_2O_2
3. If possible, reduce the subscripts to give a ratio with the smallest whole numbers.	In this case, the numbers cannot be reduced any further; the correct formula is Al_2O_3.	To reduce the subscripts, divide both subscripts by 2. $Mg_2O_2 \div 2 = MgO$
4. Check to make sure that the sum of the charges of the cations exactly cancels the sum of the charges of the anions.	Cations: $2(3+) = 6+$ Anions: $3(2-) = 6-$ The charges cancel.	Cations: $2+$ Anions: $2-$ The charges cancel.

▶SKILLBUILDER 5

Write a formula for the compound formed from strontium and chlorine.

▶SKILLBUILDER 6

Write a formula for the compound formed from aluminum and nitrogen.

▶FOR MORE PRACTICE Example 21; Problems 53, 54, 55, 56.

EXAMPLE 7 Writing Formulas for Ionic Compounds

Write a formula for the compound composed of potassium and oxygen.

SOLUTION

First write the symbol for each ion along with its appropriate charge from its group number in the periodic table.

$$K^+ \quad O^{2-}$$

Then make the magnitude of each ion's charge become the subscript for the other ion.

$$K^+ \quad O^{2-} \text{ becomes } K_2O$$

No reduction of subscripts is necessary in this case. Finally, check to see that the sum of the charges of the cations $[2(1+) = 2+]$ exactly cancels the sum of the charges of the anion $(2-)$. The correct formula is K_2O.

▶**SKILLBUILDER 7** | **Writing Formulas for Ionic Compounds**

Write a formula for the compound that forms from calcium and bromine.

▶**FOR MORE PRACTICE** Problems 57, 58.

6 Nomenclature: Naming Compounds

Since there are so many different compounds, chemists have developed systematic ways to name them. If you learn these naming rules, you can examine a compound's formula and determine its name or vice versa. Many compounds also have a common name. For example, H_2O has the common name *water* and the systematic name *dihydrogen monoxide*. A common name is like a nickname for a compound, used by those who are familiar with it. Since water is such a familiar compound, everyone uses its common name and not its systematic name. In the sections that follow, you will learn how to systematically name simple ionic and molecular compounds. Keep in mind, however, that some compounds also have common names that are often used instead of the systematic name. Common names can be learned only through familiarity.

7 Naming Ionic Compounds

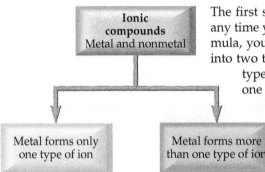

The first step in naming an ionic compound is identifying it as one. Remember, any time you have a metal and one or more nonmetals together in a chemical formula, you can assume the compound is ionic. Ionic compounds are categorized into two types (◀ Figure 12) depending on the metal in the compound. The first type (sometimes called Type I) contains a metal with an invariant charge— one that does not vary from one compound to another. Sodium, for instance, has a 1+ charge in all of its compounds. Table 3 lists more examples of metals whose charge is invariant from one compound to another. The charge of most of these metals can be inferred from their group number in the periodic table.

▲ FIGURE 12 **Classification of ionic compounds** Ionic compounds can be categorized into two types, depending on the metal in the compound.

TABLE 3 **Metals Whose Charge Is Invariant from One Compound to Another**

Metal	Ion	Name	Group Number
Li	Li^+	lithium	1A
Na	Na^+	sodium	1A
K	K^+	potassium	1A
Rb	Rb^+	rubidium	1A
Cs	Cs^+	cesium	1A
Mg	Mg^{2+}	magnesium	2A
Ca	Ca^{2+}	calcium	2A
Sr	Sr^{2+}	strontium	2A
Ba	Ba^{2+}	barium	2A
Al	Al^{3+}	aluminum	3A
Zn	Zn^{2+}	zinc	*
Ag	Ag^+	silver	*

*The charge of these metals cannot be inferred from their group number.

TABLE 4 **Some Metals That Form More Than One Type of Ion and Their Common Charges**

Metal	Symbol Ion	Name	Older Name*
chromium	Cr^{2+}	chromium(II)	chromous
	Cr^{3+}	chromium(III)	chromic
iron	Fe^{2+}	Iron(II)	ferrous
	Fe^{3+}	iron(III)	ferric
cobalt	Co^{2+}	cobalt(II)	cobaltous
	Co^{3+}	cobalt(III)	cobaltic
copper	Cu^{+}	copper(I)	cuprous
	Cu^{2+}	copper(II)	cupric
tin	Sn^{2+}	tin(II)	stannous
	Sn^{4+}	tin(IV)	stannic
mercury	Hg_2^{2+}	mercury(I)	mercurous
	Hg^{2+}	mercury(II)	mercuric
lead	Pb^{2+}	lead(II)	plumbous
	Pb^{4+}	lead(IV)	plumbic

*An older naming system substitutes the names found in this column for the name of the metal and its charge. Under this system, chromium(II) oxide is named chromous oxide. We do *not* use this older system in this text.

Main group

Main group

Transition metals

▲ **FIGURE 13** **The transition metals** The metals that form more than one type of ion are usually (but not always) transition metals.

The second type of ionic compound (sometimes called Type II) contains a metal with a charge that can differ in different compounds. In other words, the metal in this second type of ionic compound can form more than one kind of cation (depending on the compound). Iron, for instance, has a 2+ charge in some of its compounds and a 3+ charge in others. Additional examples of metals that form more than one type of cation are listed in Table 4. Such metals are usually (but not always) found in the **transition metals** section of the periodic table (◄ Figure 13). However, some transition metals, such as Zn and Ag, form cations with the same charge in all of their compounds, and some main group metals, such as Pb and Sn, form more than one type of cation.

NAMING BINARY IONIC COMPOUNDS CONTAINING A METAL THAT FORMS ONLY ONE TYPE OF CATION

Binary compounds are those that contain only two different elements. The names for binary ionic compounds containing a metal that forms only one type of ion have the form:

| name of cation (metal) | base name of anion (nonmetal) + -*ide* |

Since the charge of the metal is always the same for these types of compounds, it need not be specified in the compound's name. For example, the name for NaCl consists of the name of the cation, *sodium*, followed by the base name of the anion, *chlor*, with the ending -*ide*. The full name is *sodium chloride*.

The name of the cation in ionic compounds is the same as the name of the metal.

NaCl   sodium chloride

The name for MgO consists of the name of the cation, *magnesium*, followed by the base name of the anion, *ox*, with the ending -*ide*. The full name is *magnesium oxide*.

MgO   magnesium oxide

Table 5 contains the base names for various nonmetals and their most common charges in ionic compounds.

TABLE 5 Some Common Anions

Nonmetal	Symbol for Ion	Base Name	Anion Name
fluorine	F^-	fluor-	fluoride
chlorine	Cl^-	chlor-	chloride
bromine	Br^-	brom-	bromide
iodine	I^-	iod-	iodide
oxygen	O^{2-}	ox-	oxide
sulfur	S^{2-}	sulf-	sulfide
nitrogen	N^{3-}	nitr-	nitride

EXAMPLE 8 Naming Ionic Compounds Containing a Metal That Forms Only One Type of Cation

Name the compound MgF_2.

SOLUTION

The cation is magnesium. The anion is fluorine, which becomes *fluoride*. Its correct name is *magnesium fluoride*.

▶**SKILLBUILDER 8 | Naming Ionic Compounds Containing a Metal That Forms Only One Type of Ion**

Name the compound KBr.

▶**SKILLBUILDER PLUS 2**

Name the compound $Zn_3 N_2$.

▶**FOR MORE PRACTICE**   Example 22; Problems 59, 60.

NAMING BINARY IONIC COMPOUNDS CONTAINING A METAL THAT FORMS MORE THAN ONE TYPE OF CATION

Since the charge of the metal cation in these types of compounds is not always the same, the charge must be specified in the metal's name. We specify the charge with a roman numeral (in parentheses) following the name of the metal. For example, we distinguish between Cu^+ and Cu^{2+} by writing a (I) to indicate the 1+ ion or a (II) to indicate the 2+ ion:

$$Cu^+ \quad Copper(I)$$

$$Cu^{2+} \quad Copper(II)$$

The full name for these types of compounds have the form:

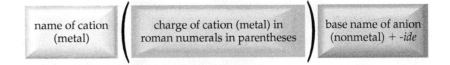

name of cation (metal) (charge of cation (metal) in roman numerals in parentheses) base name of anion (nonmetal) + *-ide*

We can determine the charge of the metal from the chemical formula of the compound—remember that the sum of all the charges must be zero. For example, the charge of iron in $FeCl_3$ must be 3+ in order for the compound to be charge neutral with the three Cl^- anions. The name for $FeCl_3$ is therefore the name of the cation, *iron*, followed by the charge of the cation in parentheses *(III)*, followed by the base name of the anion, *chlor*, with the ending *-ide*. The full name is *iron(III) chloride*.

> $FeCl_3$ iron(III) chloride

Likewise, the name for CrO consists of the name of the cation, *chromium*, followed by the charge of the cation in parentheses *(II)*, followed by the base name of the anion, *ox-*, with the ending *-ide*. The full name is *chromium(II) oxide*.

> CrO chromium(II) oxide

The charge of chromium must be 2+ in order for the compound to be charge-neutral with one O^{2-} anion.

EXAMPLE 9 **Naming Ionic Compounds Containing a Metal That Forms More Than One Type of Cation**

Name the compound $PbCl_4$.

SOLUTION

The name for $PbCl_4$ consists of the name of the cation, *lead*, followed by the charge of the cation in parentheses *(IV)*, followed by the base name of the anion, *chlor-*, with the ending *-ide*. The full name is *lead(IV) chloride*. We know the charge on Pb is 4+ because the charge on Cl is 1−. Since there are 4 Cl^- anions, the Pb cation must be Pb^{4+}.

> $PbCl_4$ lead(IV) chloride

▶**SKILLBUILDER 9 | Naming Ionic Compounds Containing a Metal That Forms More Than One Type of Cation**

Name the compound PbO.

▶**FOR MORE PRACTICE** Example 23; Problems 61, 62.

 CONCEPTUAL CHECKPOINT 3

Explain why CaO is NOT named calcium(II) oxide.

NAMING IONIC COMPOUNDS CONTAINING A POLYATOMIC ION

As we saw previously, some ionic compounds contain polyatomic ions (ions that are themselves composed of a group of atoms with an overall charge). The most common polyatomic ions are listed in Table 6. We name ionic compounds containing polyatomic ions using the same procedure we apply to other ionic compounds, except that we use the name of the polyatomic ion whenever it occurs. For example, KNO_3 is named using its cation, K^+, *potassium*, and its polyatomic anion, NO_3^-, *nitrate*. The full name is *potassium nitrate*.

> KNO_3 potassium nitrate

$Fe(OH)_2$ is named according to its cation, *iron*, its charge *(II)*, and its polyatomic ion, *hydroxide*. Its full name is *iron(II) hydroxide*.

> $Fe(OH)_2$ iron(II) hydroxide

If the compound contains both a polyatomic cation and a polyatomic anion, use the names of both polyatomic ions. For example, NH_4NO_3 is *ammonium nitrate*.

> NH_4NO_3 ammonium nitrate

EVERYDAY CHEMISTRY

Polyatomic Ions

A glance at the labels of household products reveals the importance of polyatomic ions in everyday compounds. For example, the active ingredient in household bleach is sodium hypochlorite, which acts to decompose color-causing molecules in clothes (bleaching action) and to kill bacteria (disinfection). A box of baking soda contains sodium bicarbonate (sodium hydrogen carbonate), which acts as an antacid when consumed in small quantities and as a source of carbon dioxide gas in baking. The pockets of carbon dioxide gas make baked goods fluffy rather than flat.

Calcium carbonate is the active ingredient in many antacids such as Tums™ and Alka-Mints™. It neutralizes stomach acids, relieving the symptoms of indigestion and heartburn. Too much calcium carbonate, however, can cause constipation, so Tums should not be overused. Sodium nitrite is a common food additive used to preserve packaged meats such as ham, hot dogs, and bologna. Sodium nitrite inhibits the growth of bacteria, especially those that cause botulism, an often fatal type of food poisoning.

◄ Compounds containing polyatomic ions are present in many consumer products.

► The active ingredient in bleach is sodium hypochlorite.

CAN YOU ANSWER THIS? *Write a formula for each of these compounds that contain polyatomic ions: sodium hypochlorite, sodium bicarbonate, calcium carbonate, sodium nitrite.*

TABLE 6   Some Common Polyatomic Ions

Name	Formula	Name	Formula
acetate	$C_2H_3O_2^-$	hypochlorite	ClO^-
carbonate	CO_3^{2-}	chlorite	ClO_2^-
hydrogen carbonate (or bicarbonate)	HCO_3^-	chlorate	ClO_3^-
hydroxide	OH^-	perchlorate	ClO_4^-
nitrate	NO_3^-	permanganate	MnO_4^-
nitrite	NO_2^-	sulfate	SO_4^{2-}
chromate	CrO_4^{2-}	sulfite	SO_3^{2-}
dichromate	$Cr_2O_7^{2-}$	hydrogen sulfite (or bisulfite)	HSO_3^-
phosphate	PO_4^{3-}	hydrogen sulfate (or bisulfate)	HSO_4^-
hydrogen phosphate	HPO_4^{2-}	peroxide	O_2^{2-}
ammonium	NH_4^+	cyanide	CN^-

You will need to be able to recognize polyatomic ions in a chemical formula, so become familiar with Table 6. Most polyatomic ions are **oxyanions**, anions containing oxygen. Notice that when a series of oxyanions contain different numbers of oxygen atoms, they are named systematically according to the number of oxygen atoms in the ion. If there are two ions in the series, the one with more oxygen atoms is given the ending *-ate* and the one with fewer is given the ending *-ite*. For example, NO_3^- is called *nitrate* and NO_2^- is called *nitrite*.

NO_3^- nitrate
NO_2^- nitrite

If there are more than two ions in the series, then the prefixes *hypo-*, meaning "less than," and *per-*, meaning "more than," are used. So ClO^- is called *hypochlorite*, meaning "less oxygen than chlorite," and ClO_4^- is called *perchlorate*, meaning "more oxygen than chlorate."

ClO^- hypochlorite
ClO_2^- chlorite
ClO_3^- chlorate
ClO_4^- perchlorate

EXAMPLE 10   Naming Ionic Compounds Containing a Polyatomic Ion

Name the compound K_2CrO_4.

SOLUTION

The name for K_2CrO_4 consists of the name of the cation, *potassium*, followed by the name of the polyatomic ion, *chromate*.

K_2CrO_4 potassium chromate

▶**SKILLBUILDER 10 | Naming Ionic Compounds Containing a Polyatomic Ion**

Name the compound $Mn(NO_3)_2$.

▶**FOR MORE PRACTICE**   Example 24; Problems 65, 66.

 CONCEPTUAL CHECKPOINT 4

You have just learned that the anion ClO_3^- is named chlorate. What is the name of the anion IO_3^-?

---

8   Naming Molecular Compounds

The first step in naming a molecular compound is identifying it as one. Remember, nearly all molecular compounds form from two or more nonmetals. In this section, we learn how to name binary (two-element) molecular compounds. Their names have the form:

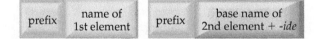

When writing the name of a molecular compound, as when writing the formula, the first element is the more metal-like one (see Table 1). The prefixes given to each element indicate the number of atoms present.

mono- 1	*hexa-* 6
di- 2	*hepta-* 7
tri- 3	*octa-* 8
tetra- 4	*nona-* 9
penta- 5	*deca-* 10

If there is only one atom of the *first element* in the formula, the prefix *mono-* is normally omitted. For example, CO_2 is named according to the first element, *carbon*, with no prefix because *mono-* is omitted for the first element, followed by the prefix *di-*, to indicate two oxygen atoms, followed by the base name of the second element, *ox*, with the ending *-ide*.

carbon di- ox -ide

The full name is *carbon dioxide*.

CO_2 carbon dioxide

The compound N_2O, also called laughing gas, is named according to the first element, *nitrogen*, with the prefix *di-*, to indicate that there are two of them, followed by the base name of the second element, *ox*, prefixed by *mono-*, to indicate one, and the suffix *-ide*. Since *mono-* ends with a vowel and *oxide* begins with one, an *o* is dropped and the two are combined as *monoxide*. The entire name is *dinitrogen monoxide*.

N_2O dinitrogen monoxide

When the prefix ends with a vowel and the base name starts with a vowel, the first vowel is sometimes dropped, especially in the case of mono oxide, which becomes monoxide.

EXAMPLE 11   Naming Molecular Compounds

Name each compound.

(a) CCl_4
(b) BCl_3
(c) SF_6

SOLUTION

(a) The name of the compound is the name of the first element, *carbon*, followed by the base name of the second element, *chlor*, prefixed by *tetra-* to indicate four, and the suffix *–ide*.

CCl_4 carbon tetrachloride

(b) The name of the compound is the name of the first element, *boron*, followed by the base name of the second element, *chlor*, prefixed by *tri-* to indicate three, and the suffix *-ide*.

BCl_3 boron trichloride

(c) The name of the compound is the name of the first element, *sulfur*, followed by the base name of the second element, *fluor*, prefixed by *hexa-* to indicate six, and the suffix *-ide*. The entire name is *sulfur hexafluoride*.

SF_6 sulfur hexafluoride

▶**SKILLBUILDER 11** | **Naming Molecular Compounds**
Name the compound N_2O_4.

▶**FOR MORE PRACTICE**   Example 25; Problems 71, 72.

9 Naming Acids

Acids are molecular compounds that produce H^+ ions when dissolved in water. They are composed of hydrogen, usually written first in their formula, and one or more nonmetals, written second. Acids are characterized by their sour taste and their ability to dissolve some metals. For example, HCl(*aq*) is an acid—the (*aq*) indicates that the compound is "aqueous" or "dissolved in water". HCl(*aq*) has a characteristically sour taste. Since HCl(*aq*) is present in stomach fluids, its sour taste becomes painfully obvious during vomiting. HCl(*aq*) also dissolves some metals. If you drop a strip of zinc into a beaker of HCl(*aq*), it will slowly disappear as the acid converts the zinc metal into dissolved Zn^{2+} cations.

> HCl(*g*) refers to HCl molecules in the gas phase.

Acids are present in many foods, such as lemons and limes, and they are used in some household products such as toilet bowl cleaner and Lime-A-Way. In this section, we simply learn how to name them. We can categorize acids into two groups: **binary acids**, those containing only hydrogen and a nonmetal, and **oxyacids**, those containing hydrogen, a nonmetal, and oxygen (◄ Figure 14).

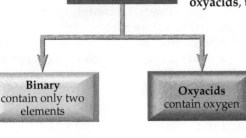

◄ **FIGURE 14** **Classification of acids** Acids are classified into two types, depending on the number of elements in the acid. If the acid contains only two elements, it is a binary acid. If it contains oxygen, it is an oxyacid.

NAMING BINARY ACIDS

Binary acids are composed of hydrogen and a nonmetal. The names for binary acids have the following form:

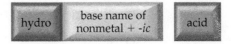

For example, HCl(*aq*) is hydro*chlor*ic acid and HBr(*aq*) is hydro*brom*ic acid.

HCl(*aq*)   hydrochloric acid   HBr(*aq*)   hydrobromic acid

EXAMPLE 12   Naming Binary Acids

Give the name of H_2S (*aq*).

The base name of S is *sulfur*, so the name is *hydrosulfuric acid*	**SOLUTION** H_2S (*aq*) hydrosulfuric acid

▶**SKILLBUILDER 12** │ **Naming Binary Acids**
Name HF(*aq*).

▶**FOR MORE PRACTICE**   Example 26; Problems 77b, 78d.

NAMING OXYACIDS

Oxyacids are acids that contain oxyanions, which can be found in the table of polyatomic ions (Table 6). For example, HNO_3 (*aq*) contains the nitrate (NO_3^-) ion, H_2SO_3(*aq*) contains the sulfite (SO_3^{2-}) ion, and H_2SO_4 (*aq*) contains the sulfate (SO_4^{2-}) ion. All of these acids are a combination of one or more H^+ ions with an oxyanion. The number of H^+ ions depends on the charge of the oxyanion, so that the formula is always charge-neutral. The names of oxyacids depend on the ending of the oxyanion (▶ Figure 15).

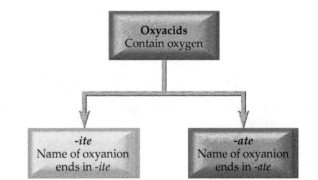

► FIGURE 15 **Classification of oxyacids** Oxyacids are classified into two types, depending on the endings of the oxyanions that they contain.

The names of acids containing oxyanions ending with -*ite* take this form:

base name of oxyanion + -*ous*   acid

The saying, "*ic I ate an acid*" is sometimes used to help remember the association of -ic with -*ate*.

The names of acids containing oxyanions ending with -*ate* take this form:

base name of oxyanion + -*ic*   acid

So H_2SO_3 is *sulfurous acid* (oxyanion is sulfite), and HNO_3 is *nitric acid* (oxyanion is nitrate).

$H_2SO_3(aq)$ sulfurous acid $HNO_3(aq)$ nitric acid

Table 7 lists the names of some common oxyacids and their oxyanions.

EXAMPLE 13   Naming Oxyacids

Name $HC_2H_3O_2(aq)$.

The oxyanion is acetate, which ends in -*ate*; therefore, the name of the acid is *acetic acid*.	**SOLUTION** $HC_2H_3O_2(aq)$ acetic acid

►**SKILLBUILDER 13 | Naming Oxyacids**
Name $HNO_2(aq)$.

►**FOR MORE PRACTICE**   Examples 27, 28; Problems 77acd, 78abc.

TABLE 7   Names of Some Common Oxyacids and Their Oxyanions

Acid Formula	Acid Name	Oxyanion Name	Oxyanion Formula
HNO_2	nitrous acid	nitrite	NO_2^-
HNO_3	nitric acid	nitrate	NO_3^-
H_2SO_3	sulfurous acid	sulfite	SO_3^-
H_2SO_4	sulfuric acid	sulfate	SO_4^{2-}
$HClO_2$	chlorous acid	chorite	ClO_2^-
$HClO_3$	chloric acid	chlorate	ClO_3^-
$H_2C_2H_3O_2$	acetic acid	acetate	$C_2H_3O_2^-$
H_2CO_3	carbonic acid	carbonate	CO_3^{2-}

CHEMISTRY IN THE ENVIRONMENT

Acid Rain

Acid rain occurs when rainwater mixes with air pollutants—such as NO, NO$_2$, and SO$_2$—that form acids. NO and NO$_2$, primarily from vehicular emission, combine with water to form HNO$_3$ (aq). SO$_2$, primarily from coal-powered electricity generation, combines with water and oxygen in air to form H$_2$SO$_4$ (aq). HNO$_3$ (aq) and H$_2$SO$_4$ (aq) both cause rainwater to become acidic. The problem is greatest in the northeastern United States, where pollutants from midwestern electrical power plants combine with rainwater to produce rain with acid levels that are up to 10 times higher than normal.

When acid rain falls or flows into lakes and streams, it makes them more acidic. Some species of aquatic animals—such as trout, bass, snails, salamanders, and clams—cannot tolerate the increased acidity and die. This then disturbs the ecosystem of the lake, resulting in imbalances that may lead to the death of other aquatic species. Acid rain also weakens trees by dissolving nutrients in the soil and by damaging their leaves. Appalachian red spruce trees have been the hardest hit, with many forests showing significant acid rain damage.

Acid rain also damages building materials. Acids dissolve CaCO$_3$ (limestone), a main component of marble and concrete, and iron, the main component of steel. Consequently, many statues, buildings, and bridges in the northeastern United States show significant deterioration, and some historical gravestones made of limestone are barely legible due to acid rain damage.

Although acid rain has been a problem for many years, innovative legislation has offered hope for change. In 1990, Congress passed several amendments to the Clean Air Act that included provisions requiring electrical utilities to reduce SO$_2$ emissions. Since then, SO$_2$ emissions have decreased, and rain in the northeastern United States has become somewhat less acidic. For example, in the early 1990s, scientists categorized 30% of the lakes in the Northeast as being of *acute concern*; today, the percentage of lakes in that category has been reduced to 18%. With time, and continued enforcement of the acid rain program, lakes, streams, and forests damaged by acid rain should recover. However, acid rain continues to worsen in countries such as China, where industrial growth is outpacing environmental controls. International cooperation is essential to solving environmental problems such as acid rain.

CAN YOU ANSWER THIS? *Name each compound, given here as formulas:*

NO, NO$_2$, SO$_2$, HNO$_3$ *(aq)*, CaCO$_3$

▲ A forest damaged by acid rain.

▲ Acid rain harms many materials, including the limestone often used for tombstones, buildings, and statues.

10   Nomenclature Summary

Acids are technically a subclass of molecular compounds; that is, they are molecular compounds that form H$^+$ ions when dissolved in water.

Naming compounds requires several steps. The flowchart in ▶ Figure 16 summarizes the different categories of compounds that we have covered in the chapter and how to identify and name them. The first step is to decide whether the compound is ionic, molecular, or an acid. You can recognize ionic compounds by the presence of a metal and a nonmetal, molecular compounds by two or more nonmetals, and acids by the presence of hydrogen (written first) and one or more nonmetals.

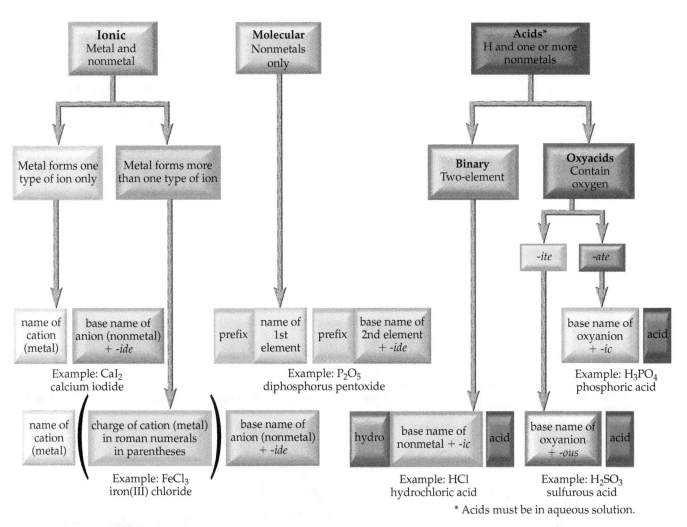

▲ FIGURE 16 **Nomenclature flowchart**

IONIC COMPOUNDS

For an ionic compound, you must next decide whether the metal forms only one type of ion or more than one type of ion. Group 1A (alkali) metals, Group 2A (alkaline earth) metals, and aluminum will always form only one type of ion. Most of the transition metals will form more than one type of ion. Once you have identified the type of ionic compound, name it according to the scheme in the chart. If the ionic compound contains a polyatomic ion—something you must learn to recognize by familiarity—insert the name of the polyatomic ion in place of the metal (positive polyatomic ion) or the nonmetal (negative polyatomic ion).

Zinc (Zn^{2+}), scandium (Sc^{3+}), and silver (Ag^+) also form only one type of ion.

MOLECULAR COMPOUNDS

We have learned how to name only one type of molecular compound, the binary (two-element) compound. If you identify a compound as molecular, name it according to the scheme in Figure 16.

ACIDS

To name an acid, you must first decide whether it is a binary (two-element) acid or an oxyacid (an acid containing oxygen). Binary acids are named according to the scheme in Figure 16. Oxyacids must be further subdivided based on the name of their corresponding oxyanion. If the oxyanion ends in -ite, use one scheme; if it ends with -ate, use the other.

EXAMPLE 14   Nomenclature Using Figure 16

Name each compound: CO, CaF_2, HF(*aq*), $Fe(NO_3)_3$, $HClO_4$ (*aq*), H_2SO_3 (*aq*).

SOLUTION

For each compound, the following table shows how to use Figure 16 to arrive at a name for the compound.

Formula	Flowchart Path	Name
CO	molecular	carbon monoxide
CaF_2	ionic ⟶ one type of ion ⟶	calcium fluoride
HF(*aq*)	acid ⟶ binary ⟶	hydrofluoric acid
$Fe(NO_3)_3$	ionic ⟶ more than one type of ion ⟶	iron(III) nitrate
$HClO_4$ (*aq*)	acid ⟶ oxyacid ⟶ *-ate* ⟶	perchloric acid
H_2SO_3 (*aq*)	acid ⟶ oxyacid ⟶ *-ite* ⟶	sulfurous acid

▶**FOR MORE PRACTICE**   Problems 93, 94.

11   Formula Mass: The Mass of a Molecule or Formula Unit

The terms *molecular mass* and *molecular weight*, which are also commonly used, have the same meaning as formula mass.

In this chapter, which introduces molecules and compounds, we designate the average mass of the molecules (or formula units) that compose a compound as the **formula mass**.

For any compound, the formula mass is the sum of the atomic masses of all the atoms in its chemical formula:

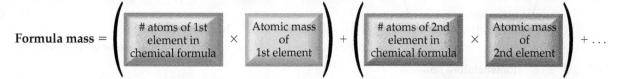

Formula mass = (# atoms of 1st element in chemical formula × Atomic mass of 1st element) + (# atoms of 2nd element in chemical formula × Atomic mass of 2nd element) + ...

Like atomic mass for atoms, formula mass characterizes the average mass of a molecule or formula unit. For example, the formula mass of water, H_2O, is:

$$\text{Formula mass} = 2(1.01 \text{ amu}) + 16.00 \text{ amu}$$
$$= 18.02 \text{ amu}$$

and that of sodium chloride, NaCl, is:

$$\text{Formula mass} = 22.99 \text{ amu} + 35.45 \text{ amu}$$
$$= 58.44 \text{ amu}$$

In addition to giving a characteristic mass to the molecules or formula units of a compound, formula mass allows us to quantify the number of molecules or formula units in a sample of a given mass.

EXAMPLE 15   Calculating Formula Mass

Calculate the formula mass of carbon tetrachloride, CCl_4.

SOLUTION

To find the formula mass, sum the atomic masses of each atom in the chemical formula.

$$\text{Formula mass} = 1 \times (\text{Atomic mass C}) + 4 \times (\text{Atomic mass Cl})$$

$$= 12.01 \text{ amu} + 4(35.45 \text{ amu})$$

$$= 12.01 \text{ amu} + 141.\underline{8}0 \text{ amu}$$

$$= 153.8 \text{ amu}$$

▶**SKILLBUILDER 15 | Calculating Formula Masses**

Calculate the formula mass of dinitrogen monoxide, N_2O, also called laughing gas.

▶**FOR MORE PRACTICE**   Example 29; Problems 83, 84.

CONCEPTUAL CHECKPOINT 5

Which compound has the greatest formula mass?

    (a) O_2 **(b)** O_3 **(c)** H_2O **(d)** H_2O_2

CHAPTER IN REVIEW

CHEMICAL PRINCIPLES

RELEVANCE

Compounds: Matter is ultimately composed of atoms, but those atoms are often combined in compounds. The most important characteristic of a compound is its constant composition. The elements that make up a particular compound are in fixed, definite proportions in all samples of the compound.

Compounds: Most of the matter we encounter is in the form of compounds. Water, salt, and carbon dioxide are all examples of common simple compounds. More complex compounds include caffeine, aspirin, acetone, and testosterone.

Chemical Formulas: Compounds are represented by chemical formulas, which indicate the elements present in the compound and the relative number of atoms of each. These formulas represent the basic units that make up a compound. Pure substances can be categorized according to the basic units that compose them. Elements can be composed of atoms or molecules. Compounds can be molecular, in which case their basic units are molecules, or ionic, in which case their basic units are ions. The formulas for many ionic compounds can be written simply by knowing the elements in the compound.

Chemical Formulas: To understand compounds, we must understand their composition, which is represented by a chemical formula. The connection between the microscopic world and the macroscopic world hinges on the particles that compose matter. Since most matter is in the form of compounds, the properties of most matter depend on the molecules or ions that compose it. Molecular matter does what its molecules do; ionic matter does what its ions do. The world we see and experience is governed by what these particles are doing.

Chemical Nomenclature: The names of simple ionic compounds, molecular compounds, and acids can all be written by examining their chemical formula. The nomenclature flowchart (Figure 16) shows the basic procedure for determining these names.

Chemical Nomenclature: Since there are so many compounds, we need a systematic way to name them. By learning these few simple rules, you will be able to name thousands of different compounds. The next time you look at the label on a consumer product, try to identify as many of the compounds as you can by examining their names.

Formula Mass: The formula mass of a compound is the sum of the atomic masses of all the atoms in the chemical formula for the compound. Like atomic mass for elements, formula mass characterizes the average mass of a molecule or formula unit.

Formula Mass: Besides being the characteristic mass of a molecule or formula unit, formula mass is important in many calculations involving the composition of compounds and quantities in chemical reactions.

CHEMICAL SKILLS

EXAMPLES

Constant Composition of Compounds (Section 2)

The law of constant composition states that all samples of a given compound should have the same ratio of their constituent elements.

To determine whether experimental data are consistent with the law of constant composition, compute the ratios of the masses of each element in all samples. When computing these ratios, it is most convenient to put the larger number in the numerator (top) and the smaller one in the denominator (bottom); that way, the ratio is greater than 1. If the ratios are the same, then the data are consistent with the law of constant composition.

EXAMPLE 16   Constant Composition of Compounds

Two samples said to be carbon disulfide (CS_2) are decomposed into their constituent elements. One sample produced 8.08 g S and 1.51 g C, while the other produced 31.3 g S and 3.85 g C. Are these results consistent with the law of constant composition?

SOLUTION

Sample 1

$$\frac{\text{Mass S}}{\text{Mass C}} = \frac{8.08 \text{ g}}{1.51 \text{ g}} = 5.35$$

Sample 2

$$\frac{\text{Mass S}}{\text{Mass C}} = \frac{31.3 \text{ g}}{3.85 \text{ g}} = 8.13$$

These results are not consistent with the law of constant composition, so the information that the two samples are the same substance must therefore be in error.

Writing Chemical Formulas (Section 3)

Chemical formulas indicate the elements present in a compound and the relative number of atoms of each. When writing formulas, put the more metallic element first.

EXAMPLE 17   Writing Chemical Formulas

Write a chemical formula for the compound containing one nitrogen atom for every two oxygen atoms.

SOLUTION

NO_2

Total Number of Each Type of Atom in a Chemical Formula (Section 3)

The numbers of atoms not enclosed in parentheses are given directly by their subscript.

Find the numbers of atoms within parentheses by multiplying their subscript within the parentheses by their subscript outside the parentheses.

EXAMPLE 18   Total Number of Each Type of Atom in a Chemical Formula

Determine the number of each type of atom in $Pb(ClO_3)_2$.

SOLUTION

One Pb atom

Two Cl atoms

Six O atoms

Classifying Elements as Atomic or Molecular (Section 4)

Most elements exist as atomic elements, their basic units in nature being individual atoms. However, several elements (H_2, N_2, O_2, F_2, Cl_2, Br_2, and I_2) exist as molecular elements, their basic units in nature being diatomic molecules.

EXAMPLE 19   Classifying Elements as Atomic or Molecular

Classify each element as atomic or molecular: sodium, iodine, and nitrogen.

SOLUTION

sodium: atomic

iodine: molecular (I_2)

nitrogen: molecular (N_2)

Classifying Compounds as Ionic or Molecular (Section 4)

Compounds containing a metal and a nonmetal are ionic. If the metal is a transition metal, it will likely form more than one type of ion (see exceptions in Tables 3 and 4). If the metal is not a transition metal, it will likely form only one type of ion (see exceptions in Tables 3 and 4).

Compounds composed of nonmetals are molecular.

EXAMPLE 20   Classifying Compounds as Ionic or Molecular

Classify each compound as ionic or molecular. If they are ionic, determine whether the metal forms only one type of ion or more than one type of ion.

$$FeCl_3, K_2SO_4, CCl_4$$

SOLUTION

$FeCl_3$: ionic, metal forms more than one type of ion

K_2SO_4: ionic, metal forms only one type of ion

CCl_4: molecular

Writing Formulas for Ionic Compounds (Section 5)

1. Write the symbol for the metal ion followed by the symbol for the nonmetal ion (or polyatomic ion) and their charges. These charges can be deduced from the group numbers in the periodic table. (In the case of polyatomic ions, the charges come from Table 6.)
2. Make the magnitude of the charge on each ion become the subscript for the other ion.

3. Check to see if the subscripts can be reduced to simpler whole numbers. Subscripts of 1 can be dropped, since they are normally implied.
4. Check that the sum of the charges of the cations exactly cancels the sum of the charges of the anions.

EXAMPLE 21   Writing Formulas for Ionic Compounds

Write a formula for the compound that forms from lithium and sulfate ions.

SOLUTION

$$Li^+ \quad SO_4^{2-}$$
$$Li_2(SO_4)$$

In this case, the subscripts cannot be further reduced.

$$Li_2SO_4$$

Cations	Anions
$2(1+) = 2+$	$2-$

Naming Binary Ionic Compounds Containing a Metal That Forms Only One Type of Ion (Section 7)

The name of the metal is unchanged. The name of the nonmetal is its base name with the ending -*ide*.

EXAMPLE 22   Naming Binary Ionic Compounds Containing a Metal That Forms Only One Type of Ion

Name the compound Al_2O_3.

SOLUTION

aluminum oxide

Naming Binary Ionic Compounds Containing a Metal That Forms More than One Type of Ion (Section 7)

Since the names of these compounds include the charge of the metal ion, you must first determine that charge. To do this, calculate the total charge of the nonmetal ions.

The total charge of the metal ions must equal the total charge of the nonmetal ions, but have the opposite sign.

The name of the compound is the name of the metal ion, followed by the charge of the metal ion, followed by the base name of the nonmetal + *-ide*.

EXAMPLE 23 Naming Binary Ionic Compounds Containing a Metal that Forms More than One Type of Ion

Name the compound Fe_2S_3.

SOLUTION

3 sulfide ions $\times$ (2−) = 6−

2 iron ions $\times$ (*ion charge*) = 6+

ion charge = 3+

Charge of each iron ion = 3+

iron (III) sulfide

Naming Compounds Containing a Polyatomic Ion (Section 7)

Name ionic compounds containing a polyatomic ion in the normal way, except substitute the name of the polyatomic ion (from Table 6) in place of the nonmetal.

Since the metal in this example forms more than one type of ion, you need to determine the charge on the metal ion. The charge of the metal ion must be equal in magnitude to the sum of the charges of the polyatomic ions but opposite in sign.

The name of the compound is the name of the metal ion, followed by the charge of the metal ion, followed by the name of the polyatomic ion.

EXAMPLE 24 Naming Compounds Containing a Polyatomic Ion

Name the compound $Co(ClO_4)_2$.

SOLUTION

2 perchlorate ions $\times$ (1−) = 2−

Charge of cobalt ion = 2+

cobalt(II) perchlorate

Naming Molecular Compounds (Section 8)

The name consists of a prefix indicating the number of atoms of the first element, followed by the name of the first element, and a prefix for the number of atoms of the second element followed by the base name of the second element plus the suffix *-ide*. When *mono-* occurs on the first element, it is normally dropped.

EXAMPLE 25 Naming Molecular Compounds

Name the compound NO_2.

SOLUTION

nitrogen dioxide

Naming Binary Acids (Section 9)

The name begins with *hydro-*, followed by the base name of the nonmetal, plus the suffix *-ic* and then the word *acid*.

EXAMPLE 26 Naming Binary Acids

Name the acid HI(*aq*).

SOLUTION

hydroiodic acid

Naming Oxyacids with an Oxyanion Ending in *-ate* (Section 9)

The name is the base name of the oxyanion + *-ic*, followed by the word *acid* (sulfate violates the rule somewhat, since in strict term, the base name would be *sulf*).

EXAMPLE 27 Naming Oxyacids with an Oxyanion Ending in *-ate*

Name the acid H_2SO_4 (*aq*).

SOLUTION

The oxyanion is sulfate. The name of the acid is *sulfuric acid*.

Naming Oxyacids with an Oxyanion Ending in *-ite* (Section 9)

The name is the base name of the oxyanion + *-ous*, followed by the word *acid*.

EXAMPLE 28   Naming Oxyacids with an Oxyanion Ending in *-ite*

Name the acid $HClO_2(aq)$.

SOLUTION

The oxyanion is chlorite. The name of the acid is *chlorous acid*.

Calculating Formula Mass (Section 11)

The formula mass is the sum of the atomic masses of all the atoms in the chemical formula. In determining the number of each type of atom, don't forget to multiply subscripts inside parentheses by subscripts outside parentheses.

EXAMPLE 29   Calculating Formula Mass

Calculate the formula mass of $Mg(NO_3)_2$.

SOLUTION

$$\text{Formula mass} = 24.31 + 2(14.01) + 6(16.00)$$
$$= 148.33 \text{ amu}$$

KEY TERMS

acid [**Section 9**]
atomic element [**Section 4**]
ball-and-stick model [**Section 3**]
binary acid [**Section 9**]
binary compound [**Section 7**]

chemical formula [**Section 3**]
empirical formula [**Section 3**]
formula mass [**Section 11**]
formula unit [**Section 4**]
ionic compound [**Section 4**]

law of constant composition [**Section 2**]
molecular compound [**Section 4**]
molecular element [**Section 4**]
molecular formula [**Section 3**]

molecular model [**Section 3**]
oxyacid [**Section 9**]
oxyanion [**Section 7**]
polyatomic ion [**Section 7**]
space-filling model [**Section 3**]
transition metals [**Section 7**]

EXERCISES

QUESTIONS

1. Do the properties of an element change when it combines with another element to form a compound? Explain.
2. How might the world be different if elements did not combine to form compounds?
3. What is the law of constant composition? Who discovered it?
4. What is a chemical formula? List some examples.
5. In a chemical formula, which element is listed first?
6. In a chemical formula, how do you calculate the number of atoms of an element within parentheses? Give an example.
7. Explain the difference between a molecular formula and an empirical formula.
8. What is structural formula? What is the difference between a structural formula and a molecular model?
9. What is the difference between a molecular element and an atomic element? List the elements that occur as diatomic molecules.
10. What is the difference between an ionic compound and a molecular compound?

11. What is the difference between a common name for a compound and a systematic name?
12. List the metals that form only one type of ion (that is, metals whose charge is invariant from one compound to another). What are the group numbers of these metals?
13. Find the block in the periodic table of metals that tend to form more than one type of ion. What is the name of this block?
14. What is the basic form for the names of ionic compounds containing a metal that forms only one type of ion?
15. What is the basic form for the names of ionic compounds containing a metal that forms more than one type of ion?
16. Why are numbers needed in the names of ionic compounds containing a metal that forms more than one type of ion?
17. How are compounds containing a polyatomic ion named?
18. What polyatomic ions have a 2− charge? What polyatomic ions have a 3− charge?

19. What is the basic form for the names of molecular compounds?
20. How many atoms does each prefix specify? *mono-, di-, tri-, tetra-, penta-, hexa-*.
21. What is the basic form for the names of binary acids?

22. What is the basic form for the name of oxyacids whose oxyanions end with *-ate*?
23. What is the basic form for the name of oxyacids whose oxyanions end with *-ite*?
24. What is the formula mass of a compound?

PROBLEMS

CONSTANT COMPOSITION OF COMPOUNDS

25. Two samples of sodium chloride were decomposed into their constituent elements. One sample produced 4.65 g of sodium and 7.16 g of chlorine, and the other sample produced 7.45 g of sodium and 11.5 g of chlorine. Are these results consistent with the law of constant composition? Explain your answer.

26. Two samples of carbon tetrachloride were decomposed into their constituent elements. One sample produced 32.4 g of carbon and 373 g of chlorine, and the other sample produced 12.3 g of carbon and 112 g of chlorine. Are these results consistent with the law of constant composition? Explain your answer.

27. Upon decomposition, one sample of magnesium fluoride produced 1.65 kg of magnesium and 2.57 kg of fluorine. A second sample produced 1.32 kg of magnesium. How much fluorine (in grams) did the second sample produce?

28. The mass ratio of sodium to fluorine in sodium fluoride is 1.21:1. A sample of sodium fluoride produced 34.5 g of sodium upon decomposition. How much fluorine (in grams) was formed?

29. Use the law of constant composition to complete the table summarizing the amounts of nitrogen and oxygen produced upon the decomposition of several samples of dinitrogen monoxide.

	Mass N_2O	Mass N	Mass O
Sample A	2.85 g	1.82 g	1.03 g
Sample B	4.55 g	_____	_____
Sample C	_____	_____	1.35 g
Sample D	_____	1.11 g	_____

30. Use the law of constant composition to complete the table summarizing the amounts of iron and chlorine produced upon the decomposition of several samples of iron(III) chloride.

	Mass $FeCl_3$	Mass Fe	Mass Cl
Sample A	3.785 g	1.302 g	2.483 g
Sample B	2.175 g	_____	_____
Sample C	_____	2.012 g	_____
Sample D	_____	_____	2.329 g

CHEMICAL FORMULAS

31. Write a chemical formula for the compound containing one nitrogen atom for every three iodine atoms.

32. Write a chemical formula for the compound containing one carbon atom for every four bromine atoms.

33. Write chemical formulas for compounds containing:
    (a) three iron atoms for every four oxygen atoms
    (b) one phosphorus atom for every three chlorine atoms
    (c) one phosphorus atom for every five chlorine atoms
    (d) two silver atoms for every oxygen atom

34. Write chemical formulas for compounds containing:
    (a) one calcium atom for every two iodine atoms
    (b) two nitrogen atoms for every four oxygen atoms
    (c) one silicon atom for every two oxygen atoms
    (d) one zinc atom for every two chlorine atoms

35. How many oxygen atoms are in each chemical formula?
    (a) H_3PO_4
    (b) Na_2HPO_4
    (c) $Ca(HCO_3)_2$
    (d) $Ba(C_2H_3O_2)_2$

36. How many hydrogen atoms are in each of the formulas in Problem 35?

37. Determine the number of each type of atom in each formula.
  (a) $MgCl_2$
  (b) $NaNO_3$
  (c) $Ca(NO_2)_2$
  (d) $Sr(OH)_2$

38. Determine the number of each type of atom in each formula.
  (a) NH_4Cl
  (b) $Mg_3(PO_4)_2$
  (c) $NaCN$
  (d) $Ba(HCO_3)_2$

39. Complete the table.

Formula	Number of $C_2H_3O_2^-$ Units	Number of Carbon Atoms	Number of Hydrogen Atoms	Number of Oxygen Atoms	Number of Metal Atoms
$Mg(C_2H_3O_2)_2$	___	___	___	___	___
$NaC_2H_3O_2$	___	___	___	___	___
$Cr_2(C_2H_3O_2)_4$	___	___	___	___	___

40. Complete the table.

Formula	Number of SO_4^{2-} Units	Number of Sulfur Atoms	Number of Oxygen Atoms	Number of Metal Atoms
$CaSO_4$	___	___	___	___
$Al_2(SO_4)_3$	___	___	___	___
K_2SO_4	___	___	___	___

41. Give the empirical formula that corresponds to each molecular formula.
  (a) C_2H_6
  (b) N_2O_4
  (c) $C_4H_6O_2$
  (d) NH_3

42. Give the empirical formula that corresponds to each molecular formula.
  (a) C_2H_2
  (b) CO_2
  (c) $C_6H_{12}O_6$
  (d) B_2H_6

MOLECULAR VIEW OF ELEMENTS AND COMPOUNDS

43. Classify each element as atomic or molecular.
  (a) chlorine
  (b) argon
  (c) cobalt
  (d) hydrogen

44. Which elements have molecules as their basic units?
  (a) helium
  (b) oxygen
  (c) iron
  (d) bromine

45. Classify each compound as ionic or molecular.
  (a) CS_2
  (b) CuO
  (c) KI
  (d) PCl_3

46. Classify each compound as ionic or molecular.
  (a) PtO_2
  (b) CF_2Cl_2
  (c) CO
  (d) SO_3

47. Match the substances on the left with the basic units that compose them on the right.

helium	molecules
CCl_4	formula units
K_2SO_4	diatomic molecules
bromine	single atoms

48. Match the substances on the left with the basic units that compose them on the right.

NI_3	molecules
copper metal	single atoms
$SrCl_2$	diatomic molecules
nitrogen	formula units

49. What are the basic units—single atoms, molecules, or formula units—that compose each substance?
  (a) $BaBr_2$
  (b) Ne
  (c) I_2
  (d) CO

50. What are the basic units—single atoms, molecules, or formula units—that compose each substance?
  (a) Rb_2O
  (b) N_2
  (c) $Fe(NO_3)_2$
  (d) N_2F_4

51. Classify each compound as ionic or molecular. If it is ionic, determine whether the metal forms only one type of ion or more than one type of ion.
    (a) KCl
    (b) CBr_4
    (c) NO_2
    (d) $Sn(SO_4)_2$

52. Classify each compound as ionic or molecular. If it is ionic, determine whether the metal forms only one type of ion or more than one type of ion.
    (a) $CoCl_2$
    (b) CF_4
    (c) $BaSO_4$
    (d) NO

WRITING FORMULAS FOR IONIC COMPOUNDS

53. Write a formula for the ionic compound that forms from each pair of elements.
    (a) sodium and sulfur
    (b) strontium and oxygen
    (c) aluminum and sulfur
    (d) magnesium and chlorine

54. Write a formula for the ionic compound that forms from each pair of elements.
    (a) aluminum and oxygen
    (b) beryllium and iodine
    (c) calcium and sulfur
    (d) calcium and iodine

55. Write a formula for the compound that forms from potassium and
    (a) acetate
    (b) chromate
    (c) phosphate
    (d) cyanide

56. Write a formula for the compound that forms from calcium and
    (a) hydroxide
    (b) carbonate
    (c) phosphate
    (d) hydrogen phosphate

57. Write formulas for the compounds formed from the element on the left and each element on the right.
    (a) Li   N, O, F
    (b) Ba   N, O, F
    (c) Al   N, O, F

58. Write formulas for the compounds formed from the element on the left and each polyatomic ion on the right.
    (a) Rb $NO_3^-, SO_4^{2-}, PO_4^{3-}$
    (b) Sr $NO_3^-, SO_4^{2-}, PO_4^{3-}$
    (c) In $NO_3^-, SO_4^{2-}, PO_4^{3-}$
    (Assume In charge is 3+.)

NAMING IONIC COMPOUNDS

59. Name each ionic compound. In each of these compounds, the metal forms only one type of ion.
    (a) CsCl
    (b) $SrBr_2$
    (c) K_2O
    (d) LiF

60. Name each ionic compound. In each of these compounds, the metal forms only one type of ion.
    (a) LiI
    (b) MgS
    (c) BaF_2
    (d) NaF

61. Name each ionic compound. In each of these compounds, the metal forms more than one type of ion.
    (a) $CrCl_2$
    (b) $CrCl_3$
    (c) SnO_2
    (d) PbI_2

62. Name each ionic compound. In each of these compounds, the metal forms more than one type of ion.
    (a) $HgBr_2$
    (b) Fe_2O_3
    (c) CuI_2
    (d) $SnCl_4$

63. Determine whether the metal in each ionic compound forms only one type of ion or more than one type of ion and name the compound accordingly.
    (a) Cr_2O_3
    (b) NaI
    (c) $CaBr_2$
    (d) SnO

64. Determine whether the metal in each ionic compound forms only one type of ion or more than one type of ion and name the compound accordingly.
    (a) FeI_3
    (b) $PbCl_4$
    (c) SrI_2
    (d) BaO

65. Name each ionic compound containing a polyatomic ion.
    (a) $Ba(NO_3)_2$
    (b) $Pb(C_2H_3O_2)_2$
    (c) NH_4I
    (d) $KClO_3$
    (e) $CoSO_4$
    (f) $NaClO_4$

66. Name each ionic compound containing a polyatomic ion.
    (a) $Ba(OH)_2$
    (b) $Fe(OH)_3$
    (c) $Cu(NO_2)_2$
    (d) $PbSO_4$
    (e) KClO
    (f) $Mg(C_2H_3O_2)_2$

67. Name each polyatomic ion.
    (a) BrO^-
    (b) BrO_2^-
    (c) BrO_3^-
    (d) BrO_4^-

68. Name each polyatomic ion.
    (a) IO^-
    (b) IO_2^-
    (c) IO_3^-
    (d) IO_4^-

69. Write a formula for each ionic compound.
    (a) copper(II) bromide
    (b) silver nitrate
    (c) potassium hydroxide
    (d) sodium sulfate
    (e) potassium hydrogen sulfate
    (f) sodium hydrogen carbonate

70. Write a formula for each ionic compound.
    (a) copper(I) chlorate
    (b) potassium permanganate
    (c) lead(II) chromate
    (d) calcium fluoride
    (e) iron(II) phosphate
    (f) lithium hydrogen sulfite

NAMING MOLECULAR COMPOUNDS

71. Name each molecular compound.
    (a) SO_2
    (b) NI_3
    (c) BrF_5
    (d) NO
    (e) N_4Se_4

72. Name each molecular compound.
    (a) XeF_4
    (b) PI_3
    (c) SO_3
    (d) $SiCl_4$
    (e) I_2O_5

73. Write a formula for each molecular compound.
    (a) carbon monoxide
    (b) disulfur tetrafluoride
    (c) dichlorine monoxide
    (d) phosphorus pentafluoride
    (e) boron tribromide
    (f) diphosphorus pentasulfide

74. Write a formula for each molecular compound.
    (a) chlorine monoxide
    (b) xenon tetroxide
    (c) xenon hexafluoride
    (d) carbon tetrabromide
    (e) diboron tetrachloride
    (f) tetraphosphorus triselenide

75. Determine whether the name shown for each molecular compound is correct. If not, provide the compound's correct name.

(a) PBr_5 phosphorus(V) pentabromide

(b) P_2O_3 phosphorus trioxide

(c) SF_4 monosulfur hexafluoride

(d) NF_3 nitrogen trifluoride

76. Determine whether the name shown for each molecular compound is correct. If not, provide the compound's correct name.

(a) NCl_3 nitrogen chloride

(b) CI_4 carbon(IV) iodide

(c) CO carbon oxide

(d) SCl_4 sulfur tetrachloride

NAMING ACIDS

77. Determine whether each acid is a binary acid or an oxyacid and name each acid. If the acid is an oxyacid, also provide the name of the oxyanion.

(a) $HNO_2 (aq)$

(b) $HI (aq)$

(c) $H_2SO_4 (aq)$

(d) $HNO_3 (aq)$

78. Determine whether each acid is a binary acid or an oxyacid and name each acid. If the acid is an oxyacid, also provide the name of the oxyanion.

(a) $H_2CO_3 (aq)$

(b) $HC_2H_3O_2 (aq)$

(c) $H_3PO_4 (aq)$

(d) $HCl (aq)$

79. Name each acid.

(a) $HClO$

(b) $HClO_2$

(c) $HClO_3$

(d) $HClO_4$

80. Name each acid. (*Hint:* The names of the oxyanions are analogous to the names of the oxyanions of chlorine.)

(a) $HBrO_3$

(b) HIO_3

81. Write a formula for each acid.

(a) phosphoric acid

(b) hydrobromic acid

(c) sulfurous acid

82. Write a formula for each acid.

(a) hydrofluoric acid

(b) hydrocyanic acid

(c) chlorous acid

FORMULA MASS

83. Calculate the formula mass for each compound.

(a) HNO_3

(b) $CaBr_2$

(c) CCl_4

(d) $Sr(NO_3)_2$

84. Calculate the formula mass for each compound.

(a) CS_2

(b) $C_6H_{12}O_6$

(c) $Fe(NO_3)_3$

(d) C_7H_{16}

85. Arrange the compounds in order of decreasing formula mass.

Ag_2O, PtO_2, $Al(NO_3)_3$, PBr_3

86. Arrange the compounds in order of decreasing formula mass.

WO_2, Rb_2SO_4, $Pb(C_2H_3O_2)_2$, RbI

CUMULATIVE PROBLEMS

87. Write a molecular formula for each molecular model. (White = hydrogen; red = oxygen; black = carbon; blue = nitrogen; yellow = sulfur)

(a)

(b)

(c)

88. Write a molecular formula for each molecular model. (White = hydrogen; red = oxygen; black = carbon; blue = nitrogen; yellow = sulfur)

(a)

(b)

(c)

89. How many chlorine atoms are in each set?

   (a) three carbon tetrachloride molecules

   (b) two calcium chloride formula units

   (c) four phosphorus trichloride molecules

   (d) seven sodium chloride formula units

90. How many oxygen atoms are in each set?

   (a) four dinitrogen monoxide molecules

   (b) two calcium carbonate formula units

   (c) three sulfur dioxide molecules

   (d) five perchlorate ions

91. Specify the number of hydrogen atoms (white) represented in each set of molecular models:

(a)   (b)   (c)

92. Specify the number of oxygen atoms (red) represented in each set of molecular models:

(a)   (b)   (c)

93. Complete the table:

Formula	Type of Compound (Ionic, Molecular, Acid)	Name
N_2H_4	molecular	_____
_____	_____	potassium chloride
H_2CrO_4 (aq)	_____	_____
_____	_____	cobalt(III) cyanide

94. Complete the table:

Formula	Type of Compound (Ionic, Molecular, Acid)	Name
$K_2Cr_2O_7$	ionic	_____
HBr (aq)	_____	hydrobromic acid
_____	_____	dinitrogen pentoxide
PbO_2	_____	_____

95. Determine whether each name is correct for the given formula. If not, provide the correct name.

   (a) $Ca(NO_2)_2$ calcium nitrate

   (b) K_2O dipotassium monoxide

   (c) PCl_3 phosphorus chloride

   (d) $PbCO_3$ lead(II) carbonate

   (e) KIO_2 potassium hypoiodite

96. Determine whether each name is correct for the given formula. If not, provide the correct name.

   (a) HNO_3 (aq)   hydrogen nitrate

   (b) NaClO   sodium hypochlorite

   (c) CaI_2 calcium diiodide

   (d) $SnCrO_4$ tin chromate

   (e) $NaBrO_3$ sodium bromite

97. For each compound, list the correct formula and calculate the formula mass.

   (a) tin(IV) sulfate

   (b) nitrous acid

   (c) sodium bicarbonate

   (d) phosphorus pentafluoride

98. For each compound, list the correct formula and calculate the formula mass.

   (a) barium bromide

   (b) dinitrogen trioxide

   (c) copper(I) sulfate

   (d) hydrobromic acid

99. Name each compound and calculate its formula mass.

   (a) PtO_2

   (b) N_2O_5

   (c) $Al(ClO_3)_3$

   (d) PBr_5

100. Name each compound and calculate its formula mass.

   (a) $Al_2(SO_4)_3$

   (b) P_2O_3

   (c) HClO (aq)

   (d) $Cr(C_2H_3O_2)_3$

101. A compound contains only carbon and hydrogen and has a formula mass of 28.06 amu. What is its molecular formula?

102. A compound contains only nitrogen and oxygen and has a formula mass of 44.02 amu. What is its molecular formula?

103. Carbon has two naturally occurring isotopes: carbon-12 (mass = 12.00 amu) and carbon-13 (mass = 13.00 amu). Chlorine also has two naturally occurring isotopes: chlorine-35 (mass = 34.97 amu) and chlorine-37 (mass = 36.97 amu). How many CCl_4 molecules of different masses can exist? Determine the mass (in amu) of each of them.

104. Nitrogen has two naturally occurring isotopes: nitrogen-14 (mass = 14.00 amu) and nitrogen-15 (mass = 15.00 amu). Bromine also has two naturally occurring isotopes: bromine-79 (mass = 78.92 amu) and bromine-81 (mass = 80.92 amu). How many NBr_3 molecules of different masses can exist? Determine the mass (in amu) of each of them.

HIGHLIGHT PROBLEMS

105. Examine each substance and the corresponding molecular view and classify it as an atomic element, a molecular element, a molecular compound, or an ionic compound.

(a)

Charles D. Winters/Photo Researchers.

(b)

Richard Megna/Fundamental Photographs.

Richard Megna/Fundamental Photographs.

(c)

(d)

106. Molecules can be as small as two atoms or as large as thousands of atoms. In 1962, Max F. Perutz and John C. Kendrew were awarded the Nobel Prize for their discovery of the structure of hemoglobin, a very large molecule that transports oxygen from the lungs to cells through the bloodstream. The chemical formula of hemoglobin is $C_{2952}H_{4664}O_{832}N_{812}S_8Fe_4$. Calculate the formula mass of hemoglobin.

▶ Max Perutz and John C. Kendrew won a Nobel Prize in 1962 for determining the structure of hemoglobin by X-ray diffraction.

Getty Images.

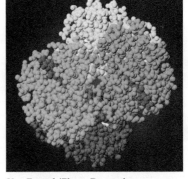

Ken Eward/Photo Researchers.

◀ Computer generated model of hemoglobin.

107. Examine each consumer product label. Write chemical formulas for as many of the compounds as possible based on what you have learned in this chapter.

(a)

Active Ingredient:
Sodium Hypochlorite 6.0%
Other Ingredients: 94.0%
Total: 100.0%
(Yields 5.7% available chlorine)

KEEP OUT OF REACH OF CHILDREN
DANGER: CORROSIVE.
FIRST AID: IF IN EYES: Hold eye open and rinse slowly and gently with water for 15–20 minutes. Remove contact lenses, if present, after the first 5 minutes, then continue rinsing eye. IF ON SKIN OR CLOTHING: Take off contaminated clothing. Rinse skin immediately with plenty of water for 15–20 minutes. IN EITHER CASE, CALL A POISON CONTROL CENTER OR DOCTOR IMMEDIATELY FOR TREATMENT ADVICE. See back panel for additional precautionary labeling.
Kills Methicillin Resistant Staphylococcus aureus (MRSA) *Staphylococcus aureus, Streptococcus pyogenes, Salmonella enterica, Escherichia coli 0157:H7 and Influenza A2

3 QT (96 FL OZ) 2.83 L

(b)

NOTICE! PROTECTIVE INNER SEAL BENEATH CAP. IF MISSING OR DAMAGED, DO NOT USE CONTENTS.

Drug Facts

Active ingredients (in each tablet)	Purpose
Calcium carbonate 1000 mg	Antacid
Simethicone 60 mg	Antigas

Uses for the relief of
• acid indigestion
• heartburn
• sour stomach
• upset stomach associated with these symptoms
• bloating and pressure commonly referred to as gas

Warning
Do not take more than 8 tablets in a 24-hour period or use the maximum dosage for more than 2 weeks except under the advice and supervision of a physician

Ask a doctor before use if you have
• kidney stones   • a calcium-restricted diet

Ask a doctor or pharmacist before use if your are presently taking a prescription drug. Antacids may interact with certain prescription drugs.

When using this product
• at maximum dose, constipation may occur

Stop use and ask a doctor if
• symptoms last more than two weeks

Keep out of reach of children.

(c)

Drug Facts

Active ingredients (in each 5 mL teaspoon)	Purposes
Aluminum hydroxide (equivalent to dried gel, USP) 400 mg	Antacid
Magnesium hydroxide 400 mg	Antacid
Simethicone 40 mg	Antigas

Use relieves: ■ heartburn ■ acid indigestion ■ sour stomach ■ upset stomach due to these symptoms ■ pressure and bloating commonly referred to as gas

Warnings
Ask a doctor before use if you have
■ kidney disease ■ a magnesium-restricted diet

Ask a doctor or pharmacist if you are taking a prescription drug. Antacids may interact with certain prescription drugs.

Stop use and ask a doctor if symptoms last more than 2 weeks.

Keep out of reach of children.

Directions ■ shake well ■ adults/children 12 years and older: take 2-4 teaspoonfuls between meals, at bedtime, or as directed by a doctor ■ do not take more than 12 teaspoonfuls in a 24-hour period, or use the maximum dosage for more than 2 weeks ■ children under 12 years: ask a doctor

Other information ■ each teaspoon contains: magnesium 171 mg ■ do not use if breakaway band on plastic cap is broken or missing ■ does not meet USP requirements for preservative effectiveness ■ do not freeze

Inactive ingredients butylparaben, carboxymethylcellulose sodium, flavors, hypromellose, microcrystalline cellulose, propylparaben, purified water, sodium saccharin, sorbitol

Questions or comments?
1-800-469-5268 (English) or
1-888-466-8746 (Spanish)

Johnson-Johnson • MERCK
Consumer Pharmaceuticals Co.
FORT WASHINGTON, PA 19034 USA

(d)

Nutrition Facts
Serving Size 1/8 tsp (0.6g)
Servings Per Container about 472

Amount Per Serving

Calories 0

	% Daily Value*
Total Fat 0g	0%
Sodium 65mg	3%
Total Carb. 0g	0%
Protein 0g	
Calcium 2%	

Not a significant source of calories from fat, saturated fat, trans fat, cholesterol, dietary fiber, sugars, vitamin A, vitamin C and iron.
*Percent Daily Values are based on a 2,000 calorie diet.

Ingredients: Cornstarch, Sodium Bicarbonate, Sodium Aluminum Sulfate, Monocalcium Phosphate.

CLABBER GIRL CORPORATION TERRE HAUTE, IN 47808

davisbakingpowder.com
MADE IN USA

Maxwellartandphoto.com.

▶ANSWERS TO SKILLBUILDER EXERCISES

Skillbuilder 1	Yes, because in both cases
	$$\frac{\text{Mass O}}{\text{Mass C}} = 1.3$$
Skillbuilder 2	(a) Ag_2S (b) N_2O (c) TiO_2
Skillbuilder 3	two K atoms, one S atom, four O atoms
Skillbuilder Plus 1	two Al atoms, three S atoms, twelve O atoms
Skillbuilder 4	
	(a) molecular element
	(b) molecular compound
	(c) atomic element
	(d) ionic compound
	(e) ionic compound

Skillbuilder 5	$SrCl_2$
Skillbuilder 6	AlN
Skillbuilder 7	$CaBr_2$
Skillbuilder 8	potassium bromide
Skillbuilder Plus 2	zinc nitride
Skillbuilder 9	lead(II) oxide
Skillbuilder 10	manganese(II) nitrate
Skillbuilder 11	dinitrogen tetroxide
Skillbuilder 12	hydrofluoric acid
Skillbuilder 13	nitrous acid
Skillbuilder 15	44.02 amu

▶ANSWERS TO CONCEPTUAL CHECKPOINTS

1 (b) This formula represents 2 Al atoms + 3 (2 Cr atoms + 7 O atoms) = 29 atoms.

2 (b) The figure represents a molecular compound because the compound exists as individual molecules. Figure (a) represents an ionic compound with formula units in a lattice structure.

3 Because calcium forms only one type of ion (Ca^{2+}); therefore, the charge of the ion is not included in the name (because it is always the same, 2+).

4 Iodate

5 (b)

ANSWERS TO ODD-NUMBERED EXERCISES

QUESTIONS

1. Yes; when elements combine with other elements, a compound is created. Each compound is unique and contains properties different from those of the elements that compose it.

3. The law of constant composition states that all samples of a given compound have the same proportions of their constituent elements. Joseph Proust formulated this law.

5. The more metallic element is generally listed first in a chemical formula.

7. The empirical formula gives the relative number of atoms of each element in a compound. The molecular formula gives the actual number of atoms of each element in a molecule of the compound.

9. An atomic element is one that exists in nature with a single atom as the basic unit. A molecular element is one that exists as a diatomic molecule as the basic unit. Molecular elements include H_2, N_2, O_2, F_2, Cl_2, Br_2, and I_2.

11. The systematic name can be directly derived by looking at the compound's formula. The common name for a compound acts like a nickname and can only be learned through familiarity.

13. The block that contains the elements for Type II compounds is known as the transition metals.

15. The basic form for the names of Type II ionic compounds is to have the name of the metal cation first, followed by the charge of the metal cation (in parentheses, using Roman numerals), and finally the base name of the nonmetal anion with -ide attached to the end.

17. For compounds containing a polyatomic anion, the name of the cation is first, followed by the name for the polyatomic anion. Also, if the compound contains both a polyatomic cation and a polyatomic anion, one would just use the names of both polyatomic ions.

19. The form for naming molecular compounds is to have the first element preceded by a prefix to indicate the number of atoms present. This is then followed by the second element with its corresponding prefix and -ide placed on the end of the second element.

21. To correctly name a binary acid, one must begin the first word with *hydro-*, which is followed by the base name of the nonmetal plus -ic added on the end. Finally, the word *acid* follows the first word.

23. To name an acid with oxyanions ending with -ite, one must take the base name of the oxyanion and attach -ous to it; the word *acid* follows this.

PROBLEMS

25. Yes; the ratios of sodium to chlorine in both samples were equal.

27. 2.06×10^3 g

29.

	Mass N_2O	Mass N	Mass O
Sample A	2.85	1.82	1.03
Sample B	4.55	2.91	1.64
Sample C	3.74	2.39	1.35
Sample D	1.74	1.11	0.63

31. NI_3

33. **a.** Fe_3O_4 **b.** PCl_3
    c. PCl_5 **d.** Ag_2O

35. **a.** 4 **b.** 4
    c. 6 **d.** 4

37. **a.** magnesium, 1; chlorine, 2
    b. sodium, 1; nitrogen, 1; oxygen, 3
    c. calcium, 1; nitrogen, 2; oxygen, 4
    d. strontium, 1; oxygen, 2; hydrogen, 2

39.

Formula	Number of $C_2H_3O_2$	Number of C Atoms	Number of H Atoms	Number of O Atoms	Number of Metal Atoms
$Mg(C_2H_3O_2)_2$	2	4	6	4	1
$NaC_2H_3O_2$	1	2	3	2	1
$Cr_2(C_2H_3O_2)_4$	4	8	12	8	2

41. **a.** CH_3 **b.** NO_2
    c. C_2H_3O **d.** NH_3

43. **a.** molecular **b.** atomic
    c. atomic **d.** molecular

45. **a.** molecular **b.** ionic
    c. ionic **d.** molecular

47. helium $\longrightarrow$ single atoms
    CCl_4 $\longrightarrow$ molecules
    K_2SO_4 $\longrightarrow$ formula units
    bromine $\longrightarrow$ diatomic molecules

49. **a.** formula units **b.** single atoms
    c. molecules **d.** molecules

51. **a.** ionic; forms only one type of ion
    b. molecular
    c. molecular
    d. ionic; forms only one type of ion

53. **a.** Na_2S **b.** SrO
    c. Al_2S_3 **d.** $MgCl_2$

55. **a.** $KC_2H_3O_2$ **b.** K_2CrO_4
    c. K_3PO_4 **d.** KCN

57. **a.** Li_3N, Li_2O, LiF **b.** Ba_3N_2, BaO, BaF_2

c. AlN, Al_2O_3, AlF_3

59. a. cesium chloride   **b.** strontium bromide

     c. potassium oxide   **d.** lithium fluoride

61. a. chromium(II) chloride   **b.** chromium(III) chloride

     c. tin(IV) oxide   **d.** lead(II) iodide

63. a. forms more than one type of ion, chromium(III) oxide

     b. forms only one type of ion, sodium iodide

     c. forms only one type of ion, calcium bromide

     d. forms more than one type of ion, tin(II) oxide

65. a. barium nitrate   **b.** lead(II) acetate

     c. ammonium iodide   **d.** potassium chlorate

     e. cobalt(II) sulfate   **f.** sodium perchlorate

67. a. hypobromite ion   **b.** bromite ion

     c. bromate ion   **d.** perbromate ion

69. a. $CuBr_2$ **b.** $AgNO_3$

     c. KOH **d.** Na_2SO_4

     e. $KHSO_4$ **f.** $NaHCO_3$

71. a. sulfur dioxide

     b. nitrogen triiodide

     c. bromine pentafluoride

     d. nitrogen monoxide

     e. tetranitrogen tetraselenide

73. a. CO **b.** S_2F_4

     c. Cl_2O **d.** PF_5

     e. BBr_3 **f.** P_2S_5

75. a. PBr_5 phosphorus pentabromide

     b. P_2O_3 diphosphorus trioxide

     c. SF_4 sulfur tetraflouride

     d. correct

77. a. oxyacid, nitrous acid, nitrite

     b. binary acid, hydroiodic acid

     c. oxyacid, sulfuric acid, sulfate

     d. oxyacid, nitric acid, nitrate

79. a. hypochlorous acid   **b.** chlorous acid

     c. chloric acid   **d.** perchloric acid

81. a. H_3PO_4 **b.** HBr

     c. H_2SO_3

83. a. 63.02 amu   **b.** 199.88 amu

     c. 153.81 amu   **d.** 211.64 amu

85. PBr_3, Ag_2O, PtO_2, $Al(NO_3)_3$

87. a. CH_4 **b.** SO_3

     c. NO_2

89. a. 12   **b.** 4

     c. 12   **d.** 7

91. a. 8   **b.** 12

     c. 12

93.

Formula	Type	Name
N_2H_4	molecular	dinitrogen tetrahydride
KCl	ionic	potassium chloride
H_2CrO_4	acid	chromic acid
$Co(CN)_3$	ionic	cobalt(III) cyanide

95. a. calcium nitrite

     b. potassium oxide

     c. phosphorus trichloride

     d. correct

     e. potassium iodite

97. a. $Sn(SO_4)_2$ 310.9 amu   **b.** HNO_2 47.02 amu

     c. $NaHCO_3$ 84.01 amu   **d.** PF_5 125.97 amu

99. a. platinum(IV) oxide 227.08 amu

     b. dinitrogen pentoxide 108.02 amu

     c. aluminum chlorate 277.33 amu

     d. phosphorus pentabromide 430.47 amu

101. C_2H_4

103. 10 different isotopes can exist. 151.88 amu, 152.88 amu, 153.88 amu, 154.88 amu, 155.88 amu, 156.88 amu, 157.88 amu, 158.88 amu, 159.88 amu, and 160.88 amu.

105. a. molecular element   **b.** atomic element

     c. ionic compound   **d.** molecular compound

107. a. $NaOCl$; $NaOH$ **b.** $Al(OH)_3$; $Mg(OH)_2$

     c. $CaCO_3$

     d. $NaHCO_3$, $Ca_3(PO_4)_2$, $NaAl(SO_4)_2$

Electrons in Atoms and the Periodic Table

From Chapter 9 of *Introductory Chemistry,* Fourth Edition, Nivaldo J. Tro. Copyright © 2011 by Pearson Education, Inc. Published by Pearson Prentice Hall. All rights reserved.

Electrons in Atoms and the Periodic Table

"Anyone who is not shocked by quantum mechanics has not understood it."

NIELS BOHR (1885–1962)

1 Blimps, Balloons, and Models of the Atom

Associated Press.

▲ The *Hindenburg* was filled with hydrogen, a reactive and flammable gas. **Question:** What makes hydrogen reactive?

◄ Modern blimps are filled with helium, an inert gas. The nucleus of the helium atom (inset) has two protons, so the neutral helium atom has two electrons—a highly stable configuration. In this chapter we learn about models that explain the inertness of helium and the reactivity of other elements.

You have probably seen one of the Goodyear blimps floating in the sky. A Goodyear blimp is often present at championship sporting events such as the Rose Bowl, the Indy 500, or the U.S. Open golf tournament. One was present at the Statue of Liberty's 100th birthday party, and blimps have made appearances in countless movies and television shows. The blimp's inherent stability allows it to provide spectacular views of the world below for television and film.

The Goodyear blimp is similar to a large balloon. Unlike airplanes, which must be moving fast to stay in flight, a blimp or *airship* floats in air because it is filled with a gas that is less dense than air. The Goodyear blimp is filled with helium. Other airships in history, however, have used hydrogen for buoyancy. For example, the *Hindenburg*—the largest airship ever constructed—was filled with hydrogen, which turned out to be a poor choice. Hydrogen is a reactive and flammable gas. On May 6, 1937, while landing in New Jersey on its first transatlantic crossing, the *Hindenburg* burst into flames, destroying the airship and killing 36 of the 97 passengers. Apparently, as the *Hindenburg* was landing, leaking hydrogen gas ignited, resulting in an explosion that destroyed the ship. (The skin of the *Hindenburg*, which was constructed of a flammable material, may have also been partially to blame for its demise.) A similar accident cannot happen to the Goodyear blimp thanks to the inert and therefore nonflammable nature of its helium gas contents. A spark or even a flame would actually be *extinguished* by helium.

Why is helium inert? What is it about helium *atoms* that makes helium *gas* inert? By contrast, why is hydrogen so reactive? Recall that elemental hydrogen exists as a diatomic element. Hydrogen atoms are so reactive that they react with each other to form hydrogen molecules. What is it about

173

hydrogen atoms that makes them so reactive? What is the difference between hydrogen and helium that accounts for their different reactivities?

When we examine the properties of hydrogen and helium, we make observations about nature. Mendeleev's periodic law, summarizes the results of many similar observations on the properties of elements:

> When the elements are arranged in order of increasing atomic number, certain sets of properties recur periodically.

The reactivity exhibited by hydrogen is also seen in other Group I elements, such as lithium and sodium. Likewise, the inertness of helium is seen in neon, argon, and the other noble gases. In this chapter, we consider models and theories that help explain the observed behaviors of groups of elements such as the Group I metals and noble gases. We examine two important models in particular—the **Bohr model** and the **quantum-mechanical model**—that propose explanations for the inertness of helium, the reactivity of hydrogen, and the periodic law. These models explain how electrons exist in atoms and how those electrons affect the chemical and physical properties of elements. You have already learned much about the behavior of elements. You know, for example, that sodium tends to form 1+ ions and that fluorine tends to form 1− ions. You know that some elements are metals and that others are nonmetals. And you know that the noble gases are chemically inert and that the alkali metals are chemically reactive. But you do not know *why*. The models in this chapter explain why.

The Bohr model and the quantum-mechanical model were developed in the early 1900s, and they caused a revolution in the physical sciences, changing our fundamental view of matter at its most basic level. The scientists who devised these models—including Niels Bohr, Erwin Schrödinger, and Albert Einstein—were bewildered by their discoveries. Bohr claimed, "Anyone who is not shocked by quantum mechanics has not understood it." Schrödinger lamented, "I don't like it, and I am sorry I ever had anything to do with it." Einstein disbelieved it, insisting that "God does not play dice with the universe." However, the quantum-mechanical model has such explanatory power that it is rarely questioned today. It forms the basis of the modern periodic table and our understanding of chemical bonding. Its applications include lasers, computers, and semiconductor devices, and it has given us new ways to design drugs that cure disease. The quantum-mechanical model for the atom is, in many ways, the foundation of modern chemistry.

The periodic law stated here is a modification of Mendeleev's original formulation. Mendeleev listed elements in order of increasing *mass*; today we list them in order of increasing *atomic number*.

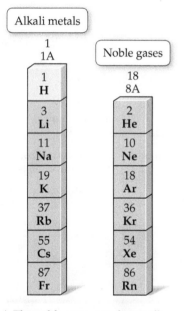

▲ The noble gases are chemically inert, and the alkali metals are chemically reactive. Why? (Hydrogen is a group I element, but it is not considered an alkali metal.)

Burgess Companies.

American Institute of Physics/Emilio Segre Visual Archives.

▲ Niels Bohr (left) and Erwin Schrödinger (right), along with Albert Einstein, played a role in the development of quantum mechanics, yet they were bewildered by their own theory.

2 Light: Electromagnetic Radiation

▲ When a water surface is disturbed, waves are created that radiate outward from the site.

| The Greek letter *lambda* (λ) is pronounced "lam-duh."

| Helpful mnemonic: ROY G BIV—Red, Orange, Yellow, Green, Blue, Indigo, Violet

Before we explore models of the atom, we must understand a few things about light, because the interaction of light with atoms helped to shape these models. Light is familiar to all of us—we see the world by it—but what is light? Unlike most of what we have encountered so far in this book, light is not matter—it has no mass. Light is a form of **electromagnetic radiation**, a type of energy that travels through space at a constant speed of 3.0×10^8 m/s (186,000 mi/s). At this speed, a flash of light generated at the equator would travel around the world in one-seventh of a second. This extremely fast speed is part of the reason that you *see* a firework in the sky before you *hear* the sound of its explosion. The light from the exploding firework reaches your eye almost instantaneously. The sound, traveling much more slowly, takes longer.

Before the advent of quantum mechanics, light was described exclusively as a wave of electromagnetic energy traveling through space. You are probably familiar with water waves (think of the waves created by a rock dropped into a still pond), or you may have created a wave on a rope by moving the end of the rope up and down in a quick motion. In either case, the wave carries energy as it moves through the water or along the rope.

Waves are generally characterized by their **wavelength** (λ), the distance between adjacent wave crests (▼ Figure 1). For visible light, wavelength determines color. For example, orange light has a longer wavelength than blue light. White light, as produced by the sun or by a lightbulb, contains a spectrum of wavelengths and therefore a spectrum of color. We can see these colors—red, orange, yellow, green, blue, indigo, and violet—in a rainbow or when white light is passed through a prism (▼ Figure 2). Red light, with a wavelength of 750 nm (nanometers), has the longest wavelength of visible light. Violet light, with a wavelength of 400 nm, has the shortest (1 nm = 10^{-9} m). The presence of color in

▶ FIGURE 1 **Wavelength** The wavelength of light (λ) is defined as the distance between adjacent wave crests.

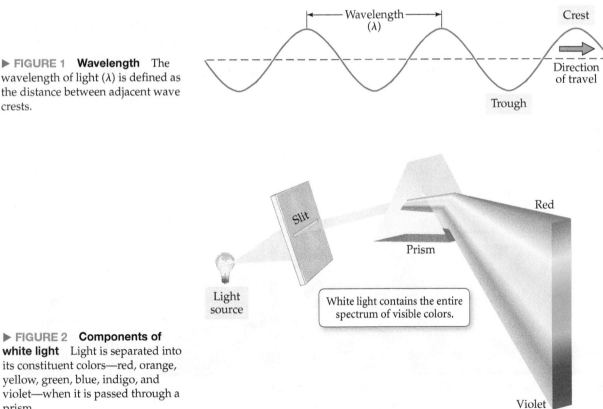

▶ FIGURE 2 **Components of white light** Light is separated into its constituent colors—red, orange, yellow, green, blue, indigo, and violet—when it is passed through a prism.

▲ FIGURE 3 **Color in objects** A red shirt appears red because it absorbs all colors except red, which it reflects.

❙ The Greek letter *nu* (*ν*) is pronounced "noo."

white light is responsible for the colors we see in our everyday vision. For example, a red shirt is red because it reflects red light (◄ Figure 3). Our eyes see only the reflected light, making the shirt appear red.

Light waves are also often characterized by their **frequency** (*ν*), the number of cycles or crests that pass through a stationary point in one second. Wavelength and frequency are inversely related—the shorter the wavelength, the higher the frequency. Blue light, for example, has a higher frequency than red light.

In the early twentieth century, scientists such as Albert Einstein discovered that the results of certain experiments could be explained only by describing light, not as waves, but as particles. In this description, the light leaving a flashlight, for example, is viewed as a stream of particles. A particle of light is called a **photon**, and we can think of a photon as a single packet of light energy. The amount of energy carried in the packet depends on the wavelength of the light—the shorter the wavelength, the greater the energy. Just as water waves carry more energy if their crests are closer together—think about surf pounding a beach—light waves carry more energy if their crests are closer together. Therefore, violet light (shorter wavelength) carries more energy per photon than red light (longer wavelength).

To summarize:

- Electromagnetic radiation is a form of energy that travels through space at a constant speed of 3.0×10^8 m/s and can exhibit wavelike or particle-like properties.
- The wavelength of electromagnetic radiation determines the amount of energy carried by one of its photons. The shorter the wavelength, the greater the energy of each photon.
- The frequency and energy of electromagnetic radiation are inversely related to its wavelength.

3 The Electromagnetic Spectrum

Electromagnetic radiation ranges in wavelength from 10^{-16} m (gamma rays) to 10^6 m (radio waves). Visible light composes only a tiny portion of that range. The entire range of electromagnetic radiation is called the **electromagnetic spectrum**. ▼ Figure 4 shows the entire electromagnetic spectrum, with short-wavelength, high-frequency radiation on the right and long-wavelength, low-frequency radiation on the left. Visible light is the small sliver in the middle.

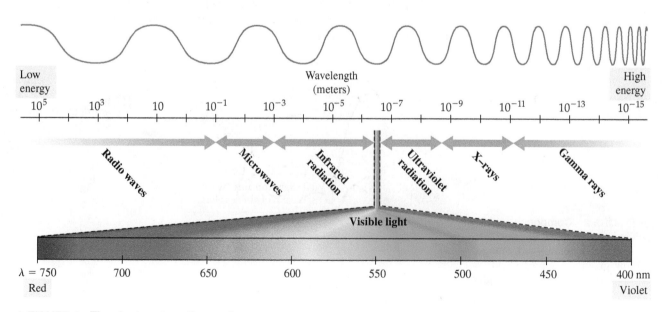

▲ FIGURE 4 **The electromagnetic spectrum**

Remember that the energy carried per photon is greater for short-wavelength light than for long-wavelength light. The shortest wavelength (and therefore most energetic) photons are those of **gamma rays**, shown on the far right of Figure 4. Gamma rays are produced by the sun, by stars, and by certain unstable atomic nuclei on Earth. Excessive human exposure to gamma rays is dangerous because the high energy of gamma-ray photons can damage biological molecules.

Next on the electromagnetic spectrum (to the left in Figure 4), with longer wavelengths (and lower energy) than gamma rays are **X-rays**, familiar to us from their medical use. X-rays pass through many substances that block visible light and are therefore used to image internal bones and organs. Like gamma-ray photons, X-ray photons carry enough energy to damage biological molecules. While several yearly exposures to X-rays are relatively harmless, excessive exposure to X-rays increases cancer risk.

Sandwiched between X-rays and visible light in the electromagnetic spectrum is **ultraviolet** or **UV light**, most familiar to us as the component of sunlight that produces a sunburn or suntan. While not as energetic as gamma-ray or X-ray photons, ultraviolet photons still carry enough energy to damage biological molecules. Excessive exposure to ultraviolet light increases the risk of skin cancer and cataracts and causes premature wrinkling of the skin. Next on the spectrum is **visible light**, ranging from violet (shorter wavelength, higher energy) to red (longer wavelength, lower energy). Photons of visible light do not damage biological molecules. They do, however, cause molecules in our eyes to rearrange, which sends a signal to our brains that results in vision.

Infrared light is next, with even longer wavelengths than visible light. The heat you feel when you place your hand near a hot object is infrared light. All warm objects, including human bodies, emit infrared light. While infrared light is invisible to our eyes, infrared sensors can detect it and are often used in night-vision technology to "see" in the dark. In the infrared region of the spectrum, warm objects—such as human bodies—glow, much as a lightbulb glows in the visible region of the spectrum.

Beyond infrared light, at longer wavelengths still, are **microwaves**, used for radar and in microwave ovens. Although microwave light has longer wavelengths—and therefore lower energy per photon—than visible or infrared light, it is efficiently absorbed by water and can therefore heat substances that contain water. For this reason substances that contain water, such as food, are warmed when placed in a microwave oven, but substances that do not contain water, such as a plate, are not.

The longest wavelengths of light are **radio waves**, which are used to transmit the signals used by AM and FM radio, cellular telephones, television, and other forms of communication.

Some types of dishes contain substances that absorb microwave radiation, but most do not.

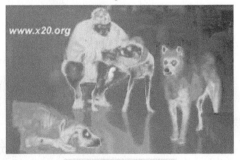

Normal photograph   Infrared photograph

▲ Warm objects, such as human or animal bodies, give off infrared light that is easily detected with an infrared camera. In the infrared photograph, the warmest areas appear as red and the coolest as dark blue. (Note that the photo confirms the familiar idea that healthy dogs have cold noses.) (*Source:* Sierra Pacific Innovations. All rights reserved. SPI CORP, www.x20.org)

Radiation Treatment for Cancer

X-rays and gamma rays are sometimes called ionizing radiation because the high energy in their photons can ionize atoms and molecules. When ionizing radiation interacts with biological molecules, it can permanently change or even destroy them. Consequently, we normally try to limit our exposure to ionizing radiation. However, doctors can use ionizing radiation to destroy molecules within unwanted cells such as cancer cells.

In radiation therapy (or radiotherapy), doctors aim X-ray or gamma-ray beams at cancerous tumors. The ionizing radiation damages the molecules within the tumor's cells that carry genetic information—information necessary for the cell to grow and divide—and the cell dies or stops dividing. Ionizing radiation also damages molecules within healthy cells; however, cancerous cells divide more quickly than healthy cells, making them more susceptible to genetic damage. Nonetheless, healthy cells often inadvertently sustain damage during treatments, resulting in side effects such as fatigue, skin lesions, and hair loss. Doctors try to minimize the exposure of healthy cells by appropriate shielding and by targeting the tumor from multiple directions, minimizing the exposure of healthy cells while maximizing the exposure of cancerous cells (▶ Figure 5).

Another side effect of exposing healthy cells to radiation is that they too may become cancerous. So a treatment for cancer may cause cancer. So why do we continue to use it? Radiation therapy, as most other disease therapies, has associated risks. However, we take risks all the time, many for lesser reasons. For example, every time we drive a car, we risk injury or even death. Why? Because we perceive the benefit—such as getting to the grocery store to buy food—to be worth the risk. The situation is similar in cancer therapy or any other therapy for that matter. The benefit of cancer therapy (possibly curing a cancer that will certainly kill you) is worth the risk (a slight increase in the chance of developing a future cancer).

CAN YOU ANSWER THIS? *Why would visible light not work to destroy cancerous tumors?*

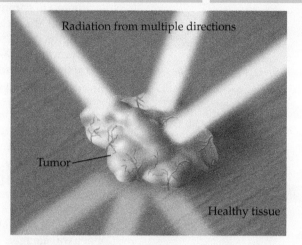

▲ **FIGURE 5 Radiation therapy** By targeting the tumor from various different directions, radiologists attempt to limit damage to healthy tissue.

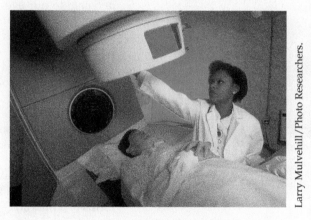

▲ Cancer patient undergoing radiation therapy.

Larry Mulvehill/Photo Researchers.

EXAMPLE 1 Wavelength, Energy, and Frequency

Arrange the three types of electromagnetic radiation—visible light, X-rays, and microwaves—in order of increasing:

(a) wavelength   **(b)** frequency   **(c)** energy per photon

	SOLUTION
(a) wavelength Figure 4 indicates that X-rays have the shortest wavelength, followed by visible light and then microwaves.	X-rays, visible light, microwaves
(b) frequency Since frequency and wavelength are inversely proportional—the longer the wavelength, the shorter the frequency—the ordering with respect to frequency is exactly the reverse of the ordering with respect to wavelength.	microwaves, visible light, X-rays

(c) energy per photon

microwaves, visible light, X-rays

Energy per photon decreases with increasing wavelength but increases with increasing frequency; therefore, the ordering with respect to energy per photon is the same as frequency.

▶**SKILLBUILDER 1** | **Wavelength, Energy, and Frequency**

Arrange the colors of visible light—green, red, and blue—in order of increasing:

(a) wavelength   **(b)** frequency   **(c)** energy per photon

▶**FOR MORE PRACTICE**   Example 9; Problems 31, 32, 33, 34, 35, 36, 37, 38.

 CONCEPTUAL CHECKPOINT 1

Yellow light has a longer wavelength than violet light. Therefore:

(a) Yellow light has more energy per photon than violet light.

(b) Yellow light has less energy per photon than violet light.

(c) Both yellow light and violet light have the same energy per photon.

4   The Bohr Model: Atoms with Orbits

▲ **FIGURE 6**   **A neon sign**   Neon atoms inside a glass tube absorb electrical energy and then re-emit the energy as light.

When an atom absorbs energy—in the form of heat, light, or electricity—it often re-emits that energy as light. For example, a neon sign is composed of one or more glass tubes filled with gaseous neon atoms. When an electrical current is passed through the tube, the neon atoms absorb some of the electrical energy and re-emit it as the familiar red light of a neon sign (◀ Figure 6). If the atoms in the tube are different, the emitted light is a different color. In other words, atoms of a given element emit light of unique colors (or unique wavelengths). Mercury atoms, for example, emit light that appears blue, hydrogen atoms emit light that appears pink (▼ Figure 7), and helium atoms emit light that appears yellow-orange.

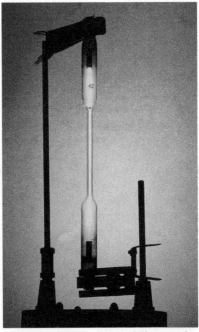 

▶ **FIGURE 7**   **Light emission by different elements**   Light emitted from a mercury lamp (left) appears blue, and light emitted from a hydrogen lamp (right) appears pink.

Richard Megna/Fundamental Photographs.

179

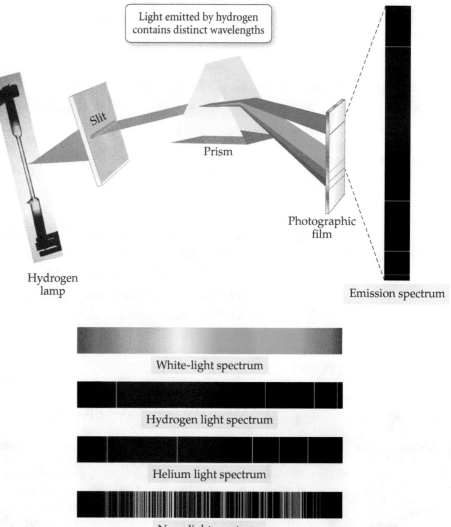

▲ **FIGURE 8** **Emission spectra** A white-light spectrum is continuous, with some radiation emitted at every wavelength. The emission spectrum of an individual element, however, includes only certain specific wavelengths. (The different wavelengths appear as *lines* because the light from the source passes through a slit before entering the prism.) Each element produces its own unique and distinctive emission spectrum.

Closer inspection of the light emitted by hydrogen, helium, and neon atoms reveals that the light contains several distinct colors or wavelengths. Just as the white light from a lightbulb can be separated into its constituent wavelengths by passing it through a prism, so the light emitted by glowing hydrogen, helium, or neon can also be separated into its constituent wavelengths (▲ Figure 8) by passing it through a prism. The result is called an **emission spectrum**. Notice the differences between a white-light spectrum and the emission spectra of hydrogen, helium, and neon. The white-light spectrum is *continuous*, meaning that the light intensity is uninterrupted or smooth across the entire visible range—there is some radiation at all wavelengths, with no gaps. The emission spectra of hydrogen, helium, and neon, however, are not continuous. They consist of bright spots or lines at specific wavelengths with complete darkness in between. Since the emission of light in atoms is related to the motions of electrons within the atoms, a model for how electrons exist in atoms must account for these spectra.

A major challenge in developing a model for electrons in atoms was the discrete or bright-line nature of the emission spectra. Why did atoms, when excit-

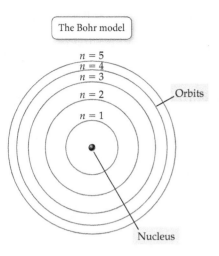

▲ FIGURE 9 **Bohr orbits**

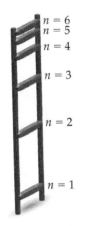

▲ FIGURE 10 **The Bohr energy ladder** Bohr orbits are like steps on a ladder. It is possible to stand on one step or another, but impossible to stand between steps.

ed with energy, emit light only at particular wavelengths? Why did they *not* emit a continuous spectrum? Niels Bohr developed a simple model to explain these results. In his model, now called the Bohr model, electrons travel around the nucleus in circular orbits that are similar to planetary orbits around the sun. However, unlike planets revolving around the sun—which can theoretically orbit at any distance whatsoever from the sun—electrons in the Bohr model can orbit only at *specific, fixed* distances from the nucleus (◄ Figure 9).

The *energy* of each Bohr orbit, specified by a **quantum number** $n = 1, 2, 3 \ldots$, is also fixed, or **quantized**. The energy of each orbit increases with increasing value of n, but the levels become more closely spaced as n increases. Bohr orbits are like steps of a ladder (◄ Figure 10), each at a specific distance from the nucleus and each at a specific energy. Just as it is impossible to stand *between steps* on a ladder, so it is impossible for an electron to exist *between orbits* in the Bohr model. An electron in an $n = 3$ orbit, for example, is farther from the nucleus and has more energy than an electron in an $n = 2$ orbit. And an electron cannot exist at an intermediate distance or energy between the two orbits—the orbits are *quantized*. As long as an electron remains in a given orbit, it does not absorb or emit light, and its energy remains fixed and constant.

When an atom absorbs energy, an electron in one of these fixed orbits is *excited* or promoted to an orbit that is farther away from the nucleus (◄ Figure 11) and therefore higher in energy (this is analogous to moving up a step on the ladder). However, in this new configuration, the atom is less stable, and the electron quickly falls back or *relaxes* to a lower-energy orbit (this is analogous to moving down a step on the ladder). As it does so, it releases a photon of light containing the precise amount of energy—called a **quantum** of energy—that corresponds to the energy difference between the two orbits.

Since the amount of energy in a photon is directly related to its wavelength, the photon has a specific wavelength. *Consequently, the light emitted by excited atoms consists of specific lines at specific wavelengths, each corresponding to a specific transition between two orbits.* For example, the line at 486 nm in the hydrogen emission spectrum corresponds to an electron relaxing from the $n = 4$ orbit to the $n = 2$ orbit (▼ Figure 12). In the same way, the line at 657 nm (longer wavelength and therefore lower energy) corresponds to an electron relaxing from the $n = 3$ orbit to the $n = 2$ orbit. Notice that transitions between orbits that are closer together produce lower-energy (and therefore longer-wavelength) light than transitions between orbits that are farther apart.

The great success of the Bohr model of the atom was that it predicted the lines of the hydrogen emission spectrum. However, it failed to predict the emission

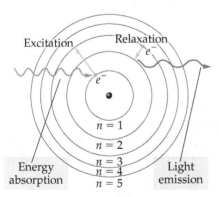

▲ FIGURE 11 **Excitation and emission** When a hydrogen atom absorbs energy, an electron is excited to a higher-energy orbit. The electron then relaxes back to a lower-energy orbit, emitting a photon of light.

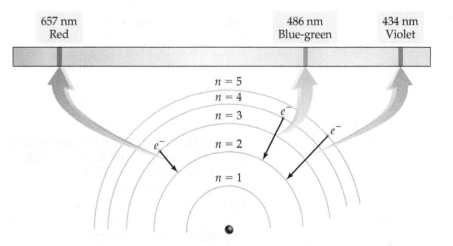

▲ FIGURE 12 **Hydrogen emission lines** The 657-nm line of the hydrogen emission spectrum corresponds to an electron relaxing from the $n = 3$ orbit to the $n = 2$ orbit. The 486-nm line corresponds to an electron relaxing from the $n = 4$ orbit to the $n = 2$ orbit, and the 434-nm line corresponds to an electron relaxing from $n = 5$ to $n = 2$.

The Bohr model is still important because it provides a logical foundation to the quantum-mechanical model and reveals the historical development of scientific understanding.

spectra of other elements that contained more than one electron. For this, and other reasons, the Bohr model was replaced with a more sophisticated model called the quantum-mechanical or wave-mechanical model.

To summarize:

- Electrons exist in quantized orbits at specific, fixed energies and specific, fixed distances from the nucleus.
- When energy is put into an atom, electrons are excited to higher-energy orbits.
- When an electron relaxes (or falls) from a higher-energy orbit to a lower-energy orbit, the atom emits light.
- The energy (and therefore the wavelength) of the emitted light corresponds to the energy difference between the two orbits in the transition. Since these energies are fixed and discrete, the energy (and therefore the wavelength) of the emitted light is fixed and discrete.

✔ CONCEPTUAL CHECKPOINT 2

In one transition, an electron in a hydrogen atom falls from the $n = 3$ level to the $n = 2$ level. In a second transition, an electron in a hydrogen atom falls from the $n = 2$ level to the $n = 1$ level. Compared to the radiation emitted by the first of these transitions, the radiation emitted by the second will have:

(a) a lower frequency

(b) a smaller energy per photon

(c) a shorter wavelength

(d) a longer wavelength

5 The Quantum-Mechanical Model: Atoms with Orbitals

The quantum-mechanical model of the atom replaced the Bohr model in the early twentieth century. In the quantum-mechanical model *Bohr orbits* are replaced with *quantum-mechanical* **orbitals**. Orbitals are different from orbits in that they represent, not specific paths that electrons follow, but probability maps that show a statistical distribution of where the electron is likely to be found. The idea of an orbital is not easy to visualize. Quantum mechanics revolutionized physics and chemistry because in the quantums-mechanical model, electrons *do not* behave like particles flying through space. We cannot, in general, describe their exact paths. An orbital is a probability map that shows where the electron is *likely* to be found when the atom is probed; it does not represent the exact path that an electron takes as it travels through space.

BASEBALL PATHS AND ELECTRON PROBABILITY MAPS

To understand orbitals, let's contrast the behavior of a baseball with that of an electron. Imagine a baseball thrown from the pitcher's mound to a catcher at home plate (▶ Figure 13). The baseball's path can easily be traced as it travels from the pitcher to the catcher. The catcher can watch the baseball as it travels through the air, and he can predict exactly where the baseball will cross over home plate. He can even place his mitt in the correct place to catch it. *This would be impossible for an electron.* Like photons, electrons exhibit a *wave–particle duality*; sometimes they act as particles, and other times as waves. This duality leads to behavior that makes it impossible to trace an electron's path. If an electron were "thrown" from the pitcher's mound to home plate, it would land in a different place every time, *even if it were thrown in exactly the same way.* Baseballs have predictable paths—electrons do not.

Associated Press.

▶ FIGURE 13 **Baseballs follow predictable paths** A baseball follows a well-defined path as it travels from the pitcher to the catcher.

Joe Sohm/Photo Researchers.

▲ FIGURE 14 **Electrons are unpredictable** To describe the behavior of a "pitched" electron, you would have to construct a probability map of where it would cross home plate.

In the quantum-mechanical world of the electron, the catcher could not know exactly where the electron would cross the plate for any given throw. He would have no way of putting his mitt in the right place to catch it. However, if the catcher kept track of hundreds of electron throws, he could observe a reproducible, statistical pattern of where the electron crosses the plate. He could even draw maps in the strike zone showing the probability of an electron crossing a certain area (◀ Figure 14). These maps are called *probability maps*.

FROM ORBITS TO ORBITALS

In the Bohr model, an *orbit* is a circular path—analogous to a baseball's path—that shows the electron's motion around an atomic nucleus. In the quantum-mechanical model, an *orbital* is a probability map, analogous to the probability map drawn by our catcher. It shows the relative likelihood of the electron being found at various locations when the atom is probed. Just as the Bohr model has different orbits with different radii, the quantum-mechanical model has different orbitals with different shapes.

6 Quantum-Mechanical Orbitals

In the Bohr model of the atom, a single quantum number (n) specifies each orbit. In the quantum-mechanical model, a number and a letter specify an orbital (or orbitals). For example, the lowest-energy orbital in the quantum-mechanical model—analogous to the $n = 1$ orbit in the Bohr model—is called the *1s orbital*. It is specified by the number 1 and the letter *s*. The number is called the **principal quantum number** (n)

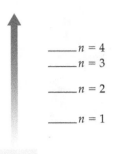

Energy

▲ **FIGURE 15 Principal quantum numbers** The principal quantum numbers ($n = 1, 2, 3 \ldots$) determine the energy of the hydrogen quantum-mechanical orbitals.

This analogy is purely hypothetical. It is impossible to photograph electrons in this way.

and specifies the **principal shell** of the orbital. The higher the principal quantum number, the higher the energy of the orbital. The possible principal quantum numbers are $n = 1, 2, 3 \ldots$, with energy increasing as n increases (◄ Figure 15). Since the 1s orbital has the lowest possible principal quantum number, it is in the lowest-energy shell and has the lowest possible energy.

The letter indicates the **subshell** of the orbital and specifies its shape. The possible letters are s, p, d, and f, each with a different shape. Orbitals within the s subshell have a spherical shape. Unlike the $n = 1$ Bohr orbit, which shows the electron's path, the 1s quantum-mechanical orbital is a three-dimensional probability map. Orbitals are sometimes represented by dots (◄ Figure 16), where the dot density is proportional to the probability of finding the electron.

We can understand the dot representation of an orbital better with another analogy. Imagine taking a photograph of an electron in an atom every second for 10 or 15 minutes. One second the electron is very close to the nucleus; the next second it is farther away and so on. Each photo shows a dot representing the electron's position relative to the nucleus at that time. If you took hundreds of photos and superimposed all of them, you would have an image like Figure 16—a statistical representation of where the electron is found. Notice that the dot density for the 1s orbital is greatest near the nucleus and decreases farther away from the nucleus. This means that the electron is more likely to be found close to the nucleus than far away from it.

Orbitals can also be represented as geometric shapes that encompass most of the volume where the electron is likely to be found. For example, the 1s orbital can be represented as a sphere (▼ Figure 17) that encompasses the volume within which the electron is found 90% of the time. If we superimpose the dot representation of the 1s orbital on the shape representation (▼ Figure 18), we can see that most of the dots are within the sphere, meaning that the electron is most likely to be found within the sphere when it is in the 1s orbital.

The single electron of an undisturbed hydrogen atom at room temperature is in the 1s orbital. This is called the **ground state**, or lowest energy state, of the hydrogen atom. However, like the Bohr model, the quantum-mechanical model allows transitions to higher-energy orbitals upon the absorption of energy. What are these higher-energy orbitals? What do they look like?

Dot representation of 1s orbital

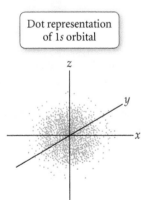

▲ **FIGURE 16 1s orbital** The dot density in this plot is proportional to the probability of finding the electron. The greater dot density near the middle represents a higher probability of finding the electron near the nucleus.

Shape representation of 1s orbital

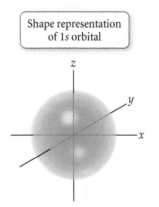

▲ **FIGURE 17 Shape representation of the 1s orbital** Because the distribution of electron density around the nucleus in Figure 16 is symmetrical—the same in all directions—we can represent the 1s orbital as a sphere.

Both representations of 1s superimposed

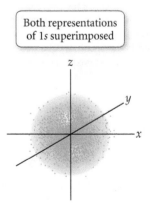

▲ **FIGURE 18 Orbital shape and dot representation for the 1s orbital** The shape representation of the 1s orbital superimposed on the dot density representation. We can see that when the electron is in the 1s orbital, it is most likely to be found within the sphere.

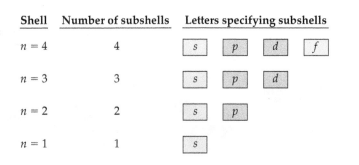

Shell	Number of subshells	Letters specifying subshells			
$n = 4$	4	s	p	d	f
$n = 3$	3	s	p	d	
$n = 2$	2	s	p		
$n = 1$	1	s			

► FIGURE 19 **Subshells** The number of subshells in a given principal shell is equal to the value of n.

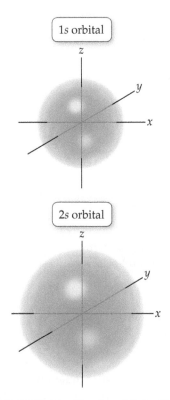

▲ FIGURE 20 **The 2s orbital** The 2s orbital is similar to the 1s orbital, but larger in size.

The next orbitals in the quantum-mechanical model are those with principal quantum number $n = 2$. Unlike the $n = 1$ principal shell, which contains only one subshell (specified by s), the $n = 2$ principal shell contains two subshells, specified by s and p.

The number of subshells in a given principal shell is equal to the value of n.

Therefore the $n = 1$ principal shell has one subshell, the $n = 2$ principal shell has two subshells, and so on (▲ Figure 19). The s subshell contains the 2s orbital, higher in energy than the 1s orbital and slightly larger (◄ Figure 20), but otherwise similar in shape. The p subshell contains three 2p orbitals (▼ Figure 21), all with the same dumbbell-like shape but with different orientations.

The next principal shell, $n = 3$, contains three subshells specified by s, p, and d. The s and p subshells contain the 3s and 3p orbitals, similar in shape to the 2s and 2p orbitals, but slightly larger and higher in energy. The d subshell contains the five d orbitals shown in ► Figure 22 on the next page. The next principal shell, $n = 4$, contains four subshells specified by s, p, d, and f. The s, p, and d subshells are similar to those in $n = 3$. The f subshell contains seven orbitals (called the 4f orbitals), whose shape we do not consider in this text.

As we have already discussed, hydrogen's single electron is usually in the 1s orbital because electrons generally seek out the lowest-energy orbital available. In hydrogen, the rest of the orbitals are normally empty. However, the absorption of energy by a hydrogen atom can cause the electron to jump (or make a transition) from the 1s orbital to a higher-energy orbital. When the electron is in a higher-energy orbital, the hydrogen atom is said to be in an **excited state**.

Because of their higher energy, excited states are unstable, and the electron will usually fall (or relax) back to a lower-energy orbital. In the process the electron emits energy, often in the form of light. As in the Bohr model, the energy difference between the two orbitals involved in the transition determines the wavelength of the emitted light (the greater the energy difference, the shorter the wavelength). The quantum-mechanical model predicts the bright-line spectrum of hydrogen as well as the Bohr model. However, it can also predict the bright-line spectra of other elements as well.

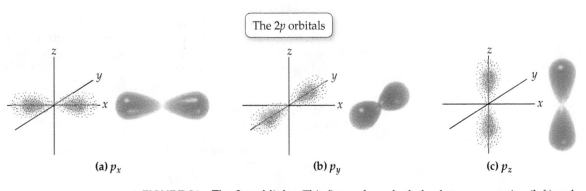

▲ FIGURE 21 **The 2p orbitals** This figure shows both the dot representation (left) and shape representation (right) for each p-orbital.

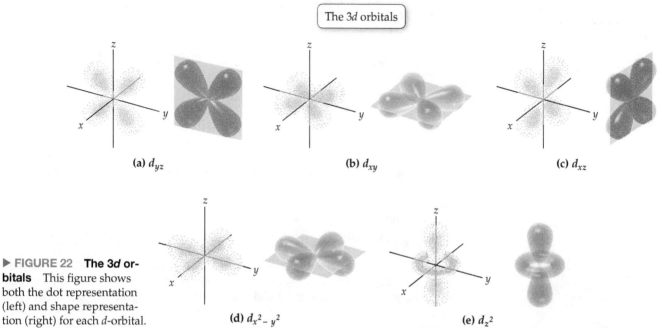

The 3d orbitals

(a) d_{yz}

(b) d_{xy}

(c) d_{xz}

▶ FIGURE 22 **The 3d orbitals** This figure shows both the dot representation (left) and shape representation (right) for each d-orbital.

(d) $d_{x^2-y^2}$

(e) d_{z^2}

ELECTRON CONFIGURATIONS: HOW ELECTRONS OCCUPY ORBITALS

An **electron configuration** shows the occupation of orbitals by electrons for a particular atom. For example, the electron configuration for a ground-state (or lowest energy) hydrogen atom is:

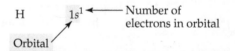

The electron configuration tells us that hydrogen's single electron is in the 1s orbital.

Another way to represent this information is with an **orbital diagram**, which gives similar information but shows the electrons as arrows in a box representing the orbital. The orbital diagram for a ground-state hydrogen atom is:

H   ↑

1s

The box represents the 1s orbital, and the arrow within the box represents the electron in the 1s orbital. In orbital diagrams, the direction of the arrow (pointing up or pointing down) represents **electron spin**, a fundamental property of electrons. All electrons have spin. The **Pauli exclusion principle** states that *orbitals may hold no more than two electrons with opposing spins*. We symbolize this as two arrows pointing in opposite directions

↑↓

A helium atom, for example, has two electrons. The electron configuration and orbital diagram for helium are:

Electron configuration	Orbital diagram
He $1s^2$	
	1s

▶ FIGURE 23 **Energy ordering of orbitals for multi-electron atoms**
Different subshells within the same principal shell have different energies.

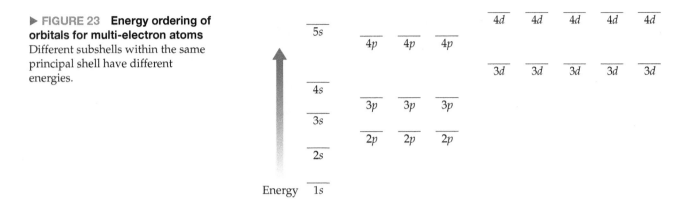

▶ FIGURE 23 **Energy ordering of orbitals for multi-electron atoms**
Different subshells within the same principal shell have different energies.

In multi-electron atoms, the subshells within a principal shell do not have the same energy because of electron–electron interactions.

Remember that the number of electrons in an atom is equal to its atomic number.

Since we know that electrons occupy the lowest-energy orbitals available, and since we know that only two electrons (with opposing spins) are allowed in each orbital, we can continue to build ground-state electron configurations for the rest of the elements as long as we know the energy ordering of the orbitals. ▲ Figure 23 shows the energy ordering of a number of orbitals for multi-electron atoms.

Notice that, for multi-electron atoms (in contrast to hydrogen which has only one electron), the subshells within a principal shell *do not* have the same energy. In elements other than hydrogen, the energy ordering is not determined by the principal quantum number alone. For example, in multi-electron atoms, the $4s$ subshell is lower in energy than the $3d$ subshell, even though its principal quantum number is higher. Using this relative energy ordering, we can write ground-state electron configurations and orbital diagrams for other elements. For lithium, which has three electrons, the electron configuration and orbital diagram are:

Electron configuration	Orbital diagram
Li $\quad 1s^2 2s^1$	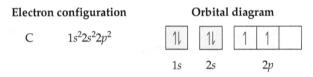

For carbon, which has six electrons, the electron configuration and orbital diagram are:

Electron configuration $\qquad$ Orbital diagram

C $\qquad 1s^2 2s^2 2p^2$

Notice that the $2p$ electrons occupy the p orbitals (of equal energy) singly rather than pairing in one orbital. This is the result of **Hund's rule**, which states that *when filling orbitals of equal energy, electrons fill them singly first, with parallel spins.*

Before we write electron configurations for other elements, let us summarize what we have learned so far:

- Electrons occupy orbitals so as to minimize the energy of the atom; therefore, lower-energy orbitals fill before higher-energy orbitals. Orbitals fill in the following order: $1s\ 2s\ 2p\ 3s\ 3p\ 4s\ 3d\ 4p\ 5s\ 4d\ 5p\ 6s$ (◀ Figure 24).
- Orbitals can hold no more than two electrons each. When two electrons occupy the same orbital, they must have opposing spins. This is known as the Pauli exclusion principle.
- When orbitals of identical energy are available, these are first occupied singly with parallel spins rather than in pairs. This is known as Hund's rule.

Consider the electron configurations and orbital diagrams for elements with atomic numbers 3 through 10.

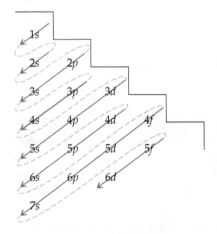

▲ FIGURE 24 **Orbital filling order**
The arrows indicate the order in which orbitals fill.

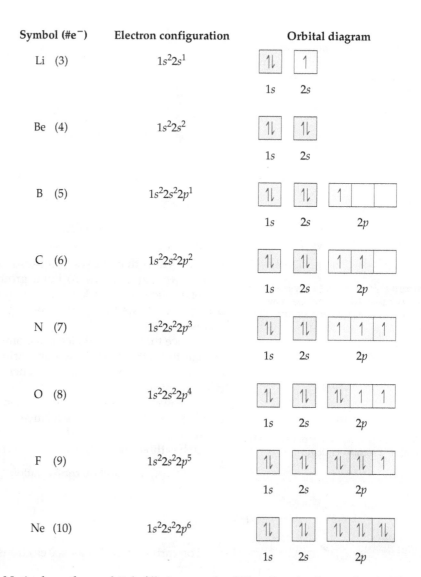

Symbol (#e⁻)	Electron configuration	Orbital diagram

Li (3) — $1s^2 2s^1$

Be (4) — $1s^2 2s^2$

B (5) — $1s^2 2s^2 2p^1$

C (6) — $1s^2 2s^2 2p^2$

N (7) — $1s^2 2s^2 2p^3$

O (8) — $1s^2 2s^2 2p^4$

F (9) — $1s^2 2s^2 2p^5$

Ne (10) — $1s^2 2s^2 2p^6$

Notice how the p orbitals fill. As a result of Hund's rule, the p orbitals fill with single electrons before they fill with paired electrons. The electron configuration of neon represents the complete filling of the $n = 2$ principal shell. When writing electron configurations for elements beyond neon—or beyond any other noble gas—the electron configuration of the previous noble gas is often abbreviated by the symbol for the noble gas in brackets. For example, the electron configuration of sodium is:

$$\text{Na} \quad 1s^2 2s^2 2p^6 3s^1$$

This can also be written using the noble gas core notation as:

$$\text{Na} \quad [\text{Ne}]3s^1$$

where [Ne] represents $1s^2 2s^2 2p^6$, the electron configuration for neon.

To write an electron configuration for an element, first find its atomic number from the periodic table—this number equals the number of electrons in the neutral atom. Then use the order of filling from Figure 23 or 24 to distribute the electrons in the appropriate orbitals. Remember that each orbital can hold a maximum of 2 electrons. Consequently:

- the s subshell has only 1 orbital and therefore can hold only 2 electrons.
- the p subshell has 3 orbitals and therefore can hold 6 electrons.
- the d subshell has 5 orbitals and therefore can hold 10 electrons.
- the f subshell has 7 orbitals and therefore can hold 14 electrons.

EXAMPLE 2 Electron Configurations

Write electron configurations for each element.

(a) Mg   (b) S   (c) Ga

	SOLUTION
(a) Magnesium has 12 electrons. Distribute two of these into the 1s orbital, two into the 2s orbital, six into the 2p orbitals, and two into the 3s orbital. You can also write the electron configuration more compactly using the noble gas core notation. For magnesium, use [Ne] to represent $1s^2 2s^2 2p^6$.	Mg $1s^2 2s^2 2p^6 3s^2$ or Mg $[Ne]3s^2$
(b) Sulfur has 16 electrons. Distribute two of these into the 1s orbital, two into the 2s orbital, six into the 2p orbitals, two into the 3s orbital, and four into the 3p orbitals. You can write the electron configuration more compactly by using [Ne] to represent $1s^2 2s^2 2p^6$.	S $1s^2 2s^2 2p^6 3s^2 3p^4$ or S $[Ne]3s^2 3p^4$
(c) Gallium has 31 electrons. Distribute two of these into the 1s orbital, two into the 2s orbital, six into the 2p orbitals, two into the 3s orbital, six into the 3p orbitals, two into the 4s orbital, ten into the 3d orbitals, and one into the 4p orbitals. Notice that the d subshell has five orbitals and can therefore hold 10 electrons. You can write the electron configuration more compactly by using [Ar] to represent $1s^2 2s^2 2p^6 3s^2 3p^6$.	Ga $1s^2 2s^2 2p^6 3s^2 3p^6 4s^2 3d^{10} 4p^1$ or Ga $[Ar]4s^2 3d^{10} 4p^1$

▶SKILLBUILDER 2 | Electron Configurations

Write electron configurations for each element.

(a) Al   (b) Br   (c) Sr

▶SKILLBUILDER PLUS 1

Write electron configurations for each ion. (*Hint:* To determine the number of electrons to include in the electron configuration of an ion, make sure to add or subtract electrons as needed to account for the charge of the ion.)

(a) Al^{3+} (b) Cl^- (c) O^{2-}

▶FOR MORE PRACTICE   Problems 49, 50, 53, 54, 55, 56.

EXAMPLE 3 Writing Orbital Diagrams

Write an orbital diagram for silicon.

SOLUTION

Since silicon is atomic number 14, it has 14 electrons. Draw a box for each orbital, putting the lowest-energy orbital (1s) on the far left and proceeding to orbitals of higher energy to the right.

☐ ☐ ☐☐☐ ☐ ☐☐☐
1s   2s   2p   3s   3p

Distribute the 14 electrons into the orbitals, allowing a maximum of 2 electrons per orbital and remembering Hund's rule. The complete orbital diagram is:

Si   ↑↓ ↑↓ ↑↓ ↑↓ ↑↓ ↑↓ ↑ ↑ ☐
      1s   2s   2p   3s   3p

▶SKILLBUILDER 3 | Writing Orbital Diagrams

Write an orbital diagram for argon.

▶FOR MORE PRACTICE   Example 10; Problems 51, 52.

✔ **CONCEPTUAL CHECKPOINT 3**

Which pair of elements has the same *total* number of electrons in *p* orbitals?

(a) Na and K

(b) K and Kr

(c) P and N

(d) Ar and Ca

7 Electron Configurations and the Periodic Table

VALENCE ELECTRONS

Valence electrons are the electrons in the outermost principal shell (the principal shell with the highest principal quantum number, n). These electrons are important because, as we will see in the next chapter, they are involved in chemical bonding. Electrons that are *not* in the outermost principal shell are called **core electrons**. For example, silicon, with the electron configuration of $1s^2 2s^2 2p^6 3s^2 3p^2$, has 4 valence electrons (those in the $n = 3$ principal shell) and 10 core electrons.

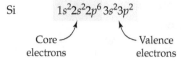

Si $\quad 1s^2 2s^2 2p^6\ 3s^2 3p^2$

Core electrons — Valence electrons

EXAMPLE 4   Valence Electrons and Core Electrons

Write an electron configuraton for selenium and identify the valence electrons and the core electrons.

SOLUTION

Write the electron configuration for selenium by determining the total number of electrons from selenium's atomic number (34) and then distributing them into the appropriate orbitals.

$$\text{Se} \qquad 1s^2 2s^2 2p^6 3s^2 3p^6 4s^2 3d^{10} 4p^4$$

The valence electrons are those in the outermost principal shell. For selenium, the outermost principal shell is the $n = 4$ shell, which contains 6 electrons (2 in the $4s$ orbital and 4 in the three $4p$ orbitals). All other electrons, including those in the $3d$ orbitals, are core electrons.

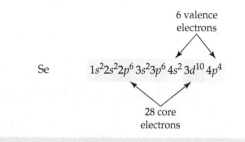

6 valence electrons

Se $\quad 1s^2 2s^2 2p^6\ 3s^2 3p^6\ 4s^2\ 3d^{10}\ 4p^4$

28 core electrons

▶**SKILLBUILDER 4 | Valence Electrons and Core Electrons**

Write an electron configuration for chlorine and identify the valence electrons and core electrons.

▶**FOR MORE PRACTICE**   Example 11; Problems 57, 58, 61, 62.

1A	2A	3A	4A	5A	6A	7A	8A
1 **H** $1s^1$							2 **He** $1s^2$
3 **Li** $2s^1$	4 **Be** $2s^2$	5 **B** $2s^2 2p^1$	6 **C** $2s^2 2p^2$	7 **N** $2s^2 2p^3$	8 **O** $2s^2 2p^4$	9 **F** $2s^2 2p^5$	10 **Ne** $2s^2 2p^6$
11 **Na** $3s^1$	12 **Mg** $3s^2$	13 **Al** $3s^2 3p^1$	14 **Si** $3s^2 3p^2$	15 **P** $3s^2 3p^3$	16 **S** $3s^2 3p^4$	17 **Cl** $3s^2 3p^5$	18 **Ar** $3s^2 3p^6$

▶ **FIGURE 25** Outer electron configurations of the first 18 elements

▲ Figure 25 shows the first 18 elements in the periodic table with an outer electron configuration listed below each one. As you move across a row, the orbitals are simply filling in the correct order. As you move down a column, the highest principal quantum number increases, but the number of electrons in each subshell remains the same. Consequently, the elements within a column (or family) all have the same number of valence electrons and similar outer electron configurations.

A similar pattern exists for the entire periodic table (▼ Figure 26). Notice that, because of the filling order of orbitals, the periodic table can be divided into blocks representing the filling of particular subshells.

- The first two columns on the left side of the periodic table are the *s* block with outer electron configurations of ns^1 (first column) and ns^2 (second column).
- The six columns on the right side of the periodic table are the *p* block with outer electron configurations of: $ns^2 np^1$, $ns^2 np^2$, $ns^2 np^3$, $ns^2 np^4$, $ns^2 np^5$ (halogens), and $ns^2 np^6$ (noble gases).
- The transition metals are the *d* block.
- The lanthanides and actinides (also called the inner transition metals) are the *f* block.

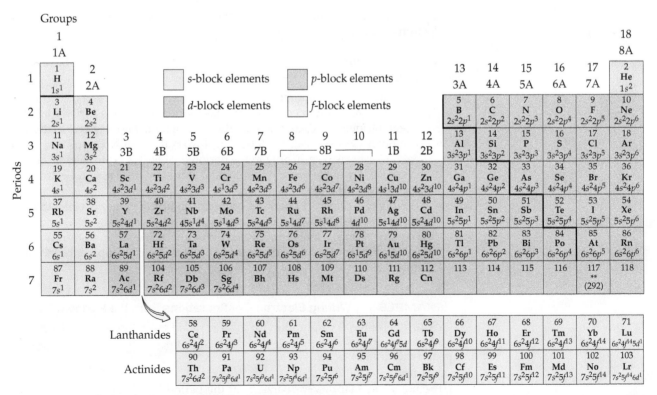

▲ **FIGURE 26** Outer electron configurations of the elements

Remember that main-group elements are those in the two far left columns (1A, 2A) and the six far right columns (3A–8A) of the periodic table.

Notice that, except for helium, the number of valence electrons for any main-group element is equal to the group number of its column. For example, we can tell that chlorine has 7 valence electrons because it is in the column with group number 7A. The row number in the periodic table is equal to the number of the highest principal shell (n value). For example, since chlorine is in row 3, its highest principal shell is the $n = 3$ shell.

The transition metals have electron configurations with trends that differ somewhat from main-group elements. As you move across a row in the d block, the d orbitals are filling (Figure 26). However, the principal quantum number of the d orbital being filled across each row in the transition series is equal to the row number minus one (in the fourth row, the $3d$ orbitals fill; in the fifth row, the $4d$ orbitals fill; and so on). For the first transition series, the outer configuration is $4s^2 3d^x$ (x = number of d electrons) with two exceptions: Cr is $4s^1 3d^5$ and Cu is $4s^1 3d^{10}$. These exceptions occur because a half-filled d subshell and a completely filled d subshell are particularly stable. Otherwise, the number of outershell electrons in a transition series does not change as you move across a period. In other words, *the transition series represents the filling of core orbitals, and the number of outershell electrons is mostly constant.*

We can now see that the organization of the periodic table allows us to write the electron configuration for any element based simply on its position in the periodic table. For example, suppose we want to write an electron configuration for P. The inner electrons of P are simply those of the noble gas that precedes P in the periodic table, Ne. So we can represent the inner electrons with [Ne]. We obtain the outer electron configuration by tracing the elements between Ne and P and assigning electrons to the appropriate orbitals (◄ Figure 27). Remember that the highest n value is given by the row number (3 for phosphorus). So we begin with [Ne], then add in the two $3s$ electrons as we trace across the s block, followed by three $3p$ electrons as we trace across the p block to P, which is in the third column of the p block. The electron configuration is:

$$\text{P} \qquad [\text{Ne}]3s^2 3p^3$$

Notice that P is in column 5A and therefore has 5 valence electrons and an outer electron configuration of $ns^2 np^3$.

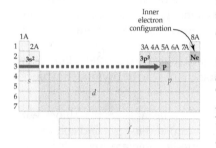

▲ FIGURE 27 **Electron configuration of phosphorus** Determining the electron configuration for P from its position in the periodic table.

To summarize writing an electron configuration for an element based on its position in the periodic table:

- The inner electron configuration for any element is the electron configuration of the noble gas that immediately precedes that element in the periodic table. Represent the inner configuration with the symbol for the noble gas in brackets.
- The outer electrons can be determined from the element's position within a particular block (s, p, d, or f) in the periodic table. Trace the elements between the preceding noble gas and the element of interest, and assign electrons to the appropriate orbitals.
- The highest principal quantum number (highest n value) is equal to the row number of the element in the periodic table.
- For any element containing d electrons, the principal quantum number (n value) of the outermost d electrons is equal to the row number of the element minus 1.

EXAMPLE 5 Writing Electron Configurations from the Periodic Table

Write an electron configuration for arsenic based on its position in the periodic table.

SOLUTION

The noble gas that precedes arsenic in the periodic table is argon, so the inner electron configuration is [Ar]. We can obtain the outer electron configuration by

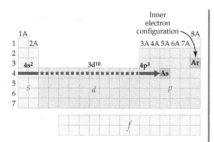

▲ FIGURE 28 Electron configuration of arsenic Determining the electron configuration for As from its position in the periodic table.

tracing the elements between Ar and As and assigning electrons to the appropriate orbitals. Remember that the highest *n* value is given by the row number (4 for arsenic). So, we begin with [Ar], then add in the two 4*s* electrons as we trace across the *s* block, followed by ten 3*d* electrons as we trace across the *d* block (the *n* value for *d* subshells is equal to the row number minus one), and finally the three 4*p* electrons as we trace across the *p* block to As, which is in the third column of the *p* block (◄ Figure 28).

The electron configuration is:

$$\text{As} \qquad [\text{Ar}]4s^2 3d^{10} 4p^3$$

▶**SKILLBUILDER 5 | Writing Electron Configurations from the Periodic Table**

Use the periodic table to determine the electron configuration for tin.

▶**FOR MORE PRACTICE** Example 12; Problems 65, 66, 67, 68.

✔ CONCEPTUAL CHECKPOINT 4

Which element has the *fewest* valence electrons?

(a) B

(b) Ca

(c) O

(d) K

(e) Ga

8 The Explanatory Power of the Quantum-Mechanical Model

Noble gases

| 18 |
| 8A |

| 2 |
| **He** |
| $1s^2$ |

| 10 |
| **Ne** |
| $2s^2 2p^6$ |

| 18 |
| **Ar** |
| $3s^2 3p^6$ |

| 36 |
| **Kr** |
| $4s^2 4p^6$ |

| 54 |
| **Xe** |
| $5s^2 5p^6$ |

| 86 |
| **Rn** |
| $6s^2 6p^6$ |

▲ FIGURE 29 Electron configurations of the noble gases The noble gases (except for helium) all have 8 valence electrons and completely full outer principal shells.

At the beginning of this chapter, we learned that the quantum-mechanical model explained the chemical properties of the elements such as the inertness of helium, the reactivity of hydrogen, and the periodic law. We can now see how: *The chemical properties of elements are largely determined by the number of valence electrons they contain.* Their properties vary in a periodic fashion because the number of valence electrons is periodic.

Since elements within a column in the periodic table have the same number of valence electrons, they also have similar chemical properties. The noble gases, for example, all have 8 valence electrons, except for helium, which has 2 (◄ Figure 29). Although we don't get into the quantitative (or numerical) aspects of the quantum-mechanical model in this text, calculations show that atoms with 8 valence electrons (or 2 for helium) are particularly low in energy, and therefore stable. The noble gases are indeed chemically stable, and thus relatively inert or nonreactive as accounted for by the quantum model.

Elements with electron configurations close to the noble gases are the most reactive because they can attain noble gas electron configurations by losing or gaining a small number of electrons. Alkali metals (Group 1) are among the most reactive metals since their outer electron configuration (ns^1) is 1 electron beyond a noble gas configuration (◄ Figure 30). If they can react to lose the

Alkali metals

| 1 |
| 1A |

| 3 |
| **Li** |
| $2s^1$ |

| 11 |
| **Na** |
| $3s^1$ |

| 19 |
| **K** |
| $4s^1$ |

| 37 |
| **Rb** |
| $5s^1$ |

| 55 |
| **Cs** |
| $6s^1$ |

| 87 |
| **Fr** |
| $7s^1$ |

◄ FIGURE 30 Electron configurations of the alkali metals The alkali metals all have ns^1 electron configurations and are therefore 1 electron beyond a noble gas configuration. In their reactions, they tend to lose that electron, forming 1+ ions and attaining a noble gas configuration.

ns^1 electron, they attain a noble gas configuration. This explains why the Group 1A metals tend to form 1+ cations. As an example, consider the electron configuration of sodium:

$$\text{Na} \qquad 1s^2 2s^2 2p^6 3s^1$$

In reactions, sodium loses its $3s$ electron, forming a 1+ ion with the electron configuration of neon.

$$\text{Na}^+ \qquad 1s^2 2s^2 2p^6$$

$$\text{Ne} \qquad 1s^2 2s^2 2p^6$$

Similarly, alkaline earth metals, with an outer electron configuration of ns^2, also tend to be reactive metals, losing their ns^2 electrons to form 2+ cations (▼ Figure 31). For example, consider magnesium:

$$\text{Mg} \qquad 1s^2 2s^2 2p^6 3s^2$$

In reactions, magnesium loses its two $3s$ electrons, forming a 2− ion with the electron configuration of neon.

$$\text{Mg}^{2+} \qquad 1s^2 2s^2 2p^6$$

On the other side of the periodic table, halogens are among the most reactive nonmetals because of their $ns^2 np^5$ electron configurations (▼ Figure 32). They are only one electron away from a noble gas configuration and tend to react to gain that one electron, forming 1− ions. For example, consider fluorine:

$$\text{F} \qquad 1s^2 2s^2 2p^5$$

In reactions, fluorine gains an additional $2p$ electron, forming a 1− ion with the electron configuration of neon.

$$\text{F}^- \qquad 1s^2 2s^2 2p^6$$

Atoms and/or ions that have the same electron configuration are termed isoelectronic.

The elements that form predictable ions are shown in ▶ Figure 33. Notice how the charge of these ions reflects their electron configurations—these elements form ions with noble gas electron configurations.

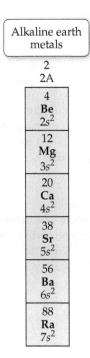

◀ FIGURE 31 **Electron configurations of the alkaline earth metals** The alkaline earth metals all have ns^2 electron configurations and are therefore 2 electrons beyond a noble gas configuration. In their reactions, they tend to lose 2 electrons, forming 2+ ions and attaining a noble gas configuration.

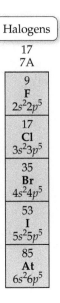

▶ FIGURE 32 **Electron configurations of the halogens** The halogens all have $ns^2 np^5$ electron configurations and are therefore 1 electron short of a noble gas configuration. In their reactions, they tend to gain 1 electron, forming 1− ions and attaining a noble gas configuration.

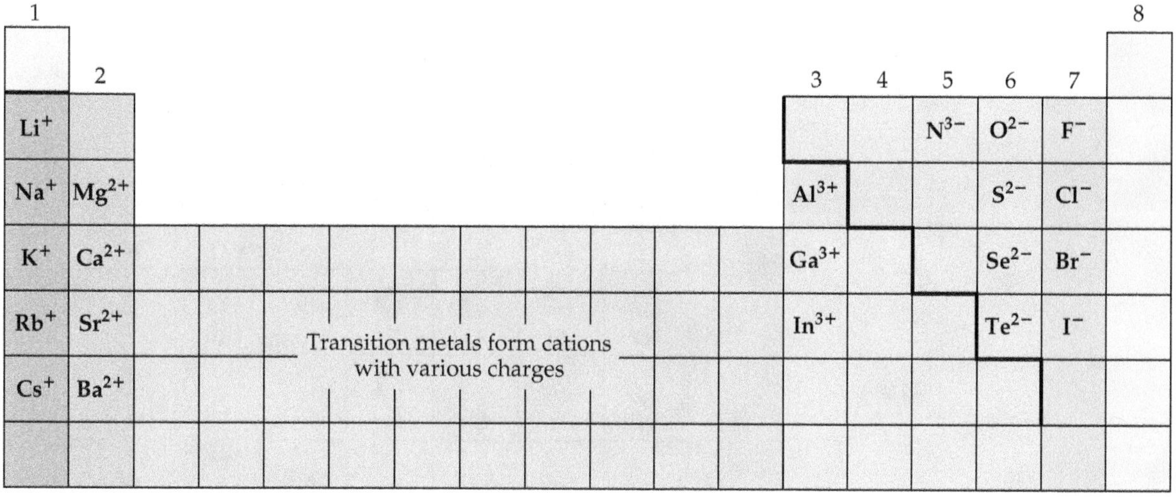

1	2											3	4	5	6	7	8
Li^+														N^{3-}	O^{2-}	F^-	
Na^+	Mg^{2+}											Al^{3+}			S^{2-}	Cl^-	
K^+	Ca^{2+}											Ga^{3+}			Se^{2-}	Br^-	
Rb^+	Sr^{2+}			Transition metals form cations								In^{3+}			Te^{2-}	I^-	
Cs^+	Ba^{2+}			with various charges													

▲ FIGURE 33   **Elements that form predictable ions**

✔ CONCEPTUAL CHECKPOINT 5

Below is the electron configuration of calcium:

$$Ca \qquad 1s^2 2s^2 2p^6 3s^2 3p^6 4s^2$$

In its reactions, calcium tends to form the Ca^{2+} ion. Which electrons are lost upon ionization?

(a) the $4s$ electrons

(b) two of the $3p$ electrons

(c) the $3s$ electrons

(d) the $1s$ electrons

9 Periodic Trends: Atomic Size, Ionization Energy, and Metallic Character

The quantum-mechanical model also explains other periodic trends such as atomic size, ionization energy, and metallic character. We will examine these one at a time.

ATOMIC SIZE

The **atomic size** of an atom is determined by the distance between the outermost electrons and the nucleus. As we move across a period in the periodic table, we know that electrons occupy orbitals with the same principal quantum number, n. Since the principal quantum number largely determines the size of an orbital, electrons are therefore filling orbitals of approximately the same size, and we might expect atomic size to remain constant across a period. However, with each step across a period, the number of protons in the nucleus is also increasing. This increase in the number of protons results in a greater pull on the electrons from the nucleus, causing atomic size to actually decrease. Therefore:

As you move to the right across a period, or row, in the periodic table, atomic size decreases, as shown in ▶ Figure 34 on the next page.

As you move down a column in the periodic table, the highest principal quantum number, n, increases. Since the size of an orbital increases with increasing principal quantum number, the electrons that occupy the outermost orbitals are farther from the nucleus as you move down a column. Therefore:

As you move down a column, or family, in the periodic table, atomic size increases, as shown in Figure 34.

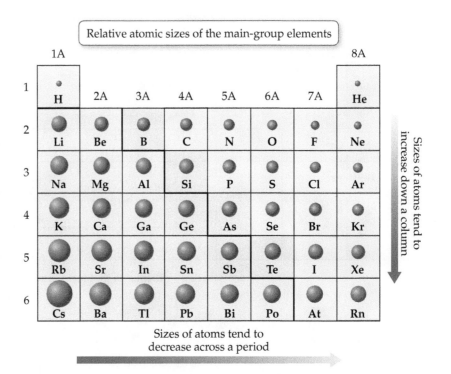

▶ FIGURE 34 **Periodic properties: atomic size** Atomic size decreases as you move to the right across a period and increases as you move down a column in the periodic table.

Sizes of atoms tend to increase down a column

Sizes of atoms tend to decrease across a period

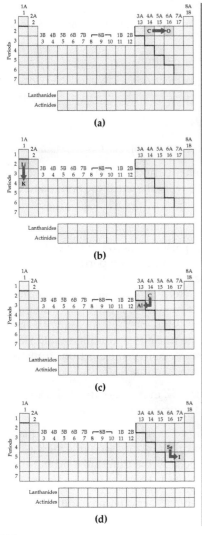

(a)

(b)

(c)

(d)

EXAMPLE 6 Atomic Size

Choose the larger atom in each pair.

(a) C or O   **(b)** Li or K   **(c)** C or Al   **(d)** Se or I

SOLUTION

(a) C or O
Carbon atoms are larger than O atoms because, as you trace the path between C and O on the periodic table (see margin), you move to the right within the same period. Atomic size decreases as you go to the right.

(b) Li or K
Potassium atoms are larger than Li atoms because, as you trace the path between Li and K on the periodic table (see margin), you move down a column. Atomic size increases as you go down a column.

(c) C or Al
Aluminum atoms are larger than C atoms because, as you trace the path between C and Al on the periodic table (see margin), you move down a column (atomic size increases) and then to the left across a period (atomic size increases). These effects add together for an overall increase.

(d) Se or I
Based on periodic properties alone, you cannot tell which atom is larger because as you trace the path between Se and I (see margin) you go down a column (atomic size increases) and then to the right across a period (atomic size decreases). These effects tend to cancel one another.

▶**SKILLBUILDER 6 | Atomic Size**

Choose the larger atom in each pair.

(a) Pb or Po   **(b)** Rb or Na   **(c)** Sn or Bi   **(d)** F or Se

▶**FOR MORE PRACTICE** Example 13a; Problems 81, 82, 83, 84.

CHEMISTRY AND HEALTH
Pumping Ions: Atomic Size and Nerve Impulses

No matter what you are doing at this moment, tiny pumps in each of the trillions of cells that make up your body are hard at work. These pumps, located in the cell membrane, move a number of different ions into and out of the cell. The most important such ions are sodium (Na^+) and potassium (K^+), which happen to be pumped in opposite directions. Sodium ions are pumped *out of cells*, while potassium ions are pumped *into cells*. The result is a *chemical gradient* for each ion: The concentration of sodium is higher outside the cell than within, while exactly the opposite is true for potassium.

The ion pumps within the cell membrane are analogous to water pumps in a high-rise building that pump water against the force of gravity to a tank on the roof. Other structures within the membrane, called ion channels, are like the building's faucets. When they open momentarily, bursts of sodium and potassium ions, driven by their concentration gradients, flow back across the membrane—sodium flowing in and potassium flowing out. These ion pulses are the basis for the transmission of nerve signals in the brain, heart, and throughout the body. Consequently, every move you make or every thought you have is mediated by the flow of these ions.

How do the pumps and channels differentiate between sodium and potassium ions? How do the ion pumps selectively move sodium out of the cell and potassium into the cell? To answer this question, we must examine the sodium and potassium ions more closely. In what ways do they differ? Both are cations of Group I metals. All Group I metals tend to lose one electron to form cations with 1+ charge, so the magnitude of the charge cannot be the decisive factor. But potassium (atomic number 19) lies directly below sodium in the periodic table (atomic number 11) and based on periodic properties is therefore larger than sodium. The potassium ion has a radius of 133 pm, while the sodium ion has a radius of 95 pm. (Recall from Chapter 2 that 1 pm = 10^{-12} m.) The pumps and channels within cell membranes are so sensitive that they can distinguish between the sizes of these two ions and selectively allow only one or the other to pass. The result is the transmission of nerve signals that allows you to read this page.

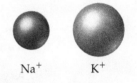

Na^+ K^+

CAN YOU ANSWER THIS? *Other ions, including calcium and magnesium, are also important to nerve signal transmission. Arrange these four ions in order of increasing size: K^+, Na^+, Mg^{2+}, and Ca^{2+}.*

IONIZATION ENERGY

The **ionization energy** of an atom is the energy required to remove an electron from the atom in the gaseous state. For example, the ionization of sodium can be represented with the equation:

$$Na + \text{Ionization energy} \longrightarrow Na^+ + 1e^-$$

Based on what you know about electron configurations, what would you predict about ionization energy trends? Would it take more or less energy to remove an electron from Na than from Cl? We know that Na has an outer electron configuration of $3s^1$ and Cl has an outer electron configuration of $3s^2 3p^5$. Since removing an electron from Na gives it a noble gas configuration—and removing an electron from Cl does not—we would expect sodium to have a lower ionization energy, and that is the case. It is easier to remove an electron from sodium than it is from chlorine. We can generalize this idea in this statement:

As you move across a period, or row, to the right in the periodic table, ionization energy increases (▶ Figure 35 on the next page).

What happens to ionization energy as you move down a column? As we have learned, the principal quantum number, n, increases as you move down a column. Within a given subshell, orbitals with higher principal quantum numbers are larger than orbitals with smaller principal quantum numbers. Consequently, electrons in the outermost principal shell are farther away from the positively charged nucleus—and therefore held less tightly—as you move down a column. This

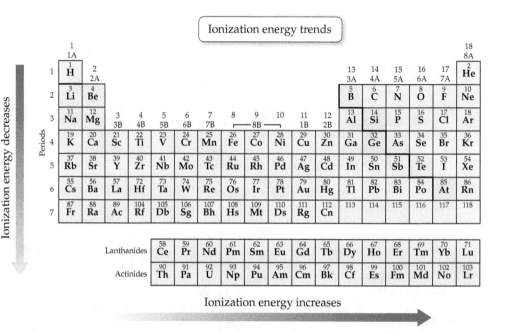

▶ FIGURE 35 **Periodic properties: ionization energy**
Ionization energy increases as you move to the right across a period and decreases as you move down a column in the periodic table.

results in a lower ionization energy (if the electron is held less tightly, it is easier to pull away) as you move down a column. Therefore:

As you move down a column (or family) in the periodic table, ionization energy decreases (Figure 35).

Notice that the trends in ionization energy are consistent with the trends in atomic size. Smaller atoms are more difficult to ionize because their electrons are held more tightly. Therefore, as you go across a period, atomic size decreases and ionization energy increases. Similarly, as you go down a column, atomic size increases and ionization energy decreases since electrons are farther from the nucleus and therefore less tightly held.

EXAMPLE 7 **Ionization Energy**

Choose the element with the higher ionization energy from each pair.

(a) Mg or P
(b) As or Sb
(c) N or Si
(d) O or Cl

SOLUTION

(a) Mg or P
P has a higher ionization than Mg because, as you trace the path between Mg and P on the periodic table (see margin), you move to the right within the same period. Ionization energy increases as you go to the right.

(b) As or Sb
As has a higher ionization energy than Sb because, as you trace the path between As and Sb on the periodic table (see margin), you move down a column. Ionization energy decreases as you go down a column.

(c) N or Si
N has a higher ionization energy than Si because, as you trace the path between N and Si on the periodic table (see margin), you move down a column (ionization energy decreases) and then to the left across a period (ionization energy decreases). These effects sum together for an overall decrease.

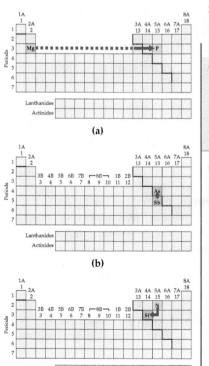

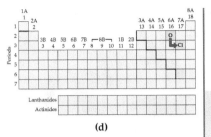

(d)

(d) O or Cl

Based on periodic properties alone, you cannot tell which has a higher ionization energy because, as you trace the path between O and Cl (see margin), you go down a column (ionization energy decreases) and then to the right across a period (ionization energy increases). These effects tend to cancel.

▶**SKILLBUILDER 7 | Ionization Energy**

Choose the element with the higher ionization energy from each pair.

(a) Mg or Sr
(b) In or Te
(c) C or P
(d) F or S

▶**FOR MORE PRACTICE**   Example 13b; Problems 77, 78, 79, 80.

METALLIC CHARACTER

Metals tend to lose electrons in their chemical reactions, while nonmetals tend to gain electrons. As you move across a period in the periodic table, ionization energy increases, which means that electrons are less likely to be lost in chemical reactions. Consequently:

As you move across a period, or row, to the right in the periodic table, **metallic character** decreases (▼ Figure 36).

As you move down a column in the periodic table, ionization energy decreases, making electrons more likely to be lost in chemical reactions. Consequently:

As you move down a column, or family, in the periodic table, metallic character increases (Figure 36).

These trends, based on the quantum-mechanical model, explain the distribution of metals and nonmetals. Metals are found toward the left side of the periodic table and nonmetals (with the exception of hydrogen) toward the upper right.

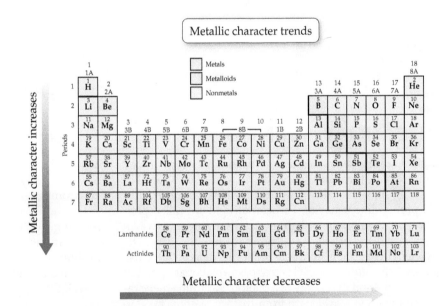

▲ **FIGURE 36   Periodic properties: metallic character**   Metallic character decreases as you move to the right across a period and increases as you move down a column in the periodic table.

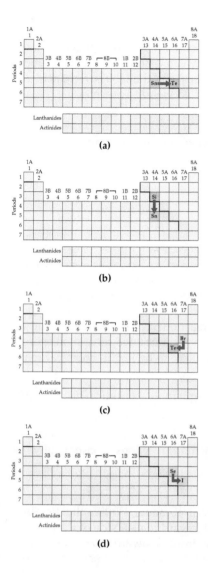

(a)

(b)

(c)

(d)

EXAMPLE 8 Metallic Character

Choose the more metallic element from each pair.

(a) Sn or Te

(b) Si or Sn

(c) Br or Te

(d) Se or I

SOLUTION

(a) Sn or Te

Sn is more metallic than Te because, as you trace the path between Sn and Te on the periodic table (see margin), you move to the right within the same period. Metallic character decreases as you go to the right.

(b) Si or Sn

Sn is more metallic than Si because, as you trace the path between Si and Sn on the periodic table (see margin), you move down a column. Metallic character increases as you go down a column.

(c) Br or Te

Te is more metallic than Br because, as you trace the path between Br and Te on the periodic table (see margin), you move down a column (metallic character increases) and then to the left across a period (metallic character increases). These effects add together for an overall increase.

(d) Se or I

Based on periodic properties alone, you cannot tell which is more metallic because as you trace the path between Se and I (see margin), you go down a column (metallic character increases) and then to the right across a period (metallic character decreases). These effects tend to cancel.

▶**SKILLBUILDER 8 | Metallic Character**

Choose the more metallic element from each pair.

(a) Ge or In   **(b)** Ga or Sn   **(c)** P or Bi   **(d)** B or N

▶**FOR MORE PRACTICE**   Example 13; Problems 85, 86, 87, 88.

CHAPTER IN REVIEW

CHEMICAL PRINCIPLES

Light: Light is electromagnetic radiation, a kind of energy that travels through space at a constant speed of 3.0×10^8 m/s (186,000 mi/s) and exhibits both wavelike and particle-like behavior. Particles of light are called photons. The wave nature of light is characterized by its wavelength, the distance between adjacent crests in the wave. The wavelength of light is inversely proportional to both the frequency—the number of cycles that pass a stationary point in one second—and the energy of a photon. Electromagnetic radiation ranges in wavelength from 10^{-16} m (gamma rays) to 10^6 m (radio waves). In between these lie X-rays, ultraviolet light, visible light, infrared light, and microwaves.

RELEVANCE

Light: Light enables us to see the world. However, we see only visible light, a small sliver in the center of the electromagnetic spectrum. Other forms of electromagnetic radiation are used for cancer therapy, X-ray imaging, night vision, microwave cooking, and communications. Light is also important to many chemical problems. We can learn about the electronic structure of atoms, for example, by examining their interaction with light.

The Bohr Model: The emission spectrum of hydrogen, consisting of bright lines at specific wavelengths, can be explained by the Bohr model for the hydrogen atom. In this model, electrons occupy circular orbits at specific fixed distances from the nucleus. Each orbit is specified by a quantum number (n), which also specifies the orbit's energy. While an electron is in a given orbit, its energy remains constant. When it jumps between orbits, a quantum of energy is absorbed or emitted. Since the difference in energy between orbits is fixed, the energy emitted or absorbed is also fixed. Emitted energy is carried away in the form of a photon of specific wavelength.

The Bohr Model: The Bohr model was a first attempt to explain the bright-line spectra of atoms. While it did predict the spectrum of the hydrogen atom, it failed to predict the spectra of other atoms and was consequently replaced by the quantum-mechanical model.

The Quantum-Mechanical Model: The quantum-mechanical model for the atom describes electron orbitals, which are electron probability maps that show the relative probability of finding an electron in various places surrounding the atomic nucleus. Orbitals are specified with a number (n), called the principal quantum number, and a letter. The principal quantum number ($n = 1, 2, 3 . . .$) specifies the principal shell, and the letter (s, p, d, or f) specifies the subshell of the orbital. In the hydrogen atom, the energy of orbitals depends only on n. In multi-electron atoms, the energy ordering is $1s$ $2s$ $2p$ $3s$ $3p$ $4s$ $3d$ $4p$ $5s$ $4d$ $5p$ $6s$.

An electron configuration indicates which orbitals are occupied for a particular atom. Orbitals are filled in order of increasing energy and obey the Pauli exclusion principle (each orbital can hold a maximum of two electrons with opposing spins) and Hund's rule (electrons occupy orbitals of identical energy singly before pairing).

The Quantum-Mechanical Model: The quantum-mechanical model changed the way we view nature. Before the quantum-mechanical model, electrons were viewed as small particles, much like any other particle. Electrons were supposed to follow the normal laws of motion, just as a baseball does. However, the electron, with its wavelike properties, does not follow these laws. Instead, electron motion is describable only through probabilistic predictions. Quantum theory single-handedly changed the predictability of nature at its most fundamental level.

The quantum-mechanical model of the atom predicts and explains many chemical properties.

The Periodic Table: Elements within the same column of the periodic table have similar outer electron configurations and the same number of valence electrons (electrons in the outermost principal shell), and therefore similar chemical properties. The periodic table is divisible into blocks (s block, p block, d block, and f block) in which particular sublevels are filled. As you move across a period to the right in the periodic table, atomic size decreases, ionization energy increases, and metallic character decreases. As you move down a column in the periodic table, atomic size increases, ionization energy decreases, and metallic character increases.

The Periodic Table: The periodic law exists because the number of valence electrons is periodic, and valence electrons determine chemical properties. Quantum theory also predicts that atoms with 8 outershell electrons (or 2 for helium) are particularly stable, thus explaining the inertness of the noble gases. Atoms without noble gas configurations undergo chemical reactions to attain them, explaining the reactivity of the alkali metals and the halogens as well as the tendency of several families to form ions with certain charges.

CHEMICAL SKILLS

EXAMPLES

Predicting Relative Wavelength, Energy, and Frequency of Light (Section 3)

* Relative wavelengths can be obtained from Figure 4.

* Energy per photon increases with decreasing (shorter) wavelength.

* Frequency increases with decreasing (shorter) wavelength.

EXAMPLE 9 Predicting Relative Wavelength, Energy, and Frequency of Light

Which type of light—infrared or ultraviolet—has the longer wavelength? Higher frequency? Higher energy per photon?

SOLUTION

Infrared light has the longer wavelength (Figure 4). Ultraviolet light has the higher frequency and the higher energy per photon.

Writing Electron Configurations and Orbital Diagrams (Section 6)

To write electron configurations, determine the number of electrons in the atom from the element's atomic number and then follow these rules:

- Electrons occupy orbitals so as to minimize the energy of the atom; therefore, lower-energy orbitals fill before higher-energy orbitals. Orbitals fill in the order: 1s 2s 2p 3s 3p 4s 3d 4p 5s 4d 5p 6s (Figure 24). The s subshells hold up to 2 electrons, p subshells hold up to 6, d subshells hold up to 10, and f subshells hold up to 14.

- Orbitals can hold no more than 2 electrons each. When 2 electrons occupy the same orbital, they must have opposing spins.

- When orbitals of identical energy are available, these are first occupied singly with parallel spins rather than in pairs.

EXAMPLE 10 Writing Electron Configurations and Orbital Diagrams

Write an electron configuration and orbital diagram (outer electrons only) for germanium.

SOLUTION

Germanium is atomic number 32; therefore, it has 32 electrons.

ELECTRON CONFIGURATION

$$Ge \quad 1s^2 2s^2 2p^6 3s^2 3p^6 4s^2 3d^{10} 4p^2$$

or

$$Ge \quad [Ar]4s^2 3d^{10} 4p^2$$

ORBITAL DIAGRAM (OUTER ELECTRONS)

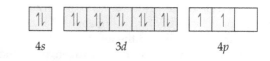

4s   3d   4p

Identifying Valence Electrons and Core Electrons (Section 7)

- Valence electrons are the electrons in the outermost principal energy shell (the principal shell with the highest principal quantum number).

- Core electrons are those that are not in the outermost principal shell.

EXAMPLE 11 Identifying Valence Electrons and Core Electrons

Identify the valence electrons and core electrons in the electron configuration of germanium (given in Example 10).

SOLUTION

$$Ge \quad 1s^2 2s^2 2p^6 3s^2 3p^6 \; 4s^2 \; 3d^{10} \; 4p^2$$

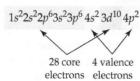

28 core   4 valence
electrons   electrons

Writing Electron Configurations for an Element Based on Its Position in the Periodic Table (Section 7)

1. The inner electron configuration for any element is the electron configuration of the noble gas that immediately precedes that element in the periodic table. Represent the inner configuration with the symbol for the noble gas in brackets.

2. The outer electrons can be determined from the element's position within a particular block (s, p, d, or f) in the periodic table. Trace the elements between the preceding noble gas and the element of interest and assign electrons to the appropriate orbitals. Figure 26 shows the outer electron configuration based on the position of an element in the periodic table.

3. The highest principal quantum number (highest n value) is equal to the row number of the element in the periodic table.

4. The principal quantum number (n value) of the outermost d electrons for any element containing d electrons is equal to the row number of the element minus 1.

EXAMPLE 12 Writing Electron Configurations for an Element Based on Its Position in the Periodic Table

Write an electron configuration for iodine based on its position in the periodic table.

SOLUTION

The inner configuration for I is [Kr].

Begin with the [Kr] inner electron configuration. As you trace from Kr to I, add 2 5s electrons, 10 4d electrons, and 5 5p electrons. The overall configuration is:

$$I \quad [Kr]5s^2 4d^{10} 5p^5$$

Periodic Trends: Atomic Size, Ionization Energy, and Metallic Character (Section 9)

On the periodic table:

- Atomic size decreases as you move to the right and increases as you move down.

- Ionization energy increases as you move to the right and decreases as you move down.

- Metallic character decreases as you move to the right and increases as you move down.

EXAMPLE 13 **Periodic Trends: Atomic Size, Ionization Energy, and Metallic Character**

Arrange Si, In, and S in order of **(a)** increasing atomic size, **(b)** increasing ionization energy, and **(c)** increasing metallic character.

SOLUTION

(a) S, Si, In

(b) In, Si, S

(c) S, Si, In

KEY TERMS

atomic size [**Section 9**]
Bohr model [**Section 1**]
core electrons [**Section 7**]
electromagnetic radiation [**Section 2**]
electromagnetic spectrum [**Section 3**]
electron configuration [**Section 6**]
electron spin [**Section 6**]
emission spectrum [**Section 4**]

excited state [**Section 6**]
frequency (ν) [**Section 2**]
gamma rays [**Section 3**]
ground state [**Section 6**]
Hund's rule [**Section 6**]
infrared light [**Section 3**]
ionization energy [**Section 9**]
metallic character [**Section 9**]
microwaves [**Section 3**]
orbital [**Section 5**]
orbital diagram [**Section 6**]

Pauli exclusion principle [**Section 6**]
photon [**Section 2**]
principal quantum number [**Section 6**]
principal shell [**Section 6**]
quantized [**Section 4**]
quantum (plural, *quanta*) [**Section 4**]
quantum-mechanical model [**Section 1**]

quantum number [**Section 4**]
radio waves [**Section 3**]
subshell [**Section 6**]
ultraviolet (UV) light [**Section 3**]
valence electron [**Section 7**]
visible light [**Section 3**]
wavelength (λ) [**Section 2**]
X-rays [**Section 3**]

EXERCISES

QUESTIONS

1. When were the Bohr model and the quantum-mechanical model for the atom developed? What purpose do these models serve?
2. What is light? How fast does light travel?
3. What is white light? Colored light?
4. Explain, in terms of absorbed and reflected light, why a blue object appears blue.
5. What is the relationship between the wavelength of light and the amount of energy carried by its photons? How are wavelength and frequency of light related?
6. List some sources of gamma rays.
7. How are X-rays used?
8. Why should excess exposure to gamma rays and X-rays be avoided?
9. Why should excess exposure to ultraviolet light be avoided?
10. What objects emit infrared light? What technology exploits this?
11. Why do microwave ovens heat food, but tend not to heat the dish the food is on?
12. What type of electromagnetic radiation is used in communications devices such as cellular telephones?
13. Describe the Bohr model for the hydrogen atom.
14. What is an emission spectrum? Use the Bohr model to explain why the emission spectrum of the

hydrogen atom consists of distinct lines at specific wavelengths.
15. Explain the difference between a Bohr orbit and a quantum-mechanical orbital.
16. What is the difference between the ground state of an atom and an excited state of an atom?
17. Explain how the motion of an electron is different from the motion of a baseball. What is a probability map?
18. Explain why quantum-mechanical orbitals have "fuzzy" boundaries.
19. List the four possible subshells in the quantum-mechanical model, the number of orbitals in each subshell, and the maximum number of electrons that can be contained in each subshell.
20. List all of the quantum-mechanical orbitals through 5*s*, in the correct energy order for multi-electron atoms.
21. What is the Pauli exclusion principle? Why is it important when writing electron configurations?
22. What is Hund's rule? Why is it important when writing orbital diagrams?
23. Within an electron configuration, what do symbols such as [Ne] and [Kr] represent?
24. Explain the difference between valence electrons and core electrons.

25. Identify each block in the blank periodic table.

  (a) *s* block

  (b) *p* block

  (c) *d* block

  (d) *f* block

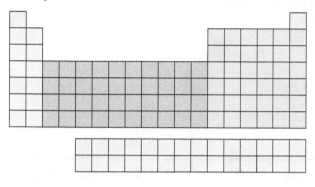

26. Give some examples of the explanatory power of the quantum-mechanical model.

27. Explain why Group 1 elements tend to form 1+ ions and Group 7 elements tend to form 1− ions.

28. Explain the periodic trends in each chemical property:

  (a) ionization energy

  (b) atomic size

  (c) metallic character

PROBLEMS

WAVELENGTH, ENERGY, AND FREQUENCY OF ELECTROMAGNETIC RADIATION

29. How long does it take light to travel in:

  (a) 1.0 ft (report answer in nanoseconds)

  (b) 2462 mi, the distance between Los Angeles and New York (report answer in milliseconds)

  (c) 4.5 billion km, the average separation between the sun and Neptune (report answer in hours and minutes)

30. How far does light travel in:

  (a) 1.0 s

  (b) 1.0 day

  (c) 1.0 yr

31. Which type of electromagnetic radiation has the longest wavelength?

  (a) visible

  (b) ultraviolet

  (c) infrared

  (d) X-ray

32. Which type of electromagnetic radiation has the shortest wavelength?

  (a) radio waves

  (b) microwaves

  (c) infrared

  (d) ultraviolet

33. List the types of electromagnetic radiation in order of increasing energy per photon.

  (a) radio waves

  (b) microwaves

  (c) infrared

  (d) ultraviolet

34. List the types of electromagnetic radiation in order of decreasing energy per photon.

  (a) gamma rays

  (b) radio waves

  (c) microwaves

  (d) visible light

35. List two types of electromagnetic radiation with frequencies higher than visible light.

36. List two types of electromagnetic radiation with frequencies lower than infrared light.

37. List these three types of radiation—infrared, X-ray, and radio waves—in order of:

  (a) increasing energy per photon

  (b) increasing frequency

  (c) increasing wavelength

38. List these three types of electromagnetic radiation—visible, gamma rays, and microwaves—in order of:

  (a) decreasing energy per photon

  (b) decreasing frequency

  (c) decreasing wavelength

THE BOHR MODEL

39. Bohr orbits have fixed _____ and fixed _____.

40. In the Bohr model, what happens when an electron makes a transition between orbits?

41. Two of the emission wavelengths in the hydrogen emission spectrum are 410 nm and 434 nm. One of these is due to the $n = 6$ to $n = 2$ transition, and the other is due to the $n = 5$ to $n = 2$ transition. Which wavelength goes with which transition?

42. Two of the emission wavelengths in the hydrogen emission spectrum are 656 nm and 486 nm. One of these is due to the $n = 4$ to $n = 2$ transition, and the other is due to the $n = 3$ to $n = 2$ transition. Which wavelength goes with which transition?

THE QUANTUM-MECHANICAL MODEL

43. Sketch the $1s$ and $2p$ orbitals. How would the $2s$ and $3p$ orbitals differ from the $1s$ and $2p$ orbitals?

44. Sketch the $3d$ orbitals. How would the $4d$ orbitals differ from the $3d$ orbitals?

45. Which electron is, on average, closer to the nucleus: an electron in a $2s$ orbital or an electron in a $3s$ orbital?

46. Which electron is, on average, farther from the nucleus: an electron in a $3p$ orbital or an electron in a $4p$ orbital?

47. According to the quantum-mechanical model for the hydrogen atom, which electron transition would produce light with longer wavelength: $2p$ to $1s$ or $3p$ to $1s$?

48. According to the quantum-mechanical model for the hydrogen atom, which transition would produce light with longer wavelength: $3p$ to $2s$ or $4p$ to $2s$?

ELECTRON CONFIGURATIONS

49. Write full electron configurations for each element.
    (a) Sr
    (b) Ge
    (c) Li
    (d) Kr

50. Write full electron configurations for each element.
    (a) N
    (b) Mg
    (c) Ar
    (d) Se

51. Write full orbital diagrams and indicate the number of unpaired electrons for each element.
    (a) He
    (b) B
    (c) Li
    (d) N

52. Write full orbital diagrams and indicate the number of unpaired electrons for each element.
    (a) F
    (b) C
    (c) Ne
    (d) Be

53. Write electron configurations for each element. Use the symbol of the previous noble gas in brackets to represent the core electrons.
    (a) Ga
    (b) As
    (c) Rb
    (d) Sn

54. Write electron configurations for each element. Use the symbol of the previous noble gas in brackets to represent the core electrons.
    (a) Te
    (b) Br
    (c) I
    (d) Cs

55. Write electron configurations for each transition metal.
    (a) Zn
    (b) Cu
    (c) Zr
    (d) Fe

56. Write electron configurations for each transition metal.
    (a) Mn
    (b) Ti
    (c) Cd
    (d) V

VALENCE ELECTRONS AND CORE ELECTRONS

57. Write full electron configurations and indicate the valence electrons and the core electrons for each element.
    (a) Kr
    (b) Ge
    (c) Cl
    (d) Sr

58. Write full electron configurations and indicate the valence electrons and the core electrons for each element.
    (a) Sb
    (b) N
    (c) B
    (d) K

59. Write orbital diagrams for the valence electrons and indicate the number of unpaired electrons for each element.
    (a) Br
    (b) Kr
    (c) Na
    (d) In

60. Write orbital diagrams for the valence electrons and indicate the number of unpaired electrons for each element.
    (a) Ne
    (b) I
    (c) Sr
    (d) Ge

61. How many valence electrons are in each element?
    (a) O
    (b) S
    (c) Br
    (d) Rb

62. How many valence electrons are in each element?
    (a) Ba
    (b) Al
    (c) Be
    (d) Se

ELECTRON CONFIGURATIONS AND THE PERIODIC TABLE

63. List the outer electron configuration for each column in the periodic table.
    (a) 1A
    (b) 2A
    (c) 5A
    (d) 7A

64. List the outer electron configuration for each column in the periodic table.
    (a) 3A
    (b) 4A
    (c) 6A
    (d) 8A

65. Use the periodic table to write electron configurations for each element.
    (a) Al
    (b) Be
    (c) In
    (d) Zr

66. Use the periodic table to write electron configurations for each element.
    (a) Tl
    (b) Co
    (c) Ba
    (d) Sb

67. Use the periodic table to write electron configurations for each element.
    (a) Sr
    (b) Y
    (c) Ti
    (d) Te

68. Use the periodic table to write electron configurations for each element.
    (a) Se
    (b) Sn
    (c) Pb
    (d) Cd

69. How many $2p$ electrons are in an atom of each element?

(a) C

(b) N

(c) F

(d) P

70. How many $3d$ electrons are in an atom of each element?

(a) Fe

(b) Zn

(c) K

(d) As

71. List the number of elements in periods 1 and 2 of the periodic table. Why do the two periods have a different number of elements?

72. List the number of elements in periods 3 and 4 of the periodic table. Why do the two periods have a different number of elements?

73. Name an element in the third period (row) of the periodic table with:

(a) 3 valence electrons

(b) a total of 4 $3p$ electrons

(c) 6 $3p$ electrons

(d) 2 $3s$ electrons and no $3p$ electrons

74. Name an element in the fourth period of the periodic table with:

(a) 5 valence electrons

(b) a total of 4 $4p$ electrons

(c) a total of 3 $3d$ electrons

(d) a complete outer shell

75. Use the periodic table to identify the element with each electron configuration.

(a) $[Ne]3s^23p^5$

(b) $[Ar]4s^23d^{10}4p^1$

(c) $[Ar]4s^23d^6$

(d) $[Kr]5s^1$

76. Use the periodic table to identify the element with each electron configuration.

(a) $[Ne]3s^1$

(b) $[Kr]5s^24d^{10}$

(c) $[Xe]6s^2$

(d) $[Kr]5s^24d^{10}5p^3$

PERIODIC TRENDS

77. Choose the element with the higher ionization energy from each pair.

(a) As or Bi

(b) As or Br

(c) S or I

(d) S or Sb

78. Choose the element with the higher ionization energy from each pair.

(a) Al or In

(b) Cl or Sb

(c) K or Ge

(d) S or Se

79. Arrange the elements in order of increasing ionization energy: Te, Pb, Cl, S, Sn.

80. Arrange the elements in order of increasing ionization energy: Ga, In, F, Si, N.

81. Choose the element with the larger atoms from each pair.

(a) Al or In

(b) Si or N

(c) P or Pb

(d) C or F

82. Choose the element with the larger atoms from each pair.

(a) Sn or Si

(b) Br or Ga

(c) Sn or Bi

(d) Se or Sn

83. Arrange these elements in order of increasing atomic size: Ca, Rb, S, Si, Ge, F.

84. Arrange these elements in order of increasing atomic size: Cs, Sb, S, Pb, Se.

85. Choose the more metallic element from each pair.
    (a) Sr or Sb
    (b) As or Bi
    (c) Cl or O
    (d) S or As

86. Choose the more metallic element from each pair.
    (a) Sb or Pb
    (b) K or Ge
    (c) Ge or Sb
    (d) As or Sn

87. Arrange these elements in order of increasing metallic character: Fr, Sb, In, S, Ba, Se.

88. Arrange these elements in order of increasing metallic character: Sr, N, Si, P, Ga, Al.

CUMULATIVE PROBLEMS

89. What is the maximum number of electrons that can occupy the $n = 3$ quantum shell?

90. What is the maximum number of electrons that can occupy the $n = 4$ quantum shell?

91. Use the electron configurations of the alkaline earth metals to explain why they tend to form 2+ ions.

92. Use the electron configuration of oxygen to explain why it tends to form a 2− ion.

93. Write the electron configuration for each ion. What do all of the electron configurations have in common?
    (a) Ca^{2+} (b) K^+ (c) S^{2-} (d) Br^-

94. Write the electron configuration for each ion. What do all of the electron configurations have in common?
    (a) F^- (b) P^{3-} (c) Li^+ (d) Al^{3+}

95. Examine the Periodic Table which shows the division of the periodic table into metals, nonmetals, and metalloids. Use what you know about electron configurations to explain these divisions.

96. Examine the Periodic Table which shows the elements that form predictable ions. Use what you know about electron configurations to explain these trends.

97. Explain what is wrong with each electron configuration and write the correct ground state (or lowest energy) configuration based on the number of electrons.
    (a) $1s^3 2s^3 2p^9$
    (b) $1s^2 2s^2 2p^6 2d^4$
    (c) $1s^2 1p^5$
    (d) $1s^2 2s^2 2p^8 3s^2 3p^1$

98. Explain what is wrong with each electron configuration and write the correct ground state (or lowest energy) configuration based on the number of electrons.
    (a) $1s^4 2s^4 2p^{12}$
    (b) $1s^2 2s^2 2p^6 3s^2 3p^6 3d^{10}$
    (c) $1s^2 2p^6 3s^2$
    (d) $1s^2 2s^2 2p^6 3s^2 3p^6 4s^2 4d^{10} 4p^3$

99. Bromine is a highly reactive liquid, while krypton is an inert gas. Explain this difference based on their electron configurations.

100. Potassium is a highly reactive metal, while argon is an inert gas. Explain this difference based on their electron configurations.

101. Based on periodic trends, which one of these elements would you expect to be most easily oxidized: Ge, K, S, or N?

102. Based on periodic trends, which one of these elements would you expect to be most easily reduced: Ca, Sr, P, or Cl?

103. When an electron makes a transition from the $n = 3$ to the $n = 2$ hydrogen atom Bohr orbit, the energy difference between these two orbits (3.0×10^{-19} J) is emitted as a photon of light. The relationship between the energy of a photon and its wavelength is given by $E = hc/\lambda$, where E is the energy of the photon in J, h is Planck's constant (6.626×10^{-34} J·s), and c is the speed of light (3.00×10^8 m/s). Find the wavelength of light emitted by hydrogen atoms when an electron makes this transition.

104. When an electron makes a transition from the $n = 4$ to the $n = 2$ hydrogen atom Bohr orbit, the energy difference between these two orbits (4.1×10^{-19} J) is emitted as a photon of light. The relationship between the energy of a photon and its wavelength is given by $E = hc/\lambda$, where E is the energy of the photon in J, h is Planck's constant (6.626×10^{-34} J·s), and c is the speed of light (3.00×10^8 m/s). Find the wavelength of light emitted by hydrogen atoms when an electron makes this transition.

105. The distance from the sun to Earth is 1.496×10^8 km. How long does it take light to travel from the sun to Earth?

106. The nearest star is Alpha Centauri, at a distance of 4.3 light-years from Earth. A light-year is the distance that light travels in one year (365 days). How far away, in kilometers, is Alpha Centauri from Earth?

107. In the beginning of this chapter, we learned that the quantum-mechanical model for the atom is the foundation for modern chemical understanding. Explain why this is so.

108. Niels Bohr said, "Anyone who is not shocked by quantum mechanics has not understood it." What do you think he meant by this statement?

109. The wave nature of matter was first proposed by Louis de Broglie, who suggested that the wavelength (λ) of a particle was related to its mass (m) and its velocity (v) by the equation: $\lambda = h/mv$, where h is Planck's constant (6.626×10^{-34} J$\cdot$s). Calculate the de Broglie wavelength of: (a) a 0.0459-kg golf ball traveling at 95 m/s; (b) an electron traveling at 3.88×10^6 m/s. Can you explain why the wave nature of matter is significant for the electron but not for the golf ball? (*Hint:* Express mass in kilograms.)

110. The particle nature of light was first proposed by Albert Einstein, who suggested that light could be described as a stream of particles called photons. A photon of wavelength λ has an energy (E) given by the equation: $E = hc/\lambda$, where E is the energy of the photon in J, h is Planck's constant (6.626×10^{-34} J$\cdot$s), and c is the speed of light (3.00×10^8 m/s). Calculate the energy of 1 mol of photons with a wavelength of 632 nm.

111. We learned in this chapter that ionization generally increases as you move from left to right across the periodic table. However, consider the data below, which shows the ionization energies of the period 2 and 3 elements:

Group	Period 2 Elements	Ionization Energy (kJ/mole)	Period 3 Elements	Ionization Energy
1A	Li	520	Na	496
2A	Be	899	Mg	738
3A	B	801	Al	578
4A	C	1086	Si	786
5A	N	1402	P	1012
6A	O	1314	S	1000
7A	F	1681	Cl	1251
8A	Ne	2081	Ar	1521

Notice that the increase is not uniform. In fact, ionization energy actually decreases a bit in going from elements in group 2A to 3A and then again from 5A to 6A. Use what you know about electron configurations to explain why these dips in ionization energy exist.

112. When atoms lose more than one electron, the ionization energy to remove the second electron is always more than the ionization energy to remove the first. Similarly, the ionization energy to remove the third electron is more than the second and so on. However, the increase in ionization energy upon the removal of subsequent electrons is not necessarily uniform. For example, consider the first three ionization energies of magnesium:

First ionization energy	738 kJ/mol
Second ionization energy	1450 kJ/mol
Third ionization energy	7730 kJ/mol

The second ionization energy is roughly twice the first ionization energy, but then the third ionization energy is over five times the second. Use the electron configuration of magnesium to explain why this is so. Would you expect the same behavior in sodium? Why or why not?

HIGHLIGHT PROBLEMS

113. Excessive exposure to sunlight increases the risk of skin cancer because some of the photons have enough energy to break chemical bonds in biological molecules. These bonds require approximately 250–800 kJ/mol of energy to break. The energy of a single photon is given by $E = hc/\lambda$, where E is the energy of the photon in J, h is Planck's constant (6.626×10^{-34} J·s), and c is the speed of light (3.00×10^8 m/s). Determine which kinds of light contain enough energy to break chemical bonds in biological molecules by calculating the total energy in 1 mol of photons for light of each wavelength.

(a) infrared light (1500 nm)

(b) visible light (500 nm)

(c) ultraviolet light (150 nm)

114. The quantum-mechanical model, besides revolutionizing chemistry, shook the philosophical world because of its implications regarding determinism. Determinism is the idea that the outcomes of future events are determined by preceding events. The trajectory of a baseball, for example, is deterministic; that is, its trajectory—and therefore its landing place—is determined by its position, speed, and direction of travel. Before quantum mechanics, most scientists thought that fundamental particles—such as electrons and protons—also behaved deterministically. The implication of this belief was that the entire universe must behave deterministically—the future must be determined by preceding events. Quantum mechanics challenged this reasoning because fundamental particles do not behave deterministically—their future paths are not determined by preceding events. Some scientists struggled with this idea. Einstein himself refused to believe it, stating, "God does not play dice with the universe." Explain what Einstein meant by this statement.

▲ "God does not play dice with the universe."

►ANSWERS TO SKILLBUILDER EXERCISES

Skillbuilder 1
 (a) blue, green, red
 (b) red, green, blue
 (c) red, green, blue

Skillbuilder 2
 (a) Al $1s^2 2s^2 2p^6 3s^2 3p^1$ or
  $[Ne]3s^2 3p^1$
 (b) Br $1s^2 2s^2 2p^6 3s^2 3p^6 4s^2 3d^{10} 4p^5$ or
  $[Ar]4s^2 3d^{10} 4p^5$
 (c) Sr $1s^2 2s^2 2p^6 3s^2 3p^6 4s^2 3d^{10} 4p^6 5s^2$ or
  $[Kr]5s^2$

Skillbuilder Plus 1 Subtract 1 electron for each unit of positive charge. Add 1 electron for each unit of negative charge.
 (a) Al^{3+} $1s^2 2s^2 2p^6$
 (b) Cl^- $1s^2 2s^2 2p^6 3s^2 3p^6$
 (c) O^{2-} $1s^2 2s^2 2p^6$

Skillbuilder 3

Ar

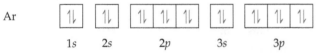

1s   2s   2p   3s   3p

Skillbuilder 4

Cl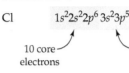

10 core electrons   7 valence electrons

Skillbuilder 5 $[Kr]5s^2 4d^{10} 5p^2$

Skillbuilder 6
 (a) Pb
 (b) Rb
 (c) cannot determine based on periodic properties
 (d) Se

Skillbuilder 7
 (a) Mg
 (b) Te
 (c) cannot determine based on periodic properties
 (d) F

Skillbuilder 8
 (a) In
 (b) cannot determine based on periodic properties
 (c) Bi
 (d) B

►ANSWERS TO CONCEPTUAL CHECKPOINTS

1 (b) Wavelength and energy per photon are inversely related. Since yellow light has a longer wavelength, it has less energy per photon than violet light.

2 (c) The higher energy levels are more closely spaced than the lower ones, so the difference in energy between $n = 2$ and $n = 1$ is greater than the difference in energy between $n = 3$ and $n = 2$. The photon emitted when an electron falls from $n = 2$ to $n = 1$ therefore carries more energy, corresponding to radiation with a shorter wavelength and higher frequency.

3 (d) Both have 6 electrons in $2p$ orbitals and 6 electrons in $3p$ orbitals.

4 (d) The outermost principal shell for K is $n = 4$, which contains only a single valence electron, $4s^1$.

5 (a) Calcium loses its 4s electron and attains a noble gas configuration (that of Ar).

ANSWERS TO ODD-NUMBERED EXERCISES

QUESTIONS

1. Both the Bohr model and the quantum-mechanical model for the atom were developed in the early 1900s. These models serve to explain how electrons are arranged within the atomic structure and how the electrons affect the chemical and physical properties of each element.

3. White light contains a spectrum of wavelengths and therefore a spectrum of color. Colored light is produced by a single wavelength and is therefore a single color.

5. Energy carried per photon is greater for shorter wavelengths than for longer wavelengths. Wavelength and frequency are inversely related—the shorter the wavelength, the higher the frequency.

7. X-rays pass through many substances that block visible light and are therefore used to image bones and organs.

9. Ultraviolet light contains enough energy to damage biological molecules, and excessive exposure increases the risk of skin cancer and cataracts.

11. Microwaves can only heat things containing water, and therefore the food, which contains water, becomes hot, but the plate does not.

13. The Bohr model is a representation for the atom in which electrons travel around the nucleus in circular orbits with a fixed energy at specific, fixed distances from the nucleus.

15. The Bohr orbit describes the path of an electron as an orbit or trajectory (a specified path). A quantum-mechanical orbital describes the path of an electron using a probability map.

17. The e^- has wave particle duality, which means the path of an electron is not predictable. The motion of a baseball is predictable. A probability map shows a statistical, reproducible pattern of where the electron is located.

19. The subshells are s (1 orbital, which contains a maximum of 2 electrons); p (3 orbitals, which contain a maximum of 6 electrons); d (5 orbitals, which contain a maximum of 10 electrons); and f (7 orbitals, which contain a maximum of 14 electrons).

21. The Pauli exclusion principle states that separate orbitals may hold no more than 2 electrons, and when 2 electrons are present in a single orbital, they must have opposite spins. When writing electron configurations, the principle means that no box can have more than 2 arrows, and the arrows will point in opposite directions.

23. [Ne] represents $1s^2 2s^2 2p^6$.

   [Kr] represents $1s^2 2s^2 2p^6 3s^2 3p^6 4s^2 3d^{10} 4p^6$.

25.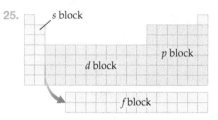

27. Group 1 elements form 1+ ions because they lose one valence electron in the outer s shell to obtain a noble gas configuration. Group 7 elements form 1− ions because they gain an electron to fill their outer p orbital to obtain a noble gas configuration.

PROBLEMS

29. **a.** 1.0 ns

   b. 13.21 ms

   c. 4 hrs 10 min

31. infrared

33. radiowaves < microwaves < infrared < ultraviolet

35. gamma, ultraviolet, or X-rays

37. **a.** radio waves < infrared < X-rays

   b. radio waves < infrared < X-rays

   c. X-rays < infrared < radio waves

39. energies, distances

41. $n = 6 \longrightarrow n = 2$: 410 nm

   $n = 5 \longrightarrow n = 2$: 434 nm

43.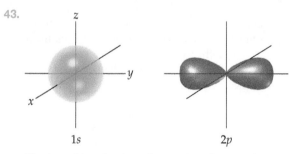

   The 2s and 3p orbitals are bigger than the 1s and 2p orbitals.

45. Electron in the 2s orbital

47. $2p \longrightarrow 1s$

49. **a.** $1s^2 2p^2 2p^6 3s^2 3p^6 4s^2 3d^{10} 4p^6 5s^2$

   b. $1s^2 2s^2 2p^6 3s^2 3p^6 4s^2 3d^{10} 4p^2$

   c. $1s^2 2s^1$

   d. $1s^2 2s^2 2p^6 3s^2 3p^6 4s^2 3d^{10} 4p^6$

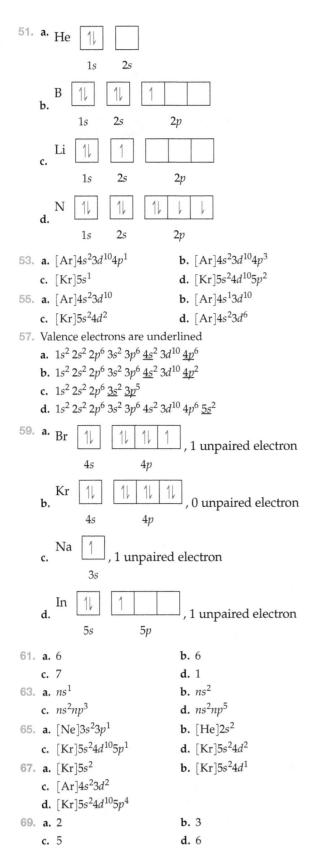

51. **a.** He

$1s$ $2s$

b. B

$1s$ $2s$ $2p$

c. Li

$1s$ $2s$ $2p$

d. N

$1s$ $2s$ $2p$

53. **a.** $[Ar]4s^23d^{10}4p^1$ **b.** $[Ar]4s^23d^{10}4p^3$
   c. $[Kr]5s^1$ **d.** $[Kr]5s^24d^{10}5p^2$

55. **a.** $[Ar]4s^23d^{10}$ **b.** $[Ar]4s^13d^{10}$
   c. $[Kr]5s^24d^2$ **d.** $[Ar]4s^23d^6$

57. Valence electrons are underlined

   a. $1s^2\,2s^2\,2p^6\,3s^2\,3p^6\,\underline{4s^2}\,3d^{10}\,\underline{4p^6}$

   b. $1s^2\,2s^2\,2p^6\,3s^2\,3p^6\,\underline{4s^2}\,3d^{10}\,\underline{4p^2}$

   c. $1s^2\,2s^2\,2p^6\,\underline{3s^2}\,\underline{3p^5}$

   d. $1s^2\,2s^2\,2p^6\,3s^2\,3p^6\,4s^2\,3d^{10}\,4p^6\,\underline{5s^2}$

59. **a.** Br , 1 unpaired electron

$4s$ $4p$

b. Kr , 0 unpaired electron

$4s$ $4p$

c. Na , 1 unpaired electron

$3s$

d. In , 1 unpaired electron

$5s$ $5p$

61. **a.** 6   **b.** 6
   c. 7   **d.** 1

63. **a.** ns^1 **b.** ns^2
   c. ns^2np^3 **d.** ns^2np^5

65. **a.** $[Ne]3s^23p^1$ **b.** $[He]2s^2$
   c. $[Kr]5s^24d^{10}5p^1$ **d.** $[Kr]5s^24d^2$

67. **a.** $[Kr]5s^2$ **b.** $[Kr]5s^24d^1$
   c. $[Ar]4s^23d^2$
   d. $[Kr]5s^24d^{10}5p^4$

69. **a.** 2   **b.** 3
   c. 5   **d.** 6

71. Period 1 has two elements. Period 2 has eight elements. The number of subshells is equal to the principal quantum number. For Period 1, $n = 1$ and the s subshell contains only two elements. For Period 2, $n = 2$ and contains s and p subshells that have a total of 8 elements.

73. **a.** Al   **b.** S
   c. Ar   **d.** Mg

75. **a.** Cl   **b.** Ga
   c. Fe   **d.** Rb

77. **a.** As   **b.** Br
   c. cannot tell   **d.** S

79. Pb < Sn < Te < S < Cl

81. **a.** In   **b.** Si
   c. Pb   **d.** C

83. F < S < Si < Ge < Ca < Rb

85. **a.** Sr   **b.** Bi
   c. cannot tell   **d.** As

87. S < Se < Sb < In < Ba < Fr

89. $18\,e^-$

91. Alkaline earth metals have the general electron configuration of ns^2. If they lose their two s electrons, they will obtain the stable electron configuration of a noble gas. This loss of electrons will give the metal a +2 charge.

93. **a.** $1s^22s^22p^63s^23p^6$

   b. $1s^22s^22p^63s^23p^6$

   c. $1s^22s^22p^63s^23p^6$

   d. $1s^22s^22p^63s^23p^64s^23d^{10}4p^6$

   They all have noble gas electron configurations.

95. Metals tend to form positive ions because they tend to lose electrons. Elements on the left side of the periodic table have only a few extra electrons, which they will lose to gain a noble gas configuration. Metalloids tend to be elements with 3 to 5 valence electrons; they could lose or gain electrons to obtain a noble gas configuration. Nonmetals tend to gain electrons to fill their almost full valence shell, so they tend to form negative ions and are on the right side of the table.

97. **a.** Can only have 2 in the s shell and 6 in the p shell: $1s^22s^22p^63s^23p^3$.

   b. There is no $2d$ subshell: $1s^22s^22p^63s^23p^2$.

   c. There is no $1p$ subshell: $1s^22s^22p^3$.

   d. Can only have 6 in the p shell: $1s^22s^22p^63s^23p^3$.

99. Bromine is highly reactive because it reacts quickly to gain an electron and obtain a stable valence shell. Krypton is a noble gas because it already has a stable valence shell.

101. K

103. 660 nm

105. 8 min, 19 sec

107. The quantum-mechanical model provided the ability to understand and predict chemical bonding, which is the basic level of understanding of matter and how it interacts. This model was critical in the areas of lasers, computers, semiconductors, and drug design. The quantum-mechanical model for the atom is considered the foundation of modern chemistry.

109. **a.** 1.5×10^{-34} m   **b.** 1.88×10^{-10} m

   Electrons have wave-particle duality, whereas golf balls do not.

111. The ionization energy dips at column 3A because removing an electron from one of those atoms leaves the atom with a fairly stable, filled s-orbital as its valence shell. For the group 6A elements, special stability occurs when those elements lose an electron and achieve a half-filled p-orbital as their valence shell.

113. Ultraviolet light is the only one of these three types of light that contains enough energy to break chemical bonds in biological molecules.

Chemical Bonding

From Chapter 10 of *Introductory Chemistry*, Fourth Edition, Nivaldo J. Tro. Copyright © 2011 by Pearson Education, Inc. Published by Pearson Prentice Hall. All rights reserved.

Indinavir

Chemical Bonding

"The fascination of a growing science lies in the work of the pioneers at the very borderland of the unknown, but to reach this frontier one must pass over well traveled roads."

GILBERT N. LEWIS (1875–1946)

1   Bonding Models and AIDS Drugs

In 1989, researchers discovered the structure of a molecule called HIV-protease. HIV-protease is a protein (a class of biological molecules) synthesized by the human immunodeficiency virus (HIV), which causes AIDS. HIV-protease is crucial to the virus's ability to replicate itself. Without HIV-protease, HIV could not spread in the human body because the virus could not copy itself, and AIDS would not develop.

With knowledge of the HIV-protease structure, drug companies set out to design a molecule that would disable protease by sticking to the working part of the molecule (called the *active site*). To design such a molecule, researchers used **bonding theories**—models that predict how atoms bond together to form molecules—to simulate how potential drug molecules would interact with the protease molecule. By the early 1990s, these companies had developed several drug molecules that seemed to work. Since these molecules inhibit the action of HIV-protease, they are called *protease inhibitors.* In human trials, protease inhibitors in combination with other drugs have decreased the viral count in HIV-infected individuals to undetectable levels. Although these drugs do not cure AIDS, HIV-infected individuals who regularly take their medication can now expect nearly normal life spans.

Bonding theories are central to chemistry because they predict how atoms bond together to form compounds. They predict what combinations of atoms form compounds and what combinations do not. Bonding theories predict why salt is NaCl and not $NaCl_2$ and why water is H_2O and not H_3O. Bonding theories also explain the shapes of molecules, which in turn determine many of their physical and chemical properties. The bonding theory you will learn in this chapter is called **Lewis theory**, named after G. N. Lewis (1875–1946), the American chemist

◄ The gold-colored structure on the computer screen is a representation of HIV-protease. The molecule shown in the center is Indinavir, a protease inhibitor.

217

who developed it. In this model, we represent electrons as dots and draw what are called *dot structures* or *Lewis structures* to represent molecules. These structures, which are fairly simple to draw, have tremendous predictive power. It takes just a few minutes to apply Lewis theory to determine whether a particular set of atoms will form a stable molecule and what that molecule might look like. Although modern chemists also use more advanced bonding theories to better predict molecular properties, Lewis theory remains the simplest method for making quick, everyday predictions about molecules.

2 Representing Valence Electrons with Dots

Valence electrons are those in the outermost principal shell. Since valence electrons are most important in bonding, Lewis theory focuses on these. In Lewis theory, the valence electrons of main-group elements are represented as dots surrounding the symbol of the element. The result is called a **Lewis structure**, or **dot structure**. For example, the electron configuration of O is:

$$1s^2\,2s^2 2p^4$$

6 valence electrons

and its Lewis structure is:

6 dots representing valence electrons

·Ö:

> Remember, the number of valence electrons for any main-group element (except helium, which has two valence electrons but is in Group 8A) is equal to the group number of the element.

Each dot represents a valence electron. The dots are placed around the element's symbol with a maximum of two dots per side. Although the exact location of dots is not critical, in this book we fill in the dots singly first and then pair them (with the exception of helium, described shortly).

The Lewis structures for all of the period 2 elements are:

Li·   ·Be·   ·Ḃ·   ·Ċ·   ·Ṅ: ·Ö: :Ḟ: :Ṅe:

Lewis structures allow us to easily see the number of valence electrons in an atom. Atoms with eight valence electrons—which are particularly stable—are easily identified because they have eight dots, an **octet**.

Helium is somewhat of an exception. Its electron configuration and Lewis structure are:

$$1s^2 \quad \text{He:}$$

The Lewis structure of helium contains two paired dots (a **duet**). For helium, a duet represents a stable electron configuration.

In Lewis theory, a **chemical bond** involves the sharing or transfer of electrons to attain stable electron configurations for the bonding atoms. If the electrons are transferred, the bond is an **ionic bond**. If the electrons are shared, the bond is a **covalent bond**. In either case, the bonding atoms attain stable electron configurations. As we have seen, a stable configuration usually consists of eight electrons in the outermost or valence shell. This observation leads to the **octet rule**:

> In chemical bonding, atoms transfer or share electrons to obtain outer shells with eight electrons.

The octet rule generally applies to all main-group elements except hydrogen and lithium. Each of these elements achieves stability when it has two electrons (a duet) in its outermost shell.

EXAMPLE 1   Writing Lewis Structures for Elements

Write the Lewis structure of phosphorus.

Since phosphorus is in Group 5A in the periodic table, it has five valence electrons. Represent these as five dots surrounding the symbol for phosphorus.	**SOLUTION** $\cdot \ddot{P} :$

▶**SKILLBUILDER 1** | Writing Lewis Structures for Elements

Write the Lewis structure of Mg.

▶**FOR MORE PRACTICE**   Example 12; Problems 25, 26.

✔ CONCEPTUAL CHECKPOINT 1

Which two elements have the most similar Lewis structures?

(a) C and Si   **(b)** O and P   **(c)** Li and F   **(d)** S and Br

---

3   Lewis Structures of Ionic Compounds: Electrons Transferred

Recall that when metals bond with nonmetals, electrons are transferred from the metal to the nonmetal. The metal becomes a cation and the nonmetal becomes an anion. The attraction between the cation and the anion results in an ionic compound. In Lewis theory, we represent this by moving electron dots from the metal to the nonmetal. For example, potassium and chlorine have the Lewis structures:

$$K \cdot \qquad : \ddot{Cl} :$$

When potassium and chlorine bond, potassium transfers its valence electron to chlorine.

$$K \cdot \quad : \ddot{Cl} : \quad \longrightarrow \quad K^+ \ [: \ddot{Cl} :]^-$$

Recall that atoms that lose electrons become positively charged and atoms that gain electrons become negatively charged.

The transfer of the electron gives chlorine an octet (shown as eight dots around chlorine) and leaves potassium with an octet in the previous principal shell, which is now the valence shell. Because the potassium lost an electron, it becomes positively charged, while the chlorine, which gained an electron, becomes negatively charged. The Lewis structure of an anion is usually written within brackets with the charge in the upper right corner (outside the brackets). The positive and negative charges attract one another, forming the compound KCl.

EXAMPLE 2   Writing Ionic Lewis Structures

Write the Lewis structure of the compound MgO.

Draw the Lewis structures of magnesium and oxygen by drawing two dots around the symbol for magnesium and six dots around the symbol for oxygen.	**SOLUTION** $\cdot Mg \cdot \quad \cdot \ddot{O} :$
In MgO, magnesium loses its two valence electrons, resulting in a 2+ charge, and oxygen gains two electrons, attaining a 2− charge and an octet.	$Mg^{2+} \ [: \ddot{O} :]^{2-}$

▶**SKILLBUILDER 2** | Writing Ionic Lewis Structures

Write the Lewis structure of the compound NaBr.

▶**FOR MORE PRACTICE**   Example 13; Problems 37, 38.

Lewis theory predicts the correct chemical formulas for ionic compounds. For the compound that forms between K and Cl, for example, Lewis theory predicts one potassium cation to every chlorine anion, KCl. As another example, consider the ionic compound formed between sodium and sulfur. The Lewis structures for sodium and sulfur are:

$$\text{Na·} \quad \text{·}\ddot{\text{S}}\text{:}$$

Notice that sodium must lose its one valence electron to obtain an octet (in the previous principal shell), while sulfur must gain two electrons to obtain an octet. Consequently, the compound that forms between sodium and sulfur requires two sodium atoms to every one sulfur atom. The Lewis structure is:

$$\text{Na}^+ \ [\text{:}\ddot{\text{S}}\text{:}]^{2-} \ \text{Na}^+$$

The two sodium atoms each lose their one valence electron, while the sulfur atom gains two electrons and obtains an octet. The correct chemical formula is Na_2S.

> Recall that ionic compounds do not exist as distinct molecules, but rather as part of a large lattice of alternating cations and anions.

EXAMPLE 3 Using Lewis Theory to Predict the Chemical Formula of an Ionic Compound

Use Lewis theory to predict the formula of the compound that forms between calcium and chlorine.

	SOLUTION
Draw the Lewis structures of calcium and chlorine by drawing two dots around the symbol for calcium and seven dots around the symbol for chlorine.	$\text{·Ca·} \quad \text{:}\ddot{\text{C}}\text{l:}$
Calcium must lose its two valence electrons (to effectively attain an octet in its previous principal shell), while chlorine needs to gain only one electron to obtain an octet. Consequently, the compound that forms between Ca and Cl has two chlorine atoms to every one calcium atom.	$[\text{:}\ddot{\text{C}}\text{l:}]^- \ \text{Ca}^{2+} \ [\text{:}\ddot{\text{C}}\text{l:}]^-$ The formula is therefore $CaCl_2$.

▶SKILLBUILDER 3 | Using Lewis Theory to Predict the Chemical Formula of an Ionic Compound

Use Lewis theory to predict the formula of the compound that forms between magnesium and nitrogen.

▶FOR MORE PRACTICE   Example 14; Problems 39, 40, 41, 42.

CONCEPTUAL CHECKPOINT 2

Which nonmetal forms an ionic compound with aluminum with the formula Al_2X_3 (where X represents the nonmetal)?

(a) Cl   (b) S   (c) N   (d) C

4   Covalent Lewis Structures: Electrons Shared

Recall that when nonmetals bond with other nonmetals, a molecular compound results. Molecular compounds contain covalent bonds in which electrons are shared between atoms rather than transferred. In Lewis theory, we represent covalent bonding by allowing neighboring atoms to share some of their valence electrons in order to attain octets (or duets for hydrogen). For example, hydrogen and oxygen have the Lewis structures:

$$\text{H·} \quad \text{·}\ddot{\text{O}}\text{:}$$

In water, hydrogen and oxygen share their electrons so that each hydrogen atom gets a duet and the oxygen atom gets an octet.

$$\text{H:}\ddot{\text{O}}\text{:H}$$

The shared electrons—those that appear in the space between the two atoms—count toward the octets (or duets) of *both of the atoms*.

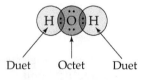

Duet   Octet   Duet

Electrons that are shared between two atoms are called **bonding pair** electrons, while those that are only on one atom are called **lone pair** (or nonbonding) electrons.

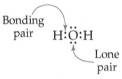

Bonding pair   H:Ö:H   Lone pair

Bonding pair electrons are often represented by dashes to emphasize that they are a chemical bond.

$$H—\ddot{O}—H$$

Remember that each dash represents a *pair* of shared electrons.

Lewis theory also explains why the halogens form diatomic molecules. Consider the Lewis structure of chlorine.

$$:\ddot{\underset{..}{C}l}:$$

If two Cl atoms pair together, they can each attain an octet.

$$:\ddot{\underset{..}{C}l}:\ddot{\underset{..}{C}l}: \quad or \quad :\ddot{\underset{..}{C}l}—\ddot{\underset{..}{C}l}:$$

When we examine elemental chlorine, we find that it indeed exists as a diatomic molecule, just as Lewis theory predicts. The same is true for the other halogens.

Similarly, Lewis theory predicts that hydrogen, which has the Lewis structure:

$$H·$$

should exist as H_2. When two hydrogen atoms share their valence electrons, they each get a duet, a stable configuration for hydrogen.

$$H:H \quad or \quad H—H$$

Again, Lewis theory is correct. In nature, elemental hydrogen exists as H_2 molecules.

DOUBLE AND TRIPLE BONDS

In Lewis theory, atoms can share more than one electron pair to attain an octet. For example, we know that oxygen exists as the diatomic molecule, O_2. The Lewis structure of an oxygen atom is:

$$·\ddot{\underset{..}{O}}:$$

If we pair two oxygen atoms together and then try to write a Lewis structure, we do not have enough electrons to give each O atom an octet.

$$:\ddot{\underset{..}{O}}:\ddot{\underset{..}{O}}:$$

However, we can convert a lone pair into an additional bonding pair by moving it into the bonding region.

$$:\ddot{\underset{..}{O}}{:}\ddot{\underset{..}{O}}: \longrightarrow :\ddot{O}::\ddot{O}: \quad or \quad :\ddot{O}=\ddot{O}:$$

221

Each oxygen atom now has an octet because the additional bonding pair counts toward the octet of both oxygen atoms.

Octet → $:\ddot{O}::\ddot{O}:$ ← Octet

When two electron pairs are shared between two atoms, the resulting bond is a **double bond**. In general, double bonds are shorter and stronger than single bonds. For example, the distance between oxygen nuclei in an oxygen–oxygen double bond is 121 pm. In a single bond, it is 148 pm.

Atoms can also share three electron pairs. Consider the Lewis structure of N_2. Since each N atom has 5 valence electrons, the Lewis structure for N_2 has 10 electrons. A first attempt at writing the Lewis structure gives:

$:\ddot{N}:\ddot{N}:$

As with O_2, we do not have enough electrons to satisfy the octet rule for both N atoms. However, if we convert two additional lone pairs into bonding pairs, each nitrogen atom can get an octet.

$:\ddot{N}:\ddot{N}: \longrightarrow :N:::N:$ *or* $:N≡N:$

The resulting bond is a **triple bond**. Triple bonds are even shorter and stronger than double bonds. The distance between nitrogen nuclei in a nitrogen–nitrogen triple bond is 110 pm. In a double bond, the distance is 124 pm. When we examine nitrogen in nature, we find that it indeed exists as a diatomic molecule with a very strong short bond between the two nitrogen atoms. The bond is so strong that it is difficult to break, making N_2 a relatively unreactive molecule.

5 Writing Lewis Structures for Covalent Compounds

> When guessing at skeletal structures, put the less metallic elements in terminal positions and the more metallic elements in central positions. Halogens, being among the least metallic elements, are nearly always terminal.

> Non-terminal hydrogen atoms exist in some compounds. However, they are rare and beyond our scope.

To write a Lewis structure for a covalent compound, follow these steps:

1. **Write the correct skeletal structure for the molecule.** The skeletal structure shows the relative positions of the atoms and does not include electrons, but it must have the atoms in the correct positions. For example, you could *not* write a Lewis structure for water if you started with the hydrogen atoms next to each other and the oxygen atom at the end (H H O). In nature, oxygen is the central atom, and the hydrogen atoms are **terminal atoms** (at the ends). The correct skeletal structure is H O H.

   The only way to absolutely know the correct skeletal structure for any molecule is to examine its structure in nature. However, we can write likely skeletal structures by remembering two guidelines. First, *hydrogen atoms will always be terminal*. Since hydrogen requires only a duet, it will never be a central atom because central atoms must be able to form at least two bonds and hydrogen can form only one. Second, *many molecules tend to be symmetrical*, so when a molecule contains several atoms of the same type, these tend to be in terminal positions. *This second guideline, however, has many exceptions.* In cases where the skeletal structure is unclear, this text will provide you with the correct skeletal structure.

2. **Calculate the total number of electrons for the Lewis structure by summing the valence electrons of each atom in the molecule.** Remember that the number of valence electrons for any main-group element is equal to its group number in the periodic table. **If you are writing a Lewis structure for a polyatomic ion, the charge of the ion must be considered when calculating the total number of electrons.** Add one electron for each negative charge and subtract one electron for each positive charge.

3. **Distribute the electrons among the atoms, giving octets (or duets for hydrogen) to as many atoms as possible.** Begin by placing two electrons between each pair of atoms. These are the minimal number of bonding electrons. Then distribute the remaining electrons, first to terminal atoms and then to the central atom, giving octets to as many atoms as possible.

4. **If any atoms lack an octet, form double or triple bonds as necessary to give them octets.** Do this by moving lone electron pairs from terminal atoms into the bonding region with the central atom.

A brief version of this procedure is shown in the left column. Two examples of applying it are shown in the center and right columns.

	EXAMPLE 4	EXAMPLE 5
Writing Lewis Structures for Covalent Compounds	Write the Lewis structure for CO_2.	Write the Lewis structure for CCl_4.
1. Write the correct skeletal structure for the molecule.	SOLUTION Following the symmetry guideline, write: O C O	SOLUTION Following the symmetry guideline, write: Cl Cl C Cl Cl
2. Calculate the total number of electrons for the Lewis structure by summing the valence electrons of each atom in the molecule.	Total number of electrons for Lewis structure = $$\left(\begin{array}{c}\text{\# valence}\\ \text{e}^- \text{ for C}\end{array}\right) + 2\left(\begin{array}{c}\text{\# valence}\\ \text{e}^- \text{ for O}\end{array}\right)$$ $$= 4 + 2(6)$$ $$= 16$$	Total number of electrons for Lewis structure = $$\left(\begin{array}{c}\text{\# valence}\\ \text{e}^- \text{ for C}\end{array}\right) + 4\left(\begin{array}{c}\text{\# valence}\\ \text{e}^- \text{ for Cl}\end{array}\right)$$ $$= 4 + 4(7)$$ $$= 32$$
3. Distribute the electrons among the atoms, giving octets (or duets for hydrogen) to as many atoms as possible. Begin with the bonding electrons, and then proceed to lone pairs on terminal atoms, and finally to lone pairs on the central atom.	Bonding electrons first. O:C:O (4 of 16 electrons used) Lone pairs on terminal atoms next. :Ö:C:Ö: (16 of 16 electrons used)	Bonding electrons first. Cl Cl:C:Cl Cl (8 of 32 electrons used) Lone pairs on terminal atoms next. :C̈l: :C̈l:C:C̈l: :C̈l: (32 of 32 electrons used)
4. If any atoms lack octets, form double or triple bonds as necessary to give them octets.	Move lone pairs from the oxygen atoms to bonding regions to form double bonds. :Ö:C:Ö: ⟶ :O::C::O: ▶SKILLBUILDER 4 Write the Lewis structure for CO.	Since all of the atoms have octets, the Lewis structure is complete. ▶SKILLBUILDER 5 Write the Lewis structure for H_2CO. ▶FOR MORE PRACTICE Example 15; Problems 47, 48, 49, 50, 51, 52.

WRITING LEWIS STRUCTURES FOR POLYATOMIC IONS

We write Lewis structures for polyatomic ions by following the same procedure, but we pay special attention to the charge of the ion when calculating the number of electrons for the Lewis structure. Add one electron for each negative charge and subtract one electron for each positive charge. We normally show the Lewis structure for a polyatomic ion within brackets and write the charge of the ion in the upper right corner. For example, suppose we want to write a Lewis structure for the CN^- ion. We begin by writing the skeletal structure.

$$CN$$

Next we calculate the total number of electrons for the Lewis structure by summing the number of valence electrons for each atom and adding one for the negative charge.

Total number of electrons
for Lewis structure = (# valence e^- in C) + (# valence e^- in N) + 1

$$= 4 + 5 + 1$$

Add one e^- to account for 1− charge of ion.

$$= 10$$

We then place two electrons between each pair of atoms

C:N   (2 of 10 electrons used)

and distribute the remaining electrons.

:C̈:N̈:   (10 of 10 electrons used)

Since neither of the atoms has octets, we move two lone pairs into the bonding region to form a triple bond, giving both atoms octets. We also enclose the Lewis structure in brackets and write the charge of the ion in the upper right corner.

$$[:C:::N:]^- \quad or \quad [:C \equiv N:]^-$$

✓ CONCEPTUAL CHECKPOINT 3

The total number of electrons in the Lewis structure of OH^- is:

(a) 6   (b) 7   (c) 8   (d) 9

EXAMPLE 6   Writing Lewis Structures for Polyatomic Ions

Write the Lewis structure for the NH_4^+ ion.

Begin by writing the skeletal structure. Hydrogen atoms must be terminal, and following the guideline of symmetry, the nitrogen atom should be in the middle surrounded by four hydrogen atoms.	SOLUTION H H N H H
Calculate the total number of electrons for the Lewis structure by summing the number of valence electrons for each atom and subtracting 1 for the positive charge.	4 × (# valence e^- in H) Total number of electrons for Lewis structure = 5 + 4 − 1 = 8 # valence e^- in N Subtract 1 e^- to account for 1+ charge of ion.
Next, place two electrons between each pair of atoms.	H H:N̈:H (8 of 8 electrons used) H

Since the nitrogen atom has an octet and since all of the hydrogen atoms have duets, the placement of electrons is complete. Write the entire Lewis structure in brackets indicating the charge of the ion in the upper right corner.

$$\left[\begin{array}{c} \text{H} \\ \text{H:N:H} \\ \text{H} \end{array}\right]^{+} \quad or \quad \left[\begin{array}{c} \text{H} \\ | \\ \text{H—N—H} \\ | \\ \text{H} \end{array}\right]^{+}$$

▶**SKILLBUILDER 6** | **Writing Lewis Structures for Polyatomic Ions**

Write the Lewis structure for the ClO^{-} ion.

▶**FOR MORE PRACTICE**   Problems 55bcd, 56abc, 57, 58.

EXCEPTIONS TO THE OCTET RULE

Lewis theory is often correct in its predictions, but exceptions exist. For example, if we try to write the Lewis structure for NO, which has 11 electrons, the best we can do is:

$$\text{:N::O:} \quad or \quad \text{:N=O:}$$

The nitrogen atom does not have an octet, so this is not a great Lewis structure. However, NO exists in nature. Why? As with any simple theory, Lewis theory is not sophisticated enough to be correct every time. It is impossible to write good Lewis structures for molecules with odd numbers of electrons, yet some of these molecules exist in nature. In such cases, we simply write the best Lewis structure that we can. Another significant exception to the octet rule is boron, which tends to form compounds with only six electrons around B, rather than eight. For example, BF_3 and BH_3—both of which exist in nature—lack an octet for B.

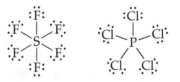

A third type of exception to the octet rule is also common. A number of molecules, such as SF_6 and PCl_5, have more than eight electrons around a central atom in their Lewis structures.

These are often referred to as *expanded octets*. Expanded octets can form for period 3 elements and beyond. Beyond mentioning them, we do not cover expanded octets in this text. In spite of these exceptions, Lewis theory remains a powerful and simple way to understand chemical bonding.

✔ **CONCEPTUAL CHECKPOINT 4**

Which two species have the same number of lone electron pairs in their Lewis structures?

(a) H_2O and H_3O^+

(b) NH_3 and H_3O^+

(c) NH_3 and CH_4

(d) NH_3 and NH_4^+

6 Resonance: Equivalent Lewis Structures for the Same Molecule

When writing Lewis structures, we may find that, for some molecules, we can write more than one good Lewis structure. For example, consider writing a Lewis structure for SO_2. We begin with the skeletal structure:

O S O

We then sum the valence electrons.

Total number of electrons for Lewis structure

$= (\# \text{ valence } e^- \text{ in S}) + 2(\# \text{ valence } e^- \text{ in O})$

$= 6 + 2(6)$

$= 18$

We next place two electrons between each pair of atoms

O:S:O   (4 of 18 electrons used)

and then distribute the remaining electrons, first to terminal atoms

:Ö:S:Ö: (16 of 18 electrons used)

and finally to the central atom.

:Ö:S̈:Ö: (18 of 18 electrons used)

Since the central atom lacks an octet, we move one lone pair from an oxygen atom into the bonding region to form a double bond, giving all of the atoms octets.

:Ö::S̈:Ö: *or*   :Ö=S̈—Ö:

However, we could have formed the double bond with the other oxygen atom.

:Ö—S̈=Ö:

These two Lewis structures are equally correct. In cases such as this—where we can write two or more equivalent (or nearly equivalent) Lewis structures for the same molecule—we find that the molecule exists in nature as an average or intermediate between the two Lewis structures. Either *one* of the two Lewis structures for SO_2 would predict that SO_2 should contain two different kinds of bonds (one double bond and one single bond). However, when we examine SO_2 in nature, we find that both of the bonds are equivalent and intermediate in strength and length between a double bond and single bond. We account for this in Lewis theory by representing the molecule with both structures, called **resonance structures**, with a double-headed arrow between them.

:Ö=S̈—Ö: ⟷   :Ö—S̈=Ö:

The true structure of SO_2 is intermediate between these two resonance structures.

EXAMPLE 7 Writing Resonance Structures

Write the Lewis structure for the NO_3^- ion. Include resonance structures.

Begin by writing the skeletal structure. Applying the guideline of symmetry, make the three oxygen atoms terminal.	**SOLUTION** <div align="center">O O N O</div>

Sum the valence electrons (adding one electron to account for the 1− charge) to determine the total number of electrons in the Lewis structure.	Total number of electrons for Lewis structure = 5 + 3(6) + 1 = 24 — 3 × (# valence e⁻ in O); # valence e⁻ in N; Add one e⁻ to account for negative charge of ion.
Place two electrons between each pair of atoms.	O:N:O with O above (6 of 24 electrons used)
Distribute the remaining electrons, first to terminal atoms.	:Ö:N:Ö: with :Ö: above (24 of 24 electrons used)
Since there are no electrons remaining to complete the octet of the central atom, form a double bond by moving a lone pair from one of the oxygen atoms into the bonding region with nitrogen. Enclose the structure in brackets and write the charge at the upper right.	[:Ö: / :Ö:N::Ö:]⁻ or [:Ö: / :Ö—N=Ö:]⁻
Notice that you could have formed the double bond with either of the other two oxygen atoms.	[:Ö: / :O=N—Ö:]⁻ or [:Ö / :Ö—N—Ö:]⁻
Since the three Lewis structures are equally correct, write the three structures as resonance structures.	[:Ö: / :O=N—Ö:]⁻ ⟷ [:Ö / :Ö—N—Ö:]⁻ ⟷ [:Ö: / :Ö—N=Ö:]⁻

▶**SKILLBUILDER 7 | Writing Resonance Structures**

Write the Lewis structure for the NO_2^- ion. Include resonance structures.

▶**FOR MORE PRACTICE**   Example 16; Problems 55, 56, 57, 58.

7 Predicting the Shapes of Molecules

Lewis theory, in combination with **valence shell electron pair repulsion (VSEPR) theory**, can be used to predict the shapes of molecules. VSEPR theory is based on the idea that **electron groups**—lone pairs, single bonds, or multiple bonds—repel each other. This repulsion between the negative charges of electron groups on the central atom determines the geometry of the molecule. For example, consider CO_2, which has the Lewis structure:

$$:\ddot{O}=C=\ddot{O}:$$

The geometry of CO_2 is determined by the repulsion between the two electron groups (the two double bonds) on the central carbon atom. These two electron groups get as far away from each other as possible, resulting in a bond angle of 180° and a **linear** geometry for CO_2.

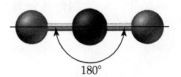

180°

CHEMISTRY IN THE ENVIRONMENT

The Lewis Structure of Ozone

Ozone is a form of oxygen in which three oxygen atoms bond together. Its Lewis structure consists of the two resonance structures:

$$:\ddot{O}=\ddot{O}-\ddot{\underset{..}{O}}: \longleftrightarrow :\ddot{\underset{..}{O}}-\ddot{O}=\ddot{O}:$$

Compare the Lewis structure of ozone to the Lewis structure of O_2:

$$:\ddot{O}=\ddot{O}:$$

Which molecule, O_3 or O_2, do you think has the stronger oxygen–oxygen bond? If you deduced O_2, you are correct. O_2 has a stronger bond because it is a pure double bond. Ozone, on the other hand, has bonds that are intermediate between single and double, so O_3 has weaker bonds. The effects of this are significant. O_3 shields us from harmful ultraviolet light entering Earth's atmosphere. O_3 is ideally suited to do this because photons at wavelengths of 280–320 nm (the most dangerous components of sunlight to humans) are just strong enough to break ozone's bonds. In the process, the photons are absorbed.

$$:\ddot{\underset{..}{O}}-\ddot{O}=\ddot{O}: + \text{UV light} \longrightarrow :\ddot{O}=\ddot{O}: + \cdot\ddot{\underset{..}{O}}\cdot$$

The same wavelengths of UV light, however, do not have sufficient energy to break the stronger double bond of O_2, which is therefore transparent to UV. Consequently, it is important that we continue, and even strengthen, the ban on ozone-depleting compounds.

CAN YOU ANSWER THIS? *Why are these Lewis structures for ozone incorrect?*

$$:\ddot{\underset{..}{O}}-\ddot{\underset{..}{O}}-\ddot{\underset{..}{O}}: \qquad :\ddot{\underset{..}{O}}=O=\ddot{\underset{..}{O}}:$$

As another example, consider the molecule H_2CO. Its Lewis structure is:

$$\begin{array}{c} :\!O\!: \\ \| \\ H\!-\!C\!-\!H \end{array}$$

This molecule has three electron groups around the central atom. These three electron groups get as far away from each other as possible, resulting in a bond angle of 120° and a **trigonal planar** geometry.

| The angles shown here for H_2CO are approximate. The C=O double bond contains more electron density than do C—H single bonds; resulting in a slightly greater repulsion; thus the HCH bond angle is actually 116°, and the HCO bond angles are actually 122°.

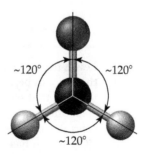

| A tetrahedron is a geometric shape with four triangular faces.

If a molecule has four electron groups around the central atom, as CH_4, does, it has a **tetrahedral** geometry with bond angles of 109.5°.

| CH_4 is shown here with both a ball-and-stick model (left) and a space-filling model (right). Although space-filling models more closely portray molecules, ball-and-stick models are often used to clearly illustrate molecular geometries.

$$\begin{array}{c} H \\ | \\ H\!-\!C\!-\!H \\ | \\ H \end{array}$$

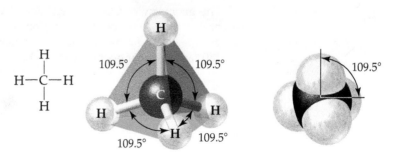

The mutual repulsion of the four electron groups causes the tetrahedral shape—the tetrahedron allows the maximum separation among the four groups. When we write the structure of CH_4 on paper, it may seem that the molecule should be square planar, with bond angles of 90°. However, in three dimensions the electron groups can get farther away from each other by forming the tetrahedral geometry.

Each of the preceding examples has only bonding groups of electrons around the central atom. What happens in molecules with lone pairs around the central atom? These lone pairs also repel other electron groups. For example, consider the NH_3 molecule:

$$H - \underset{\cdot\cdot}{N} - H$$
with H above

The four electron groups (one lone pair and three bonding pairs) get as far away from each other possible. If we look only at the electrons, we find that the **electron geometry**—the geometrical arrangement of the electron groups—is tetrahedral.

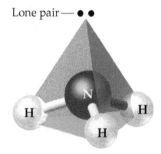

However, the **molecular geometry**—the geometrical arrangement of the atoms—is **trigonal pyramidal**.

Trigonal pyramidal
structure

Notice that, although the electron geometry and the molecular geometry are different, the electron geometry is relevant to the molecular geometry. In other words, the lone pair exerts its influence on the bonding pairs.

Consider one last example, H_2O. Its Lewis structure is:

$$H - \underset{\cdot\cdot}{\overset{\cdot\cdot}{O}} - H$$

Since it has four electron groups, its electron geometry is also tetrahedral.

For reasons we don't cover here, the bond angles in NH_3 and H_2O are actually a few degrees smaller than the ideal tetrahedral angles.

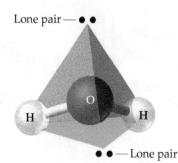

However, its molecular geometry is **bent**.

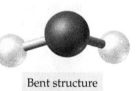

Bent structure

Table 1 summarizes the electron and molecular geometry of a molecule based on the total number of electron groups, the number of bonding groups, and the number of lone pairs.

TABLE 1 Electron and Molecular Geometries

Electron Groups*	Bonding Groups	Lone Pairs	Electron Geometry	Angle between Electron Groups**	Molecular Geometry	Example
2	2	0	linear	180°	linear	$\ddot{O}{=}C{=}\ddot{O}$
3	3	0	trigonal planar	120°	trigonal planar	$\overset{\ddot{O}}{\underset{H{-}C{-}H}{\|\|}}$
3	2	1	trigonal planar	120°	bent	$\ddot{O}{=}\ddot{S}{-}\ddot{O}$
4	4	0	tetrahedral	109.5°	tetrahedral	$H{-}\underset{H}{\overset{H}{C}}{-}H$
4	3	1	tetrahedral	109.5°	trigonal pyramidal	$H{-}\underset{H}{\overset{\cdot\cdot}{N}}{-}H$
4	2	2	tetrahedral	109.5°	bent	$H{-}\ddot{O}{-}H$

*Count only electron groups around the *central* atom. Each of the following is considered one electron group: a lone pair, a single bond, a double bond, and a triple bond.

**Angles listed here are idealized. Actual angles in specific molecules may vary by several degrees.

To determine the geometry of any molecule, use the following procedure. As usual, the steps are in the left column and two examples of applying the steps are in the center and right columns.

Predicting Geometry Using VSEPR Theory	**EXAMPLE 8** Predict the electron and molecular geometry of PCl₃.	**EXAMPLE 9** Predict the electron and molecular geometry of the [NO₃]⁻ ion.
1. Draw a Lewis structure for the molecule.	SOLUTION PCl₃ has 26 electrons. $:\!\overset{\cdot\cdot}{\underset{\cdot\cdot}{Cl}}\!:$ $:\!\ddot{Cl}\!:\!\ddot{P}\!:\!\ddot{Cl}\!:$	SOLUTION [NO₃]⁻ has 24 electrons. $\left[:\!\ddot{O}\!:\!N\!:\!:\!\ddot{O}\!:\right]^{-}$

2. Determine the total number of electron groups around the central atom. Lone pairs, single bonds, double bonds, and triple bonds each count as one group.	The central atom (P) has four electron groups.	The central atom (N) has three electron groups (the double bond counts as one group).
3. Determine the number of bonding groups and the number of lone pairs around the central atom. These should sum to the result from Step 2. Bonding groups include single bonds, double bonds, and triple bonds.	:Cl: :Cl:P:Cl: Lone pair Three of the four electron groups around P are bonding groups, and one is a lone pair.	[:O: :O:N::O:] No lone pairs All three of the electron groups around N are bonding groups.
4. Refer to Table 1 to determine the electron geometry and molecular geometry.	The electron geometry is tetrahedral (four electron groups), and the molecular geometry—the shape of the molecule—is trigonal pyramidal (four electron groups, three bonding groups, and one lone pair).	The electron geometry is trigonal planar (three electron groups), and the molecular geometry—the shape of the molecule—is trigonal planar (three electron groups, three bonding groups, and no lone pairs).
	▶**SKILLBUILDER 8** Predict the molecular geometry of ClNO (N is the central atom).	▶**SKILLBUILDER 9** Predict the molecular geometry of the SO_3^{2-} ion. ▶**FOR MORE PRACTICE** Example 17; Problems 65, 66, 69, 70, 73, 74.

✔ CONCEPTUAL CHECKPOINT 5

Which condition necessarily leads to a molecular geometry that is identical to the electron geometry?

(a) The presence of a double bond between the central atom and a terminal atom.

(b) The presence of two or more identical terminal atoms bonded to the central atom.

(c) The presence of one or more lone pairs on the central atom.

(d) The absence of any lone pairs on the central atom.

REPRESENTING MOLECULAR GEOMETRIES ON PAPER

Since molecular geometries are three-dimensional, they are often difficult to represent on two-dimensional paper. Many chemists use this notation for bonds to indicate three-dimensional structures on two-dimensional paper.

—	‖⋯	◄
Straight line	*Hashed lines*	*Wedge*
Bond in plane of paper	Bond projecting into the paper	Bond projecting out of the paper

CHEMISTRY AND HEALTH

Fooled by Molecular Shape

Artificial sweeteners, such as aspartame (Nutrasweet™), taste sweet but have few or no calories. Why? Because taste and caloric value are entirely separate properties of foods. The caloric value of a food depends on the amount of energy released when the food is metabolized. Sucrose (table sugar) is metabolized by oxidation to carbon dioxide and water:

$$C_{12}H_{22}O_{11} + 6\,O_2 \longrightarrow 12\,CO_2 + 11\,H_2O$$
$$\Delta H = -5644\ kJ$$

When your body metabolizes one mole of sucrose, it obtains 5644 kJ of energy. Some artificial sweeteners, such as saccharin, are not metabolized at all—they just pass through the body unchanged—and therefore have no caloric value. Other artificial sweeteners, such as aspartame, are metabolized but have a much lower caloric content (for a given amount of sweetness) than sucrose.

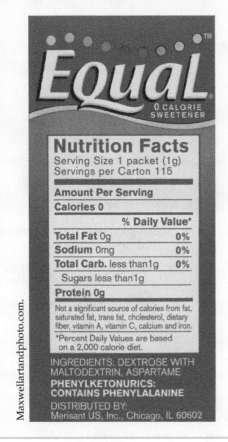

INGREDIENTS: DEXTROSE WITH MALTODEXTRIN, ASPARTAME
PHENYLKETONURICS: CONTAINS PHENYLALANINE
DISTRIBUTED BY: Merisant US, Inc., Chicago, IL 60602

The *taste* of a food, however, is independent of its metabolism. The sensation of taste originates in the tongue, where specialized cells called taste cells act as highly sensitive and specific molecular detectors. These cells can distinguish the sugar molecules from the thousands of different types of molecules present in a mouthful of food. The main basis for this discrimination is the molecule's *shape*.

The surface of a taste cell contains specialized protein molecules called taste receptors. Each particular *tastant*—a molecule that we can taste—fits snugly into a special pocket on the taste receptor protein called the *active site*, just as a key fits into a lock. For example, a sugar molecule fits only into the active site of the sugar receptor protein called Tlr3. When the sugar molecule (the key) enters the active site (the lock), the different subunits of the Tlr3 protein split apart. This split causes a series of events that result in transmission of a nerve signal, which reaches the brain and registers a sweet taste.

Artificial sweeteners taste sweet because they fit into the receptor pocket that normally binds sucrose. In fact, both aspartame and saccharin bind to the active site in the Tlr3 protein more strongly than sugar does! For this reason, artificial sweeteners are "sweeter than sugar." It takes 200 times as much sucrose as aspartame to trigger the same amount of nerve signal transmission from taste cells.

This type of lock-and-key fit between the active site of a protein and a particular molecule is important not only to taste but to many other biological functions as well. For example, immune response, the sense of smell, and many types of drug action all depend on shape-specific interactions between molecules and proteins. The ability of scientists to determine the shapes of key biological molecules is largely responsible for the revolution in biology that has occurred over the last 50 years.

CAN YOU ANSWER THIS? *Proteins are long-chain molecules in which each link is an amino acid. The simplest amino acid is glycine, which has the structure:*

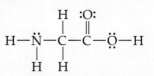

Determine the geometry around each interior atom in the glycine structure and make a three-dimensional sketch of the molecule.

The major molecular geometries used in this book are shown here using this notation:

| Linear | Trigonal planar | Bent | Tetrahedral | Trigonal pyramidal |

Maxwellartandphoto.com.

232

8 Electronegativity and Polarity: Why Oil and Water Don't Mix

▲ FIGURE 1 **Oil and water don't mix** Question: Why not?

If you combine oil and water in a container, they separate into distinct regions (◄ Figure 1). Why? Something about water molecules causes them to bunch together into one region, expelling the oil molecules into a separate region. What is that something? We can begin to understand the answer by examining the Lewis structure of water.

$$H—\overset{..}{\underset{..}{O}}—H$$

The two bonds between O and H each consist of an electron pair—two electrons shared between the oxygen atom and the hydrogen atom. The oxygen and hydrogen atoms each donate one electron to this electron pair; however, like most children, they don't share them equally. The oxygen atom takes more than its fair share of the electron pair.

ELECTRONEGATIVITY

The ability of an element to attract electrons within a covalent bond is called **electronegativity**. Oxygen is more electronegative than hydrogen, which means that, on average, the shared electrons are more likely to be found near the oxygen atom than near the hydrogen atom. Consider one of the two OH bonds:

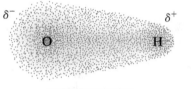

Dipole moment

The value of electronegativity is assigned using a relative scale on which fluorine, the most electronegative element, has an electronegativity of 4.0. All other electronegativities are defined relative to fluorine.

Since the electron pair is unequally shared (with oxygen getting the larger share), the oxygen atom has a partial negative charge, symbolized by $\delta-$ (delta minus). The hydrogen atom (getting the smaller share) has a partial positive charge, symbolized by $\delta+$ (delta plus). The result of this uneven electron sharing is a **dipole moment**, a separation of charge within the bond. Covalent bonds that have a dipole moment are called **polar covalent bonds**. The magnitude of the dipole moment, and therefore the degree of polarity of the bond, depend on the electronegativity difference between the two elements in the bond and the length of the bond. For a fixed bond length, the greater the electronegativity difference, the greater the dipole moment and the more polar the bond.

▼ Figure 2 shows the relative electronegativities of the elements. Notice that electronegativity increases as you go toward the right across a period in the

▶ FIGURE 2 **Electronegativity of the elements** Linus Pauling introduced the scale shown here. He arbitrarily set the electronegativity of fluorine at 4.0 and computed all other values relative to fluorine.

▲ FIGURE 3 **Pure covalent bonding** In Cl₂, the two Cl atoms share the electrons evenly. This is a pure covalent bond.

▲ FIGURE 4 **Ionic bonding** In NaCl, Na completely transfers an electron to Cl. This is an ionic bond.

The degree of bond polarity is a continuous function. The guidelines given here are approximate.

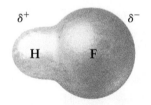

δ^+ δ^-

H   F

▲ FIGURE 5 **Polar covalent bonding** In HF, the electrons are shared, but the shared electrons are more likely to be found on F than on H. The bond is polar covalent.

periodic table and decreases as you go down a column in the periodic table. If two elements with identical electronegativities form a covalent bond, they share the electrons equally, and there is no dipole moment. For example, the chlorine molecule, composed of two chlorine atoms (which of course have identical electronegativities), has a pure covalent bond in which electrons are evenly shared (◀ Figure 3). The bond has no dipole moment, and the molecule is **nonpolar**.

If there is a large electronegativity difference between the two elements in a bond, such as normally occurs between a metal and a nonmetal, the electron is completely transferred and the bond is ionic. For example, sodium and chlorine form an ionic bond (◀ Figure 4).

If there is an intermediate electronegativity difference between the two elements, such as between two different nonmetals, then the bond is polar covalent. For example, HF forms a polar covalent bond (◀ Figure 5).

These concepts are summarized in Table 2 and ▼ Figure 6.

TABLE 2 The Effect of Electronegativity Difference on Bond Type

Electronegativity Difference (ΔEN)	Bond Type	Example
zero (0–0.4)	pure covalent	Cl₂
intermediate (0.4–2.0)	polar covalent	HF
large (2.0+)	ionic	NaCl

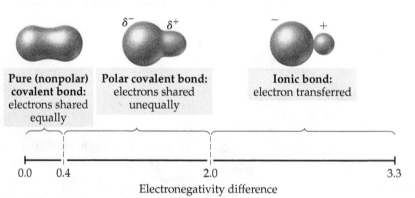

Pure (nonpolar) covalent bond: electrons shared equally   Polar covalent bond: electrons shared unequally   Ionic bond: electron transferred

0.0   0.4   2.0   3.3
Electronegativity difference

▲ FIGURE 6 **The continuum of bond types** The type of bond (pure covalent, polar covalent, or ionic) is related to the electronegativity difference between the bonded atoms.

EXAMPLE 10 Classifying Bonds as Pure Covalent, Polar Covalent, or Ionic

Determine whether the bond formed between each pair of atoms is pure covalent, polar covalent, or ionic.

(a) Sr and F
(b) N and Cl
(c) N and O

SOLUTION

(a) In Figure 2, we find the electronegativity of Sr (1.0) and of F (4.0). The electronegativity difference (ΔEN) is:

$$\Delta EN = 4.0 - 1.0 = 3.0$$

Referring to Table 2, we classify this bond as ionic.

(b) In Figure 2, we find the electronegativity of N (3.0) and of Cl (3.0). The electronegativity difference (ΔEN) is:

$$\Delta EN = 3.0 - 3.0 = 0$$

Referring to Table 2, we classify this bond as pure covalent.

(c) In Figure 2, we find the electronegativity of N (3.0) and of O (3.5). The electronegativity difference (ΔEN) is:

$$\Delta EN = 3.5 - 3.0 = 0.5$$

Referring to Table 2, we classify this bond as polar covalent.

▶**SKILLBUILDER 10 | Classifying Bonds as Pure Covalent, Polar Covalent, or Ionic**

Determine whether the bond formed between each pair of atoms is pure covalent, polar covalent, or ionic.

(a) I and I
(b) Cs and Br
(c) P and O

▶**FOR MORE PRACTICE** Problems 81, 82.

POLAR BONDS AND POLAR MOLECULES

Does the presence of one or more polar bonds in a molecule always result in a polar molecule? The answer is no. A **polar molecule** is one with polar bonds that add together—they do not cancel each other—to form a net dipole moment. For diatomic molecules, you can easily tell polar molecules from nonpolar ones. If a diatomic molecule contains a polar bond, then the molecule is polar. However, for molecules with more than two atoms, it is more difficult to tell polar molecules from nonpolar ones because two or more polar bonds may cancel one another. For example, consider carbon dioxide:

$$:\ddot{O}{=}C{=}\ddot{O}:$$

Each C=O *bond* is polar because the difference in electronegativity between oxygen and carbon is 1.0. However, since CO_2 has a linear geometry, the dipole moment of one bond completely cancels the dipole moment of the other and the *molecule* is nonpolar. We can understand this with an analogy. Imagine each polar bond to be a rope pulling on the central atom. In CO_2 we can see how the two ropes pulling in opposing directions cancel each other's effect:

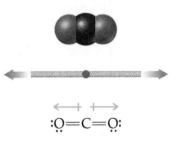

We can also represent polar bonds with arrows (or vectors) that point in the direction of the negative pole and have a plus sign at the positive pole (as just shown for carbon dioxide). If the arrows (or vectors) point in exactly opposing directions as in carbon dioxide, the dipole moments cancel.

Water, on the other hand, has two dipole moments that do not cancel. If we imagine each bond as a rope pulling on oxygen, we see that, because of the angle between the bonds, the pulls of the two ropes do not cancel:

In the vector representation of a dipole moment, the vector points in the direction of the atom with the partial negative charge.

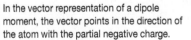

TABLE 3 Common Cases of Adding Dipole Moments to Determine Whether a Molecule Is Polar

Nonpolar

Two identical polar bonds pointing in opposite directions will cancel. The molecule is nonpolar.

Nonpolar

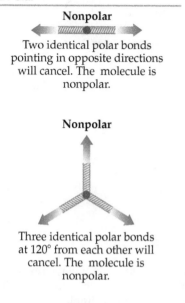

Three identical polar bonds at 120° from each other will cancel. The molecule is nonpolar.

Polar

Three polar bonds in a trigonal pyramidal arrangement (109.5°) will not cancel. The molecule is polar.

Polar

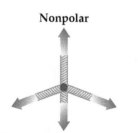

Two polar bonds with an angle of less than 180° between them will not cancel. The molecule is polar.

Nonpolar

Four identical polar bonds in a tetrahedral arrangement (109.5° from each other) will cancel. The molecule is nonpolar.

Note: In all cases where the polar bonds cancel, the bonds are assumed to be identical. If one or more of the bonds are different than the other(s), the bonds will not cancel and the molecule is polar.

Consequently, water is a polar molecule. We can use symmetry as a guide to determine whether a molecule containing polar bonds is indeed polar. Highly symmetric molecules tend to be nonpolar even if they have polar bonds because the bond dipole moments (or the pulls of the ropes) tend to cancel. Asymmetric molecules that contain polar bonds tend to be polar because the bond dipole moments (or the pulls of the ropes) tend not to cancel. Table 3 summarizes some common cases.

In summary, to determine whether a molecule is polar:

- **Determine whether the molecule contains polar bonds**. A bond is polar if the two bonding atoms have different electronegativities. If there are no polar bonds, the molecule is nonpolar.
- **Determine whether the polar bonds add together to form a net dipole moment**. You must first use VSEPR to determine the geometry of the molecule. Then visualize each bond as a rope pulling on the central atom. Is the molecule highly symmetrical? Do the pulls of the ropes cancel? If so, there is no net dipole moment and the molecule is nonpolar. If the molecule is asymmetrical and the pulls of the rope do not cancel, the molecule is polar.

EXAMPLE 11 Determining Whether a Molecule Is Polar

Determine whether NH_3 is polar.

Begin by drawing the Lewis structure of NH_3. Since N and H have different electronegativities, the bonds are polar.

SOLUTION

The geometry of NH_3 is trigonal pyramidal (four electron groups, three bonding groups, one lone pair). Draw a three-dimensional picture of NH_3 and imagine each bond as a rope that is being pulled. The pulls of the ropes do not cancel and the molecule is polar.

NH_3 is polar

▶**SKILLBUILDER 11 | Determining Whether a Molecule Is Polar**

Determine whether CH_4 is polar.

▶**FOR MORE PRACTICE** Example 18; Problems 89, 90, 91, 92.

Whether or not a molecule is polar is important because polar molecules tend to behave differently than nonpolar molecules. Water and oil do not mix, for example, because water molecules are polar and the molecules that compose oil are generally nonpolar. Polar molecules interact strongly with other polar molecules because the positive end of one molecule is attracted to the negative end of another, just as the south pole of a magnet is attracted to the north pole of another

EVERYDAY CHEMISTRY

How Soap Works

Imagine eating a greasy cheeseburger with both hands and no napkins. By the end of the meal, your hands are coated with grease and oil. If you try to wash them with only water, they remain greasy. However, if you add a little soap, the grease washes away. Why? As we learned previously, water molecules are polar and the molecules that compose grease and oil are nonpolar. As a result, water and grease repel each other.

The molecules that compose soap, however, have a special structure that allows them to interact strongly with both water and grease. One end of a soap molecule is polar, while the other end is nonpolar.

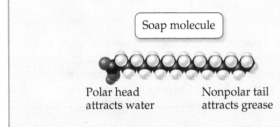

Soap molecule

Polar head
attracts water

Nonpolar tail
attracts grease

The polar head of a soap molecule strongly attracts water molecules, while the nonpolar tail strongly attracts grease and oil molecules. Soap is a sort of molecular liaison, one end interacting with water and the other end interacting with grease. Soap therefore allows water and grease to mix, removing the grease from your hands and washing it down the drain.

CAN YOU ANSWER THIS? *Consider this detergent molecule. Which end do you think is polar? Which end is nonpolar?*

$$CH_3(CH_2)_{11}OCH_2CH_2OH$$

▶ **FIGURE 7** **Dipole–dipole attraction** Just as the north pole of one magnet is attracted to the south pole of another, so the positive end of one molecule with a dipole is attracted to the negative end of another molecule with a dipole.

magnet (▲ Figure 7). A mixture of polar and nonpolar molecules is similar to a mixture of small magnetic and nonmagnetic particles. The magnetic particles clump together, excluding the nonmagnetic ones and separating into distinct regions (◄ Figure 8). Similarly, the polar water molecules attract one another, forming regions from which the nonpolar oil molecules are excluded (▼ Figure 9).

▲ **FIGURE 8** **Magnetic and non-magnetic particles** Magnetic particles attract one another, excluding nonmagnetic particles. This behavior is analogous to that of polar and nonpolar molecules.

Richard Megna/Fundamental Photographs.

◄ **FIGURE 9** **Polar and nonpolar molecules** A mixture of polar and nonpolar molecules, like a mixture of magnetic and nonmagnetic particles, separates into distinct regions because the polar molecules attract one another, excluding the nonpolar ones. **Question:** Can you think of some examples of this behavior?

CHAPTER IN REVIEW

CHEMICAL PRINCIPLES

RELEVANCE

Lewis Theory: Lewis theory is a model for chemical bonding. According to Lewis theory, chemical bonds are formed when atoms transfer valence electrons (ionic bonding) or share valence electrons (covalent bonding) to attain noble gas electron configurations. In Lewis theory, valence electrons are represented as dots surrounding the symbol for an element. When two or more elements bond together, the dots are transferred or shared so that every atom attains eight dots (an octet), or two dots (a duet) in the case of hydrogen.

Lewis Theory: Bonding theories predict what combinations of elements will form stable compounds and can also be used to predict the properties of those compounds. For example, pharmaceutical companies use bonding theories when they are designing drug molecules that must interact with a specific part of a protein molecule.

Molecular Shapes: The shapes of molecules can be predicted by combining Lewis theory with valence shell electron pair repulsion (VSEPR) theory. In this model, electron groups—lone pairs, single bonds, double bonds, and triple bonds—around the central atom repel one another and determine the geometry of the molecule.

Molecular Shapes: Molecular shapes determine many of the properties of compounds. Water's bent geometry, for example, causes it to be a liquid at room temperature instead of a gas. It is also the reason ice floats on water and snowflakes have hexagonal patterns.

Electronegativity and Polarity: Electronegativity refers to the relative ability of elements to attract electrons within a chemical bond. Electronegativity increases as you move to the right across a period in the periodic table and decreases as you move down a column. When two nonmetal atoms of different electronegativities form a covalent bond, the electrons in the bond are not evenly shared and the bond is polar. In diatomic molecules, a polar bond results in a polar molecule. In molecules with more than two atoms, polar bonds may cancel, forming a nonpolar molecule, or they may sum, forming a polar molecule.

Electronegativity and Polarity: The polarity of a molecule influences many of its properties such as whether it will be a solid, liquid, or gas at room temperature and whether it will mix with other compounds. Oil and water, for example, do not mix because water is polar while oil is nonpolar.

CHEMICAL SKILLS

EXAMPLES

Lewis Structures for Elements (Section 2)

The Lewis structure of any element is the symbol for the element with the valence electrons represented as dots drawn around the element. The number of valence electrons is equal to the group number of the element (for main-group elements).

EXAMPLE 12   Lewis Structures for Elements

Draw the Lewis structure of sulfur.

SOLUTION

Since S is in Group 6A, it has six valence electrons. We draw these as dots surrounding its symbol, S.

$\cdot \ddot{\text{S}} \colon$

Writing Lewis Structures of Ionic Compounds (Section 3)

In an ionic Lewis structure, the metal loses all of its valence electrons to the nonmetal, which attains an octet. The nonmetal, with its octet, is normally written in brackets with the charge in the upper right corner.

EXAMPLE 13 Writing Lewis Structures of Ionic Compounds

Write the Lewis structure for lithium bromide.

SOLUTION

$$Li^+ \ [:\ddot{\underset{..}{Br}}:]^-$$

Using Lewis Theory to Predict the Chemical Formula of an Ionic Compound (Section 3)

To determine the chemical formula of an ionic compound, write the Lewis structures of each of the elements. Then choose the correct number of each type of atom so that the metal atom(s) lose all of their valence electrons and the nonmetal atom(s) attain an octet.

EXAMPLE 14 Using Lewis Theory to Predict the Chemical Formula of an Ionic Compound

Use Lewis theory to predict the formula for the compound that forms between potassium and sulfur.

SOLUTION

The Lewis structures of K and S are:

$$K\cdot \qquad \cdot\ddot{\underset{..}{S}}:$$

Potassium must lose one electron and sulfur must gain two. Consequently, we need two potassium atoms to every sulfur atom. The Lewis structure is:

$$K^+[:\ddot{\underset{..}{S}}:]^{2-}K^+$$

The correct formula is K_2S.

Writing Lewis Structures for Covalent Compounds (Sections 4, 5)

To write covalent Lewis structures, follow these steps:

1. **Write the correct skeletal structure for the molecule.** Hydrogen atoms will always be terminal, halogens will usually be terminal, and many molecules tend to be symmetrical.

2. **Calculate the total number of electrons for the Lewis structure by summing the valence electrons of each atom in the molecule.** Remember that the number of valence electrons for any main-group element is equal to its group number in the periodic table. For polyatomic ions, add one electron for each negative charge and subtract one electron for each positive charge.

3. **Distribute the electrons among the atoms, giving octets (or duets for hydrogen) to as many atoms as possible.** Begin by placing two electrons between each pair of atoms. These are the bonding electrons. Then distribute the remaining electrons, first to terminal atoms and then to the central atom.

4. **If any atoms lack an octet, form double or triple bonds as necessary to give them octets.** Do this by moving lone electron pairs from terminal atoms into the bonding region with the central atom.

EXAMPLE 15 Writing Lewis Structures for Covalent Compounds

Write the Lewis structure for CS_2.

SOLUTION

S C S

$$\text{Total e}^- = 1 \times (\text{\# valence e}^- \text{ in C})$$
$$+ 2 \times (\text{\# valence e}^- \text{ in S})$$
$$= 4 + 2(6)$$
$$= 16$$

S:C:S   (4 of 16 e⁻ used)

:S̈:C:S̈:   (16 of 16 e⁻ used)

:S̈::C::S̈:   or   :S̈=C=S̈:

Writing Resonance Structures (Section 6)

When you can write two or more equivalent (or nearly equivalent) Lewis structures for a molecule, the true structure is an average between these. Represent this by writing all of the correct structures (called resonance structures) with double-headed arrows between them.

Predicting the Shapes of Molecules (Section 7)

To determine the shape of a molecule, follow these steps:

1. **Draw the Lewis structure for the molecule.**

2. **Determine the total number of electron groups around the central atom.** Lone pairs, single bonds, double bonds, and triple bonds each count as one group.

3. **Determine the number of bonding groups and the number of lone pairs around the central atom.** These should sum to the result from Step 2. Bonding groups include single bonds, double bonds, and triple bonds.

4. Refer to Table 1 to determine the electron geometry and molecular geometry.

Determining Whether a Molecule Is Polar (Section 8)

- **Determine whether the molecule contains polar bonds.** A bond is polar if the two bonding atoms have different electronegativities. If there are no polar bonds, the molecule is nonpolar.

- **Determine whether the polar bonds add together to form a net dipole moment.** Use VSEPR theory to determine the geometry of the molecule. Then visualize each bond as a rope pulling on the central atom. Is the molecule highly symmetrical? Do the pulls of the ropes cancel? If so, there is no net dipole moment and the molecule is nonpolar. If the molecule is asymmetrical and the pulls of the rope do not cancel, the molecule is polar.

EXAMPLE 16 Writing Resonance Structures

Write resonance structures for SeO_2.

SOLUTION

We can write a Lewis structure for SeO_2 by following the steps for writing covalent Lewis structures. We find that we can write two equally correct structures, so we draw them both as resonance structures.

$$:\ddot{O}-\ddot{Se}=\ddot{O}: \longleftrightarrow :\ddot{O}=\ddot{Se}-\ddot{O}:$$

EXAMPLE 17 Predicting the Shapes of Molecules

Predict the geometry of SeO_2.

SOLUTION

The Lewis structure for SeO_2 (as we saw in Example 16) is composed of the following two resonance structures.

$$:\ddot{O}-\ddot{Se}=\ddot{O}: \longleftrightarrow :\ddot{O}=\ddot{Se}-\ddot{O}:$$

Either of the resonance structures will give the same geometry.

Total number of electron groups = 3
Number of bonding groups = 2
Number of lone pairs = 1

Electron geometry = Trigonal planar
Molecular geometry = Bent

EXAMPLE 18 Determining Whether a Molecule Is Polar

Determine whether SeO_2 is polar.

SOLUTION

Se and O are nonmetals with different electronegativities (2.4 for Se and 3.5 for O). Therefore, the Se–O bonds are polar.

As we saw in Example 17, the geometry of SeO_2 is bent.

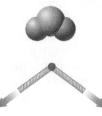

The polar bonds do not cancel but rather sum to give a net dipole moment. Therefore the molecule is polar.

KEY TERMS

bent [**Section 7**]
bonding pair [**Section 4**]
bonding theory [**Section 1**]
chemical bond [**Section 2**]
covalent bond [**Section 2**]
dipole moment [**Section 8**]
dot structure [**Section 2**]
double bond [**Section 4**]
duet [**Section 2**]

electron geometry [**Section 7**]
electron group [**Section 7**]
electronegativity [**Section 8**]
ionic bond [**Section 2**]
Lewis structure [**Section 2**]
Lewis theory [**Section 1**]
linear [**Section 7**]
lone pair [**Section 4**]
molecular geometry
 [**Section 7**]

nonpolar [**Section 8**]
octet [**Section 2**]
octet rule [**Section 2**]
polar covalent bond
 [**Section 8**]
polar molecule [**Section 8**]
resonance structures
 [**Section 6**]
terminal atom [**Section 5**]

tetrahedral [**Section 7**]
trigonal planar [**Section 7**]
trigonal pyramidal
 [**Section 7**]
triple bond [**Section 4**]
valence shell electron pair
 repulsion (VSEPR)
 theory [**Section 7**]

EXERCISES

QUESTIONS

1. Why are bonding theories important? Give some examples of what bonding theories can predict.
2. Write the electron configurations for Ne and Ar. How many valence electrons do they each have?
3. In Lewis theory, what is an octet? What is a duet? What is a chemical bond?
4. What is the difference between ionic bonding and covalent bonding?
5. How can Lewis theory be used to determine the formula of ionic compounds? You may explain this with an example.
6. What is the difference between lone pair and bonding pair electrons?
7. How are double and triple bonds physically different from single bonds?
8. What is the procedure for writing a covalent Lewis structure?
9. How do you determine the number of electrons that go into the Lewis structure of a molecule?
10. How do you determine the number of electrons that go into the Lewis structure of a polyatomic ion?
11. Why does the octet rule have exceptions? Give some examples.
12. What are resonance structures? Why are they necessary?

13. Explain how VSEPR theory predicts the shapes of molecules.
14. If all of the electron groups around a central atom are bonding groups (that is, there are no lone pairs), what is the molecular geometry for:
 (a) two electron groups
 (b) three electron groups
 (c) four electron groups
15. Give the bond angles for each of the geometries in the preceding question.
16. What is the difference between electron geometry and molecular geometry in VSEPR theory?
17. What is electronegativity?
18. What is the most electronegative element on the periodic table?
19. What is a polar covalent bond?
20. What is a dipole moment?
21. What happens when you try to mix a polar liquid with a nonpolar one?
22. If a molecule has polar bonds, will the molecule itself be polar? Why or why not?

PROBLEMS

WRITING LEWIS STRUCTURES FOR ELEMENTS

23. Write an electron configuration for each element and the corresponding Lewis structure. Indicate which electrons in the electron configuration are included in the Lewis structure.
 (a) N
 (b) C
 (c) Cl
 (d) Ar

24. Write an electron configuration for each element and the corresponding Lewis structure. Indicate which electrons in the electron configuration are included in the Lewis structure.
 (a) Li
 (b) P
 (c) F
 (d) Ne

25. Write Lewis structures for each element.
    (a) I
    (b) S
    (c) Ge
    (d) Ca

26. Write Lewis structures for each element.
    (a) Kr
    (b) P
    (c) B
    (d) Na

27. Write a generic Lewis structure for the halogens. Do the halogens tend to gain or lose electrons in chemical reactions? How many?

28. Write a generic Lewis structure for the alkali metals. Do the alkali metals tend to gain or lose electrons in chemical reactions? How many?

29. Write a generic Lewis structure for the alkaline earth metals. Do the alkaline earth metals tend to gain or lose electrons in chemical reactions? How many?

30. Write a generic Lewis structure for the elements in the oxygen family (Group 6A). Do the elements in the oxygen family tend to gain or lose electrons in chemical reactions? How many?

31. Write the Lewis structure for each ion.
    (a) Al^{3+}
    (b) Mg^{2+}
    (c) Se^{2-}
    (d) N^{3-}

32. Write a Lewis structure for each ion.
    (a) Sr^{2+}
    (b) S^{2-}
    (c) Li^+
    (d) Cl^-

33. For each ion, indicate the noble gas that has the same Lewis structure as the ion.
    (a) Br^-
    (b) O^{2-}
    (c) Rb^+
    (d) Ba^{2+}

34. For each ion, indicate the noble gas that has the same Lewis structure as the ion.
    (a) Se^{2-}
    (b) I^-
    (c) Sr^{2+}
    (d) F^-

LEWIS STRUCTURES FOR IONIC COMPOUNDS

35. Determine whether each compound is best represented by an ionic or a covalent Lewis structure.
    (a) SF_6
    (b) $MgCl_2$
    (c) BrCl
    (d) K_2S

36. Determine whether each compounds is best represented by an ionic or a covalent Lewis structure.
    (a) NO
    (b) CO_2
    (c) Rb_2O
    (d) Al_2S_3

37. Write a Lewis structure for each ionic compound.
    (a) NaF
    (b) CaO
    (c) $SrBr_2$
    (d) K_2O

38. Write a Lewis structure for each ionic compound.
    (a) SrO
    (b) Li_2S
    (c) CaI_2
    (d) RbF

39. Use Lewis theory to determine the formula for the compound that forms from:
    (a) Ca and S
    (b) Mg and Br
    (c) Cs and I
    (d) Ca and N

40. Use Lewis theory to determine the formula for the compound that forms from:
    (a) Al and S
    (b) Na and S
    (c) Sr and Se
    (d) Ba and F

41. Draw the Lewis structure for the ionic compound that forms from Mg and:

(a) F

(b) O

(c) N

42. Draw the Lewis structure for the ionic compound that forms from Al and:

(a) F

(b) O

(c) N

43. Determine what is wrong with each ionic Lewis structure and write the correct structure.

(a) $[Cs:]^+$ $[:\overset{\cdot\cdot}{\underset{\cdot\cdot}{Cl}}:]^-$

(b) Ba^+ $[:\overset{\cdot\cdot}{\underset{\cdot\cdot}{O}}:]^-$

(c) Ca^{2+} $[:\overset{\cdot\cdot}{\underset{\cdot\cdot}{I}}:]^-$

44. Determine what is wrong with each ionic Lewis structure and write the correct structure.

(a) $[:\overset{\cdot\cdot}{\underset{\cdot\cdot}{O}}:]^{2-} Na^+ [:\overset{\cdot\cdot}{\underset{\cdot\cdot}{O}}:]^{2-}$

(b) $Mg:\overset{\cdot\cdot}{\underset{\cdot\cdot}{O}}:$

(c) $[Li:]^+[:\overset{\cdot\cdot}{\underset{\cdot\cdot}{S}}:]^-$

LEWIS STRUCTURES FOR COVALENT COMPOUNDS

45. Use Lewis theory to explain why each element exists as a diatomic molecule:

(a) hydrogen

(b) iodine

(c) nitrogen

(d) oxygen

46. Use Lewis theory to explain why the compound that forms between hydrogen and sulfur has the formula H_2S. Would you expect HS to be stable? H_3S?

47. Write the Lewis structure for each molecule.

(a) PH_3

(b) SCl_2

(c) F_2

(d) HI

48. Write the Lewis structure for each molecule.

(a) CH_4

(b) NF_3

(c) OF_2

(d) H_2O

49. Write the Lewis structure for each molecule.

(a) O_2

(b) CO

(c) HONO (N is central)

(d) SO_2

50. Write the Lewis structure for each molecule.

(a) N_2O (oxygen is terminal)

(b) SiH_4

(c) CI_4

(d) Cl_2CO (carbon is central)

51. Write the Lewis structure for each molecule.

(a) C_2H_2

(b) C_2H_4

(c) N_2H_2

(d) N_2H_4

52. Write the Lewis structure for each molecule.

(a) H_2CO (carbon is central)

(b) H_3COH (carbon and oxygen are both central)

(c) H_3COCH_3 (oxygen is between the two carbon atoms)

(d) H_2O_2

53. Determine what is wrong with each Lewis structure and write the correct structure.

(a) $:\overset{\cdot}{N}=\overset{\cdot}{N}:$

(b) $:\overset{\cdot\cdot}{\underset{\cdot\cdot}{S}}-Si-\overset{\cdot\cdot}{\underset{\cdot\cdot}{S}}:$

(c) $H-H-\overset{\cdot\cdot}{\underset{\cdot\cdot}{O}}:$

(d) $:\overset{\cdot\cdot}{\underset{\cdot\cdot}{I}}-N-\overset{\cdot\cdot}{\underset{\cdot\cdot}{I}}:$
$\quad\quad\quad |$
$\quad\quad\; :\overset{\cdot\cdot}{\underset{\cdot\cdot}{I}}:$

54. Determine what is wrong with each Lewis structure and write the correct structure.

(a) $H-H-H-\overset{\cdot\cdot}{N}:$

(b) $:\overset{\cdot\cdot}{\underset{\cdot\cdot}{Cl}}=O=\overset{\cdot\cdot}{\underset{\cdot\cdot}{Cl}}:$

(c) $\quad\quad :\overset{\cdot\cdot}{O}:$
$\quad\quad\quad |$
$H-C-\overset{\cdot\cdot}{\underset{\cdot\cdot}{O}}-H$

(d) $H=\overset{\cdot\cdot}{\underset{\cdot\cdot}{Br}}:$

55. Write a Lewis structure for each molecule or ion. Include resonance structures if necessary.
    (a) SeO_2
    (b) CO_3^{2-}
    (c) ClO^-
    (d) ClO_2^-

56. Write a Lewis structure for each molecule or ion. Include resonance structures if necessary.
    (a) ClO_3^-
    (b) ClO_4^-
    (c) NO_3^-
    (d) SO_3

57. Write a Lewis structure for each ion. Include resonance structures if necessary.
    (a) PO_4^{3-}
    (b) CN^-
    (c) NO_2^-
    (d) SO_3^{2-}

58. Write a Lewis structure for each ion. Include resonance structures if necessary.
    (a) SO_4^{2-}
    (b) HSO_4^- (S is central; H is attached to one of the O atoms)
    (c) NH_4^+
    (d) BrO_2^- (Br is central)

59. Write the Lewis structure for each molecule. These molecules do not follow the octet rule.
    (a) BCl_3
    (b) NO_2
    (c) BH_3

60. Write the Lewis structure for each molecule. These molecules do not follow the octet rule.
    (a) BBr_3
    (b) NO

PREDICTING THE SHAPES OF MOLECULES

61. Determine the number of electron groups around the central atom for each molecule.
    (a) OF_2
    (b) NF_3
    (c) CS_2
    (d) CH_4

62. Determine the number of electron groups around the central atom for each molecule.
    (a) CH_2Cl_2
    (b) SBr_2
    (c) H_2S
    (d) PCl_3

63. Determine the number of bonding groups and the number of lone pairs for each of the molecules in Problem 61. The sum of these should equal your answer to Problem 61.

64. Determine the number of bonding groups and the number of lone pairs for each of the molecules in Problem 62. The sum of these should equal your answer to Problem 62.

65. Determine the molecular geometry of each molecule.
    (a) CBr_4
    (b) H_2CO
    (c) CS_2
    (d) BH_3

66. Determine the molecular geometry of each molecule.
    (a) SiO_2
    (b) BF_3
    (c) $CFCl_3$ (carbon is central)
    (d) H_2CS (carbon is central)

67. Determine the bond angles for each molecule in Problem 65.

68. Determine the bond angles for each molecule in Problem 66.

69. Determine the electron and molecular geometries of each molecule.
    (a) N_2O (oxygen is terminal)
    (b) SO_2
    (c) H_2S
    (d) PF_3

70. Determine the electron and molecular geometries of each molecule. (*Hint:* Determine the geometry around each of the two central atoms.)
    (a) C_2H_2 (skeletal structure HCCH)
    (b) C_2H_4 (skeletal structure H_2CCH_2)
    (c) C_2H_6 (skeletal structure H_3CCH_3)

71. Determine the bond angles for each molecule in Problem 69.

72. Determine the bond angles for each molecule in Problem 70.

73. Determine the electron and molecular geometries of each molecule. For molecules with two central atoms, indicate the geometry about each central atom.
    (a) N_2
    (b) N_2H_2 (skeletal structure HNNH)
    (c) N_2H_4 (skeletal structure H_2NNH_2)

74. Determine the electron and molecular geometries of each molecule. For molecules with more than one central atom, indicate the geometry about each central atom.
    (a) CH_3OH (skeletal structure H_3COH)
    (b) H_3COCH_3 (skeletal structure H_3COCH_3)
    (c) H_2O_2 (skeletal structure HOOH)

75. Determine the molecular geometry of each polyatomic ion.
    (a) CO_3^{2-}
    (b) ClO_2^-
    (c) NO_3^-
    (d) NH_4^+

76. Determine the molecular geometry of each polyatomic ion.
    (a) ClO_4^-
    (b) BrO_2^-
    (c) NO_2^-
    (d) SO_4^{2-}

ELECTRONEGATIVITY AND POLARITY

77. Refer to Figure 2 to determine the electronegativity of each element.
    (a) Mg
    (b) Si
    (c) Br

78. Refer to Figure 2 to determine the electronegativity of each element.
    (a) F
    (b) C
    (c) S

79. List these elements in order of decreasing electronegativity: Rb, Si, Cl, Ca, Ga.

80. List these elements in order of increasing electronegativity: Ba, N, F, Si, Cs.

81. Refer to Figure 2 to find the electronegativity difference between each pair of elements; then refer to Table 2 to classify the bonds that occur between them as pure covalent, polar covalent, or ionic.
    (a) Mg and Br
    (b) Cr and F
    (c) Br and Br
    (d) Si and O

82. Refer to Figure 2 to find the electronegativity difference between each pair of elements; then refer to Table 2 to classify the bonds that occur between them as pure covalent, polar covalent, or ionic.
    (a) K and Cl
    (b) N and N
    (c) C and S
    (d) C and Cl

83. Arrange these diatomic molecules in order of increasing bond polarity: ICl, HBr, H_2, CO

84. Arrange these diatomic molecules in order of decreasing bond polarity: HCl, NO, F_2, HI

85. Classify each diatomic molecule as polar or nonpolar.
    (a) CO
    (b) O_2
    (c) F_2
    (d) HBr

86. Classify each diatomic molecule as polar or nonpolar.
    (a) I_2
    (b) NO
    (c) HCl
    (d) N_2

87. For each polar molecule in Problem 85 draw the molecule and indicate the positive and negative ends of the dipole moment.

88. For each polar molecule in Problem 86 draw the molecule and indicate the positive and negative ends of the dipole moment.

89. Classify each molecule as polar or nonpolar.
    (a) CS_2
    (b) SO_2
    (c) CH_4
    (d) CH_3Cl

90. Classify each molecule as polar or nonpolar.
    (a) H_2CO
    (b) CH_3OH
    (c) CH_2Cl_2
    (d) CO_2

91. Classify each molecule as polar or nonpolar.
    (a) BH_3
    (b) $CHCl_3$
    (c) C_2H_2
    (d) NH_3

92. Classify each molecule as polar or nonpolar.
    (a) N_2H_2
    (b) H_2O_2
    (c) CF_4
    (d) NO_2

CUMULATIVE PROBLEMS

93. Write electron configurations and Lewis structures for each element. Indicate which of the electrons in the electron configuration are shown in the Lewis structure.
    (a) Ca
    (b) Ga
    (c) As
    (d) I

94. Write electron configurations and Lewis structures for each element. Indicate which of the electrons in the electron configuration are shown in the Lewis structure.
    (a) Rb
    (b) Ge
    (c) Kr
    (d) Se

95. Determine whether each compound is ionic or covalent and write the appropriate Lewis structure.
    (a) K_2S
    (b) CHFO (carbon is central)
    (c) MgSe
    (d) PBr_3

96. Determine whether each compound is ionic or covalent and write the appropriate Lewis structure.
    (a) HCN
    (b) ClF
    (c) MgI_2
    (d) CaS

97. Write the Lewis structure for $OCCl_2$ (carbon is central) and determine whether the molecule is polar. Draw the three-dimensional structure for the molecule.

98. Write the Lewis structure for CH_3COH and determine whether the molecule is polar. Draw the three-dimensional structure for the molecule. The skeletal structure is:

$$
\begin{array}{ccc}
\text{H} & \text{O} & \\
\text{H} \quad \text{C} & \text{C} & \text{H} \\
\text{H} & &
\end{array}
$$

99. Write the Lewis structure for acetic acid (a component of vinegar), CH_3COOH, and draw the three-dimensional sketch of the molecule. Its skeletal structure is:

$$
\begin{array}{ccccc}
 & \text{H} & \text{O} & & \\
\text{H} & \text{C} & \text{C} & \text{O} & \text{H} \\
 & \text{H} & & &
\end{array}
$$

100. Write the Lewis structure for benzene, C_6H_6, and draw a three-dimensional sketch of the molecule. The skeletal structure is the ring shown here. (*Hint:* The Lewis structure consists of two resonance structures.)

$$
\begin{array}{ccc}
 & \text{H} & \\
 & \text{C} & \\
\text{HC} & & \text{CH} \\
\text{HC} & & \text{CH} \\
 & \text{C} & \\
 & \text{H} &
\end{array}
$$

101. Consider the neutralization reaction:

$$HCl(aq) + NaOH(aq) \longrightarrow H_2O(l) + NaCl(aq)$$

Write the reaction showing the Lewis structures of each of the reactants and products.

102. Consider the precipitation reaction.

$$Pb(NO_3)_2(aq) + 2\,LiCl(aq) \longrightarrow PbCl_2(s) + 2\,LiNO_3(aq)$$

Write the reaction showing the Lewis structures of each of the reactants and products.

103. Consider the redox reaction:

$$2\,K(s) + Cl_2(g) \longrightarrow 2\,KCl(s)$$

Draw the Lewis structure for each reactant and product, and determine which reactant was oxidized and which one was reduced.

104. Consider the redox reaction:

$$Ca(s) + Br_2(g) \longrightarrow CaBr_2(s)$$

Draw the Lewis structure for each reactant and product, and determine which reactant was oxidized and which one was reduced.

105. Each compound listed contains both ionic and covalent bonds. Write the ionic Lewis structure for each one, including the covalent structure for the polyatomic ion. Write resonance structures if necessary.

(a) KOH

(b) KNO_3

(c) LiIO

(d) $BaCO_3$

106. Each of the compounds listed contains both ionic and covalent bonds. Write an ionic Lewis structure for each one, including the covalent structure for the polyatomic ion. Write resonance structures if necessary.

(a) $RbIO_2$

(b) $Ca(OH)_2$

(c) NH_4Cl

(d) $Sr(CN)_2$

107. Each molecule listed contains an expanded octet (10 or 12 electrons) around the central atom. Write the Lewis structure for each molecule.

(a) PF_5

(b) SF_4

(c) SeF_4

108. Each molecule listed contains an expanded octet (10 or 12 electrons) around the central atom. Write the Lewis structure for each molecule.

(a) ClF_5

(b) SF_6

(c) IF_5

109. Formic acid is responsible for the sting in biting ants. By mass, formic acid is 26.10% C, 4.38% H, and 69.52% O. The molar mass of formic acid is 46.02 g/mol. Find the molecular formula of formic acid and draw its Lewis structure.

110. Diazomethane has the following composition by mass: 28.57% C, 4.80% H, and 66.64% N. The molar mass of diazomethane is 42.04 g/mol. Find the molecular formula of diazomethane and draw its Lewis structure.

111. Free radicals are molecules that contain an odd number of valence electrons and therefore contain an unpaired electron in their Lewis structure. Write the best possible Lewis structure for the free radical HOO. Does Lewis theory predict that HOO is stable? Predict its geometry.

112. Free radicals (as explained in the previous problem) are molecules that contain an odd number of valence electrons. Write the best possible Lewis structure for the free radical CH_3. Predict its geometry.

HIGHLIGHT PROBLEMS

113. Some theories on aging suggest that free radicals cause a variety of diseases and aging. Free radicals (as explained in Problems 111 and 112) are molecules or ions containing an unpaired electron. As you know from Lewis theory, such molecules are not chemically stable and quickly react with other molecules. Free radicals may attack molecules within the cell, such as DNA, changing them and causing cancer or other diseases. Free radicals may also attack molecules on the surfaces of cells, making them appear foreign to the body's immune system. The immune system then attacks the cell and destroys it, weakening the body. Draw the Lewis structure for each of these free radicals, which have been implicated in theories of aging.

(a) O_2^-

(b) O^-

(c) OH

(d) CH_3OO (unpaired electron on terminal oxygen)

114. Free radicals (see Problem 113) are important in many environmentally significant reactions. For example, photochemical smog, which forms as a result of the action of sunlight on air pollutants, is formed in part by these two steps:

$$NO_2 \xrightarrow{\text{UV light}} NO + O$$

$$O + O_2 \longrightarrow O_3$$

The product of this reaction, ozone, is a pollutant in the lower atmosphere. Ozone is an eye and lung irritant and also accelerates the weathering of rubber products. Write Lewis structures for each of the reactants and products in the preceding reactions.

▲ Ozone damages rubber products.

▲ Free radicals, molecules containing unpaired electrons (represented here as X·), may attack biological molecules such as the DNA molecule depicted here.

115. Examine the formulas and space-filling models of the molecules shown here. Determine whether the structure is correct and, if not, make a sketch of the correct structure.

(a) H_2Se

(b) CSe_2

(c) PCl_3

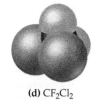

(d) CF_2Cl_2

▶ANSWERS TO SKILLBUILDER EXERCISES

Skillbuilder 1   ·Mg·

Skillbuilder 2   Na⁺ [:B̈r̈:]⁻

Skillbuilder 3 Mg_3N_2

Skillbuilder 4   :C≡O:

Skillbuilder 5
$$
\begin{array}{c}
\ddot{O}: \\
\parallel \\
H-C-H
\end{array}
$$

Skillbuilder 6   [:C̈l—Ö:]⁻

Skillbuilder 7   [:Ö=N̈—Ö:]⁻ ⟷ [:Ö—N̈=Ö:]⁻

Skillbuilder 8   bent

Skillbuilder 9   trigonal pyramidal

Skillbuilder 10
    (a) pure covalent
    (b) ionic
    (c) polar covalent

Skillbuilder 11 CH_4 is nonpolar

▶ANSWERS TO CONCEPTUAL CHECKPOINTS

1 (a)   C and Si both have four dots in their Lewis structure because they are both in the same column in the periodic table.

2 (b)   Aluminum must lose its three valence electrons to get an octet. Sulfur must gain two electrons to get an octet. Therefore, two Al atoms are required for every three S atoms.

3 (c) The Lewis structure of OH^- has eight electrons; six from oxygen, one from hydrogen, and one from the negative charge.

4 (b)   Both NH_3 and H_3O^+ have one lone electron pair.

5 (d)   If there are no lone pairs on the central atom, all of its valence electrons are involved in bonds, so the molecular geometry must be the same as the electron geometry.

ANSWERS TO ODD-NUMBERED EXERCISES

QUESTIONS

1. Bonding theories predict how atoms bond together to form molecules, and they also predict what combinations of atoms form molecules and what combinations do not. Likewise, bonding theories explain the shapes of molecules, which in turn determine many of their physical and chemical properties.

3. Atoms with eight valence electrons are particularly stable and are said to have an octet. Atoms such as hydrogen, helium, lithium, and beryllium are exceptions to the octet rule as they achieve stability when their outermost shell contains two electrons—a duet. A chemical bond is the sharing or transfer of electrons to attain stable electron configurations among the bonding atoms.

5. The Lewis structure for potassium has 1 valence electron, whereas the Lewis structure for monatomic chlorine has 7 valence electrons. From these structures we can determine that if potassium gives up its one valence electron to chlorine, K^+ and Cl^- are formed; therefore the formula must be KCl.

7. Double and triple bonds are shorter and stronger than single bonds.

9. You determine the number of electrons that go into the Lewis structure of a molecule by summing the valence electrons of each atom in the molecule.

11. The octet rule is not sophisticated enough to be correct every time. For example, some molecules that exist in nature have an odd number of valence electrons and thus will not have octets on all their constituent atoms. Some elements tend to form compounds in nature in which they have more (sulfur) or less (boron) than 8 valence electrons.

13. VSEPR theory predicts the shape of molecules using the idea that electron groups repel each other.

15. **a.** 180°   **b.** 120°
    c. 109.5°

17. Electronegativity is the ability of an element to attract electrons within a covalent bond.

19. A polar covalent bond is a covalent bond that has a dipole moment.

21. If a polar liquid and a nonpolar liquid are mixed they will separate into distinct regions because the polar molecules will be attracted to one another and will exclude the nonpolar molecules.

PROBLEMS

23. **a.** $1s^2 2s^2 2p^3$, $\cdot\ddot{N}\colon$
    b. $1s^2 2s^2 2p^2$, $\cdot\dot{C}\cdot$

c. $1s^2 2s^2 2p^6 3s^2 3p^5$, $\colon\ddot{C}l\cdot$

d. $1s^2 2s^2 2p^6 3s^2 3p^6$, $\colon\ddot{A}r\colon$

25. **a.** $\colon\dot{I}\colon$ **b.** $\cdot\ddot{S}\colon$
    c. $\cdot\dot{G}e\cdot$ **d.** $\cdot Ca\cdot$

27. $\colon\dot{X}\colon$ Halogens tend to gain one electron in a chemical reaction.

29. $M\colon$ Alkaline earth metals tend to lose two electrons in a chemical reaction.

31. **a.** Al^{3+} **b.** Mg^{2+}
    c. $\left[\colon\ddot{S}e\colon\right]^{2-}$ **d.** $\left[\colon\ddot{N}\colon\right]^{3-}$

33. **a.** Kr   **b.** Ne
    c. Kr   **d.** Xe

35. **a.** covalent   **b.** ionic
    c. covalent   **d.** ionic

37. **a.** $Na^+\left[\colon\ddot{F}\colon\right]^-$ **b.** $Ca^{2+}\left[\colon\ddot{O}\colon\right]^{2-}$
    c. $\left[\colon\ddot{B}r\colon\right]^- Sr^{2+}\left[\colon\ddot{B}r\colon\right]^-$ **d.** $K^+\left[\colon\ddot{O}\colon\right]^{2-}K^+$

39. **a.** CaS   **b.** $MgBr_2$
    c. CsI   **d.** Ca_3N_2

41. **a.** $\left[\colon\ddot{F}\colon\right]^- Mg^{2+}\left[\colon\ddot{F}\colon\right]^-$ **b.** $Mg^{2+}\left[\colon\ddot{O}\colon\right]^{2-}$
    c. $Mg^{2+}\left[\colon\ddot{N}\colon\right]^{3-} Mg^{2+}\left[\colon\ddot{N}\colon\right]^{3-} Mg^{2+}$

43. **a.** $Cs^+\left[\colon\ddot{C}l\colon\right]^-$ **b.** $Ba^{2+}\left[\colon\ddot{O}\colon\right]^{2-}$
    c. $\left[\colon\dot{I}\colon\right]^- Ca^{2+}\left[\colon\dot{I}\colon\right]^-$

45. **a.** Hydrogen exists as a diatomic molecule because two hydrogen molecules achieve a stable duet when they share their electrons and form a single covalent bond.

b. Iodine achieves a stable octet when two atoms share electrons and form a single bond.

c. Nitrogen achieves a stable octet when two atoms share electrons and form a triple bond.

d. Oxygen achieves a stable octet when two atoms share electrons and form a double bond.

47. **a.** $\begin{array}{c} H-\ddot{P}-H \\ | \\ H \end{array}$ **b.** $\colon\ddot{C}l-\ddot{S}-\ddot{C}l\colon$
    c. $\colon\ddot{F}-\ddot{F}\colon$ **d.** $H-\ddot{I}\colon$

49. **a.** $\ddot{O}=\ddot{O}$ **b.** $\colon C\equiv O\colon$
    c. $H-\ddot{O}-\dot{N}=\ddot{O}$ **d.** $\colon\ddot{O}=\ddot{S}-\ddot{O}\colon$

51. a. H—C≡C—H

b.
```
    H—C=C—H
       |  |
       H  H
```

c. H—N̈=N̈—H

d.
```
    H—N̈—N̈—H
       |   |
       H   H
```

53. a. :N≡N:

b. S̈=Si=S̈

c. H—Ö—H

d.
```
   :Ï—N̈—Ï:
        |
       :Ï:
```

55. a. Ö=S̈e—Ö: ⟷ :Ö—S̈e=Ö

b.
$$\left[\ddot{O}=C-\ddot{\underset{..}{O}}:\right]^{2-} \longleftrightarrow \left[:\ddot{O}-C=\ddot{O}\right]^{2-} \longleftrightarrow \left[:\ddot{O}-C-\ddot{O}:\right]^{2-}$$
(with :Ö: below carbon in each)

c. $\left[:\ddot{C}l-\ddot{O}:\right]^{-}$

d. $\left[:\ddot{O}-\ddot{C}l-\ddot{O}:\right]^{-}$

57. a.
$$\left[\begin{array}{c} :\ddot{O}: \\ | \\ :\ddot{O}-P-\ddot{O}: \\ | \\ :\ddot{O}: \end{array}\right]^{3-}$$

b. $[:C≡N:]^{-}$

c. $\left[:\ddot{O}=N̈-\ddot{O}:\right]^{-}$ ⟷ $\left[:\ddot{O}-N̈=\ddot{O}:\right]^{-}$

d.
$$\left[\begin{array}{c} :\ddot{O}-\ddot{S}-\ddot{O}: \\ | \\ :\ddot{O}: \end{array}\right]^{2-}$$

59. a.
```
   :C̈l—B—C̈l:
        |
       :C̈l:
```

b. Ö=N̈—Ö: ⟷ :Ö—N̈=Ö

c.
```
   H—B—H
      |
      H
```

61. a. 4   **b.** 4

c. 2   **d.** 4

63. a. 3 bonding groups, 1 lone pair

b. 2 bonding groups, 2 lone pairs

c. 4 bonding groups, 0 lone pairs

d. 2 bonding groups, 0 lone pairs

65. a. tetrahedral   **b.** trigonal planar

c. linear   **d.** trigonal planar

67. a. 109.5°   **b.** 120°

c. 180°   **d.** 120°

69. a. linear, linear

b. trigonal planar, bent

c. tetrahedral, bent

d. tetrahedral, trigonal pyramidal

71. a. 180°   **b.** 120°

c. 109.5°   **d.** 109.5°

73. a. linear, linear

b. trigonal planar, bent (about both nitrogen atoms)

c. tetrahedral, trigonal pyramidal (about both nitrogen atoms)

75. a. trigonal planar   **b.** bent

c. trigonal planar   **d.** tetrahedral

77. a. 1.2   **b.** 1.8

c. 2.8

79. Cl > Si > Ga > Ca > Rb

81. a. polar covalent   **b.** ionic

c. pure covalent   **d.** polar covalent

83. H_2 < ICl < HBr < CO

85. a. polar   **b.** nonpolar

c. nonpolar   **d.** polar

87. a. (+):C≡O:(−)

b. nonpolar

c. nonpolar

d. (+)H—B̈r:(−)

89. a. nonpolar   **b.** polar

c. nonpolar   **d.** polar

91. a. nonpolar   **b.** polar

c. nonpolar   **d.** polar

93. a. $1s^22s^22p^63s^23p^64\underline{s^2}$, Ca: (underlined electrons are the ones included)

b. $1s^22s^22p^33s^23p^64\underline{s^2}3d^{10}\underline{4p^1}$, Ġa:

c. $[Ar]4\underline{s^2}3d^{10}\underline{4p^3}$, ·Ȧs:

d. $[Kr]5\underline{s^2}4d^{10}\underline{5p^5}$, :Ï:

95. a. ionic, $K^+\left[:\ddot{S}:\right]^{2-}K^+$

b. covalent,
```
        Ö:
        ‖
   H—C—F̈:
```

c. ionic, $Mg^{2+}\left[:\ddot{S}e:\right]^{2-}$

d. covalent,
```
        :B̈r:
          |
   :B̈r—P—B̈r:
```

97.
```
        ·Ö·
        ‖
   :C̈l—C—C̈l:  polar,
```
```
        C
       ‖ \
      O
     /    \
   Cl      Cl
```

99.
```
    H  Ö:
    |  ‖
  H—C—C—ÖH
    |
    H
```
```
        H   O
        |   ‖
  H⫿⫿⫿C—C
        ▲     \
        H      OH
```

101. H:C̈l: + Na⁺[:Ö:H]⁻ ⟶ H:Ö:H + Na⁺[:C̈l:]⁻

103. K·, :C̈l—C̈l:, $K^+\left[:\ddot{C}l:\right]^{-}$, Cl reduced, K oxidized

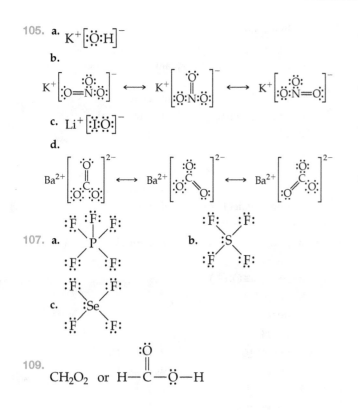

105. a. K$^+$[:Ö:H]$^-$

b.

c. Li$^+$[:Ï:Ö:]$^-$

d.

107. a.

b.

c.

109. CH$_2$O$_2$ or H—C—Ö—H (with :Ö: double bonded to C)

111. H—Ö—Ö· HOO is not stable because one oxygen atom does not have an octet. The geometry for HOO is *bent*.

113. a. [:Ö—Ö:]$^-$ b. [:Ö·]$^-$

c. ·Ö—H   d. H—C—Ö—Ö· (with H above and below C)

115. a. The structure has 2 bonding electron pairs and 2 lone pairs. The Lewis structure is analogous to that of water, and the molecular geometry is bent.

b. Correct

c. The structure has 3 bonding electron pairs and 1 lone pair. The Lewis structure is analogous to that of NH$_3$, and the geometry is trigonal pyramidal.

d. Correct

Oxidation and Reduction

From Chapter 16 of *Introductory Chemistry*, Fourth Edition, Nivaldo J. Tro. Copyright © 2011 by Pearson Education, Inc. Published by Pearson Prentice Hall. All rights reserved.

Oxidation and Reduction

"We have to learn to understand nature and not merely to observe it and endure what it imposes on us."

JOHN DESMOND BERNAL (1901–1971)

1 The End of the Internal Combustion Engine?

American Honda Motor Co. Inc.

▲ FIGURE 1 **A fuel-cell car** The Honda FCX Clarity, a hydrogen-powered, fuel-cell automobile. The only emission is water.

◀ Fuel-cell vehicles (FCVs), such as the one shown here, may someday replace vehicles powered by internal combustion engines. As you can see in this image, FCVs produce only water as exhaust.

It is possible, even likely, that you will see the end of the internal combustion engine within your lifetime. Although it has served us well—powering our airplanes, automobiles, and trains—its time is running out. What will replace it? If our cars don't run on gasoline, what will fuel them? The answers to these questions are not completely settled, but new and better technologies are on the horizon. The most promising of these is the use of **fuel cells** to power electric vehicles. Such whisper-quiet, environmentally friendly supercars are currently available only on a limited basis (◀ Figure 1), but they should become more widely available in the years to come.

In 2007, Honda's next-generation FCX Clarity fuel-cell vehicle made its European debut at the Geneva Motorshow. The four-passenger car has a top speed of 100 mph and a range of 270 miles on one tank of fuel. The electric motor is powered by hydrogen, stored as a compressed gas, and its only emission is water—which is so clean you can drink it. The FCX Clarity became available for lease on a limited basis beginning in 2008 and is slated to become available for purchase in 2015. Other automakers have similar prototype models in development. In addition, several cities around the world—including Palm Springs, California; Washington, D.C.; and Vancouver, British Columbia—are currently testing the feasibility of fuel-cell buses in a pilot program.

Fuel-cell technology is possible because of the tendency of some elements to gain electrons from other elements. The most common type of fuel cell—called the hydrogen–oxygen fuel cell—is based on the reaction between hydrogen and oxygen.

$$2\,H_2(g) + O_2(g) \longrightarrow 2\,H_2O(g)$$

In this reaction, hydrogen and oxygen form covalent bonds with one another. Recall that a single covalent bond is a shared electron pair.

However, since oxygen is more electronegative than hydrogen, the electron pair in a hydrogen–oxygen bond is *unequally* shared, with oxygen getting the larger portion. In effect, oxygen has more electrons in H_2O than in elemental O_2—it has *gained electrons* in the reaction.

In a typical reaction between hydrogen and oxygen, oxygen atoms gain the electrons directly from hydrogen atoms as the reaction proceeds. In a hydrogen–oxygen fuel cell, the same reaction occurs, but the hydrogen and oxygen are separated, forcing the electrons to move through an external wire to get from hydrogen to oxygen. These moving electrons constitute an electrical current, which is used to power the electric motor of a fuel-cell vehicle. In effect, fuel cells use the electron-gaining tendency of oxygen and the electron-losing tendency of hydrogen to force electrons to move through a wire, creating the electricity that powers the car.

Reactions involving the transfer of electrons are called **oxidation–reduction** or **redox reactions**. Besides their application to fuel-cell vehicles, redox reactions are prevalent in nature, in industry, and in many everyday processes. For example, the rusting of iron, the bleaching of hair, and the reactions occurring in batteries all involve redox reactions. Redox reactions are also responsible for providing the energy our bodies need to move, think, and stay alive.

2   Oxidation and Reduction: Some Definitions

Consider the following redox reactions:

$$2\,H_2(g) + O_2(g) \longrightarrow 2\,H_2O(g) \text{ (hydrogen–oxygen fuel-cell reaction)}$$

$$4\,Fe(s) + 3\,O_2(g) \longrightarrow 2\,Fe_2O_3(s) \text{ (rusting of iron)}$$

$$CH_4(g) + 2\,O_2(g) \longrightarrow CO_2(g) + 2\,H_2O(g) \text{ (combustion of methane)}$$

What do they all have in common? Each of these reactions involves one or more elements gaining oxygen. In the hydrogen–oxygen fuel-cell reaction, *hydrogen* gains oxygen as it turns into water. In the rusting of iron, *iron* gains oxygen as it turns into iron oxide, the familiar orange substance we call rust (▼ Figure 2). In the combustion of methane, *carbon* gains oxygen to form carbon dioxide, producing the brilliant blue flame we see on gas stoves (▼ Figure 3). In each

▼ FIGURE 2 **Slow oxidation** Rust is produced by the oxidation of iron to form iron oxide.

Ron Zmiri/Shutterstock.

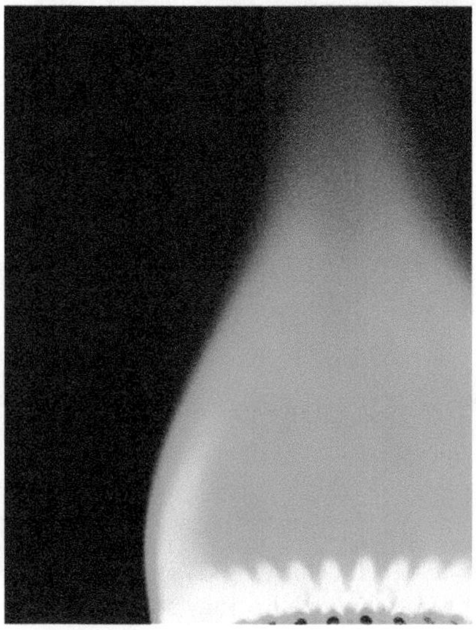

Getty Images.

▲ FIGURE 3 **Rapid oxidation** The flame on a gas stove results from the oxidation of carbon in natural gas.

case, the substance that gains oxygen is oxidized in the reaction. One definition of *oxidation*—though not the most fundamental one—is simply the *gaining of oxygen*.

Now consider these same three reactions in reverse:

$$2\,H_2O(g) \longrightarrow 2\,H_2(g) + O_2(g)$$

$$2\,Fe_2O_3(s) \longrightarrow 4\,Fe(s) + 3\,O_2(g)$$

$$CO_2(g) + 2\,H_2O(g) \longrightarrow CH_4(g) + 2\,O_2(g)$$

Each of these reactions involves loss of oxygen. In the first reaction, hydrogen loses oxygen; in the second reaction, iron loses oxygen; and in the third reaction, carbon loses oxygen. In each case, the substance that loses oxygen is reduced in the reaction. One definition of *reduction* is simply the *loss of oxygen*.

Redox reactions need not involve oxygen, however. Consider, for example, the similarities between the following two reactions:

$$4\,Li(s) + O_2(g) \longrightarrow 2\,Li_2O(s)$$

$$2\,Li(s) + Cl_2(g) \longrightarrow 2\,LiCl(s)$$

In both cases, lithium (a metal with a strong tendency to lose electrons) reacts with an electronegative nonmetal (which has a tendency to gain electrons). In both cases, lithium atoms lose electrons to become positive ions—lithium is oxidized.

$$Li \longrightarrow Li^+ + e^-$$

The electrons lost by lithium are gained by the nonmetals, which become negative ions—the nonmetals are reduced.

$$O_2 + 4e^- \longrightarrow 2\,O^{2-}$$

$$Cl_2 + 2e^- \longrightarrow 2\,Cl^-$$

A more fundamental definition of **oxidation**, then, is simply the *loss of electrons*, and a more fundamental definition of **reduction** is the *gain of electrons*.

Notice that *oxidation and reduction must occur together*. If one substance loses electrons (oxidation), then another substance must gain electrons (reduction) (◄ Figure 4). The substance that is oxidized is called the **reducing agent** because it causes the reduction of the other substance. Similarly, the substance that is reduced is called the **oxidizing agent** because it causes the oxidation of the other substance. For example, consider our hydrogen–oxygen fuel-cell reaction.

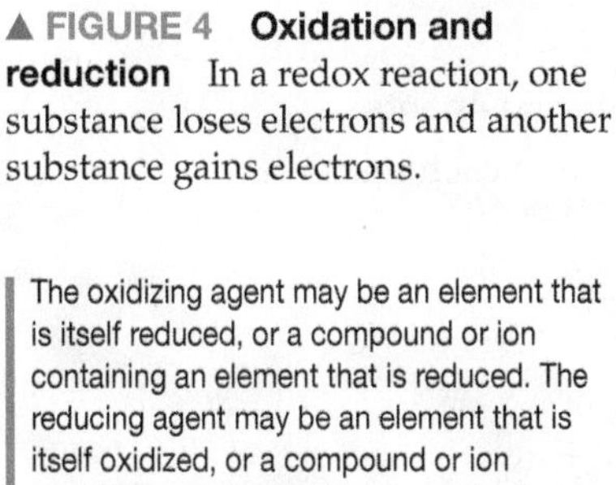

$$\underset{\text{Reducing agent}}{2\,H_2(g)} + \underset{\text{Oxidizing agent}}{O_2(g)} \longrightarrow 2\,H_2O(g)$$

In this reaction, hydrogen is oxidized, making it the reducing agent. Oxygen is reduced, making it the oxidizing agent. Substances such as oxygen, which have a strong tendency to attract electrons, are good oxidizing agents—they tend to cause the oxidation of other substances. Substances such as hydrogen, which have a strong tendency to give up electrons, are good reducing agents—they tend to cause the reduction of other substances.

To summarize:

* Oxidation—the loss of electrons
* Reduction—the gain of electrons
* Oxidizing agent—the substance being reduced
* Reducing agent—the substance being oxidized

These definitions of oxidation and reduction are useful because they show the origin of the term *oxidation*, and they allow us to quickly identify reactions involving elemental oxygen as oxidation and reduction reactions. However, as you will see, these definitions are *not* the most fundamental.

In redox reactions between a metal and a nonmetal, the metal is oxidized and the nonmetal is reduced.

Helpful mnemonics: OIL RIG—Oxidation **Is** **L**oss (of electrons); Reduction **Is** **G**ain (of electrons). LEO the lion says GER—**L**ose **E**lectrons **O**xidation; **G**ain **E**lectrons **R**eduction.

e^-

| The substance losing electrons is oxidized. | The substance gaining electrons is reduced. |

▲ **FIGURE 4** **Oxidation and reduction** In a redox reaction, one substance loses electrons and another substance gains electrons.

The oxidizing agent may be an element that is itself reduced, or a compound or ion containing an element that is reduced. The reducing agent may be an element that is itself oxidized, or a compound or ion containing an element that is oxidized.

EXAMPLE 1 Identifying Oxidation and Reduction

Identify the substance being oxidized and the substance being reduced in each reaction.

(a) $2 \, Mg(s) + O_2(g) \longrightarrow 2 \, MgO(s)$

(b) $Fe(s) + Cl_2(g) \longrightarrow FeCl_2(s)$

(c) $Zn(s) + Fe^{2+}(aq) \longrightarrow Zn^{2+}(aq) + Fe(s)$

SOLUTION

(a) In this reaction, magnesium is gaining oxygen and losing electrons to oxygen. Mg is therefore oxidized, and O_2 is reduced.

(b) In this reaction, a metal (Fe) is reacting with an electronegative nonmetal (Cl_2). Fe loses electrons and is therefore oxidized, while Cl_2 gains electrons and is therefore reduced.

(c) In this reaction, electrons are transferred from the Zn to the Fe^{2+}. Zn loses electrons and is oxidized. Fe^{2+} gains electrons and is reduced.

▶**SKILLBUILDER 1 | Identifying Oxidation and Reduction**

Identify the substance being oxidized and the substance being reduced in each reaction.

(a) $2 \, K(s) + Cl_2(g) \longrightarrow 2 \, KCl(s)$

(b) $2 \, Al(s) + 3 \, Sn^{2+}(aq) \longrightarrow 2 \, Al^{3+}(aq) + 3 \, Sn(s)$

(c) $C(s) + O_2(g) \longrightarrow CO_2(g)$

▶**FOR MORE PRACTICE** Example 11; Problems 33, 34, 35, 36.

EXAMPLE 2 Identifying Oxidizing and Reducing Agents

Identify the oxidizing agent and the reducing agent in each reaction.

(a) $2 \, Mg(s) + O_2(g) \longrightarrow 2 \, MgO(s)$

(b) $Fe(s) + Cl_2(g) \longrightarrow FeCl_2(s)$

(c) $Zn(s) + Fe^{2+}(aq) \longrightarrow Zn^{2+}(aq) + Fe(s)$

SOLUTION

In the previous example, we identified the substance being oxidized and reduced for these reactions. Recall that the substance being oxidized is the reducing agent, and the substance being reduced is the oxidizing agent.

(a) Mg is oxidized and is therefore the reducing agent; O_2 is reduced and is therefore the oxidizing agent.

(b) Fe is oxidized and is therefore the reducing agent; Cl_2 is reduced and is therefore the oxidizing agent.

(c) Zn is oxidized and is therefore the reducing agent; Fe^{2+} is reduced and is therefore the oxidizing agent.

▶**SKILLBUILDER 2 | Identifying Oxidizing and Reducing Agents**

Identify the oxidizing agent and the reducing agent in each reaction.

(a) $2 \, K(s) + Cl_2(g) \longrightarrow 2 \, KCl(s)$

(b) $2 \, Al(s) + 3 \, Sn^{2+}(aq) \longrightarrow 2 \, Al^{3+}(aq) + 3 \, Sn(s)$

(c) $C(s) + O_2(g) \longrightarrow CO_2(g)$

▶**FOR MORE PRACTICE** Example 12; Problems 37, 38.

✔ **CONCEPTUAL CHECKPOINT 1**

An oxidizing agent:

(a) is always oxidized.

(b) is always reduced.

(c) can either be oxidized or reduced, depending on the reaction.

3 Oxidation States: Electron Bookkeeping

For many redox reactions, such as those involving oxygen or other highly electronegative elements, the substances being oxidized and reduced can be identified easily by inspection. For other redox reactions, identification is more difficult. For example, consider the redox reaction between carbon and sulfur.

$$C + 2\,S \longrightarrow CS_2$$

What is oxidized here? What is reduced? In order to easily identify oxidation and reduction, chemists have devised a scheme to track electrons and where they go in chemical reactions. In this scheme—which is like bookkeeping for electrons—all shared electrons are assigned to the most electronegative element. Then a number—called the **oxidation state** or the **oxidation number**—is computed for each element based on the number of electrons assigned to it.

The procedure just described is a bit cumbersome in practice. However, its main results can be summarized in a series of rules. The easiest way to assign oxidation states is to follow these rules.

Do not confuse oxidation state with ionic charge. A substance need not be ionic to have an assigned oxidation state.

These rules are hierarchical. If any two rules conflict, follow the rule that is higher on the list.

Nonmetal	Oxidation State	Example
fluorine	−1	MgF_2 −1 ox state
hydrogen	+1	H_2O +1 ox state
oxygen	−2	CO_2 −2 ox state
Group 7A	−1	CCl_4 −1 ox state
Group 6A	−2	H_2S −2 ox state
Group 5A	−3	NH_3 −3 ox state

Rules for Assigning Oxidation States

Examples

(1) The oxidation state of an atom in a free element is 0.

Cu Cl_2
0 ox state   0 ox state

(2) The oxidation state of a monoatomic ion is equal to its charge.

Ca^{2+} Cl^-
+2 ox state   −1 ox state

(3) The sum of the oxidation states of all atoms in:
- a neutral molecule or formula unit is 0.

H_2O
$2(\text{H ox state}) + 1(\text{O ox state}) = 0$

- an ion is equal to the charge of the ion.

NO_3^-
$1(\text{N ox state}) + 3(\text{O ox state}) = -1$

(4) In their compounds,
- Group I metals have an oxidation state of +1.

NaCl
+1 ox state

- Group II metals have an oxidation state of +2.

CaF_2
+2 ox state

(5) In their compounds, nonmetals are assigned oxidation states according to the hierarchical table at left. Entries at the top of the table have priority over entries at the bottom.

EXAMPLE 3 Assigning Oxidation States

Assign an oxidation state to each atom in each of the following.

(a) Br_2 (b) K^+ (c) LiF   (d) CO_2 (e) SO_4^{2-} (f) Na_2O_2

Since Br_2 is a free element, the oxidation state of both Br atoms is 0 (Rule 1).	**SOLUTION**
	(a) Br_2
	  Br Br
	  0 0

Since K^+ is a monoatomic ion, the oxidation state of the K^+ ion is +1 (Rule 2).	**(b)** K^+
	  K^+
	  +1

The oxidation state of Li is +1 (Rule 4). The oxidation state of F is −1 (Rule 5). Since this is a neutral compound, the sum of the oxidation states is 0 (Rule 3).	**(c)** LiF
	  Li F
	  +1 −1 sum: $+1 - 1 = 0$

The oxidation state of oxygen is −2 (Rule 5). The oxidation state of carbon must be deduced from Rule 3, which states that the sum of the oxidation states of all the atoms must be 0. Since there are two oxygen atoms, the oxidation state of O must be multiplied by 2 when calculating the sum.	**(d)** CO_2
	  (C ox state) + 2(O ox state) = 0
	  (C ox state) + 2(−2) = 0
	  (C ox state) − 4 = 0
	  C ox state = +4
	  C O_2
	  +4 −2
	  sum: $+4 + 2(-2) = 0$

The oxidation state of oxygen is −2 (Rule 5). The oxidation state of S is expected to be −2 (Rule 5). However, if that were the case, the sum of the oxidation states would not equal the charge of the ion. Since O is higher on the list, it takes priority, and the oxidation state of sulfur is calculated by setting the sum of all of the oxidation states equal to −2 (the charge of the ion).	**(e)** SO_4^{2-}
	  (S ox state) + 4(O ox state) = −2
	  (S ox state) + 4(−2) = −2
	    (Oxygen takes priority over sulfur.)
	  (S ox state) − 8 = −2
	  S ox state = −2 + 8
	  S ox state = +6
	  S O_4^{2-}
	  +6 −2
	  sum: $+6 + 4(-2) = -2$

The oxidation state of sodium is +1 (Rule 4). The oxidation state of O is expected to be −2 (Rule 5). However, Na takes priority, and we deduce the oxidation state of O by setting the sum of all of the oxidation states equal to 0.	**(f)** Na_2O_2
	  2(Na ox state) + 2(O ox state) = 0
	  2(+1) + 2(O ox state) = 0
	    (Sodium takes priority over oxygen.)
	  +2 + 2(O ox state) = 0
	  O ox state = −1
	  Na_2 O_2
	  +1 −1
	  sum: $2(+1) + 2(-1) = 0$

▶**SKILLBUILDER 3 | Assigning Oxidation States**

Assign an oxidation state to each atom in each of the following.

(a) Zn   (b) Cu^{2+} (c) $CaCl_2$ (d) CF_4 (e) NO_2^- (f) SO_3

▶**FOR MORE PRACTICE**   Example 13; Problems 45, 46, 47, 48, 49, 50, 51, 52, 53, 54.

EVERYDAY CHEMISTRY

The Bleaching of Hair

College students, both male and female, with bleached hair are a common sight on most campuses. Many students bleach their own hair with home-bleaching kits available at most drugstores and supermarkets. These kits normally contain hydrogen peroxide (H_2O_2), an excellent oxidizing agent. When applied to hair, hydrogen peroxide oxidizes melanin, the dark pigment that gives hair color. Once melanin is oxidized, it no longer imparts a dark color to hair, leaving the hair with the familiar bleached look.

Hydrogen peroxide also oxidizes other components of hair. For example, the protein molecules in hair contain —SH groups called *thiols*. Thiols are normally slippery (they slide across each other). Hydrogen peroxide oxidizes these thiol groups to sulfonic acid groups (—SO_3H). Sulfonic acid groups are stickier, causing hair to tangle more easily. Consequently, people with heavily bleached hair often use conditioners. Conditioners contain compounds that form thin, lubricating coatings on individual hair shafts. These coatings prevent tangling and make hair softer and more manageable.

CAN YOU ANSWER THIS? *Assign oxidation states to the atoms of H_2O_2. Which atoms in H_2O_2 do you think change oxidation state when H_2O_2 oxidizes hair?*

▲ Hair is often bleached using hydrogen peroxide, a good oxidizing agent.

John-Francis Bourke/Digital Vision/Getty Images.

Now let's return to our original question. What is being oxidized and what is being reduced in the following reaction?

$$C + 2\,S \longrightarrow CS_2$$

We use the oxidation state rules to assign oxidation states to all elements on both sides of the equation.

$$\underset{0}{C} + 2\,\underset{0}{S} \longrightarrow \underset{+4\;-2}{CS_2}$$

Carbon went from an oxidation state of 0 to +4. In terms of our electron bookkeeping scheme (the assigned oxidation state), carbon *lost electrons* and was *oxidized*. Sulfur went from an oxidation state of 0 to −2. In terms of our electron bookkeeping scheme, sulfur *gained electrons* and was *reduced*.

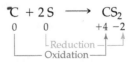

In terms of oxidation states, we define oxidation and reduction as follows.

Oxidation—an increase in oxidation state
Reduction—a decrease in oxidation state

EXAMPLE 4   Using Oxidation States to Identify Oxidation and Reduction

Use oxidation states to identify the element that is being oxidized and the element that is being reduced in the redox reaction.

$$Ca(s) + 2 H_2O(l) \longrightarrow Ca(OH)_2(aq) + H_2(g)$$

Assign an oxidation state to each atom in the reaction. Since Ca increased in oxidation state, it was oxidized. Since H decreased in oxidation state, it was reduced. (Note that oxygen has the same oxidation state on both sides of the equation and was therefore neither oxidized nor reduced.)	**SOLUTION** 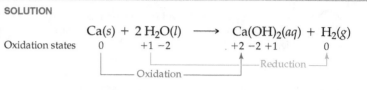

▶**SKILLBUILDER 4** | Using Oxidation States to Identify Oxidation and Reduction

Use oxidation states to identify the element that is being oxidized and the element that is being reduced in the redox reaction.

$$Sn(s) + 4 HNO_3(aq) \longrightarrow SnO_2(s) + 4 NO_2(g) + 2 H_2O(g)$$

▶**FOR MORE PRACTICE**   Problems 57, 58, 59, 60.

✓ CONCEPTUAL CHECKPOINT 2

In which of the following does nitrogen have the *lowest* oxidation state?

(a) N_2

(b) NO

(c) NO_2

(d) NH_3

---

4   Balancing Redox Equations

Some redox reactions can be balanced in a way similar to balancing chemical equations by inspection. However, redox reactions occurring in aqueous solutions are usually difficult to balance by inspection and require a special procedure called the *half-reaction method of balancing*. In this procedure, the overall equation is broken down into two **half-reactions**: one for oxidation and one for reduction. The half-reactions are balanced individually and then added together. For example, consider the redox reaction:

$$Al(s) + Ag^+(aq) \longrightarrow Al^{3+}(aq) + Ag(s)$$

We assign oxidation numbers to all atoms to determine what is being oxidized and what is being reduced.

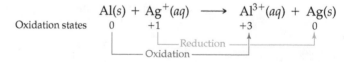

We then divide the reaction into two half-reactions, one for oxidation and one for reduction.

Oxidation: $Al(s) \longrightarrow Al^{3+}(aq)$

Reduction: $Ag^+(aq) \longrightarrow Ag(s)$

We then balance the two half-reactions individually. In this case, the half-reactions are already balanced with respect to mass—the number of each type of atom on both sides of each half-reaction is the same. However, the equations are not balanced with respect to charge—in the oxidation half-reaction, the left side of the equation has 0 charge while the right side has +3 charge, and in the reduction half-reaction, the left side has +1 charge and the right side has 0 charge. We balance the charge of each half-reaction individually by adding the appropriate number of electrons to make the charges on both sides equal.

$$Al(s) \longrightarrow Al^{3+}(aq) + 3e^- \quad \text{(zero charge on both sides)}$$

$$1e^- + Ag^+(aq) \longrightarrow Ag(s) \quad \text{(zero charge on both sides)}$$

Since these half-reactions must occur together, the number of electrons lost in the oxidation half-reaction must equal the number gained in the reduction half-reaction. We equalize these by multiplying one or both half-reactions by appropriate whole numbers to equalize the electrons lost and gained. In this case, we multiply the reduction half-reaction by 3.

$$Al(s) \longrightarrow Al^{3+}(aq) + 3e^-$$

$$3 \times [1e^- + Ag^+(aq) \longrightarrow Ag(s)]$$

We then add the half-reactions together, canceling electrons and other species as necessary.

$$Al(s) \longrightarrow Al^{3+}(aq) + 3\cancel{e}$$

$$\underline{3\cancel{e} + 3\,Ag^+(aq) \longrightarrow 3\,Ag(s)}$$

$$Al(s) + 3\,Ag^+(aq) \longrightarrow Al^{3+}(aq) + 3\,Ag(s)$$

Reactants	Products
1 Al	1 Al
3 Ag	3 Ag
+3 charge	+3 charge

Lastly, we verify that the equation is balanced, with respect to both mass and charge as shown in the margin. Notice that the charge need not be zero on both sides of the equation—it just has to be *equal* on both sides. The equation is balanced.

A general procedure for balancing redox reactions is given in the following procedure box. Since aqueous solutions are often acidic or basic, the procedure must account for the presence of H^+ ions or OH^- ions. We cover acidic solutions in the examples that follow and demonstrate how to balance redox reactions in basic solutions in Example 8.

Balancing Redox Equations Using the Half-Reaction Method	EXAMPLE 5 Balance the redox reaction.	EXAMPLE 6 Balance the redox reaction.
1. **Assign oxidation states** to all atoms and identify the substances being oxidized and reduced.	SOLUTION $$Al(s) + Cu^{2+}(aq) \longrightarrow$$ $$0 \qquad +2$$ $$Al^{3+}(aq) + Cu(s)$$ $$+3 \qquad 0$$ Oxidation / Reduction	SOLUTION $$Fe^{2+}(aq) + MnO_4^-(aq) \longrightarrow$$ $$+2 \qquad +7\ -2$$ $$Fe^{3+}(aq) + Mn^{2+}(aq)$$ $$+3 \qquad +2$$ Oxidation / Reduction
2. **Separate the overall reaction into two half-reactions,** one for oxidation and one for reduction.	OXIDATION $Al(s) \longrightarrow Al^{3+}(aq)$ REDUCTION $Cu^{2+}(aq) \longrightarrow Cu(s)$	OXIDATION $Fe^{2+}(aq) \longrightarrow Fe^{3+}(aq)$ REDUCTION $MnO_4^-(aq) \longrightarrow Mn^{2+}(aq)$

263

3. **Balance each half-reaction with respect to mass** in the following order.

   - Balance all elements other than H and O.

   - Balance O by adding H_2O.

   - Balance H by adding H^+.

All elements other than hydrogen and oxygen are balanced, so proceed to the next step. No oxygen; proceed to the next step. No hydrogen; proceed to the next step.	All elements other than hydrogen and oxygen are balanced, so proceed to next step. $Fe^{2+}(aq) \longrightarrow Fe^{3+}(aq)$ $MnO_4^-(aq) \longrightarrow$ $\qquad Mn^{2+}(aq) + \mathbf{4\ H_2O}(l)$ $Fe^{2+}(aq) \longrightarrow Fe^{3+}(aq)$ $\mathbf{8\ H^+}(aq) + MnO_4^-(aq) \longrightarrow$ $\qquad Mn^{2+}(aq) + 4\ H_2O(l)$

4. **Balance each half-reaction with respect to charge** by adding electrons to the right side of the oxidation half-reaction and the left side of the reduction half-reaction. (The sum of the charges on both sides of each equation should then be equal.)

$Al(s) \longrightarrow Al^{3+}(aq) + \mathbf{3e^-}$ $\mathbf{2e^-} + Cu^{2+}(aq) \longrightarrow Cu(s)$	$Fe^{2+}(aq) \longrightarrow Fe^{3+}(aq) + \mathbf{1e^-}$ $\mathbf{5e^-} + 8\ H^+(aq) + MnO_4^-(aq) \longrightarrow$ $\qquad Mn^{2+}(aq) + 4\ H_2O(l)$

5. **Make the number of electrons in both half-reactions equal** by multiplying one or both half-reactions by a small whole number.

$\mathbf{2} \times [Al(s) \longrightarrow Al^{3+}(aq) + 3e^-]$ $\mathbf{3} \times [2e^- + Cu^{2+}(aq) \longrightarrow Cu(s)]$	$\mathbf{5} \times [Fe^{2+}(aq) \longrightarrow Fe^{3+}(aq) + 1e^-]$ $5e^- + 8\ H^+(aq) + MnO_4^-(aq) \longrightarrow$ $\qquad Mn^{2+}(aq) + 4\ H_2O(l)$

6. **Add the two half-reactions together**, canceling electrons and other species as necessary.

$2\ Al(s) \longrightarrow 2\ Al^{3+}(aq) + \cancel{6e^-}$ $\underline{\cancel{6e^-} + 3\ Cu^{2+}(aq) \longrightarrow 3\ Cu(s)}$ $2\ Al(s) + 3\ Cu^{2+}(aq) \longrightarrow$ $\qquad 2\ Al^{3+}(aq) + 3\ Cu(s)$	$5\ Fe^{2+}(aq) \longrightarrow 5\ Fe^{3+}(aq) + \cancel{5e^-}$ $\cancel{5e^-} + 8\ H^+(aq) + MnO_4^-(aq)$ $\qquad \longrightarrow Mn^{2+}(aq) + 4\ H_2O(l)$ $\overline{5\ Fe^{2+}(aq) + 8\ H^+(aq) + MnO_4^-(aq)}$ $\longrightarrow 5\ Fe^{3+}(aq) + Mn^{2+}(aq) + 4\ H_2O(l)$

7. **Verify that the reaction is balanced** with respect to both mass and charge.

Reactants	Products
2 Al	2 Al
3 Cu	3 Cu
+6 charge	+6 charge

Reactants	Products
5 Fe	5 Fe
8 H	8 H
1 Mn	1 Mn
4 O	4 O
+17 charge	+17 charge

▶**SKILLBUILDER 5**

Balance the following redox reaction occurring in acidic solution.

$$H^+(aq) + Cr(s) \longrightarrow H_2(g) + Cr^{3+}(aq)$$

▶**SKILLBUILDER 6**

Balance the following redox reaction occurring in acidic solution.

$$Cu(s) + NO_3^-(aq) \longrightarrow Cu^{2+}(aq) + NO_2(g)$$

▶**FOR MORE PRACTICE** Example 14; Problems 61, 62, 63, 64.

EXAMPLE 7   Balancing Redox Reactions

Balance the following redox reaction occurring in acidic solution.

$$I^-(aq) + Cr_2O_7^{2-}(aq) \longrightarrow Cr^{3+}(aq) + I_2(s)$$

1. Follow the half-reaction method for balancing redox reactions. Begin by assigning oxidation states.	**SOLUTION** $$\underset{-1}{I^-}(aq) + \underset{+6 \;\; -2}{Cr_2O_7^{2-}}(aq) \longrightarrow \underset{+3}{Cr^{3+}}(aq) + \underset{0}{I_2}(s)$$ Reduction ⟶ Oxidation ⟶
2. Separate the overall reaction into two half-reactions.	**OXIDATION** $I^-(aq) \longrightarrow I_2(s)$ **REDUCTION** $Cr_2O_7^{2-}(aq) \longrightarrow Cr^{3+}(aq)$
3. Balance each half-reaction with respect to mass.	
• Balance all elements other than H and O.	$2\,I^-(aq) \longrightarrow I_2(aq)$ $Cr_2O_7^{2-}(aq) \longrightarrow 2\,Cr^{3+}(s)$
• Balance O by adding H_2O.	$2\,I^-(aq) \longrightarrow I_2(s)$ $Cr_2O_7^{2-}(aq) \longrightarrow 2\,Cr^{3+}(aq) + 7\,H_2O(l)$
• Balance H by adding H^+.	$2\,I^-(aq) \longrightarrow I_2(s)$ $14\,H^+(aq) + Cr_2O_7^{2-}(aq) \longrightarrow 2\,Cr^{3+}(aq) + 7\,H_2O(l)$
4. Balance each half-reaction with respect to charge.	$2\,I^-(aq) \longrightarrow I_2(s) + 2e^-$ $6e^- + 14\,H^+(aq) + Cr_2O_7^{2-}(aq) \longrightarrow 2\,Cr^{3+}(aq) + 7\,H_2O(l)$
5. Make the number of electrons in both half-reactions equal.	$3 \times [2\,I^-(aq) \longrightarrow I_2(s) + 2e^-]$ $6e^- + 14\,H^+(aq) + Cr_2O_7^{2-}(aq) \longrightarrow 2\,Cr^{3+}(aq) + 7\,H_2O(l)$
6. Add the half-reactions together.	$6\,I^-(aq) \longrightarrow 3\,I_2(s) + \cancel{6e^-}$ $\cancel{6e^-} + 14\,H^+(aq) + Cr_2O_7^{2-}(aq) \longrightarrow 2\,Cr^{3+}(aq) + 7\,H_2O(l)$ $\overline{6\,I^-(aq) + 14\,H^+(aq) + Cr_2O_7^{2-}(aq) \longrightarrow 3\,I_2(s) + 2\,Cr^{3+}(aq) + 7\,H_2O(l)}$
7. Verify that the reaction is balanced.	**Reactants** **Products** 6 I 6 I 14 H 14 H 2 Cr 2 Cr 7 O 7 O +6 charge +6 charge

▶ **SKILLBUILDER 7 | Balancing Redox Reactions**

Balance the following redox reaction occurring in acidic solution.

$$Sn(s) + MnO_4^-(aq) \longrightarrow Sn^{2+}(aq) + Mn^{2+}(aq)$$

▶ **FOR MORE PRACTICE**   Problems 65, 66, 67, 68.

When a redox reaction occurs in basic solution, we follow the same general procedure with one addition: the neutralization of H^+ with OH^-. The H^+ and OH^- combine to form water, as shown in the following example.

EXAMPLE 8 Balancing Redox Reactions Occurring in Basic Solution

Balance the following redox reaction occurring in basic solution.

$$CN^-(aq) + MnO_4^-(aq) \longrightarrow CNO^-(aq) + MnO_2(s) \qquad \text{(basic solution)}$$

1. Follow the half-reaction method for balancing redox reactions. Begin by assigning oxidation states.	**SOLUTION** $\quad CN^-(aq) + MnO_4^-(aq) \longrightarrow CNO^-(aq) + MnO_2(s)$ +2 −3 $\qquad$ +7 −2 $\qquad\qquad$ +4 −3 −2 $\qquad$ +4 −2 └─ Reduction ─┘ └─── Oxidation ───┘
2. Separate the overall reaction into two half-reactions.	**OXIDATION** $\ CN^-(aq) \longrightarrow CNO^-(aq)$ **REDUCTION** $\ MnO_4^-(aq) \longrightarrow MnO_2(s)$
3. Balance each half-reaction with respect to mass.	
• Balance all elements other than H and O.	All elements other than H and O are already balanced.
• Balance O by adding H_2O.	$CN^-(aq) + \mathbf{H_2O}(l) \longrightarrow CNO^-(aq)$ $MnO_4^-(aq) \longrightarrow MnO_2(s) + \mathbf{2\,H_2O}(l)$
• Balance H by adding H^+.	$CN^-(aq) + H_2O(l) \longrightarrow CNO^-(aq) + \mathbf{2\,H^+}(aq)$ $MnO_4^-(aq) + \mathbf{4\,H^+}(aq) \longrightarrow MnO_2(s) + 2\,H_2O(l)$
• Neutralize H^+ by adding OH^-. Add the same number of OH^- to each side of the equation (to preserve mass balance).	$CN^-(aq) + H_2O(l) + \mathbf{2\,OH^-}(aq) \longrightarrow CNO^-(aq) + \underline{2\,H^+(aq) + \mathbf{2\,OH^-}(aq)}$ $\ \mathbf{2\,H_2O}(l)$ $MnO_4^-(aq) + \underline{4\,H^+(aq) + \mathbf{4\,OH^-}(aq)} \longrightarrow MnO_2(s) + 2\,H_2O(l) + \mathbf{4\,OH^-}(aq)$ $\ \mathbf{4\,H_2O}(l)$
• Cancel any water molecules that occur on both sides of a half reaction.	$CN^-(aq) + \cancel{H_2O}(l) + 2\,OH^-(aq) \longrightarrow CNO^-(aq) + 2\,H_2O(l)$ $MnO_4^-(aq) + 2\cancel{4}\,H_2O(l) \longrightarrow MnO_2(s) + \cancel{2\,H_2O}(l) + 4\,OH^-(aq)$
4. Balance each half-reaction with respect to charge.	$CN^-(aq) + 2\,OH^-(aq) \longrightarrow CNO^-(aq) + H_2O(l) + \mathbf{2e^-}$ $\mathbf{3e^-} + MnO_4^-(aq) + 2\,H_2O(l) \longrightarrow MnO_2(s) + 4\,OH^-(aq)$
5. Make the number of electrons in both half-reactions equal.	$\mathbf{3} \times [CN^-(aq) + 2\,OH^-(aq) \longrightarrow CNO^-(aq) + H_2O(l) + 2e^-]$ $\mathbf{2} \times [3e^- + MnO_4^-(aq) + 2\,H_2O(l) \longrightarrow MnO_2(s) + 4\,OH^-(aq)]$
6. Add the half-reactions together and cancel.	$3\,CN^-(aq) + 6\cancel{\,OH^-}(aq) \longrightarrow 3\,CNO^-(aq) + 3\,H_2O(l) + \cancel{6e^-}$ $\cancel{6e^-} + 2\,MnO_4^-(aq) + 4\,H_2O(l) \longrightarrow 2\,MnO_2(s) + 2\,8\,OH^-(aq)$ $\overline{3\,CN^-(aq) + 2\,MnO_4^-(aq) + H_2O(l) \longrightarrow 3\,CNO^-(aq) + 2\,MnO_2(s) + 2\,OH^-(aq)}$
7. Verify that the reaction is balanced.	<table><tr><th>Reactants</th><th>Products</th></tr><tr><td>3 C</td><td>3 C</td></tr><tr><td>3 N</td><td>3 N</td></tr><tr><td>2 Mn</td><td>2 Mn</td></tr><tr><td>9 O</td><td>9 O</td></tr><tr><td>2 H</td><td>2 H</td></tr><tr><td>−5 charge</td><td>−5 charge</td></tr></table>

▶ **SKILLBUILDER 8** | **Balancing Redox Reactions**

Balance the following redox reaction occurring in basic solution.

$$H_2O_2(aq) + ClO_2(aq) \longrightarrow ClO_2^-(aq) + O_2(g)$$

▶ **FOR MORE PRACTICE** Problems 69, 70.

CHEMISTRY IN THE ENVIRONMENT

Photosynthesis and Respiration: Energy for Life

All living things require energy, and most of that energy comes from the sun. Solar energy reaches Earth in the form of electromagnetic radiation. This radiation keeps our planet at a temperature that allows life as we know it to flourish. But the wavelengths that make up visible light have an additional and very crucial role to play in the maintenance of life. Plants capture this light and use it to make energy-rich organic molecules such as carbohydrates. Animals get their energy by eating plants or by eating other animals that have eaten plants. So ultimately, virtually all of the energy for life comes from sunlight.

But in chemical terms, how is this energy captured, transferred from organism to organism, and used? *The key reactions in these processes all involve oxidation and reduction.*

Most living things use chemical energy through a process known as *respiration*. In respiration, energy-rich molecules, typified by the sugar glucose, are "burned" in a reaction that can be summarized as follows:

$$\underset{\text{Glucose}}{C_6H_{12}O_6} + \underset{\text{Oxygen}}{6\,O_2} \longrightarrow \underset{\text{Water}}{6\,CO_2} + \text{energy}$$

You can easily see that respiration is a redox reaction. On the simplest level, it is clear that some of the atoms in glucose are gaining oxygen. More precisely, we can use the rules for assigning oxidation states to show that carbon is oxidized from an oxidation number of 0 in glucose to +4 in carbon dioxide.

Respiration is also an exothermic reaction—it releases energy. If you burn glucose in a test tube, the energy is lost as heat. Living things, however, have devised ways of capturing the energy released and using it to power their life processes, such as movement, growth, and the synthesis of other life-sustaining molecules.

Respiration is one half of a larger cycle; the other half is *photosynthesis*. Photosynthesis is the series of reactions by which green plants capture the energy of sunlight and store it as chemical energy in compounds such as glucose. Photosynthesis can be summarized as follows:

$$\underset{\substack{\text{Carbon}\\\text{dioxide}}}{6\,CO_2} + \underset{\text{Water}}{6\,H_2O} + \text{energy (sunlight)} \longrightarrow \underset{\text{Glucose}}{C_6H_{12}O_6} + \underset{\text{Oxygen}}{6\,O_2}$$

This reaction—the exact reverse of respiration—is the ultimate source of the molecules that are oxidized in respiration. And just as the key process in respiration is the oxidation of carbon, the key process in photosynthesis is the reduction of carbon. This reduction is driven by solar energy—energy that is then stored in the resulting glucose molecule. Living things harvest that energy when they "burn" glucose in the respiration half of the cycle.

Thus, oxidation and reduction reactions are at the very center of all life on Earth!

CAN YOU ANSWER THIS? *What is the oxidation state of the oxygen atoms in CO_2, H_2O, and O_2? What does this information tell you about the reactions of photosynthesis and respiration?*

Yellowj/Shutterstock.

▲ Sunlight, captured by plants in photosynthesis, is the ultimate source of the chemical energy used by nearly all living things on Earth.

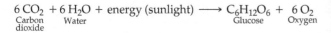

5 The Activity Series: Predicting Spontaneous Redox Reactions

As we have seen, redox reactions depend on the gaining of electrons by one substance and the losing of electrons by another. Is there a way to predict whether a particular redox reaction will spontaneously occur? Suppose we knew that substance A has a greater tendency to lose electrons than substance B (A is more easily oxidized than B). Then we could predict that if we mix A with cations of B, a redox reaction would occur in which A loses its electrons (A is oxidized) to the cations of B (B cations are reduced). For example, Mg has a greater tendency to lose electrons than Cu. Consequently, if we put solid Mg into a solution containing Cu^{2+} ions, Mg is oxidized and Cu^{2+} is reduced.

$$Mg(s) + Cu^{2+}(aq) \longrightarrow Mg^{2+}(aq) + Cu(s)$$

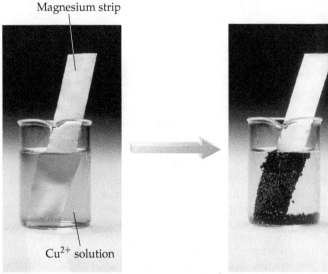

► FIGURE 5 Cu²⁺ oxidizes magnesium When a magnesium strip is put into a Cu^{2+} solution, the magnesium is oxidized to Mg^{2+} and the copper ion is reduced to $Cu(s)$. Notice the fading of the blue color (due to Cu^{2+} ions) in solution and the appearance of solid copper on the magnesium strip.

Magnesium strip

$$Mg(s) + Cu^{2+}(aq) \longrightarrow Mg^{2+}(aq) + Cu(s)$$

Cu^{2+} solution

We see this as the fading of blue (the color of the Cu^{2+} ions in solution), the dissolving of the solid magnesium, and the appearance of solid copper on the remaining magnesium surface (▲ Figure 5). This reaction is spontaneous—it occurs on its own when $Mg(s)$ and $Cu^{2+}(aq)$ come into contact. On the other hand, if we put $Cu(s)$ in a solution containing $Mg^{2+}(aq)$ ions, no reaction occurs (◄ Figure 6).

$$Cu(s) + Mg^{2+}(aq) \longrightarrow \text{NO REACTION}$$

No reaction occurs because, as we said previously, Mg atoms have a greater tendency to lose electrons than do Cu atoms; Cu atoms will therefore not lose electrons to Mg^{2+} ions.

Table 1 shows the **activity series of metals**. This table lists metals in order of decreasing tendency to lose electrons. The metals at the top of the list have the greatest tendency to lose electrons—they are most easily oxidized and therefore the most reactive. The metals at the bottom of the list have the lowest tendency to lose electrons—they are the most difficult to oxidize and therefore the least reac-

Copper strip

Mg^{2+} solution

▲ FIGURE 6 Mg²⁺ does not oxidize copper When solid copper is placed in a solution containing Mg^{2+} ions, no reaction occurs. Question: Why?

TABLE 1 Activity Series of Metals

$Li(s) \longrightarrow Li^+(aq) + e^-$	Most reactive
$K(s) \longrightarrow K^+(aq) + e^-$	Most easily oxidized
$Ca(s) \longrightarrow Ca^{2+}(aq) + 2e^-$	Strongest tendency to lose electrons
$Na(s) \longrightarrow Na^+(aq) + e^-$	
$Mg(s) \longrightarrow Mg^{2+}(aq) + 2e^-$	
$Al(s) \longrightarrow Al^{3+}(aq) + 3e^-$	
$Mn(s) \longrightarrow Mn^{2+}(aq) + 2e^-$	
$Zn(s) \longrightarrow Zn^{2+}(aq) + 2e^-$	
$Cr(s) \longrightarrow Cr^{3+}(aq) + 3e^-$	
$Fe(s) \longrightarrow Fe^{2+}(aq) + 2e^-$	
$Ni(s) \longrightarrow Ni^{2+}(aq) + 2e^-$	
$Sn(s) \longrightarrow Sn^{2+}(aq) + 2e^-$	
$Pb(s) \longrightarrow Pb^{2+}(aq) + 2e^-$	
$\mathbf{H_2(g) \longrightarrow 2\,H^+(aq) + 2e^-}$	
$Cu(s) \longrightarrow Cu^{2+}(aq) + 2e^-$	Least reactive
$Ag(s) \longrightarrow Ag^+(aq) + e^-$	Most difficult to oxidize
$Au(s) \longrightarrow Au^{3+}(aq) + 3e^-$	Least tendency to lose electrons

tive. It is not a coincidence that the metals used for jewelry, such as silver and gold, are near the bottom of the list. They are among the least reactive metals and therefore do not form compounds easily. Instead, they tend to remain as solid silver and solid gold rather than being oxidized to silver and gold cations by elements in the environment (such as the oxygen in the air).

Each reaction in the activity series is an oxidation half-reaction. The half-reactions at the top are most likely to occur in the *forward* direction, and the half-reactions at the bottom are most likely to occur in the *reverse* direction. Consequently, if we pair a half-reaction from the top of the list with the reverse of a half-reaction from the bottom of the list, we get a spontaneous reaction. More specifically,

> Any half-reaction on the list will be spontaneous when paired with the reverse of any half-reaction below it.

For example, consider the two half-reactions:

$$Mn(s) \longrightarrow Mn^{2+}(aq) + 2e^-$$
$$Ni(s) \longrightarrow Ni^{2+}(aq) + 2e^-$$

The oxidation of Mn is spontaneous when paired with the reduction of Ni^{2+}.

$$Mn(s) \longrightarrow Mn^{2+}(aq) + 2e^-$$
$$\underline{Ni^{2+}(aq) + 2e^- \longrightarrow Ni(s)}$$
$$Mn(s) + Ni^{2+}(aq) \longrightarrow Mn^{2+}(aq) + Ni(s) \quad \text{(spontaneous reaction)}$$

However, if we pair a half-reaction on the list with the reverse of a half-reaction *above it*, there is no reaction. For example,

$$Mn(s) \longrightarrow Mn^{2+}(aq) + 2e^-$$
$$\underline{Mg^{2+}(aq) + 2e^- \longrightarrow Mg(s)}$$
$$Mn(s) + Mg^{2+}(aq) \longrightarrow \text{NO REACTION}$$

No reaction occurs because Mg has a greater tendency to be oxidized than Mn. Since it is already oxidized in this reaction, nothing else happens.

EXAMPLE 9   Predicting Spontaneous Redox Reactions

Are the following redox reactions spontaneous?

(a) $Fe(s) + Mg^{2+}(aq) \longrightarrow Fe^{2+}(aq) + Mg(s)$

(b) $Fe(s) + Pb^{2+}(aq) \longrightarrow Fe^{2+}(aq) + Pb(s)$

SOLUTION

(a) $Fe(s) + Mg^{2+}(aq) \longrightarrow Fe^{2+}(aq) + Mg(s)$

This reaction involves the oxidation of Fe

$$Fe(s) \longrightarrow Fe^{2+}(aq) + 2e^-$$

with the reverse of a half-reaction *above it* in the

$$Mg^{2+}(aq) + 2e^- \text{ —}$$

Therefore, the reaction *is not* spont

(b) $Fe(s) + Pb^{2+}(aq) \longrightarrow Fe^{2+}(aq) + P$

This reaction involves the oxidation o

$$Fe(s) \longrightarrow Fe^{2}$$

with the reverse of a half-reaction *below i.*

$$Pb^{2+}(aq) + 2e^- \text{ —}$$

Therefore, the reaction *is* spontaneous.

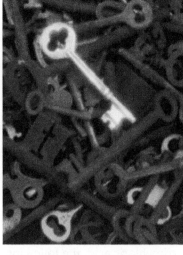

▲ Gold is very low on the activity series. Because it is so difficult to oxidize, it resists the tarnishing and corrosion that more active metals undergo.

▶ **SKILLBUILDER 9** | **Predicting Spontaneous Redox Reactions**

Are the following redox reactions spontaneous?

(a) $Zn(s) + Ni^{2+}(aq) \longrightarrow Zn^{2+}(aq) + Ni(s)$

(b) $Zn(s) + Ca^{2+}(aq) \longrightarrow Zn^{2+}(aq) + Ca(s)$

▶ **FOR MORE PRACTICE** Example 15; Problems 77, 78.

PREDICTING WHETHER A METAL WILL DISSOLVE IN ACID

As you may know, acids dissolve metals. Most acids dissolve metals by the reduction of H^+ ions to hydrogen gas and the corresponding oxidation of the metal to its ion. For example, if solid Zn is dropped into hydrochloric acid, the following reaction occurs.

$$Zn(s) \longrightarrow Zn^{2+}(aq) + 2e^-$$
$$\underline{2\,H^+(aq) + 2e^- \longrightarrow H_2(g)}$$
$$Zn(s) + 2\,H^+(aq) \longrightarrow Zn^{2+}(aq) + H_2(g)$$

We observe the reaction as the dissolving of the zinc and the bubbling of hydrogen gas (◀ Figure 7). The zinc is oxidized and the H^+ ions are reduced, dissolving the zinc. Notice that this reaction involves pairing the oxidation half-reaction of Zn with the reverse of a half-reaction below zinc on the activity series (the reduction of H^+). Therefore, this reaction is spontaneous. What happens, however, if we pair the oxidation of Cu with the reduction of H^+? The reaction would not be spontaneous because it involves pairing the oxidation of copper with the reverse of a half-reaction *above it* in the activity series. Consequently, copper does not react with H^+ and will not dissolve in acids such as HCl. In general,

> Metals above H_2 on the activity series dissolve in acids, while metals below H_2 do not dissolve in acids.

An important exception to this rule is nitric acid (HNO_3), which through a different reduction half-reaction dissolves some of the metals below H_2 in the activity series.

$Zn(s) + 2\,H^+(aq) \longrightarrow$

$Zn^{2+}(aq) + H_2(g)$

▲ **FIGURE 7** **Zinc dissolves in hydrochloric acid** The zinc metal is oxidized to Zn^{2+} ions, and the H^+ ions are reduced to hydrogen gas.

| Unlike most other acids, nitric acid dissolves some metals below H_2 in the activity series.

EXAMPLE 10 **Predicting Whether a Metal Will Dissolve in Acid**

Does Cr dissolve in hydrochloric acid?

SOLUTION

Yes. Since Cr is above H_2 in the activity series, it dissolves in HCl.

▶ **SKILLBUILDER 10** | **Predicting Whether a Metal Will Dissolve in Acid**

Does Ag dissolve in hydrobromic acid?

▶ **FOR MORE PRACTICE** Problems 83, 84.

It has been suggested that one cause of the decline of the Roman Empire was widespread chronic poisoning. The suspected source was a metal present in the vessels commonly used to store and serve acidic substances such as wine. Which metal would you expect to pose such a danger?

(a) silver

(b) gold

(c) lead

(d) copper

6 Batteries: Using Chemistry to Generate Electricity

▲ FIGURE 8 **An electrical current** Electrical current is the flow of electrical charge. In this figure, electrons are flowing through a wire.

The fuel cell that we discussed in the opening section of this chapter is a type of electrochemical cell.

Electrical current is simply the flow of electric charge (◄ Figure 8). Electrons flowing through a wire or ions flowing through a solution are both examples of electrical current. Since redox reactions involve the transfer of electrons from one species to another, they can create electrical current. For example, consider the following spontaneous redox reaction.

$$Zn(s) + Cu^{2+}(aq) \longrightarrow Zn^{2+}(aq) + Cu(s)$$

When Zn metal is placed into a Cu^{2+} solution, Zn is oxidized and Cu^{2+} is reduced—electrons are transferred directly from the Zn to the Cu^{2+}. Suppose we separate the reactants and force the electrons to travel through a wire to get from the Zn to the Cu^{2+}. The flowing electrons constitute an electrical current and can be used to do electrical work. This process is normally carried out in an **electrochemical cell**, a device that creates electrical current from a spontaneous redox reaction (or that uses electrical current to drive a nonspontaneous redox reaction). Electrochemical cells that create electrical current from spontaneous reactions are called **voltaic cells** or **galvanic cells**. A *battery* is a voltaic cell that (usually) has been designed for portability.

For example, consider the voltaic cell in ▶ Figure 9. In this cell, a solid strip of Zn is placed into a $Zn(NO_3)_2$ solution to form a **half-cell**. Similarly, a solid strip of Cu is placed into a $Cu(NO_3)_2$ solution to form a second half-cell. Then the two half-cells are connected by attaching a wire from the Zn, through a lightbulb or other electrical device, to the copper. The natural tendency of Zn to oxidize and Cu^{2+} to reduce results in the flow of electrons through the wire. The flowing electrons constitute an electrical current that lights the bulb.

In a voltaic cell, the metal strip where oxidation occurs is called the **anode** and is labeled with a negative (−) sign. The metal strip where reduction occurs is called the **cathode** and is labeled with a (+) sign. Electrons flow from the anode to the cathode (away from negative and toward positive).

As electrons flow out of the anode, positive ions form in the oxidation half-cell (Zn^{2+} forms in the preceding example). As electrons flow into the cathode, positive ions deposit as charge-neutral atoms at the reduction half-cell (Cu^{2+} deposits as $Cu(s)$ in the preceding example). However, if this were the only flow of charge, the flow would soon stop as positive charge accumulated at the anode and negative charge at the cathode. The circuit must be completed with a **salt bridge**, an inverted U-shaped tube that joins the two half-cells and contains a strong electrolyte such as KNO_3. The salt bridge allows for the flow of ions that neutralizes the charge imbalance. The negative ions within the salt bridge flow to neutralize the accumulation of positive charge at the anode, and the positive ions flow to neutralize the accumulation of negative charge at the cathode.

The salt bridge completes the circuit—it allows the flow of ions between the two half-cells.

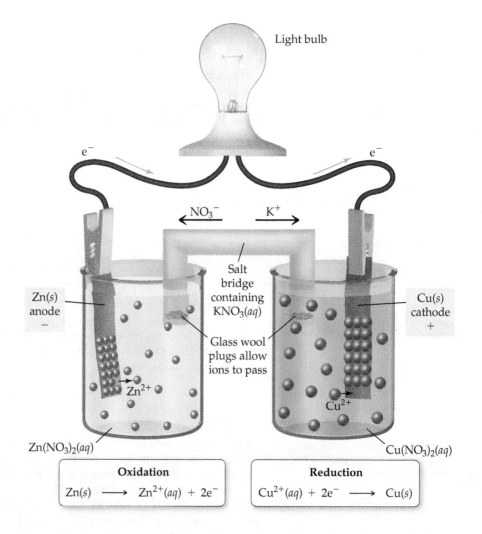

Light bulb

NO_3^- K^+

Zn(s) anode −

Salt bridge containing $KNO_3(aq)$

Cu(s) cathode +

Glass wool plugs allow ions to pass

Zn^{2+}

Cu^{2+}

$Zn(NO_3)_2(aq)$

$Cu(NO_3)_2(aq)$

Oxidation
$Zn(s) \longrightarrow Zn^{2+}(aq) + 2e^-$

Reduction
$Cu^{2+}(aq) + 2e^- \longrightarrow Cu(s)$

▶ **FIGURE 9** **A voltaic cell**
Question: Why do electrons flow from left to right in this figure?

In a voltaic cell, electrical voltage is the driving force that causes electrons to flow. A high voltage corresponds to a high driving force, while a low voltage corresponds to a low driving force. We can understand electrical voltage with an analogy. Electrons flowing through a wire are similar to water flowing in a river (▶ Figure 10). The *quantity of electrons* that flows through the wire (electrical current) is analogous to the *amount of water* that flows through the river (the river's current). The driving force that causes the electrons to flow through a wire—called *potential difference* or **voltage**—is analogous to the force of gravity that causes water to flow in a river. A high voltage is analogous to a steeply descending streambed (▶ Figure 11).

The voltage of a voltaic cell depends on the relative tendencies of the reactants to undergo oxidation and reduction. Combining the oxidation of a metal high on the activity series with the reduction of a metal ion low on the activity series produces a battery with a relatively high voltage. For example, the oxidation of Li(s) combined with the reduction of $Cu^{2+}(aq)$ results in a relatively high voltage. On the other hand, combining the oxidation of a metal on the activity series with the reduction of a metal ion just below it results in a voltaic cell with a relatively low voltage. Combining the oxidation of a metal on the activity series with the reduction of a metal ion above it on the activity series does not produce a voltaic cell at all. For example, you cannot make a voltaic cell by trying to oxidize Cu(s) and reduce $Li^+(aq)$. Such a reaction is not spontaneous and does not produce electrical current.

You can now see why voltaic cells (and batteries) go dead after extended use. As the simple voltaic cell we have just described is used, the zinc electrode dissolves away as zinc is oxidized to zinc ions. Similarly, the Cu^{2+} solution is

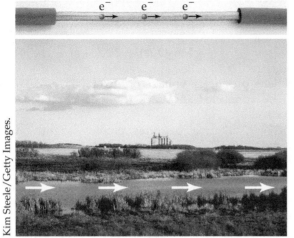

▲ FIGURE 10 **River analogy for electrical current**
The flow of electrons through a wire is similar to the flow of water in a river.

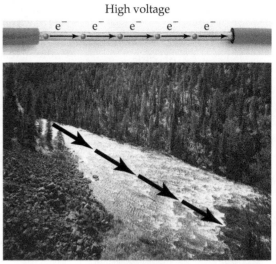

▲ FIGURE 11 **River analogy for voltage** A high voltage for electricity is analogous to a steep descent for a river.

depleted of Cu^{2+} ions as they deposit as solid Cu (▼ Figure 12). Once the zinc electrode is dissolved and the Cu^{2+} ions are depleted, the cell is dead. Some voltaic cells, such as those employed in rechargeable batteries, can be recharged by running electrical current—from an external source—in the opposite direction. This causes the regeneration of the reactants, allowing repeated use of the battery.

▶ FIGURE 12 **Dead voltaic cell**
A voltaic cell dies with extended use because the reactants [in this case $Zn(s)$ and $Cu^{2+}(aq)$] become depleted while the products [in this case $Zn^{2+}(aq)$ and $Cu(s)$] accumulate.

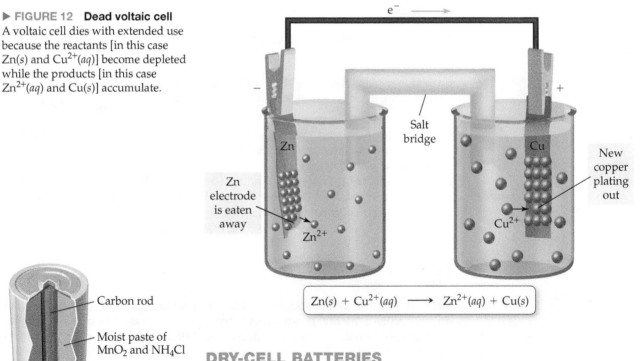

$$Zn(s) + Cu^{2+}(aq) \longrightarrow Zn^{2+}(aq) + Cu(s)$$

▲ FIGURE 13 **Common dry-cell battery**

Carbon rod

Moist paste of MnO_2 and NH_4Cl

Zn case

DRY-CELL BATTERIES

Flashlight batteries are called **dry cells** because they do not contain large amounts of liquid water. There are several common types of dry-cell batteries. The most inexpensive type of dry cell is composed of a zinc case that acts as the anode (◀ Figure 13). The zinc is oxidized according to the following reaction.

Anode reaction: $Zn(s) \longrightarrow Zn^{2+}(aq) + 2e^-$ (oxidation)

273

The cathode is a carbon rod immersed in a moist paste of MnO_2 that also contains NH_4Cl. The MnO_2 is reduced to Mn_2O_3 according to the following reaction.

Cathode reaction: $2\,MnO_2(s) + 2\,NH_4^+(aq) + 2e^- \longrightarrow$

$$Mn_2O_3(s) + 2\,NH_3(g) + H_2O(l) \quad \text{(reduction)}$$

These two half-reactions produce a voltage of about 1.5 volts. Two or more of these batteries can be connected in series (cathode-to-anode connection) to produce higher voltages.

The more expensive **alkaline batteries** employ slightly different half-reactions that use a base (therefore the name *alkaline*). In an alkaline battery, the reactions are as follows.

Anode reaction: $Zn(s) + 2\,OH^-(aq) \longrightarrow Zn(OH)_2(s) + 2e^-$

Cathode reaction: $2\,MnO_2(s) + 2\,H_2O(l) + 2e^- \longrightarrow$

$$2\,MnO(OH)(s) + 2\,OH^-(aq) \quad \text{(reduction)}$$

Alkaline batteries have a longer working life and a longer shelf life than their nonalkaline counterparts.

LEAD-ACID STORAGE BATTERIES

The batteries in most automobiles are **lead-acid storage batteries**. These batteries consist of six electrochemical cells wired in series (◄ Figure 14). Each cell produces 2 volts for a total of 12 volts. The cells each contain a porous lead anode where oxidation occurs according to the following reaction.

Anode reaction: $Pb(s) + SO_4^{2-}(aq) \longrightarrow PbSO_4(s) + 2e^-$ (oxidation)

Each cell also contains a lead(IV) oxide cathode where reduction occurs according to the following reaction.

Cathode reaction: $PbO_2(s) + 4\,H^+(aq) + SO_4^{2-}(aq) + 2e^- \longrightarrow$

$$PbSO_4(s) + 2\,H_2O(l) \quad \text{(reduction)}$$

Both the anode and the cathode are immersed in sulfuric acid (H_2SO_4). As electrical current is drawn from the battery, both the anode and the cathode become coated with $PbSO_4(s)$. If the battery is run for a long time without recharging, too much $PbSO_4(s)$ develops and the battery goes dead. The lead-acid storage battery can be recharged, however, by running electrical current through it in reverse. The electrical current has to come from an external source, such as an alternator in a car. This causes the preceding reactions to occur in reverse, converting the $PbSO_4(s)$ back to $Pb(s)$ and $PbO_2(s)$, recharging the battery.

FUEL CELLS

We discussed fuel cells in Section 1. Electric vehicles powered by fuel cells may one day replace internal combustion vehicles. Fuel cells are like batteries, but the reactants are constantly replenished. Normal batteries lose their voltage with use because the reactants are depleted as electrical current is drawn from the battery. In a fuel cell, the reactants—the fuel—constantly flow through the battery, generating electrical current as they undergo a redox reaction.

The most common fuel cell is the hydrogen–oxygen fuel cell (► Figure 15). In this cell, hydrogen gas flows past the anode (a screen coated with platinum catalyst) and undergoes oxidation.

Anode reaction: $2\,H_2(g) + 4\,OH^-(aq) \longrightarrow 4\,H_2O(l) + 4e^-$

Anode (−):
Lead grid packed
with porous lead

Anode

Cathode

Electrolyte: A 30%
solution of H_2SO_4

Cathode (+):
Lead grid packed
with PbO_2

▲ FIGURE 14 **Lead-acid storage battery** Question: Why do batteries like this become depleted? How are they recharged?

The porosity of the lead anode increases the surface area where electrons can be transferred from the solid lead to the solution.

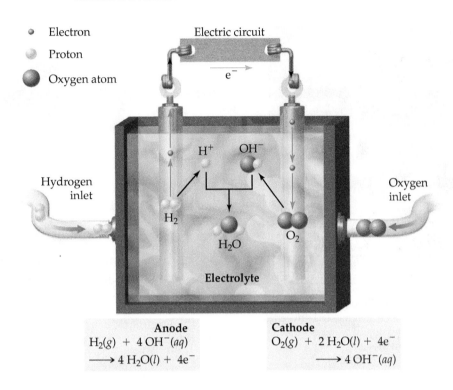

● Electron

● Proton

● Oxygen atom

Electric circuit

e^-

H$^+$ OH$^-$

Hydrogen inlet

H$_2$

H$_2$O

O$_2$

Oxygen inlet

Electrolyte

Anode	**Cathode**
H$_2(g)$ + 4 OH$^-(aq)$	O$_2(g)$ + 2 H$_2$O(l) + 4e$^-$
$\longrightarrow$ 4 H$_2$O(l) + 4e$^-$	$\longrightarrow$ 4 OH$^-(aq)$

▶ FIGURE 15 **Hydrogen–oxygen fuel cell**

Oxygen gas flows past the cathode (a similar screen) and undergoes reduction.

Cathode reaction: O$_2(g)$ + 2 H$_2$O(l) + 4e$^-$ $\longrightarrow$ 4 OH$^-(aq)$

The half-reactions sum to the following overall reaction.

Overall reaction: 2 H$_2(g)$ + O$_2(g)$ $\longrightarrow$ 2 H$_2$O(l)

Notice that the only product is water. In the space shuttle program, hydrogen–oxygen fuel cells provide electricity and astronauts drink the resulting water.

✓ CONCEPTUAL CHECKPOINT 4

Suppose you are making a battery composed of a carbon rod inserted into a moist paste of lead(II) ions, which acts as the cathode. You want the metal casing that encloses the battery to act as the anode. Which metal should you use for the casing to achieve the battery with the highest voltage?

(a) Mg   **(b)** Zn   **(c)** Ni

7 Electrolysis: Using Electricity to Do Chemistry

In a voltaic cell, a spontaneous redox reaction is used to produce electrical current. In **electrolysis**, electrical current is used to drive an otherwise nonspontaneous redox reaction. An electrochemical cell used for electrolysis is an **electrolytic cell**. We saw that the reaction of hydrogen with oxygen to form water is spontaneous and can be used to produce an electrical current in a fuel cell. By providing electrical current, we can cause the reverse reaction to occur, breaking water into hydrogen and oxygen (▶ Figure 16).

2 H$_2(g)$ + O$_2(g)$ $\longrightarrow$ 2 H$_2$O(l) (spontaneous—produces electrical current; occurs in a voltaic cell)

2 H$_2$O(l) $\longrightarrow$ 2 H$_2(g)$ + O$_2(g)$ (nonspontaneous—consumes electrical current; occurs in an electrolytic cell)

Charles Winters/Photo Researchers.

▲ FIGURE 16 **Electrolysis of water** As a current passes between the electrodes, liquid water is broken down into hydrogen gas (right tube) and oxygen gas (left tube).

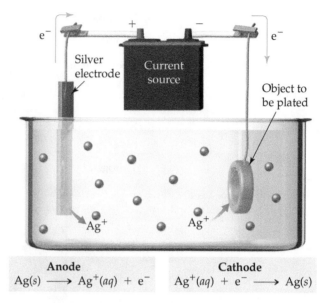

Anode	Cathode
$Ag(s) \longrightarrow Ag^+(aq) + e^-$	$Ag^+(aq) + e^- \longrightarrow Ag(s)$

▲ FIGURE 17 **Electrolytic cell for silver plating** Silver is oxidized on the left side of the cell and reduced at the right. As it is reduced, it is deposited on the object to be plated.

One of the problems associated with the widespread adoption of fuel cells is the scarcity of hydrogen. Where is the hydrogen to power these fuel cells going to come from? One possible answer is that the hydrogen can come from water through solar- or wind-powered electrolysis. In other words, a solar- or wind-powered electrolytic cell can be used to make hydrogen from water when the sun is shining or when the wind is blowing. The hydrogen can then be converted back to water to generate electricity when needed. Hydrogen made in this way could also be used to power fuel-cell vehicles.

Electrolysis also has numerous other applications. For example, most metals are found in Earth's crust as metal oxides. Converting them to pure metals requires the reduction of the metal, a nonspontaneous process. Electrolysis can be used to produce these metals. Electrolysis can also be used to plate metals onto other metals. For example, silver can be plated onto another, less expensive metal using the electrolytic cell shown in ▲ Figure 17. In this cell, a silver electrode is placed in a solution containing silver ions. An electrical current then causes the oxidation of silver at the anode (replenishing the silver ions in solution) and the reduction of silver ions at the cathode (coating the ordinary metal with solid silver).

$$\text{Anode reaction:} \quad Ag(s) \longrightarrow Ag^+(aq) + e^-$$
$$\text{Cathode reaction:} \quad Ag^+(aq) + e^- \longrightarrow Ag(s)$$

8 Corrosion: Undesirable Redox Reactions

Angus Beare/Dorling Kindersly Media Library.

▲ Paint can prevent underlying iron from rusting. However, if the paint becomes scratched, the iron will rust at the point of the chip. ·Question: Why?

Corrosion is the oxidation of metals. The most common kind of corrosion is the rusting of iron. A significant part of the iron produced each year goes to replace rusted iron. Rusting is a redox reaction in which iron is oxidized and oxygen is reduced.

Oxidation:	$2\,Fe(s) \longrightarrow 2\,Fe^{2+}(aq) + 4e^-$
Reduction:	$O_2(g) + 2\,H_2O(l) + 4e^- \longrightarrow 4\,OH^-(aq)$
Overall:	$2\,Fe(s) + O_2(g) + 2\,H_2O(l) \longrightarrow 2\,Fe(OH)_2(s)$

The $Fe(OH)_2$ formed in the overall reaction then undergoes several additional reactions to form Fe_2O_3, the familiar orange substance that we call rust. One of the main problems with Fe_2O_3 is that it crumbles off the solid iron below

EVERYDAY CHEMISTRY

The Fuel-Cell Breathalyzer

Police use a device called a breathalyzer to measure the amount of ethyl alcohol (C_2H_5OH) in the bloodstream of a person suspected of driving under the influence of alcohol.

Breathalyzers work because the amount of ethyl alcohol in the breath is proportional to the amount of ethyl alcohol in the bloodstream. One type of breathalyzer employs a fuel cell to measure the amount of alcohol in the breath. The fuel cell consists of two platinum electrodes (▼ Figure 18). When a suspect blows into the breathalyzer, any ethyl alcohol in the breath is oxidized to acetic acid at the anode.

Anode: $\underset{\text{Ethyl alcohol}}{C_2H_5OH} + 4\,OH^-(aq) \longrightarrow$

$$\underset{\text{Acetic acid}}{CH_3COOH(aq)} + 3\,H_2O + 4e^-$$

Electrolyte

C_2H_5OH

e^-

H_2O

OH^-

e^- O_2

Suspect's breath

Blood alcohol level

Anode   Cathode

CH_3COOH Air intake

▲ FIGURE 18   **Schematic diagram of a fuel-cell breathalyzer**

At the cathode, oxygen is reduced.

Cathode: $O_2(g) + 2\,H_2O(l) + 4e^- \longrightarrow 4\,OH^-(aq)$

The overall reaction is simply the oxidation of ethyl alcohol to acetic acid and water.

Overall: $C_2H_5OH(g) + O_2(g) \longrightarrow CH_3COOH(g) + H_2O$

The amount of electrical current produced depends on the amount of alcohol in the breath. A higher current reveals a higher blood alcohol level. When calibrated correctly, the fuel-cell breathalyzer can precisely measure the blood alcohol level of a suspected drunk driver.

CAN YOU ANSWER THIS? *Assign oxidation states to each element in the reactants and products in the overall equation for the fuel-cell breathalyzer. What element is oxidized, and what element is reduced in the reaction?*

Draeger Safety, Inc.

▲ **Fuel-cell breathalyzer** A suspect blows into the top of this device and blood alcohol level is determined.

277

it, exposing more iron to further rusting. Under the right conditions, an entire piece of iron can rust away.

Iron is not the only metal that undergoes oxidation. Most other metals, such as copper and aluminum, also undergo oxidation. However, the oxides of copper and aluminum do not flake off as iron oxide does. When aluminum oxidizes, the aluminum oxide actually forms a tough clear coating on the underlying metal. This coating protects the underlying metal from further oxidation.

Preventing the iron from rusting is a major industry. The most obvious way to prevent rust is to keep iron dry. Without water, the redox reaction cannot occur. Another way to prevent rust is to coat the iron with a substance that is impervious to water. Cars, for example, are painted and sealed to prevent rust. A scratch in the paint, however, can lead to rusting of the underlying iron.

Rust can also be prevented by placing a *sacrificial electrode* in electrical contact with the iron. The sacrificial electrode must be composed of a metal that is above iron on the activity series. The sacrificial electrode oxidizes in place of the iron, protecting the iron from oxidation. Another way to protect iron from rusting is to coat it with a metal above it in the activity series. Galvanized nails, for example, are coated with a thin layer of zinc. Since zinc is more active than iron, it oxidizes in place of the underlying iron (just like a sacrificial electrode does). The oxide of zinc is not crumbly and remains on the nail as a protective coating.

✔ CONCEPTUAL CHECKPOINT 5

Which metal could NOT be used as a sacrificial electrode to prevent rusting?

(a) Mg   **(b)** Mn   **(c)** Zn   **(d)** Sn

CHAPTER IN REVIEW

CHEMICAL PRINCIPLES

Oxidation and Reduction: Oxidation is:

- the loss of electrons.
- an increase in oxidation state.

Reduction is:

- the gain of electrons.
- a decrease in oxidation state.

Oxidation and reduction reactions always occur together and are sometimes called redox reactions. The substance that is oxidized is the reducing agent, and the substance that is reduced is the oxidizing agent.

Oxidation States: The oxidation state is a fictitious charge assigned to each atom in a compound. It is calculated by assigning all bonding electrons in a compound to the most electronegative element.

The Activity Series: The activity series is a listing of metals from those that are easiest to oxidize to those that are most difficult to oxidize. Any half-reaction in the activity series is spontaneous when paired with the reverse of a half-reaction below it on the list.

RELEVANCE

Oxidation and Reduction: Redox reactions are common in nature, in industry, and in many everyday processes. Batteries use redox reactions to generate electrical current. Our bodies use redox reactions to obtain energy from glucose. In addition, the bleaching of hair, the rusting of iron, and the electroplating of metals all involve redox reactions.

Good oxidizing agents, such as oxygen, hydrogen peroxide, and chlorine, have a strong tendency to gain electrons. Good reducing agents, such as sodium and hydrogen, have a strong tendency to lose electrons.

Oxidation States: Oxidation states help us more easily identify substances being oxidized and reduced in a chemical reaction.

The Activity Series: The activity series allows us to predict whether a redox reaction (involving half-reactions from the series) is spontaneous.

Batteries: In a battery, the reactants of a spontaneous redox reaction are physically separated. As the redox reaction occurs, the transferred electrons are forced to travel through a wire or other external circuit, creating an electrical current that can be used to do electrical work.

Batteries: Batteries are common as portable sources of electrical current. They are used in flashlights, watches, automobiles, and other electrical devices.

Electrolysis: In a battery, a spontaneous redox reaction is used to generate an electrical current. In electrolysis, an electrical current is used to drive a nonspontaneous redox reaction.

Electrolysis: Electrolysis has many applications. For example, electrolysis is used to reduce metal oxides found in Earth's crust to their metals and to plate metals onto other metals.

Corrosion: Corrosion is the oxidation of iron and other metals by atmospheric oxygen. Corrosion can be prevented by keeping the metal dry, sealing it with a protective coating, or depositing a more active metal onto the surface of the metal to be protected.

Corrosion: The most common form of corrosion is the rusting of iron. Since a significant fraction of all iron produced is used to replace rusted iron, the prevention of rust is a major industry.

CHEMICAL SKILLS

EXAMPLES

Identifying Oxidation and Reduction (Section 2)

Oxidation can be identified as the gain of oxygen, the loss of electrons, or an increase in oxidation state. Reduction can be identified as the loss of oxygen, the gain of electrons, or a decrease in oxidation state.

When a substance gains oxygen, the substance is oxidized and the oxygen is reduced.

When a metal reacts with an electronegative element, the metal is oxidized and the electronegative element is reduced.

When a metal transfers electrons to a metal ion, the metal is oxidized and the metal ion is reduced.

EXAMPLE 11   Identifying Oxidation and Reduction

Determine the substance being oxidized and the substance being reduced in each redox reaction.

(a) $Sn(s) + O_2(g) \longrightarrow SnO_2(s)$
(b) $2\,Na(s) + F_2(g) \longrightarrow 2\,NaF(s)$
(c) $Mg(s) + Cu^{2+}(aq) \longrightarrow Mg^{2+}(aq) + Cu(s)$

SOLUTION

(a) Sn oxidized; O_2 reduced
(b) Na oxidized; F_2 reduced
(c) Mg oxidized; Cu^{2+} reduced

Identifying Oxidizing Agents and Reducing Agents (Section 2)

The reducing agent is the substance that is oxidized. The oxidizing agent is the substance that is reduced.

EXAMPLE 12   Identifying Oxidizing Agents and Reducing Agents

Identify the oxidizing and reducing agents in each redox reaction.

(a) $Sn(s) + O_2(g) \longrightarrow SnO_2(s)$
(b) $2\,Na(s) + F_2(g) \longrightarrow 2\,NaF(s)$
(c) $Mg(s) + Cu^{2+}(aq) \longrightarrow Mg^{2+}(aq) + Cu(s)$

SOLUTION

(a) Sn is the reducing agent; O_2 is the oxidizing agent.
(b) Na is the reducing agent; F_2 is the oxidizing agent.
(c) Mg is the reducing agent; Cu^{2+} is the oxidizing agent.

Assigning Oxidation States (Section 3)

Rules for Assigning Oxidation States

(These rules are hierarchical. If two rules conflict, follow the rule higher on the list.)

1. The oxidation state of an atom in a free element is 0.
2. The oxidation state of a monoatomic ion is equal to its charge.
3. The sum of the oxidation states of all atoms in:
   - a neutral molecule or formula unit is 0.
   - an ion is equal to the charge of the ion.
4. In their compounds,
   - Group I metals have an oxidation state of +1.
   - Group II metals have an oxidation state of +2.
5. In their compounds, nonmetals are assigned oxidation states according to the following hierarchical table.

Fluorine	-1
Hydrogen	$+1$
Oxygen	-2
Group 7A	-1
Group 6A	-2
Group 5A	-3

Balancing Redox Reactions (Section 4)

To balance redox reactions in aqueous acidic solutions, follow this procedure (brief version).

1. Assign oxidation states.

2. Separate the overall reaction into two half-reactions.

3. Balance each half-reaction with respect to mass.
   - Balance all elements other than H and O.

   - Balance O by adding H_2O.

   - Balance H by adding H^+.

4. Balance each half-reaction with respect to charge by adding electrons.

EXAMPLE 13 Assigning Oxidation States

Assign an oxidation state to each atom in each compound.

(a) Al
(b) Al^{3+}
(c) N_2O
(d) CO_3^{2-}

SOLUTION

(a) $\underset{0}{Al}$ (rule 1)

(b) $\underset{+3}{Al^{3+}}$ (rule 2)

(c) $\underset{+1\ -2}{N_2O}$ (rule 5, O takes priority over N)

(d) $\underset{+4\ -2}{CO_3^{2-}}$ (rules 5, 3)

EXAMPLE 14 Balancing Redox Reactions

Balance the following reaction occurring in acidic solution.

$$IO_3^-(aq) + Fe^{2+}(aq) \longrightarrow I_2(s) + Fe^{3+}(aq)$$

SOLUTION

$$\underset{+5\ -2}{IO_3^-(aq)} + \underset{+2}{Fe^{2+}(aq)} \longrightarrow \underset{0}{I_2(s)} + \underset{+3}{Fe^{3+}(aq)}$$

Reduction / Oxidation

OXIDATION $Fe^{2+}(aq) \longrightarrow Fe^{3+}(aq)$

REDUCTION $IO_3^-(aq) \longrightarrow I_2(s)$

$Fe^{2+}(aq) \longrightarrow Fe^{3+}(aq)$
$2\,IO_3^-(aq) \longrightarrow I_2(s)$

$Fe^{2+}(aq) \longrightarrow Fe^{3+}(aq)$
$2\,IO_3^-(aq) \longrightarrow I_2(s) + \textbf{6 H}_2\textbf{O}(l)$

$Fe^{2+}(aq) \longrightarrow Fe^{3+}(aq)$
$\textbf{12 H}^+(aq) + 2\,IO_3^-(aq) \longrightarrow I_2(s) + 6\,H_2O(l)$

$Fe^{2+}(aq) \longrightarrow Fe^{3+}(aq) + e^-$
$\textbf{10e}^- + 12\,H^+(aq) + 2\,IO_3^-(aq) \longrightarrow I_2(s) + 6\,H_2O(l)$

5. Make the number of electrons in both half-reactions equal.

$$10 \times [Fe^{2+}(aq) \longrightarrow Fe^{3+}(aq) + e^-]$$

$$10e^- + 12 H^+(aq) + 2 IO_3^-(aq) \longrightarrow I_2(s) + 6 H_2O$$

6. Add the two half-reactions together.

$$10 Fe^{2+}(aq) \longrightarrow 10 Fe^{3+}(aq) + \cancel{10e^-}$$

$$\underline{\cancel{10e^-} + 12 H^+(aq) + 2 IO_3^-(aq) \longrightarrow I_2(s) + 6 H_2O}$$

$$10 Fe^{2+}(aq) + 12 H^+(aq) + 2 IO_3^-(aq) \longrightarrow$$
$$10 Fe^{3+}(aq) + I_2(s) + 6 H_2O$$

7. Verify that the reaction is balanced.

Reactants	Products
10 Fe	10 Fe
12 H	12 H
2 I	2 I
6 O	6 O
+30 charge	+30 charge

Predicting Spontaneous Redox Reactions (Section 5)

Any half-reaction in the activity series is spontaneous when paired with the reverse of any half-reaction below it.

EXAMPLE 15 Predicting Spontaneous Redox Reactions

Predict whether each redox reaction is spontaneous.

(a) $Cr(s) + 3 Ag^+(aq) \longrightarrow Cr^{3+}(aq) + 3 Ag(s)$

(b) $Mn^{2+}(aq) + Fe(s) \longrightarrow Mn(s) + Fe^{2+}(aq)$

SOLUTION

(a) **Spontaneous**

(b) **Nonspontaneous**

KEY TERMS

activity series of metals [Section 5]
alkaline battery [Section 6]
anode [Section 6]
cathode [Section 6]
corrosion [Section 8]
dry cell [Section 6]

electrical current [Section 6]
electrochemical cell [Section 6]
electrolysis [Section 7]
electrolytic cell [Section 7]
fuel cell [Section 1]
half-cell [Section 6]

half-reaction [Section 4]
lead-acid storage battery [Section 6]
oxidation [Section 2]
oxidation state (oxidation number) [Section 3]
oxidizing agent [Section 2]

redox (oxidation–reduction) reaction [Section 1]
reducing agent [Section 2]
reduction [Section 2]
salt bridge [Section 6]
voltage [Section 6]
voltaic (galvanic) cell [Section 6]

EXERCISES

QUESTIONS

1. What is a fuel-cell electric vehicle?
2. What is an oxidation–reduction or redox reaction?
3. Define oxidation and reduction with respect to:

    (a) oxygen

    (b) electrons

    (c) oxidation state

4. What is an oxidizing agent? What is a reducing agent?
5. Good oxidation agents have a strong tendency to _____ electrons in reactions.

6. Good reducing agents have a strong tendency to _____ electrons in reactions.
7. What is the oxidation state of a free element? Of a monoatomic ion?
8. For a neutral molecule, the sum of the oxidation states of the individual atoms must add up to _____.
9. For an ion, the sum of the oxidation states of the individual atoms must add up to _____.
10. In their compounds, elements have oxidation states equal to _____. Are there exceptions to this rule? Explain.

11. In a redox reaction, an atom that undergoes an increase in oxidation state is _____. An atom that undergoes a decrease in oxidation state is _____.

12. How does hydrogen peroxide cause hair to change color?

13. When balancing redox equations, the number of electrons lost in the oxidation half-reaction must _____ the number of electrons gained in the reduction half-reaction.

14. When balancing aqueous redox reactions, oxygen is balanced using _____, and hydrogen is balanced using _____.

15. When balancing aqueous redox reactions, charge is balanced using _____.

16. When balancing aqueous redox reactions in basic media, hydrogen ions are neutralized using _____.

17. Are metals at the top of the activity series the most reactive or least reactive?

18. Are metals at the top of the activity series the easiest or hardest to oxidize?

19. Are metals at the bottom of the activity series most likely or least likely to lose electrons?

20. Any half-reaction in the activity series will be spontaneous when paired with the reverse of any half-reaction _____ it.

21. How can you use the activity series to determine whether a metal will dissolve in acids such as HCl or HBr?

22. What is electrical current? Explain how a simple battery creates electrical current.

23. Oxidation occurs at the _____ of an electrochemical cell.

24. Reduction occurs at the _____ of an electrochemical cell.

25. Explain the role of a salt bridge in an electrochemical cell.

26. A high voltage in an electrochemical cell is analogous to _____ in a river.

27. Describe a common dry-cell battery. Include equations for the anode and cathode reactions.

28. Describe a lead-acid storage battery. Include equations for the anode and cathode reactions.

29. Describe a fuel cell. Include equations for the anode and cathode reactions of the hydrogen–oxygen fuel cell.

30. What is electrolysis? Why is it useful?

31. What is corrosion? List reactions for the corrosion of iron.

32. How can rust be prevented?

PROBLEMS

OXIDATION AND REDUCTION

33. What substance is oxidized in each reaction?
    (a) $2 H_2(g) + O_2(g) \longrightarrow 2 H_2O(l)$
    (b) $4 Al(s) + 3 O_2(g) \longrightarrow 2 Al_2O_3(s)$
    (c) $2 Al(s) + 3 Cl_2(g) \longrightarrow 2 AlCl_3(s)$

34. What substance is oxidized in each reaction?
    (a) $2 Zn(s) + O_2(g) \longrightarrow 2 ZnO(s)$
    (b) $CH_4(g) + 2 O_2(g) \longrightarrow CO_2(g) + 2 H_2O(g)$
    (c) $Sr(s) + F_2(g) \longrightarrow SrF_2(s)$

35. For each reaction, identify the substance being oxidized and the substance being reduced.
    (a) $2 Sr(s) + O_2(g) \longrightarrow 2 SrO(s)$
    (b) $Ca(s) + Cl_2(g) \longrightarrow CaCl_2(s)$
    (c) $Ni^{2+}(aq) + Mg(s) \longrightarrow Mg^{2+}(aq) + Ni(s)$

36. For each reaction, identify the substance being oxidized and the substance being reduced.
    (a) $Mg(s) + Br_2(g) \longrightarrow MgBr_2(s)$
    (b) $2 Cr^{3+}(aq) + 3 Mn(s) \longrightarrow 2 Cr(s) + 3 Mn^{2+}(aq)$
    (c) $2 H^+(aq) + Ni(s) \longrightarrow H_2(g) + Ni^{2+}(aq)$

37. For each of the reactions in Problem 35, identify the oxidizing agent and the reducing agent.

38. For each of the reactions in Problem 36, identify the oxidizing agent and the reducing agent.

39. Based on periodic trends, which elements would you expect to be good oxidizing agents?
    (a) potassium
    (b) fluorine
    (c) iron
    (d) chlorine

40. Based on periodic trends, which elements would you expect to be good oxidizing agents?
    (a) oxygen
    (b) bromine
    (c) lithium
    (d) sodium

41. Based on periodic trends, which elements in Problem 39 (in their elemental form) would you expect to be good reducing agents?

42. Based on periodic trends, which elements in Problem 40 (in their elemental form) would you expect to be good reducing agents?

43. For each redox reaction, identify the substance being oxidized, the substance being reduced, the oxidizing agent, and the reducing agent.

    (a) $N_2(g) + O_2(g) \longrightarrow 2\,NO(g)$

    (b) $2\,CO(g) + O_2(g) \longrightarrow 2\,CO_2(g)$

    (c) $SbCl_3(g) + Cl_2(g) \longrightarrow SbCl_5(g)$

    (d) $2\,K(s) + Pb^{2+}(aq) \longrightarrow 2\,K^+(aq) + Pb(s)$

44. For each redox reaction, identify the substance being oxidized, the substance being reduced, the oxidizing agent, and the reducing agent.

    (a) $H_2(g) + I_2(g) \longrightarrow 2\,HI(g)$

    (b) $CO(g) + H_2(g) \longrightarrow C(s) + H_2O(g)$

    (c) $2\,Al(s) + 6\,H^+(aq) \longrightarrow 2\,Al^{3+}(aq) + 3\,H_2(g)$

    (d) $2\,Li(s) + Pb^{2+}(aq) \longrightarrow 2\,Li^+(aq) + Pb(s)$

OXIDATION STATES

45. Assign an oxidation state to each element or ion:

    (a) V

    (b) Mg^{2+}

    (c) Cr^{3+}

    (d) O_2

46. Assign an oxidation state to each element or ion:

    (a) Ne

    (b) Br_2

    (c) Cu^+

    (d) Fe^{3+}

47. Assign an oxidation state to each atom in each compound.

    (a) NaCl

    (b) CaF_2

    (c) SO_2

    (d) H_2S

48. Assign an oxidation state to each atom in each compound.

    (a) CH_4

    (b) CH_2Cl_2

    (c) $CuCl_2$

    (d) HI

49. What is the oxidation state of nitrogen in each compound?

    (a) NO

    (b) NO_2

    (c) N_2O

50. What is the oxidation state of Cr in each compound?

    (a) CrO

    (b) CrO_3

    (c) Cr_2O_3

51. Assign an oxidation state to each atom in each polyatomic ion.

    (a) $CO_3{}^{2-}$

    (b) OH^-

    (c) $NO_3{}^-$

    (d) $NO_2{}^-$

52. Assign an oxidation state to each atom in each polyatomic ion.

    (a) $CrO_4{}^{2-}$

    (b) $Cr_2O_7{}^{2-}$

    (c) $PO_4{}^{3-}$

    (d) $MnO_4{}^-$

53. What is the oxidation state of Cl in each ion?

    (a) ClO^-

    (b) $ClO_2{}^-$

    (c) $ClO_3{}^-$

    (d) $ClO_4{}^-$

54. What is the oxidation state of S in each ion?

    (a) $SO_4{}^{2-}$

    (b) $SO_3{}^{2-}$

    (c) $HSO_3{}^-$

    (d) $HSO_4{}^-$

55. Assign an oxidation state to each element in each compound:

    (a) $Cu(NO_3)_2$

    (b) $Sr(OH)_2$

    (c) $K_2Cr_2O_7$

    (d) $NaHCO_3$

56. Assign an oxidation state to each element in each compound:

    (a) Na_3PO_4

    (b) Hg_2S

    (c) $Fe(CN)_3$

    (d) NH_4Cl

57. Assign an oxidation state to each element in each reaction and use the change in oxidation state to determine which element is being oxidized and which element is being reduced.

(a) $SbCl_5(g) \longrightarrow SbCl_3(g) + Cl_2(g)$

(b) $CO(g) + Cl_2(g) \longrightarrow COCl_2(g)$

(c) $2\,NO(g) + Br_2(g) \longrightarrow 2\,BrNO(g)$

(d) $H_2(g) + CO_2(g) \longrightarrow H_2O(g) + CO(g)$

58. Assign an oxidation state to each element in each reaction and use the change in oxidation state to determine which element is being oxidized and which element is being reduced.

(a) $CH_4(g) + 2\,H_2S(g) \longrightarrow CS_2(g) + 4\,H_2(g)$

(b) $2\,H_2S(g) \longrightarrow 2\,H_2(g) + S_2(g)$

(c) $C_6H_{12}O_6(s) + 6\,O_2(g) \longrightarrow$
$\qquad\qquad 6\,CO_2(g) + 6\,H_2O(g)$

(d) $C_2H_4(g) + Cl_2(g) \longrightarrow C_2H_4Cl_2(g)$

59. Use oxidation states to identify the oxidizing agent and the reducing agent in the following redox reaction.

$$2\,Na(s) + 2\,H_2O(l) \longrightarrow 2\,NaOH(aq) + H_2(g)$$

60. Use oxidation states to identify the oxidizing agent and the reducing agent in the following redox reaction.

$$N_2(g) + 3\,H_2(g) \longrightarrow 2\,NH_3(g)$$

BALANCING REDOX REACTIONS

61. Balance each redox reaction using the half-reaction method.

(a) $K(s) + Cr^{3+}(aq) \longrightarrow Cr(s) + K^+(aq)$

(b) $Mg(s) + Ag^+(aq) \longrightarrow Mg^{2+}(aq) + Ag(s)$

(c) $Al(s) + Fe^{2+}(aq) \longrightarrow Al^{3+}(aq) + Fe(s)$

62. Balance each redox reaction using the half-reaction method.

(a) $Zn(s) + Sn^{2+}(aq) \longrightarrow Zn^{2+}(aq) + Sn(s)$

(b) $Mg(s) + Cr^{3+}(aq) \longrightarrow Mg^{2+}(aq) + Cr(s)$

(c) $Al(s) + Ag^+(aq) \longrightarrow Al^{3+}(aq) + Ag(s)$

63. Classify each half-reaction occurring in acidic aqueous solution as an oxidation or a reduction and balance the half-reaction.

(a) $MnO_4^-(aq) \longrightarrow Mn^{2+}(aq)$

(b) $Pb^{2+}(aq) \longrightarrow PbO_2(s)$

(c) $IO_3^-(aq) \longrightarrow I_2(s)$

(d) $SO_2(g) \longrightarrow SO_4^{2-}(aq)$

64. Classify each half-reaction occurring in acidic aqueous solution as an oxidation or a reduction and balance the half-reaction.

(a) $S(s) \longrightarrow H_2S(g)$

(b) $S_2O_8^{2-}(aq) \longrightarrow 2\,SO_4^{2-}(aq)$

(c) $Cr_2O_7^{2-}(aq) \longrightarrow Cr^{3+}(aq)$

(d) $NO(g) \longrightarrow NO_3^-(aq)$

65. Balance each redox reaction occurring in acidic aqueous solution. Use the half-reaction method.

(a) $PbO_2(s) + I^-(aq) \longrightarrow Pb^{2+}(aq) + I_2(s)$

(b) $SO_3^{2-}(aq) + MnO_4^-(aq) \longrightarrow$
$\qquad\qquad SO_4^{2-}(aq) + Mn^{2+}(aq)$

(c) $S_2O_3^{2-}(aq) + Cl_2(g) \longrightarrow SO_4^{2-}(aq) + Cl^-(aq)$

66. Balance each redox reaction occurring in acidic aqueous solution. Use the half-reaction method.

(a) $I^-(aq) + NO_2^-(aq) \longrightarrow I_2(s) + NO(g)$

(b) $BrO_3^-(aq) + N_2H_4(g) \longrightarrow Br^-(aq) + N_2(g)$

(c) $NO_3^-(aq) + Sn^{2+}(aq) \longrightarrow Sn^{4+}(aq) + NO(g)$

67. Balance each redox reaction occurring in acidic aqueous solution. Use the half-reaction method.

(a) $ClO_4^-(aq) + Cl^-(aq) \longrightarrow ClO_3^-(aq) + Cl_2(g)$

(b) $MnO_4^-(aq) + Al(s) \longrightarrow Mn^{2+}(aq) + Al^{3+}(aq)$

(c) $Br_2(aq) + Sn(s) \longrightarrow Sn^{2+}(aq) + Br^-(aq)$

68. Balance each redox reaction occurring in acidic aqueous solution. Use the half-reaction method.

(a) $IO_3^-(aq) + SO_2(g) \longrightarrow I_2(s) + SO_4^{2-}(aq)$

(b) $Sn^{4+}(aq) + H_2(g) \longrightarrow Sn^{2+}(aq) + H^+(aq)$

(c) $Cr_2O_7^{2-}(aq) + Br^-(aq) \longrightarrow Cr^{3+}(aq) + Br_2(aq)$

69. Balance each redox reaction occurring in basic solution.

    (a) $ClO^-(aq) + Cr(OH)_4^-(aq) \longrightarrow$
    $$CrO_4^{2-}(aq) + Cl^-(aq)$$

    (b) $MnO_4^-(aq) + Br^-(aq) \longrightarrow$
    $$MnO_2(s) + BrO_3^-(aq)$$

70. Balance each redox reaction occurring in basic solution.

    (a) $NO_2^-(aq) + Al(s) \longrightarrow NH_3(g) + AlO_2^-(aq)$

    (b) $Al(s) + MnO_4^-(aq) \longrightarrow$
    $$MnO_2(s) + Al(OH)_4^-(aq)$$

THE ACTIVITY SERIES

71. Which metal has the least tendency to be oxidized?

    (a) Ag

    (b) Na

    (c) Ni

    (d) Pb

72. Which metal has the least tendency to be oxidized?

    (a) Sn

    (b) Mg

    (c) Cu

    (d) Fe

73. Which metal cation has the greatest tendency to be reduced?

    (a) Mn^{2+}

    (b) Cu^{2+}

    (c) K^+

    (d) Ni^{2+}

74. Which metal cation has the greatest tendency to be reduced?

    (a) Pb^{2+}

    (b) Cr^{3+}

    (c) Fe^{2+}

    (d) Sn^{2+}

75. Which metal is the best reducing agent?

    (a) Mn

    (b) Al

    (c) Ni

    (d) Cr

76. Which metal is the best reducing agent?

    (a) Ag

    (b) Mg

    (c) Fe

    (d) Pb

77. Determine whether or not each redox reaction occurs spontaneously in the forward direction.

    (a) $Ni(s) + Zn^{2+}(aq) \longrightarrow Ni^{2+}(aq) + Zn(s)$

    (b) $Ni(s) + Pb^{2+}(aq) \longrightarrow Ni^{2+}(aq) + Pb(s)$

    (c) $Al(s) + 3 Ag^+(aq) \longrightarrow 3 Al^{3+}(aq) + Ag(s)$

    (d) $Pb(s) + Mn^{2+}(aq) \longrightarrow Pb^{2+}(aq) + Mn(s)$

78. Determine whether or not each redox reaction occurs spontaneously in the forward direction.

    (a) $Ca^{2+}(aq) + Zn(s) \longrightarrow Ca(s) + Zn^{2+}(aq)$

    (b) $2 Ag^+(aq) + Ni(s) \longrightarrow 2 Ag(s) + Ni^{2+}(aq)$

    (c) $Fe(s) + Mn^{2+}(aq) \longrightarrow Fe^{2+}(aq) + Mn(s)$

    (d) $2 Al(s) + 3 Pb^{2+}(aq) \longrightarrow 2 Al^{3+}(aq) + 3 Pb(s)$

79. Suppose you wanted to cause Ni^{2+} ions to come out of solution as solid Ni. What metal could you use to accomplish this?

80. Suppose you wanted to cause Pb^{2+} ions to come out of solution as solid Pb. What metal could you use to accomplish this?

81. Which metal in the activity series will reduce Al^{3+} ions but not Na^+ ions?

82. Which metal in the activity series can be oxidized with a Ni^{2+} solution but not with a Cr^{3+} solution?

83. Which metals dissolve in HCl? For those metals that do dissolve, write a balanced redox reaction showing what happens when the metal dissolves.
    (a) Ag
    (b) Fe
    (c) Cu
    (d) Al

84. Which metals dissolve in HCl? For those metals that do dissolve, write a balanced redox reaction showing what happens when the metal dissolves.
    (a) Cr
    (b) Pb
    (c) Au
    (d) Zn

BATTERIES, ELECTROCHEMICAL CELLS, AND ELECTROLYSIS

85. Make a sketch of an electrochemical cell with the following overall reaction. Label the anode, the cathode, and the salt bridge. Indicate the direction of electron flow. *Hint:* When drawing electrochemical cells, the anode is usually drawn on the left side.

$$Mn(s) + Pb^{2+}(aq) \longrightarrow Mn^{2+}(aq) + Pb(s)$$

86. Make a sketch of an electrochemical cell with the following overall reaction. Label the anode, the cathode, and the salt bridge. Indicate the direction of electron flow. *Hint:* When drawing electrochemical cells, the anode is usually drawn on the left side.

$$Mg(s) + Ni^{2+}(aq) \longrightarrow Mg^{2+}(aq) + Ni(s)$$

87. An electrochemical cell has the following reaction occurring at the anode.

$$Zn(s) \longrightarrow Zn^{2+}(aq) + 2e^-$$

Which cathode reaction would produce a battery with the highest voltage?
    (a) $Mg^{2+}(aq) + 2e^- \longrightarrow Mg(s)$
    (b) $Pb^{2+}(aq) + 2e^- \longrightarrow Pb(s)$
    (c) $Cr^{3+}(aq) + 3e^- \longrightarrow Cr(s)$
    (d) $Cu^{2+}(aq) + 2e^- \longrightarrow Cu(s)$

88. An electrochemical cell has the following reaction occurring at the cathode.

$$Ni^{2+}(aq) + 2e^- \longrightarrow Ni(s)$$

Which anode reaction would produce a battery with the highest voltage?
    (a) $Ag(s) \longrightarrow Ag^+(aq) + e^-$
    (b) $Mg(s) \longrightarrow Mg^{2+}(aq) + 2e^-$
    (c) $Cr(s) \longrightarrow Cr^{3+}(aq) + 3e^-$
    (d) $Cu(s) \longrightarrow Cu^{2+}(aq) + 2e^-$

89. Use the half-cell reactions for the alkaline battery to determine the overall reaction that occurs in this battery.

90. Use the half-cell reactions for the lead-acid storage battery to determine the overall reaction that occurs in this battery.

91. Make a sketch of an electrolysis cell that could be used to electroplate copper onto other metal surfaces. Label the anode and the cathode and show the reactions that occur at each.

92. Make a sketch of an electrolysis cell that could be used to electroplate nickel onto other metal surfaces. Label the anode and the cathode and show the reactions that occur at each.

CORROSION

93. Which of the following metals, if coated onto iron, would prevent the corrosion of iron?
    (a) Zn
    (b) Sn
    (c) Mn

94. Which of the following metals, if coated onto iron, would prevent the corrosion of iron?
    (a) Mg
    (b) Cr
    (c) Cu

CUMULATIVE PROBLEMS

95. Determine whether or not each reaction is a redox reaction. For those reactions that are redox reactions, identify the substance being oxidized and the substance being reduced.

   (a) $Zn(s) + CoCl_2(aq) \longrightarrow ZnCl_2(aq) + Co(s)$

   (b) $HI(aq) + NaOH(aq) \longrightarrow H_2O(l) + NaI(aq)$

   (c) $AgNO_3(aq) + NaCl(aq) \longrightarrow$
   $$AgCl(s) + NaNO_3(aq)$$

   (d) $2 K(s) + Br_2(l) \longrightarrow 2 KBr(s)$

96. Determine whether or not each reaction is a redox reaction. For those reactions that are redox reactions, identify the substance being oxidized and the substance being reduced.

   (a) $Pb(NO_3)_2(aq) + 2 LiCl(aq) \longrightarrow$
   $$PbCl_2(s) + 2 LiNO_3(aq)$$

   (b) $2 HBr(aq) + Ca(OH)_2(aq) \longrightarrow$
   $$2 H_2O(l) + CaBr_2(aq)$$

   (c) $2 Al(s) + Fe_2O_3(s) \longrightarrow Al_2O_3(s) + 2 Fe(l)$

   (d) $Na_2O(s) + H_2O(l) \longrightarrow 2 NaOH(aq)$

97. Consider the unbalanced redox reaction:

   $$MnO_4^-(aq) + Zn(s) \longrightarrow Mn^{2+}(aq) + Zn^{2+}(aq)$$

   Balance the equation in acidic solution and determine how much of a 0.500 M $KMnO_4$ solution is required to completely dissolve 2.85 g of Zn.

98. Consider the unbalanced redox reaction:

   $$Cr_2O_7^{2-}(aq) + Cu(s) \longrightarrow Cr^{3+}(aq) + Cu^{2+}$$

   Balance the equation in acidic solution and determine how much of a 0.850 M $K_2Cr_2O_7$ solution is required to completely dissolve 5.25 g of Cu.

99. If a strip of magnesium metal is dipped into a solution containing silver ions, will a spontaneous reaction occur? If so, write the two half-reactions and the balanced overall equation for the reaction that occurs.

100. If a strip of tin metal is dipped into a solution containing zinc ions, will a spontaneous reaction occur? If so, write the two half-reactions and the balanced overall equation for the reaction that occurs.

101. A 10.0-mL sample of a commercial hydrogen peroxide (H_2O_2) solution is titrated with 0.0998 M $KMnO_4$. The end point is reached at a volume of 34.81 mL. Find the mass percent of H_2O_2 in the commercial hydrogen peroxide solution. (Assume a density of 1.00 g/mL for the hydrogen peroxide solution.) The unbalanced redox reaction that occurs in acidic solution during the titration is:

   $$H_2O_2(aq) + MnO_4^-(aq) \longrightarrow O_2(g) + Mn^{2+}(aq)$$

102. A 1.012-g sample of a salt containing Fe^{2+} is titrated with 0.1201 M $KMnO_4$. The end point of the titration is reached at 22.45 mL. Find the mass percent of Fe^{2+} in the sample. The unbalanced redox reaction that occurs in acidic solution during the titration is:

   $$Fe^{2+}(aq) + MnO_4^-(aq) \longrightarrow Fe^{3+}(aq) + Mn^{2+}(aq)$$

103. Silver is electroplated at the cathode of an electrolysis cell by the half-reaction:

   $$Ag^+(aq) + e^- \longrightarrow Ag(s)$$

   How many moles of electrons are required to electroplate 5.8 g of Ag?

104. Gold is electroplated at the cathode of an electrolysis cell by the half-reaction:

   $$Au^{3+}(aq) + 3e^- \longrightarrow Au(s)$$

   How many moles of electrons are required to electroplate 1.40 g of Au?

105. Determine whether HI can dissolve each metal sample. If it can, write a balanced chemical reaction showing how the metal dissolves in HI and determine the minimum amount of 3.5 M HI required to completely dissolve the sample.

   (a) 5.95 g Cr

   (b) 2.15 g Al

   (c) 4.85 g Cu

   (d) 2.42 g Au

106. Determine whether HCl can dissolve each metal sample. If it can, write a balanced chemical reaction showing how the metal dissolves in HCl and determine the minimum amount of 6.0 M HCl required to completely dissolve the sample.

   (a) 5.90 g Ag

   (b) 2.55 g Pb

   (c) 4.83 g Sn

   (d) 1.25 g Mg

107. One drop (assume 0.050 mL) of 6.0 M HCl is placed onto the surface of 0.028-mm-thick aluminum foil. What is the maximum diameter of the hole that will result from the HCl dissolving the aluminum? (Density of aluminum = 2.7 g/cm^3)

108. A graduated cylinder containing 1.00 mL of 12.0 M HCl is accidentally tipped over, and the contents spill onto manganese foil with a thickness of 0.055 mm. Calculate the maximum diameter of the hole that will be dissolved in the foil by the reaction between the manganese and hydrochloric acid. (Density of manganese = 7.47 g/cm^3)

109. The electrolytic cell represented in Figure 17 can be used to plate silver onto other metal surfaces. The plating reaction is: $Ag^+(aq) + e^- \longrightarrow Ag(s)$. Notice from the reaction that 1 mol e^- plates out 1 mol Ag(s). Use this stoichiometric relationship to determine how much time is required with an electrical current 0.100 amp to plate out 1.0 g Ag. The amp is a unit of electrical current equivalent to 1 C/s. (*Hint:* Recall that the charge of an electron is 1.60×10^{-19} C.)

110. An electrolytic cell similar to the one represented in Figure 17 can be used to plate gold onto other metal surfaces. The plating reaction is: $Au^+(aq) + e^- \longrightarrow Au(s)$. Notice from the reaction that 1 mol e^- plates out 1 mol Au(s). Use this stoichiometric relationship to determine how much time is required with an electrical current of 0.200 amp to plate out 0.400 g Au. The amp is a unit of electrical current equivalent to 1 C/s. (*Hint:* Recall that the charge of an electron is 1.60×10^{-19} C.)

HIGHLIGHT PROBLEMS

111. Consider the molecular views of an Al strip and Cu^{2+} solution. Draw a similar sketch showing what happens to the atoms and ions if the Al strip is submerged in the solution for a few minutes.

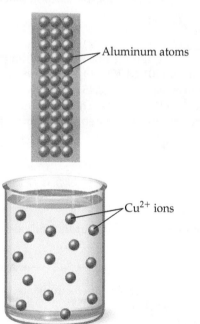

Aluminum atoms

Cu^{2+} ions

112. Suppose a fuel-cell generator produces electricity for a house. If each H_2 molecule produces $2e^-$, how many kilograms of hydrogen would be required to generate the electricity needed for a typical house? Assume the home uses about 850 kWh of electricity per month, which corresponds to approximately 2.65×10^4 mol of electrons at the voltage of a fuel cell.

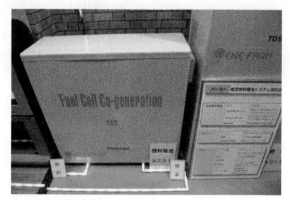

Tony McNicol/Alamy.

113. Consider the molecular view of an electrochemical cell involving the overall reaction:

$$Zn(s) + Ni^{2+}(aq) \longrightarrow Zn^{2+}(aq) + Ni(s)$$

Draw a similar sketch showing how the cell might appear after it has generated a substantial amount of electrical current.

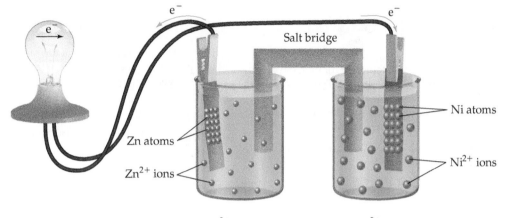

Anode: $Zn(s) \longrightarrow Zn^{2+}(aq) + 2e^-$ **Cathode:** $Ni^{2+}(aq) + 2e^- \longrightarrow Ni(s)$

▶ANSWERS TO SKILLBUILDER EXERCISES

Skillbuilder 1
  (a) K is oxidized, Cl_2 is reduced.
  (b) Al is oxidized, Sn^{2+} is reduced.
  (c) C is oxidized, O_2 is reduced.

Skillbuilder 2
  (a) K is the reducing agent; Cl_2 is the oxidizing agent.
  (b) Al is the reducing agent; Sn^{2+} is the oxidizing agent.
  (c) C is the reducing agent; O_2 is the oxidizing agent.

Skillbuilder 3   (a) $\underset{0}{Zn}$

(b) $\underset{+2}{Cu^{2+}}$

(c) $\underset{+2-1}{CaCl_2}$

(d) $\underset{+4-1}{CF_4}$

(e) $\underset{+3-2}{NO_2{}^-}$

(f) $\underset{+6-2}{SO_3}$

Skillbuilder 4
  Sn oxidized ($0 \longrightarrow +4$); N reduced ($+5 \longrightarrow +4$)

Skillbuilder 5
  $6\,H^+(aq) + 2\,Cr(s) \longrightarrow 3\,H_2(g) + 2\,Cr^{3+}(aq)$

Skillbuilder 6
  $Cu(s) + 4\,H^+(aq) + 2\,NO_3{}^-(aq) \longrightarrow$
  $\qquad\qquad Cu^{2+}(aq) + 2\,NO_2(g) + 2\,H_2O(l)$

Skillbuilder 7
  $5\,Sn(s) + 16\,H^+(aq) + 2\,MnO_4{}^-(aq) \longrightarrow$
  $\qquad\qquad 5\,Sn^{2+}(aq) + 2\,Mn^{2+}(aq) + 8\,H_2O(l)$

Skillbuilder 8
  $H_2O_2(aq) + 2\,ClO_2(aq) + 2\,OH^-(aq) \longrightarrow$
  $\qquad\qquad O_2(g) + 2\,ClO_2{}^-(aq) + 2\,H_2O(l)$

Skillbuilder 9   (a) Yes (b) No

Skillbuilder 10   No

▶ANSWERS TO CONCEPTUAL CHECKPOINTS

1 (b) The oxidizing agent oxidizes another species and is itself always reduced.

2 (d) From rule 1, we know that the oxidation state of nitrogen in N_2 is 0. According to rule 3, the sum of the oxidation states of all atoms in a compound = 0. Therefore, by applying rule 5, we can determine that the oxidation state of nitrogen in NO is +2; in NO_2 it is +4; and in NH_3 it is −3.

3 (c) Lead is the only one of these metals that lies above hydrogen in the activity series, and therefore the only one that dissolves in an acidic solution.

4 (a) Magnesium would lead to the highest voltage because it is highest on the activity series. Of the metals listed, it is most easily oxidized and therefore produces the highest voltage when combined with the reduction of Pb^{2+} ions.

5 (d) Tin is the only metal in the list that lies below iron in the activity series. Tin is therefore more difficult to oxidize than iron and cannot prevent the oxidation of the iron.

ANSWERS TO ODD-NUMBERED EXERCISES

QUESTIONS

1. A fuel-cell electric vehicle is an automobile running on an electric motor that is powered by hydrogen. The fuel cells use the electron-gaining tendency of oxygen and the electron-losing tendency of hydrogen to force electrons to move through a wire, creating the electricity that powers the car.

3. **a.** Oxidation is the gaining of oxygen, and reduction is the losing of oxygen.

   b. Oxidation is the loss of electrons, and reduction is the gain of electrons.

   c. Oxidation is an increase in oxidation state, and reduction is a decrease in oxidation state.

5. gain

7. The oxidization state of a free element is zero. The oxidization state of a monoatomic ion equals its charge.

9. For an ion, the sum of the oxidation states of the individual atoms must add up to *the charge of the ion*.

11. In a redox reaction, an atom that undergoes an increase in oxidation state is *oxidized*. An atom that undergoes a decrease in oxidation state is *reduced*.

13. When balancing redox equations, the number of electrons lost in the oxidation half-reaction must *equal* the number of electrons gained in the reduction half-reaction.

15. When balancing aqueous redox reactions, charge is balanced using *electrons*.

17. The metals at the top of the activity series are the most reactive.

19. The metals at the bottom of the activity series are least likely to lose electrons.

21. If the metal is listed above H_2 on the activity series, it will dissolve in acids such as HCl or HBr.

23. Oxidation occurs at the *anode* of an electrochemical cell.

25. The salt bridge joins the two half-cells or completes the circuit; it allows the flow of ions between the two half-cells.

27. The common dry cell battery does not contain large amounts of liquid water and is composed of a zinc case that acts as the anode. The cathode is a carbon rod immersed in a moist paste of MnO_2 that also contains NH_4Cl. The anode and cathode reactions that occur produce a voltage of about 1.5 volts.

   anode reaction:

   $$Zn(s) \longrightarrow Zn^{2+}(aq) + 2\,e^-$$

   cathode reaction:

   $$2\,MnO_2(s) + 2\,NH_2{}^+(aq) + 2\,e^- \longrightarrow$$
   $$2\,Mn_2O_3(s) + 2\,NH_3(g) + H_2O(l)$$

29. Fuel cells are like batteries, but the reactants are constantly replenished. The reactants constantly flow through the battery, generating electrical current as they undergo a redox reaction.

   anode reaction:

   $$2\,H_2(g) + 4\,OH^-(aq) \longrightarrow 4\,H_2O(g) + 4\,e^-$$

   cathode reaction:

   $$O_2(g) + 2\,H_2O(l) + 4\,e^- \longrightarrow 4\,OH^-(aq)$$

31. Corrosion is the oxidation of metals; the most common example is rusting of iron.

   oxidation:

   $$2\,Fe(s) \longrightarrow 2\,Fe^{2+}(aq) + 4\,e^-$$

   reduction:

   $$O_2(g) + 2\,H_2O(l) + 4\,e^- \longrightarrow 4\,OH^-(aq)$$

   overall:

   $$2\,Fe(s) + O_2(g) + 2\,H_2O(l) \longrightarrow 2\,Fe(OH)_2(s)$$

PROBLEMS

33. **a.** H_2 **b.** Al
   c. Al

35. **a.** Sr is oxidized, O_2 is reduced.
   b. Ca is oxidized, Cl_2 is reduced.
   c. Mg is oxidized, Ni^{2+} is reduced.

37. **a.** Sr is the reducing agent; O_2 is the oxidizing agent.
   b. Ca is the reducing agent; Cl_2 is the oxidizing agent.
   c. Mg is the reducing agent; Ni^{2+} is the oxidizing agent.

39. b (F_2), d (Cl_2)

41. a (K), c (Fe)

43. **a.** N_2 is oxidized and is the reducing agent.
   O_2 is reduced and is the oxidizing agent.
   b. C is oxidized and is the reducing agent.
   O_2 is reduced and is the oxidizing agent.
   c. Sb is oxidized and is the reducing agent.
   Cl_2 is reduced and is the oxidizing agent.
   d. K is oxidized and is the reducing agent.
   Pb^{2+} is reduced and is the oxidizing agent.

45. **a.** 0   **b.** +2
   c. +3   **d.** 0

47. **a.** Na: +1; Cl: −1   **b.** Ca: +2; F: −1
   c. S: +4; O: −2   **d.** H: +1; S: −2

49. **a.** +2   **b.** +4

     c. +1

51. **a.** C: +4; O: −2   **b.** O: −2; H: +1

     c. N: +5; O: −2   **d.** N: +3; O: −2

53. **a.** +1   **b.** +3

     c. +5   **d.** +7

55. **a.** Cu, +2; N, +5; O, −2

     b. Sr, +2; O, −2; H, +1

     c. K, +1; O, −2; Cr, +6

     d. Na, +1; H, +1; O, −2; C, +4

57. **a.** Sb + 5 $\longrightarrow$ +3, reduced

     Cl − 1 $\longrightarrow$ 0, oxidized

     b. C + 2 $\longrightarrow$ +4, oxidized

     Cl 0 $\longrightarrow$ −1, reduced

     c. N + 2 $\longrightarrow$ +3, oxidized

     Br 0 $\longrightarrow$ −1, reduced

     d. H 0 $\longrightarrow$ +1, oxidized

     C + 4 $\longrightarrow$ +2, reduced

59. Na is the reducing agent.

H is the oxidizing agent.

61. **a.** $3 K(s) + Cr^{3+}(aq) \longrightarrow Cr(s) + 3 K^+(aq)$

     b. $Mg(s) + 2 Ag^+(aq) \longrightarrow Mg^{2+}(aq) + 2 Ag(s)$

     c. $2 Al(s) + 3 Fe^{2+}(aq) \longrightarrow 2 Al^{3+}(aq) + 3 Fe(s)$

63. **a.** reduction, $5 e^- + MnO_4^-(aq) + 8 H^+(aq) \longrightarrow$

$$Mn^{2+}(aq) + 4 H_2O(l)$$

     b. oxidation, $2 H_2O(l) + Pb^{2+}(aq) \longrightarrow$

$$PbO_2(s) + 4 H^+(aq) + 2e^-$$

     c. reduction, $10 e^- + 2 IO_3^-(aq) + 12 H^+(aq) \longrightarrow$

$$I_2(s) + 6 H_2O(l)$$

     d. oxidation, $SO_2(g) + 2 H_2O(l) \longrightarrow$

$$SO_4^{2-}(aq) + 4 H^+(aq) + 2 e^-$$

65. **a.** $PbO_2(s) + 4 H^+(aq) + 2 I^-(aq) \longrightarrow$

$$I_2(s) + Pb^{2+}(aq) + 2 H_2O(l)$$

     b. $5 SO_3^{2-}(aq) + 6 H^+(aq) + 2 MnO_4^-(aq) \longrightarrow$

$$5 SO_4^{2-}(aq) + 2 Mn^{2+}(aq) + 3 H_2O(l)$$

     c. $S_2O_3^{2-}(aq) + 4 Cl_2(g) + 5 H_2O(l) \longrightarrow$

$$2 SO_4^{2-}(aq) + 8 Cl^-(aq) + 10 H^+(aq)$$

67. **a.** $ClO_4^-(aq) + 2 H^+(aq) + 2 Cl^-(aq) \longrightarrow$

$$ClO_3^-(aq) + Cl_2(aq) + H_2O(l)$$

     b. $3 MnO_4^-(aq) + 24 H^+(aq) + 5 Al(s) \longrightarrow$

$$3 Mn^{2+}(aq) + 5 Al^{3+}(aq) + 12 H_2O(l)$$

     c. $Br_2(aq) + Sn(s) \longrightarrow Sn^{2+}(aq) + 2 Br^-(aq)$

69. **a.** $3 ClO^-(aq) + 2 Cr(OH)_4^-(aq) + 2 OH^-(aq) \rightarrow$

$$3 Cl^-(aq) + 2 CrO_4^{2-}(aq) + 5 H_2O(l)$$

     b. $2 MnO_4^-(aq) + Br(aq) + H_2O(l) \longrightarrow$

$$2 MnO_2(s) + BrO_3^-(aq) + 2 OH^-(aq)$$

71. a, Ag

73. b, Cu^{2+}

75. b, Al

77. b and c occur spontaneously in the forward direction

79. Fe, Cr, Zn, Mn, Al, Mg, Na, Ca, K, Li

81. Mg

83. **a.** no reaction

     b. $2 HCl(aq) + Fe(s) \longrightarrow H_2(g) + FeCl_2(aq)$

     c. no reaction

     d. $6 HCl(aq) + 2 Al(s) \longrightarrow 3 H_2(g) + 2 AlCl_3(aq)$

85.

87. d

89. $Zn(s) + 2 MnO_2(s) + 2 H_2O(l) \longrightarrow$

$$Zn(OH)_2(s) + 2 MnO(OH)(s)$$

91.

93. a, Zn; c, Mn

95. **a.** redox; Zn is oxidized; Co is reduced.

     b. not redox

     c. not redox

     d. redox; K is oxidized; Br is reduced.

97. $16 H^+(aq) + 2 MnO_4^-(aq) + 5 Zn(s) \longrightarrow$

$$2 Mn^{2+}(aq) + 5 Zn^{2+}(aq) + 8 H_2O(l); 34.9 \text{ mL}$$

99. Yes, the reaction will occur spontaneously.

$Mg(s) \longrightarrow Mg^{2+}(aq) + 2 e^-$

$Ag^+(aq) + e^- \longrightarrow Ag(s)$

$2 Ag^+(aq) + Mg(s) \longrightarrow Mg^{2+}(aq) + 2 Ag(s)$

101. 2.95%

103. 0.054 mol

105. a. $2\,Cr(s) + 6\,HI(aq) \longrightarrow$
$2\,Cr^{3+}(aq) + 6\,I^-(aq) + 3\,H_2(g)$, 98 mL HI

  b. $2\,Al(s) + 6\,HI(aq) \longrightarrow$
$2\,Al^{3+}(aq) + 6\,I^-(aq) + 3\,H_2(g)$, 68 mL HI

  c. no

  d. no

107. 0.67 cm

109. 8.9×10^3 s or 2.5 hrs

111.

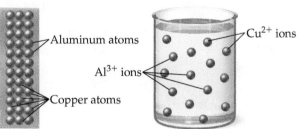

113. Many of the Zn atoms on the electrode would become Zn^{2+} ions in solution. Many Ni^{2+} ions in solution would become Ni atoms on the electrode.

Chemical Composition

Chemical
Composition

"In science, you don't ask why, you ask how much."

ERWIN CHARGAFF (1905–2002)

1 How Much Sodium?

Sodium is an important dietary mineral that we eat in our food, primarily as sodium chloride (table salt). Sodium is involved in the regulation of body fluids, and eating too much of it can lead to high blood pressure. High blood pressure, in turn, increases the risk of stroke and heart attack. Consequently, people with high blood pressure should limit their sodium intake. The FDA recommends that a person consume less than 2.4 g (2400 mg) of sodium per day. However, sodium is usually consumed as sodium chloride, so the mass of sodium that we eat is not the same as the mass of sodium chloride that we eat. How many grams of sodium chloride can we consume and still stay below the FDA recommendation for sodium?

To answer this question, we need to know the *chemical composition* of sodium chloride. We are familiar with its formula, NaCl, so we know that there is one sodium ion to every chloride ion. However, since the masses of sodium and chlorine are different, the relationship between the mass of sodium and the mass of sodium chloride is not clear from the chemical formula alone. In this chapter, we learn how to use the information in a chemical formula, together with atomic and formula masses, to calculate the amount of a constituent element in a given amount of a compound (or vice versa).

Chemical composition is important not just for assessing dietary sodium intake, but for addressing many other issues as well. A company that mines iron, for example, wants to know how much iron it can extract from a given amount of iron ore; a company interested in developing hydrogen as a potential fuel would want to know how much hydrogen it can extract from a given amount of water. Many environmental issues also require knowledge of chemical composition. An estimate of the threat of ozone depletion requires knowing how much chlorine is in a given amount of a particular chlorofluorocarbon such as freon-12. To determine

◄ Ordinary table salt is a compound called sodium chloride. The sodium within sodium chloride is linked to high blood pressure. In this chapter, we learn how to determine how much sodium is in a given amount of sodium chloride.

295

▲ The mining of iron requires knowing how much iron is in a given amount of iron ore.

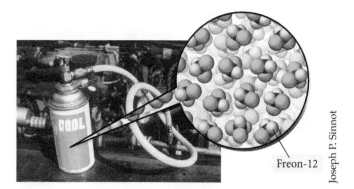

Freon-12

▲ Estimating the threat of ozone depletion requires knowing the amount of chlorine in a given amount of a chlorofluoro-carbon.

these kinds of quantities, we must understand the relationships inherent in a chemical formula and the relationship between numbers of atoms or molecules and their masses. In this chapter, we examine these relationships.

2 Counting Nails by the Pound

3.4 lbs nails

8.25 grams carbon

▲ Asking how many nails are in a given weight of nails is similar to asking how many atoms are in a given mass of an element. In both cases, we count the objects by weighing them.

Some hardware stores sell nails by the pound, which is easier than selling them by the nail because customers often need hundreds of nails and counting them takes too long. However, a customer may still want to know the number of nails contained in a given weight of nails. This problem is similar to asking how many atoms are in a given mass of an element. With atoms, however, we *must* use their mass as a way to count them because atoms are too small and too numerous to count individually. Even if you could see atoms and counted them 24 hours a day for as long as you lived, you would barely begin to count the number of atoms in something as small as a grain of sand. However, just as the hardware store customer wants to know the number of nails in a given weight, we want to know the number of atoms in a given mass. How do we do that?

Suppose the hardware store customer buys 2.60 lb of medium-sized nails and a dozen nails weigh 0.150 lb. How many nails did the customer buy? This calculation requires two conversions: one between pounds and dozens and another between dozens and number of nails. The conversion factor for the first part is the weight per dozen nails.

$$0.150 \text{ lb nails} = 1 \text{ doz nails}$$

The conversion factor for the second part is the number of nails in one dozen.

$$1 \text{ doz nails} = 12 \text{ nails}$$

The solution map for the problem is:

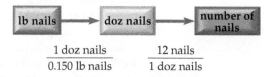

Beginning with 2.60 lb and using the solution map as a guide, we convert from lb to number of nails.

$$2.60 \text{ lb nails} \times \frac{1 \text{ doz nails}}{0.150 \text{ lb nails}} \times \frac{12 \text{ nails}}{1 \text{ doz nails}} = 208 \text{ nails}$$

The customer who bought 2.60 lb of nails has 208 nails. He counted the nails by weighing them. If the customer purchased a different size of nail, the first conversion factor—relating pounds to dozens—would change, but the second conversion factor would not. One dozen corresponds to 12 nails, regardless of their size.

3 Counting Atoms by the Gram

1 mole of copper atoms

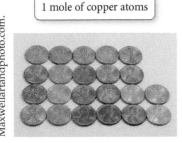

▲ Twenty-two *copper* pennies contain approximately 1 mol of copper atoms. Pennies were mostly copper until 1982, at which point the U.S. Mint started making them out of zinc with only a copper coating (because copper became too valuable).

Maxwellartandphoto.com.

The value of the mole is actually an empirically measured quantity.

Determining the number of atoms in a sample with a certain mass is similar to determining the number of nails in a sample with a certain weight. With nails, we used a dozen as a convenient number in our conversions, but a dozen is too small to use with atoms. We need a larger number because atoms are so small. The chemist's "dozen" is called the **mole (mol)** and has a value of 6.022×10^{23}.

$$1 \text{ mol} = 6.022 \times 10^{23}$$

This number is also called **Avogadro's number**, named after Amadeo Avogadro (1776–1856).

The first thing to understand about the mole is that it can specify Avogadro's number of anything. *One mole of anything is 6.022×10^{23} units of that thing.* For example, one mole of marbles corresponds to 6.022×10^{23} marbles, and one mole of sand grains corresponds to 6.022×10^{23} sand grains. One mole of atoms, ions, or molecules generally makes up objects of reasonable size. For example, 22 *copper* pennies (pennies were mostly copper until 1982) contain approximately 1 mol of copper (Cu) atoms, and a couple of large helium balloons contain approximately 1 mol of helium (He) atoms.

The second thing to understand about the mole is how it gets its specific value. *The numerical value of the mole is defined as being equal to the number of atoms in exactly 12 g of pure carbon-12.*

This definition of the mole establishes a relationship between mass (grams of carbon) and number of atoms (Avogadro's number). This relationship, as we will see shortly, allows us to count atoms by weighing them.

CONVERTING BETWEEN MOLES AND NUMBER OF ATOMS

Converting between moles and number of atoms is similar to converting between dozens and number of nails. To convert between moles of atoms and number of atoms, we use the conversion factors:

$$\frac{1 \text{ mol}}{6.022 \times 10^{23} \text{ atoms}} \quad \text{or} \quad \frac{6.022 \times 10^{23} \text{ atoms}}{1 \text{ mol}}$$

For example, suppose we want to convert 3.5 mol of helium to a number of helium atoms. We set up the problem in the standard way.

GIVEN: 3.5 mol He

FIND: He atoms

RELATIONSHIPS USED   1 mol He = 6.022×10^{23} He atoms

SOLUTION MAP   We draw a solution map showing the conversion from moles of He to He atoms.

1 mole of helium atoms

▲ Two large helium balloons contain approximately 1 mol of helium atoms.

Getty Images.

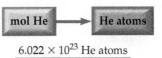

$$\frac{6.022 \times 10^{23} \text{ He atoms}}{1 \text{ mol He}}$$

SOLUTION

Beginning with 3.5 mol He, we use the conversion factor to get to He atoms.

$$3.5 \ \text{mol He} \times \frac{6.022 \times 10^{23} \ \text{He atoms}}{1 \ \text{mol He}} = 2.1 \times 10^{24} \ \text{He atoms}$$

EXAMPLE 1   **Converting between Moles and Number of Atoms**

A silver ring contains 1.1×10^{22} silver atoms. How many moles of silver are in the ring?

SORT You are given the number of silver atoms and asked to find the number of moles.	**GIVEN:** 1.1×10^{22} Ag atoms **FIND:** mol Ag
STRATEGIZE Draw a solution map, beginning with silver atoms and ending at moles. The conversion factor is Avogadro's number.	**SOLUTION MAP** $$\frac{1 \ \text{mol Ag}}{6.022 \times 10^{23} \ \text{Ag atoms}}$$ **RELATIONSHIPS USED** $1 \ \text{mol Ag} = 6.022 \times 10^{23}$ Ag atoms (Avogadro's number)
SOLVE Follow the solution map to solve the problem. Beginning with 1.1×10^{22} Ag atoms, use the conversion factor to get to moles of Ag.	**SOLUTION** $$1.1 \times 10^{22} \ \text{Ag atoms} \ \times \frac{1 \ \text{mol Ag}}{6.022 \times 10^{23} \ \text{Ag atoms}} = 1.8 \times 10^{-2} \ \text{mol Ag}$$
CHECK Are the units correct? Does the answer make physical sense?	The units, mol Ag, are the desired units. The magnitude of the answer is orders of magnitude smaller than the given quantity because it takes many atoms to make a mole, so we expect the answer to be orders of magnitude smaller than the given quantity.

▶**SKILLBUILDER 1 | Converting between Moles and Number of Atoms**

How many gold atoms are in a pure gold ring containing 8.83×10^{-2} mol Au?

▶**FOR MORE PRACTICE**   Example 13, Problems 17, 18, 19, 20.

CONVERTING BETWEEN GRAMS AND MOLES OF AN ELEMENT

We just learned how to convert between moles and number of atoms, which is like converting between dozens and number of nails. We need one more conversion factor to convert from the mass of a sample to the number of atoms in the sample. For nails, we used the weight of one dozen nails; for atoms, we use the mass of one mole of atoms.

> The mass of 1 mol of atoms of an element is its **molar mass**. The value of an element's molar mass in grams per mole is numerically equal to the element's atomic mass in atomic mass units.

Recall that Avogadro's number, the number of atoms in a mole, is defined as the number of atoms in exactly 12 g of carbon-12. Since the atomic mass unit is defined as one-twelfth of the mass of a carbon-12 atom, it follows that the molar mass of any element—the mass of 1 mol of atoms in grams of that element—is equal to the atomic mass of that element expressed in atomic mass units. For example, copper has an atomic mass of 63.55 amu; therefore, 1 mol of copper atoms has a mass of 63.55 g, and the molar mass of copper is 63.55 g/mol. Just as the weight of 1 doz nails changes for different nails, so the mass of 1 mol of atoms changes for different elements: 1 mol of sulfur atoms (sulfur atoms are lighter than copper atoms) has a mass of 32.07 g; 1 mol of carbon atoms (lighter than sulfur) has a mass of 12.01 g; and 1 mol of lithium atoms (lighter yet) has a mass of 6.94 g.

$$32.07 \text{ g sulfur} = 1 \text{ mol sulfur} = 6.022 \times 10^{23} \text{ S atoms}$$

$$12.01 \text{ g carbon} = 1 \text{ mol carbon} = 6.022 \times 10^{23} \text{ C atoms}$$

$$6.94 \text{ g lithium} = 1 \text{ mol lithium} = 6.022 \times 10^{23} \text{ Li atoms}$$

The lighter the atom, the less mass in one mole of that atom (▼ Figure 1).

Therefore, the molar mass of any element becomes a conversion factor between grams of that element and moles of that element. For carbon:

$$12.01 \text{ g C} = 1 \text{ mol C} \quad \text{or} \quad \frac{12.01 \text{ g C}}{1 \text{ mol C}} \quad \text{or} \quad \frac{1 \text{ mol C}}{12.01 \text{ g C}}$$

1 dozen large nails

1 dozen small nails

Maxwellartandphoto.com.

(a)

1 mole S (32.07 g)

1 mole C (12.01 g)

Richard Megna/Fundamental Photographs.

(b)

▶ FIGURE 1 **The mass of 1 mol** **(a)** Each of these pictures shows the same number of nails: 12. As you can see, 12 large nails have more weight and occupy more space than 12 small nails. The same is true for atoms. **(b)** Each of these samples has the same number of atoms: 6.022×10^{23}. Since sulfur atoms are more massive and larger than carbon atoms, 1 mol of S atoms is heavier and occupies more space than 1 mol of C atoms.

A 0.58-g diamond would be about a three-carat diamond.

Suppose we want to calculate the number of moles of carbon in a 0.58-g diamond (pure carbon).

We first sort the information in the problem.

GIVEN: 0.58 g C

FIND: mol C

SOLUTION MAP We then strategize by drawing a solution map showing the conversion from grams of C to moles of C. The conversion factor is the molar mass of carbon.

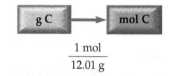

$$\frac{1\ \text{mol}}{12.01\ \text{g}}$$

RELATIONSHIPS USED

12.01 g C = 1 mol C (molar mass of carbon, from periodic table)

SOLUTION

Finally, we solve the problem by following the solution map.

$$0.58\ \cancel{\text{g C}} \times \frac{1\ \text{mol C}}{12.01\ \cancel{\text{g C}}} = 4.8 \times 10^{-2}\ \text{mol C}$$

EXAMPLE 2   The Mole Concept—Converting between Grams and Moles

Calculate the number of moles of sulfur in 57.8 g of sulfur.

SORT Begin by sorting the information in the problem. You are given the mass of sulfur and asked to find the number of moles.	GIVEN: 57.8 g S FIND: mol S
STRATEGIZE Draw a solution map showing the conversion from g S to mol S. The conversion factor is the molar mass of sulfur.	SOLUTION MAP g S → mol S $$\frac{1\ \text{mol S}}{32.07\ \text{g S}}$$ RELATIONSHIPS USED 32.07 g S = 1 mol S (molar mass of sulfur, from periodic table)
SOLVE Follow the solution map to solve the problem. Begin with 57.8 g S and use the conversion factor to get to mol S.	SOLUTION $$57.8\ \cancel{\text{g S}} \times \frac{1\ \text{mol S}}{32.07\ \cancel{\text{g S}}} = 1.80\ \text{mol S}$$
CHECK Check your answer. Are the units correct? Does the answer make physical sense?	The units (mol S) are correct. The magnitude of the answer makes sense because 1 mole of S has a mass of 32.07 g; therefore, 57.8 g of S should be close to 2 moles.

▶SKILLBUILDER 2 | The Mole Concept—Converting between Grams and Moles

Calculate the number of grams of sulfur in 2.78 mol of sulfur.

▶FOR MORE PRACTICE   Example 14; Problems 25, 26, 27, 28, 29, 30.

CONVERTING BETWEEN GRAMS OF AN ELEMENT AND NUMBER OF ATOMS

Now, suppose we want to know the number of carbon *atoms* in the 0.58-g diamond. We first convert from grams to moles and then from moles to number of atoms. The solution map is:

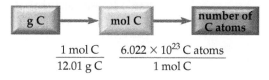

$$\frac{1 \text{ mol C}}{12.01 \text{ g C}} \qquad \frac{6.022 \times 10^{23} \text{ C atoms}}{1 \text{ mol C}}$$

Notice the similarity between this solution map and the one we used for nails:

$$\frac{1 \text{ doz nails}}{0.150 \text{ lb nails}} \qquad \frac{12 \text{ nails}}{1 \text{ doz nails}}$$

Beginning with 0.58 g carbon and using the solution map as a guide, we convert to the number of carbon atoms.

$$0.58 \text{ g C} \times \frac{1 \text{ mol C}}{12.01 \text{ g C}} \times \frac{6.022 \times 10^{23} \text{ C atoms}}{1 \text{ mol C}} = 2.9 \times 10^{22} \text{ C atoms}$$

EXAMPLE 3   The Mole Concept—Converting between Grams and Number of Atoms

How many aluminum atoms are in an aluminum can with a mass of 16.2 g?

SORT You are given the mass of aluminum and asked to find the number of aluminum atoms.	**GIVEN:** 16.2 g Al **FIND:** Al atoms
STRATEGIZE The solution map has two steps. In the first step, convert from g Al to mol Al. In the second step, convert from mol Al to the number of Al atoms. The required conversion factors are the molar mass of aluminum and the number of atoms in a mole.	**SOLUTION MAP** g Al → mol Al → number of Al atoms $\dfrac{1 \text{ mol Al}}{26.98 \text{ g Al}} \qquad \dfrac{6.022 \times 10^{23} \text{ Al atoms}}{1 \text{ mol Al}}$ **RELATIONSHIPS USED** 26.98 g Al = 1 mol Al (molar mass of aluminum, from periodic table) $6.022 \times 10^{23} = 1$ mol (Avogadro's number)
SOLVE Follow the solution map to solve the problem, beginning with 16.2 g Al and multiplying by the appropriate conversion factors to arrive at Al atoms.	**SOLUTION** $16.2 \text{ g Al} \times \dfrac{1 \text{ mol Al}}{26.98 \text{ g Al}} \times \dfrac{6.022 \times 10^{23} \text{ Al atoms}}{1 \text{ mol Al}} = 3.62 \times 10^{23} \text{ Al atoms}$
CHECK Are the units correct? Does the answer make physical sense?	The units, Al atoms, are correct. The answer makes sense because the number of atoms in any macroscopic-sized sample of matter should be very large.

▶**SKILLBUILDER 3 │ The Mole Concept—Converting between Grams and Number of Atoms**

Calculate the mass of 1.23×10^{24} helium atoms.

▶**FOR MORE PRACTICE**   Example 15; Problems 35, 36, 37, 38, 39, 40, 41, 42.

Before we move on, notice that numbers with large exponents, such as 6.022×10^{23}, are almost unimaginably large. Twenty-two copper pennies contain 6.022×10^{23} or 1 mol of copper atoms, but 6.022×10^{23} pennies would cover Earth's entire surface to a depth of 300 m. Even objects that are small by everyday standards occupy a huge space when we have a mole of them. For example, one crystal of granulated sugar has a mass of less than 1 mg and a diameter of less than 0.1 mm, yet 1 mol of sugar crystals would cover the state of Texas to a depth of several feet. For every increase of 1 in the exponent of a number, the number increases by 10. So a number with an exponent of 23 is incredibly large. A mole has to be a large number because atoms are so small.

✔ CONCEPTUAL CHECKPOINT 1

Which statement is *always* true for samples of atomic elements, regardless of the type of element present in the samples?

(a) If two samples of different elements contain the same number of atoms, they contain the same number of moles.

(b) If two samples of different elements have the same mass, they contain the same number of moles.

(c) If two samples of different elements have the same mass, they contain the same number of atoms.

✔ CONCEPTUAL CHECKPOINT 2

Without doing any calculations, determine which sample contains the most atoms.

(a) one gram of cobalt

(b) one gram of carbon

(c) one gram of lead

4 Counting Molecules by the Gram

Remember, ionic compounds do not contain individual molecules. In loose language, the smallest electrically neutral collection of ions is sometimes called a molecule but is more correctly called a formula unit.

The calculations we just performed for atoms can also be applied to molecules for covalent compounds or formula units for ionic compounds. We first convert between the mass of a compound and moles of the compound, and then we calculate the number of molecules (or formula units) from moles.

CONVERTING BETWEEN GRAMS AND MOLES OF A COMPOUND

Remember, the formula mass for a compound is the sum of the atomic masses of all of the atoms in a chemical formula.

For elements, the molar mass is the mass of 1 mol of atoms of that element. For compounds, the molar mass is the mass of 1 mol of molecules or formula units of that compound. The molar mass of a compound in grams per mole is numerically equal to the formula mass of the compound in atomic mass units. For example, the formula mass of CO_2 is:

$$\text{Formula mass} = 1(\text{Atomic mass of C}) + 2(\text{Atomic mass of O})$$

$$= 1(12.01 \text{ amu}) + 2(16.00 \text{ amu})$$

$$= 44.01 \text{ amu}$$

The molar mass of CO_2 is therefore:

$$\text{Molar mass} = 44.01 \text{ g/mol}$$

Just as the molar mass of an element serves as a conversion factor between grams and moles of that element, the molar mass of a compound serves as a conversion factor between grams and moles of that compound. For example, suppose we want to find the number of moles in a 22.5-g sample of dry ice (solid CO_2). We set up the problem in the normal way.

We begin by sorting the information.

GIVEN: 22.5 g CO_2

FIND: mol CO_2

SOLUTION MAP

We then strategize by drawing a solution map which shows how the molar mass converts grams of the compound to moles of the compound.

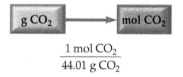

$$\frac{1 \text{ mol } CO_2}{44.01 \text{ g } CO_2}$$

RELATIONSHIPS USED

44.01 g CO_2 = 1 mol CO_2 (molar mass of CO_2)

SOLUTION

Finally, we solve the problem.

$$22.5 \text{ g} \times \frac{1 \text{ mol } CO_2}{44.01 \text{ g}} = 0.511 \text{ mol } CO_2$$

EXAMPLE 4 The Mole Concept—Converting between Grams and Moles for Compounds

Calculate the mass (in grams) of 1.75 mol of water.

SORT You are given moles of water and asked to find the mass.	GIVEN: 1.75 mol H_2O FIND: g H_2O
STRATEGIZE Draw a solution map showing the conversion from mol H_2O to g H_2O. The conversion factor is the molar mass of water, which you can determine by summing the atomic masses of all the atoms in the chemical formula.	SOLUTION MAP $\boxed{\text{mol } H_2O} \longrightarrow \boxed{\text{g } H_2O}$ $\dfrac{18.02 \text{ g } H_2O}{1 \text{ mol } H_2O}$ RELATIONSHIPS USED H_2O molar mass = 2(Atomic mass H) + 1(Atomic mass O) = 2(1.01) + 1(16.00) = 18.02 g/mol
SOLVE Follow the solution map to solve the problem. Begin with 1.75 mol of water and use the molar mass to convert to grams of water.	SOLUTION $1.75 \text{ mol } H_2O \times \dfrac{18.02 \text{ g } H_2O}{\text{mol } H_2O} = 31.5 \text{ g } H_2O$
CHECK Check your answer. Are the units correct? Does the answer make physical sense?	The units (g H_2O) are the desired units. The magnitude of the answer makes sense because 1 mole of water has a mass of 18.02 g; therefore, 1.75 moles should have a mass that is slightly less than 36 g.

▶ **SKILLBUILDER 4** | **The Mole Concept—Converting between Grams and Moles**

Calculate the number of moles of NO_2 in 1.18 g of NO_2.

▶ **FOR MORE PRACTICE** Problems 47, 48, 49, 50.

CONVERTING BETWEEN GRAMS OF A COMPOUND AND NUMBER OF MOLECULES

Suppose that we want to find the *number of CO_2 molecules* in a sample of dry ice (solid CO_2) with a mass of 22.5 g.

The solution map for the problem is:

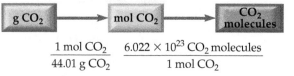

$$\frac{1 \text{ mol CO}_2}{44.01 \text{ g CO}_2} \qquad \frac{6.022 \times 10^{23} \text{ CO}_2 \text{ molecules}}{1 \text{ mol CO}_2}$$

Notice that the first part of the solution map is identical to computing the number of moles of CO_2 in 22.5 g of dry ice. The second part of the solution map shows the conversion from moles to number of molecules. Following the solution map, we calculate:

$$22.5 \text{ g } \cancel{CO_2} \times \frac{1 \text{ mol } \cancel{CO_2}}{44.01 \text{ g } \cancel{CO_2}} \times \frac{6.022 \times 10^{23} \text{ CO}_2 \text{ molecules}}{\cancel{\text{mol CO}_2}}$$

$$= 3.08 \times 10^{23} \text{ CO}_2 \text{ molecules}$$

EXAMPLE 5   The Mole Concept—Converting between Mass of a Compound and Number of Molecules

What is the mass of 4.78×10^{24} NO_2 molecules?

SORT You are given the number of NO_2 molecules and asked to find the mass.	**GIVEN:** 4.78×10^{24} NO_2 molecules **FIND:** g NO_2
STRATEGIZE The solution map has two steps. In the first step, convert from molecules of NO_2 to moles of NO_2. In the second step, convert from moles of NO_2 to mass of NO_2. The required conversion factors are the molar mass of NO_2 and the number of molecules in a mole.	**SOLUTION MAP** $$NO_2 \text{ molecules} \longrightarrow \text{mol } NO_2 \longrightarrow \text{g } NO_2$$ $$\frac{1 \text{ mol NO}_2}{6.022 \times 10^{23} \text{ NO}_2 \text{ molecules}} \qquad \frac{46.01 \text{ g NO}_2}{1 \text{ mol NO}_2}$$ **RELATIONSHIPS USED** 6.022×10^{23} molecules = 1 mol (Avogadro's number) NO_2 molar mass = 1(Atomic mass N) + 2(Atomic mass O) $\qquad\qquad = 14.01 + 2(16.00)$ $\qquad\qquad = 46.01$ g/mol
SOLVE Using the solution map as a guide, begin with molecules of NO_2 and multiply by the appropriate conversion factors to arrive at g NO_2.	**SOLUTION** $$4.78 \times 10^{24} \text{ } \cancel{NO_2 \text{ molecules}} \times \frac{1 \text{ mol } \cancel{NO_2}}{6.022 \times 10^{23} \text{ } \cancel{NO_2 \text{ molecules}}}$$ $$\times \frac{46.1 \text{ g NO}_2}{1 \text{ mol } \cancel{NO_2}} = 365 \text{ g NO}_2$$
CHECK Check your answer. Are the units correct? Does the answer make physical sense?	The units, g NO_2, are correct. Since the number of NO_2 molecules is more than one mole, the answer should be more than one molar mass (more than 46.01 g), which it is; therefore, the magnitude of the answer is reasonable.

▶ **SKILLBUILDER 5** | The Mole Concept—Converting between Mass and Number of Molecules

How many H_2O molecules are in a sample of water with a mass of 3.64 g?

▶ **FOR MORE PRACTICE**   Problems 51, 52, 53, 54.

✓ **CONCEPTUAL CHECKPOINT 3**

Compound A has a molar mass of 100 g/mol and Compound B has a molar mass of 200 g/mol. If you have samples of equal mass of both compounds, which sample contains the greatest number of molecules?

5   Chemical Formulas as Conversion Factors

3 leaves : 1 clover

▲ From our knowledge of clovers, we know that each clover has three leaves. We can express that as a ratio: 3 leaves : 1 clover.

We are almost ready to address the sodium problem in our opening example. To determine how much of a particular element (such as sodium) is in a given amount of a particular compound (such as sodium chloride), we must understand the numerical relationships inherent in a chemical formula. We can understand these relationships with a simple analogy: Asking how much sodium is in a given amount of sodium chloride is similar to asking how many leaves are on a given number of clovers. For example, suppose we want to know the number of leaves on 14 clovers. We need a conversion factor between leaves and clovers. For clovers, the conversion factor comes from our knowledge about them—we know that each clover has 3 leaves. We can express that relationship as a ratio between clovers and leaves.

3 leaves : 1 clover

Like other conversion factors, this ratio gives the relationship between leaves and clovers. With this ratio, we can write a conversion factor to determine the number of leaves in 14 clovers. The solution map is:

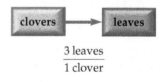

$$\frac{3\ \text{leaves}}{1\ \text{clover}}$$

We solve the problem by beginning with clovers and converting to leaves.

$$14\ \text{clovers} \times \frac{3\ \text{leaves}}{1\ \text{clover}} = 42\ \text{leaves}$$

Similarly, a chemical formula gives us ratios between elements and molecules for a particular compound. For example, the formula for carbon dioxide (CO_2) means there are two O atoms per CO_2 molecule. We write this as:

2 O atoms : 1 CO_2 molecule

Just as 3 leaves : 1 clover can also be written as 3 dozen leaves : 1 dozen clovers, for molecules we can write:

2 doz O atoms : 1 doz CO_2 molecules

However, for atoms and molecules, we normally work in moles.

$$2 \text{ mol O} : 1 \text{ mol CO}_2$$

With conversion factors such as these—which come directly from the chemical formula—we can determine the amounts of the constituent elements present in a given amount of a compound.

▶ Each of these shows a ratio.

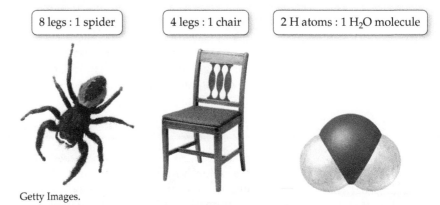

| 8 legs : 1 spider | 4 legs : 1 chair | 2 H atoms : 1 H_2O molecule |

Getty Images.

CONVERTING BETWEEN MOLES OF A COMPOUND AND MOLES OF A CONSTITUENT ELEMENT

Suppose we want to know the number of moles of O in 18 mol of CO_2. Our solution map is:

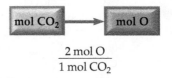

$$\frac{2 \text{ mol O}}{1 \text{ mol CO}_2}$$

We can then calculate the moles of O.

$$18 \text{ mol CO}_2 \times \frac{2 \text{ mol O}}{1 \text{ mol CO}_2} = 36 \text{ mol O}$$

EXAMPLE 6   Chemical Formulas as Conversion Factors—Converting between Moles of a Compound and Moles of a Constituent Element

Determine the number of moles of O in 1.7 mol of $CaCO_3$.

SORT	
You are given the number of moles of $CaCO_3$ and asked to find the number of moles of O.	**GIVEN:** 1.7 mol $CaCO_3$ **FIND:** mol O

STRATEGIZE	
The solution map begins with moles of calcium carbonate and ends with moles of oxygen. Determine the conversion factor from the chemical formula, which indicates three O atoms for every $CaCO_3$ unit.	**SOLUTION MAP** mol $CaCO_3$ ⟶ mol O $\dfrac{3 \text{ mol O}}{1 \text{ mol CaCO}_3}$ **RELATIONSHIPS USED** 3 mol O : 1 mol $CaCO_3$ (from chemical formula)

SOLVE	
Follow the solution map to solve the problem. The subscripts in a chemical formula are exact, so they never limit significant figures.	**SOLUTION** $1.7 \text{ mol CaCO}_3 \times \dfrac{3 \text{ mol O}}{1 \text{ mol CaCO}_3} = 5.1 \text{ mol O}$

CHECK

Check your answer. Are the units correct? Does the answer make physical sense?

The units (mol O) are correct. The magnitude is reasonable as the number of moles of oxygen should be larger than the number of moles of $CaCO_3$ (because each $CaCO_3$ unit contains 3 O atoms).

▶**SKILLBUILDER 6** | **Chemical Formulas as Conversion Factors—Converting between Moles of a Compound and Moles of a Constituent Element**

Determine the number of moles of O in 1.4 mol of H_2SO_4.

▶**FOR MORE PRACTICE**   Example 16; Problems 63, 64.

CONVERTING BETWEEN GRAMS OF A COMPOUND AND GRAMS OF A CONSTITUENT ELEMENT

Now, we have the tools we need to solve our sodium problem. Suppose we want to know the mass of sodium in 15 g of NaCl. The chemical formula gives us the relationship between moles of Na and moles of NaCl:

$$1 \text{ mol Na} : 1 \text{ mol NaCl}$$

To use this relationship, we need *mol* NaCl, but we have *g* NaCl. We can, however, use the *molar mass* of NaCl to convert from g NaCl to mol NaCl. Then we use the conversion factor from the chemical formula to convert to mol Na. Finally, we use the molar mass of Na to convert to g Na. The solution map is:

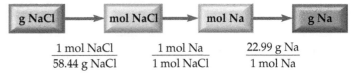

$$\frac{1 \text{ mol NaCl}}{58.44 \text{ g NaCl}} \qquad \frac{1 \text{ mol Na}}{1 \text{ mol NaCl}} \qquad \frac{22.99 \text{ g Na}}{1 \text{ mol Na}}$$

Notice that we must convert from g NaCl to mol NaCl *before* we can use the chemical formula as a conversion factor.

> The chemical formula gives us a relationship between moles of substances, not between grams.

We follow the solution map to solve the problem.

$$15 \text{ g NaCl} \times \frac{1 \text{ mol NaCl}}{58.44 \text{ g NaCl}} \times \frac{1 \text{ mol Na}}{1 \text{ mol NaCl}} \times \frac{22.99 \text{ g Na}}{1 \text{ mol Na}} = 5.9 \text{ g Na}$$

The general form for solving problems where you are asked to find the mass of an element present in a given mass of a compound is:

Mass compound ⟶ **Moles** compound ⟶ **Moles** element ⟶ **Mass** element

Use the atomic or molar mass to convert between mass and moles, and use the relationships inherent in the chemical formula to convert between moles and moles (▼ Figure 2).

▶ **FIGURE 2   Mole relationships from a chemical formula**   The relationships inherent in a chemical formula allow us to convert between moles of the compound and moles of a constituent element (or vice versa).

$$1 \text{ mol } CCl_4 : 4 \text{ mol Cl}$$

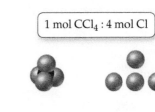

EXAMPLE 7 Chemical Formulas as Conversion Factors—Converting between Grams of a Compound and Grams of a Constituent Element

Carvone ($C_{10}H_{14}O$) is the main component of spearmint oil. It has a pleasant aroma and mint flavor. Carvone is often added to chewing gum, liqueurs, soaps, and perfumes. Calculate the mass of carbon in 55.4 g of carvone.

SORT You are given the mass of carvone and asked to find the mass of one of its constituent elements.	**GIVEN:** 55.4 g $C_{10}H_{14}O$ **FIND:** g C
STRATEGIZE Base the solution map on Grams $\longrightarrow$ Mole $\longrightarrow$ Mole $\longrightarrow$ Grams	**SOLUTION MAP** $$\boxed{\text{g } C_{10}H_{14}O} \longrightarrow \boxed{\text{mol } C_{10}H_{14}O} \longrightarrow \boxed{\text{mol C}} \longrightarrow \boxed{\text{g C}}$$ $$\frac{1 \text{ mol } C_{10}H_{14}O}{150.2 \text{ g } C_{10}H_{14}O} \qquad \frac{10 \text{ mol C}}{1 \text{ mol } C_{10}H_{14}O} \qquad \frac{12.01 \text{ g C}}{1 \text{ mol C}}$$
You need three conversion factors. The first is the molar mass of carvone.	**RELATIONSHIPS USED** $$\text{Molar mass carvone} = 10(12.01) + 14(1.01) + 1(16.00)$$ $$= 120.1 + 14.14 + 16.00$$ $$= 150.2 \text{ g/mol}$$
The second conversion factor is the relationship between moles of carbon and moles of carvone from the molecular formula.	10 mol C : 1 mol $C_{10}H_{14}O$ (from chemical formula)
The third conversion factor is the molar mass of carbon.	1 mol C = 12.01 g C (molar mass C, from periodic table)
SOLVE Follow the solution map to solve the problem, beginning with g $C_{10}H_{14}O$ and multiplying by the appropriate conversion factors to arrive at g C.	**SOLUTION** $$55.4 \text{ g } C_{10}H_{14}O \times \frac{1 \text{ mol } C_{10}H_{14}O}{150.2 \text{ g } C_{10}H_{14}O} \times$$ $$\frac{10 \text{ mol C}}{1 \text{ mol } C_{10}H_{14}O} \times \frac{12.01 \text{ g C}}{1 \text{ mol C}} = 44.3 \text{ g C}$$
CHECK Check your answer. Are the units correct? Does the answer make physical sense?	The units, g C, are correct. The magnitude of the answer is reasonable since the mass of carbon with the compound must be less than the mass of the compound itself. If you had arrived at a mass of carbon that was greater than the mass of the compound, you would immediately know that you had made a mistake; the mass of a constituent element can never be greater than the mass of the compound itself.

▶**SKILLBUILDER 7** | Chemical Formulas as Conversion Factors—Converting between Grams of a Compound and Grams of a Constituent Element

Determine the mass of oxygen in a 5.8-g sample of sodium bicarbonate ($NaHCO_3$).

▶**SKILLBUILDER PLUS 1**

Determine the mass of oxygen in a 7.20-g sample of $Al_2(SO_4)_3$.

▶**FOR MORE PRACTICE** Example 17; Problems 67, 68, 69, 70.

About 30 years ago, scientists began to suspect that synthetic compounds known as chlorofluorocarbons (CFCs) were destroying a vital compound called ozone (O_3) in Earth's upper atmosphere. Upper atmospheric ozone is important because it acts as a shield to protect life on Earth from harmful ultraviolet light (▼ Figure 3). CFCs are chemically inert molecules (they do not readily react with other substances) used primarily as refrigerants and industrial

solvents. Their inertness has allowed them to leak into the atmosphere and stay there for many years. In the upper atmosphere, however, sunlight eventually breaks bonds within CFCs, resulting in the release of chlorine atoms. The chlorine atoms then react with ozone and destroy it by converting it from O_3 into O_2.

In 1985, scientists discovered a large hole in the ozone layer over Antarctica that has since been attributed to CFCs. The amount of ozone over Antarctica had depleted by a startling 50%. The ozone hole is transient, existing only in the Antarctic spring, from late August to November. Examination of data from previous years showed that this gradually expanding ozone hole has formed each spring since 1977 (▼ Figure 4), and it continues to form today.

A similar hole has been observed during some years over the North Pole, and a smaller, but still significant, drop in ozone has been observed over more populated areas such as the northern United States and Canada. The thinning of ozone over these areas is dangerous because ultraviolet light can harm living things and induce skin cancer in humans. Based on this evidence, most developed nations banned the production of CFCs on January 1, 1996. However, CFCs still lurk in most older refrigerators and air conditioning units and can leak into the atmosphere and destroy ozone.

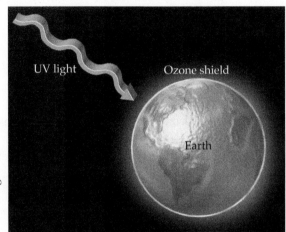

Tom Pantages.

▲ **FIGURE 3** **The ozone shield** Atmospheric ozone shields life on Earth from harmful ultraviolet light.

CAN YOU ANSWER THIS? *Suppose a car air conditioner contains 2.5 kg of freon-12 (CCl_2F_2), a CFC. How many kilograms of Cl are contained within the freon?*

► **FIGURE 4**
Growth of the ozone hole
Antarctic ozone levels in three Septembers from 1979 to 2000. The darkest blue colors indicate the lowest ozone levels.

Sep 1979

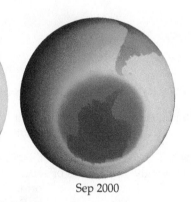

Sep 1991   Sep 2000

✔ CONCEPTUAL CHECKPOINT 4

Without doing any detailed calculations, determine which sample contains the most fluorine atoms.

(a) 25 g of HF

(b) 1.5 mol of CH_3F

(c) 1.0 mol of F_2

6 Mass Percent Composition of Compounds

Another way to express how much of an element is in a given compound is to use the element's mass percent composition for that compound. The **mass percent composition** or simply **mass percent** of an element is the element's percentage of the total mass of the compound. For example, the mass percent composition of sodium in sodium chloride is 39%. This information tells us that a 100-g sample of sodium chloride contains 39 g of sodium. The mass percent composition for a compound can be determined from experimental data using the formula:

$$\text{Mass percent of element } X = \frac{\text{Mass of } X \text{ in a sample of the compound}}{\text{Mass of the sample of the compound}} \times 100\%$$

For example, suppose a 0.358-g sample of chromium reacts with oxygen to form 0.523 g of the metal oxide. Then the mass percent of chromium is:

$$\text{Mass percent Cr} = \frac{\text{Mass Cr}}{\text{Mass metal oxide}} \times 100\%$$

$$= \frac{0.358 \text{ g}}{0.523 \text{ g}} \times 100\% = 68.5\%$$

We can use mass percent composition as a conversion factor between grams of a constituent element and grams of the compound. For example, we just saw that the mass percent composition of sodium in sodium chloride is 39%. This can be written as:

$$39 \text{ g sodium} : 100 \text{ g sodium chloride}$$

or in fractional form:

$$\frac{39 \text{ g Na}}{100 \text{ g NaCl}} \quad \text{or} \quad \frac{100 \text{ g NaCl}}{39 \text{ g Na}}$$

These fractions are conversion factors between g Na and g NaCl, as shown in Example 8.

EXAMPLE 8 Using Mass Percent Composition as a Conversion Factor

The FDA recommends that adults consume less than 2.4 g of sodium per day. How many grams of sodium chloride can you consume and still be within the FDA guidelines? Sodium chloride is 39% sodium by mass.

SORT You are given the mass of sodium and the mass percent of sodium in sodium chloride. When mass percent is given, write it as a fraction. *Percent* means *per hundred*, so 39% sodium indicates that there are 39 g Na per 100 g NaCl. You are asked to find the mass of sodium chloride that contains the given mass of sodium.	**GIVEN:** 2.4 g Na $\dfrac{39 \text{ g Na}}{100 \text{ g NaCl}}$ **FIND:** g NaCl
STRATEGIZE Draw a solution map that starts with the mass of sodium and uses the mass percent as a conversion factor to get to the mass of sodium chloride.	**SOLUTION MAP** g Na → g NaCl $\dfrac{100 \text{ g NaCl}}{39 \text{ g Na}}$ **RELATIONSHIPS USED** 39 g Na : 100 g NaCl (given in the problem)

SOLVE

Follow the solution map to solve the problem, beginning with grams Na and ending with grams of NaCl. The amount of salt you can consume and still be within the FDA guideline is 6.2 g NaCl.

SOLUTION

$$2.4 \text{ g Na} \times \frac{100 \text{ g NaCl}}{39 \text{ g Na}} = 6.2 \text{ g NaCl}$$

CHECK

Check your answer. Are the units correct? Does the answer make physical sense?

The units, g NaCl, are correct. The answer makes physical sense because the mass of NaCl should be *larger* than the mass of Na. The mass of a compound containing a given mass of a particular element is always larger than the mass of the element itself.

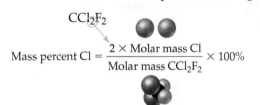

▲ Twelve and a half salt packets contain 6.2 g NaCl.

Maxwellartandphoto.com.

▶**SKILLBUILDER 8 | Using Mass Percent Composition as a Conversion Factor**

If a woman consumes 22 g of sodium chloride, how much sodium does she consume? Sodium chloride is 39% sodium by mass.

▶**FOR MORE PRACTICE** Example 19; Problems 75, 76, 77, 78.

7 Mass Percent Composition from a Chemical Formula

In the previous section, we learned how to calculate mass percent composition from experimental data and how to use mass percent composition as a conversion factor. We can also calculate the mass percent of any element in a compound from the chemical formula for the compound. Based on the chemical formula, the mass percent of element X in a compound is:

$$\text{Mass percent of element } X = \frac{\text{Mass of element } X \text{ in 1 mol of compound}}{\text{Mass of 1 mol of compound}} \times 100\%$$

Suppose, for example, that we want to calculate the mass percent composition of Cl in the chlorofluorocarbon CCl_2F_2. The mass percent of Cl is given by:

$$\text{Mass percent Cl} = \frac{2 \times \text{Molar mass Cl}}{\text{Molar mass } CCl_2F_2} \times 100\%$$

We must multiply the molar mass of Cl by 2 because the chemical formula has a subscript of 2 for Cl, meaning that 1 mol of CCl_2F_2 contains 2 mol of Cl atoms. We calculate the molar mass of CCl_2F_2 as follows:

$$\text{Molar mass} = 1(12.01) + 2(35.45) + 2(19.00) = 120.91 \text{ g/mol}$$

So the mass percent of Cl in CCl_2F_2 is

$$\text{Mass percent Cl} = \frac{2 \times \text{Molar mass Cl}}{\text{Molar mass } CCl_2F_2} \times 100\% = \frac{2 \times 35.45 \text{ g}}{120.91 \text{ g}} \times 100\%$$
$$= 58.64\%$$

EXAMPLE 9 Mass Percent Composition

Calculate the mass percent of Cl in freon-114 ($C_2Cl_4F_2$).

SORT	GIVEN: $C_2Cl_4F_2$
You are given the molecular formula of freon-114 and asked to find the mass percent of Cl.	FIND: Mass % Cl

STRATEGIZE	SOLUTION MAP
The solution map shows how you can use the information in the chemical formula to substitute into the mass percent equation and obtain the mass percent Cl.	Chemical formula → mass % Cl $$\text{Mass \% Cl} = \frac{4 \times \text{Molar mass Cl}}{\text{Molar mass } C_2Cl_4F_2} \times 100\%$$ **RELATIONSHIPS USED** Mass percent of element X = $$\frac{\text{Mass of element } X \text{ in 1 mol of compound}}{\text{Mass of 1 mol of compound}} \times 100\%$$ (mass percent equation, introduced in this section)

SOLVE	SOLUTION
Calculate the molar mass of freon-114 and substitute the values into the equation to find mass percent Cl.	$4 \times$ Molar mass Cl $= 4(35.45 \text{ g}) = 141.8 \text{ g}$ Molar mass $C_2Cl_4F_2 = 2(12.01) + 4(35.45) + 2(19)$ $\qquad = 24.02 + 141.8 + 38.00$ $\qquad = \dfrac{203.8 \text{ g}}{\text{mol}}$ $$\text{Mass \% Cl} = \frac{4 \times \text{Molar mass Cl}}{\text{Molar mass } C_2Cl_4F_2} \times 100\%$$ $$= \frac{141.8 \text{ g}}{203.8 \text{ g}} \times 100\%$$ $$= 69.58\%$$

CHECK	
Check your answer. Are the units correct? Does the answer make physical sense?	The units (%) are correct. The answer makes physical sense. Mass percent composition should never exceed 100%. If your answer is greater than 100%, you have made an error.

▶**SKILLBUILDER 9** | **Mass Percent Composition**

Acetic acid ($HC_2H_3O_2$) is the active ingredient in vinegar. Calculate the mass percent composition of O in acetic acid.

▶**FOR MORE PRACTICE**   Example 20; Problems 79, 80, 81, 82, 83, 84.

 CONCEPTUAL CHECKPOINT 5

Which compound has the highest mass percent of O? (You should not have to perform any detailed calculations to answer this question.)

(a) CrO

(b) CrO_2

(c) Cr_2O_3

CHEMISTRY AND HEALTH

Fluoridation of Drinking Water

In the early 1900s, scientists discovered that people whose drinking water naturally contained fluoride (F^-) ions had fewer cavities than people whose water did not. At the proper levels, fluoride strengthens tooth enamel, which prevents tooth decay. In an effort to improve public health, fluoride has been artificially added to drinking water supplies since 1945. In the United States today, about 62% of the population drinks artificially fluoridated drinking water. The American Dental Association and public health agencies estimate that water fluoridation reduces tooth decay by 40 to 65%.

The fluoridation of public drinking water, however, is often controversial. Some opponents argue that fluoride is available from other sources—such as toothpaste, mouthwash, drops, and pills—and therefore should not be added to drinking water. Anyone who wants fluoride can get it from these optional sources, they argue, and the government should not impose fluoride on the general population. Other opponents argue that the risks associated with fluoridation are too great. Indeed, too much fluoride can

cause teeth to become brown and spotted, a condition known as dental fluorosis. Extremely high levels can lead to skeletal fluorosis, a condition in which the bones become brittle and arthritic.

The scientific consensus is that, like many minerals, fluoride shows some health benefits at certain levels—about 1–4 mg/day for adults—but can have detrimental effects at higher levels. Consequently, most major cities fluoridate their drinking water at a level of about 1 mg/L. Since adults drink between 1 and 2 L of water per day, they should receive the beneficial amounts of fluoride from the water. Bottled water does not normally contain fluoride, and therefore does not have the benefit of fluoride to teeth. Fluoridated bottled water can sometimes be found in the infant section of supermarkets.

CAN YOU ANSWER THIS? *Fluoride is often added to water as sodium fluoride (NaF). What is the mass percent composition of F^- in NaF? How many grams of NaF should be added to 1500 L of water to fluoridate it at a level of 1.0 mg F^-/L?*

---

8 Calculating Empirical Formulas for Compounds

In Section 7, we learned how to calculate mass percent composition from a chemical formula. But can we go the other way? Can we calculate a chemical formula from mass percent composition? This is important because laboratory analyses of compounds do not often give chemical formulas directly; rather, they give the relative masses of each element present in a compound. For example, if we decompose water into hydrogen and oxygen in the laboratory, we could measure the masses of hydrogen and oxygen produced. Can we determine a chemical formula for water from this kind of data?

▶ We just learned how to go from the chemical formula of a compound to its mass percent composition. Can we also go the other way?

| Chemical formula | ⟶ ⟵ | Mass percent composition |

?

The answer is a qualified yes. We can determine a chemical formula, but it is the **empirical formula**, not the molecular formula. An empirical formula only gives the smallest whole-number ratio of each type of atom in a compound, not the specific number of each type of atom in a molecule. Recall that the **molecular formula** is always a whole-number multiple of the empirical formula:
Molecular formula = Empirical formula × n, where $n = 1, 2, 3 \ldots$

A chemical formula represents a ratio of atoms or moles of atoms, not a ratio of masses.

For example, the molecular formula for hydrogen peroxide is H_2O_2, and its empirical formula is HO.

$$HO \times 2 \longrightarrow H_2O_2$$

CALCULATING AN EMPIRICAL FORMULA FROM EXPERIMENTAL DATA

Suppose we decompose a sample of water in the laboratory and find that it produces 3.0 g of hydrogen and 24 g of oxygen. How do we determine an empirical formula from these data?

oxygen gas   hydrogen gas

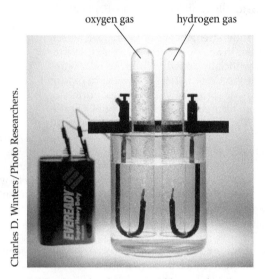

Charles D. Winters/Photo Researchers.

▲ Water can be decomposed by an electric current into hydrogen and oxygen. How can we find the empirical formula for water from the masses of its component elements?

We know that an empirical formula represents a ratio of atoms or a ratio of moles of atoms, but it *does not* represent a ratio of masses. So the first thing we must do is convert our data from grams to moles. How many moles of each element formed during the decomposition? To convert to moles, we divide each mass by the molar mass of that element.

$$\text{Moles H} = 3.0 \text{ g H} \times \frac{1 \text{ mol H}}{1.01 \text{ g H}} = 3.0 \text{ mol H}$$

$$\text{Moles O} = 24 \text{ g O} \times \frac{1 \text{ mol O}}{16.00 \text{ g O}} = 1.5 \text{ mol O}$$

From these data, we know there are 3 mol of H for every 1.5 mol of O. We can now write a pseudoformula for water:

$$H_3O_{1.5}$$

To get whole-number subscripts in our formula, we divide all the subscripts by the smallest one, in this case 1.5.

$$H_{\frac{3}{1.5}}O_{\frac{1.5}{1.5}} = H_2O$$

Our empirical formula for water, which in this case also happens to be the molecular formula, is H_2O. The following procedure can be used to obtain the empirical formula of any compound from experimental data. The left column outlines the procedure, and the center and right columns show two examples of how to apply the procedure.

	EXAMPLE 10	**EXAMPLE 11**
Obtaining an Empirical Formula from Experimental Data	A compound containing nitrogen and oxygen is decomposed in the laboratory and produces 24.5 g of nitrogen and 70.0 g of oxygen. Calculate the empirical formula of the compound.	A laboratory analysis of aspirin determines the following mass percent composition: C 60.00% H 4.48% O 35.53% Find the empirical formula.
1. Write down (or calculate) as given the masses of each element present in a sample of the compound. If you are given mass percent composition, assume a 100-g sample and calculate the masses of each element from the given percentages.	GIVEN: 24.5 g N 70.0 g O FIND: empirical formula	GIVEN: In a 100-g sample: 60.00 g C 4.48 g H 35.53 g O FIND: empirical formula
2. Convert each of the masses in Step 1 to moles by using the appropriate molar mass for each element as a conversion factor.	SOLUTION $$24.5 \text{ g N} \times \frac{1 \text{ mol N}}{14.01 \text{ g N}}$$ $$= 1.75 \text{ mol N}$$ $$70.0 \text{ g O} \times \frac{1 \text{ mol O}}{16.00 \text{ g O}}$$ $$= 4.38 \text{ mol O}$$	SOLUTION $$60.00 \text{ g C} \times \frac{1 \text{ mol C}}{12.01 \text{ g C}}$$ $$= 4.996 \text{ mol C}$$ $$4.48 \text{ g H} \times \frac{1 \text{ mol H}}{1.01 \text{ g H}}$$ $$= 4.44 \text{ mol H}$$ $$35.53 \text{ g O} \times \frac{1 \text{ mol O}}{16.00 \text{ g O}}$$ $$= 2.221 \text{ mol O}$$
3. Write down a pseudoformula for the compound, using the moles of each element (from Step 2) as subscripts.	$N_{1.75}O_{4.38}$	$C_{4.996}H_{4.44}O_{2.221}$
4. Divide all the subscripts in the formula by the smallest subscript.	$N_{\frac{1.75}{1.75}}O_{\frac{4.38}{1.75}} \longrightarrow N_1O_{2.5}$	$C_{\frac{4.996}{2.221}}H_{\frac{4.44}{2.221}}O_{\frac{2.221}{2.221}} \longrightarrow C_{2.25}H_2O_1$
5. If the subscripts are not whole numbers, multiply all the subscripts by a small whole number (see the following table) to arrive at whole-number subscripts.	$N_1O_{2.5} \times 2 \longrightarrow N_2O_5$ The correct empirical formula is N_2O_5.	$C_{2.25}H_2O_1 \times 4 \longrightarrow C_9H_8O_4$ The correct empirical formula is $C_9H_8O_4$.

Fractional Subscript	Multiply by This Number to Get Whole-Number Subscripts
_.10	10
_.20	5
_.25	4
_.33	3
_.50	2
_.66	3
_.75	4

▶**SKILLBUILDER 10**

A sample of a compound is decomposed in the laboratory and produces 165 g of carbon, 27.8 g of hydrogen, and 220.2 g O. Calculate the empirical formula of the compound.

▶**FOR MORE PRACTICE**
Problems 85, 86, 87, 88.

▶**SKILLBUILDER 11**

Ibuprofen, an aspirin substitute, has the mass percent composition: C 75.69%; H 8.80%; O 15.51%. Calculate the empirical formula of the ibuprofen.

▶**FOR MORE PRACTICE**
Example 21; Problems 89, 90, 91, 92.

EXAMPLE 12 Calculating an Empirical Formula from Reaction Data

A 3.24-g sample of titanium reacts with oxygen to form 5.40 g of the metal oxide. What is the empirical formula of the metal oxide?

You are given the mass of titanium and the mass of the metal oxide that forms. You are asked to find the empirical formula. You must recognize this problem as one requiring a special procedure and apply that procedure, which is outlined below.	GIVEN: 3.24 g Ti 5.40 g metal oxide FIND: empirical formula
1. Write down (or calculate) the masses of each element present in a sample of the compound. In this case, you are given the mass of the initial Ti sample and the mass of its oxide after the sample reacts with oxygen. The mass of oxygen is the difference between the mass of the oxide and the mass of titanium.	SOLUTION 3.24 g Ti Mass O = Mass oxide − Mass titanium $\quad\quad$ = 5.40 g − 3.24 g $\quad\quad$ = 2.16 g O
2. Convert each of the masses in Step 1 to moles by using the appropriate molar mass for each element as a conversion factor.	$3.24 \text{ g Ti} \times \dfrac{1 \text{ mol Ti}}{47.88 \text{ g Ti}} = 0.0677 \text{ mol Ti}$ $2.16 \text{ g O} \times \dfrac{1 \text{ mol O}}{16.00 \text{ g O}} = 0.135 \text{ mol O}$
3. Write down a pseudoformula for the compound, using the moles of each element obtained in Step 2 as subscripts.	$Ti_{0.0677}O_{0.135}$
4. Divide all the subscripts in the formula by the smallest subscript.	$Ti_{\frac{0.0677}{0.0677}} O_{\frac{0.135}{0.0677}} \longrightarrow TiO_2$
5. If the subscripts are not whole numbers, multiply all the subscripts by a small whole number to arrive at whole-number subscripts.	Since the subscripts are already whole numbers, this last step is unnecessary. The correct empirical formula is TiO_2.

▶SKILLBUILDER 12 | Calculating an Empirical Formula from Reaction Data

A 1.56-g sample of copper reacts with oxygen to form 1.95 g of the metal oxide. What is the formula of the metal oxide?

▶FOR MORE PRACTICE   Problems 93, 94, 95, 96.

9 Calculating Molecular Formulas for Compounds

▲ Fructose, a sugar found in fruit.

You can determine the *molecular* formula of a compound from the empirical formula if you also know the molar mass of the compound. Recall from Section 8 that the molecular formula is always a whole-number multiple of the empirical formula.

$$\text{Molecular formula} = \text{Empirical formula} \times n, \text{ where } n = 1, 2, 3 \ldots$$

Suppose we want to find the molecular formula for fructose (a sugar found in fruit) from its empirical formula, CH_2O, and its molar mass, 180.2 g/mol. We know that the molecular formula is a whole-number multiple of CH_2O.

$$\text{Molecular formula} = CH_2O \times n$$

We also know that the molar mass is a whole-number multiple of the **empirical formula molar mass**, the sum of the masses of all the atoms in the empirical formula.

$$\text{Molar mass} = \text{Empirical formula molar mass} \times n$$

For a particular compound, the value of n in both cases is the same. Therefore, we can find n by calculating the ratio of the molar mass to the empirical formula molar mass.

$$n = \frac{\text{Molar mass}}{\text{Empirical formula molar mass}}$$

For fructose, the empirical formula molar mass is:

Empirical formula molar mass = $1(12.01) + 2(1.01) + 16.00 = 30.03$ g/mol

Therefore, n is:

$$n = \frac{180.2 \text{ g/mol}}{30.03 \text{ g/mol}} = 6$$

We can then use this value of n to find the molecular formula.

Molecular formula = $CH_2O \times 6 = C_6H_{12}O_6$

EXAMPLE 13 Calculating Molecular Formula from Empirical Formula and Molar Mass

Naphthalene is a compound containing carbon and hydrogen that is often used in mothballs. Its empirical formula is C_5H_4 and its molar mass is 128.16 g/mol. What is its molecular formula?

SORT You are given the empirical formula and the molar mass of a compound and asked to find its molecular formula.	**GIVEN:** empirical formula = C_5H_4 molar mass = 128.16 g/mol **FIND:** molecular formula
STRATEGIZE In the first step, use the molar mass (which is given) and the empirical formula molar mass (which you can calculate based on the empirical formula) to determine n (the integer by which you must multiply the empirical formula to get the molecular formula). In the second step, multiply the subscripts in the empirical formula by n to arrive at the molecular formula.	**SOLUTION MAP** molar mass, empirical formula molar mass $\rightarrow$ n $n = \dfrac{\text{Molar mass}}{\text{Empirical formula molar mass}}$ n, empirical formula $\rightarrow$ molecular formula Molecular formula = Empirical formula $\times$ n
SOLVE First find the empirical formula molar mass. Now follow the solution map. Find n by dividing the molar mass by the empirical formula molar mass (which you just calculated). Multiply the empirical formula by n to get the molecular formula.	**SOLUTION** Empirical formula molar mass = $5(12.01) + 4(1.01)$ $= 64.09$ g/mol $n = \dfrac{\text{Molar mass}}{\text{Empirical formula mass}} = \dfrac{128.16 \text{ g/mol}}{64.09 \text{ g/mol}} = 2$ Molecular formula = $C_5H_4 \times 2 = C_{10}H_8$
CHECK Check your answer. Does the answer make physical sense?	The answer makes physical sense because it is a whole-number multiple of the empirical formula. Any answer containing fractional subscripts would be an error.

▶**SKILLBUILDER 13** | Calculating Molecular Formula from Empirical Formula and Molar Mass

Butane is a compound containing carbon and hydrogen that is used as a fuel in butane lighters. Its empirical formula is C_2H_5, and its molar mass is 58.12 g/mol. Find its molecular formula.

▶**SKILLBUILDER PLUS 2**

A compound with the following mass percent composition has a molar mass of 60.10 g/mol. Find its molecular formula.

C   39.97%   H   13.41%   N   46.62%

▶**FOR MORE PRACTICE**   Example 22; Problems 97, 98, 99, 100.

CHAPTER IN REVIEW

CHEMICAL PRINCIPLES

The Mole Concept: The mole is a specific number (6.022×10^{23}) that allows us to easily count atoms or molecules by weighing them. One mole of any element has a mass equivalent to its atomic mass in grams, and a mole of any compound has a mass equivalent to its formula mass in grams. The mass of 1 mol of an element or compound is its molar mass.

Chemical Formulas and Chemical Composition: Chemical formulas indicate the relative number of each kind of element in a compound. These numbers are based on atoms or moles. By using molar masses, we can use the information in a chemical formula to determine the relative masses of each kind of element in a compound. We can then relate the mass of a sample of a compound to the masses of the elements contained in the compound.

Empirical and Molecular Formulas from Laboratory Data: We can refer to the relative masses of the elements within a compound to determine the empirical formula of the compound. If the chemist also knows the molar mass of the compound, he or she can also determine its molecular formula.

RELEVANCE

The Mole Concept: The mole concept allows us to determine the number of atoms or molecules in a sample from its mass. Just as a hardware store customer wants to know the number of nails in a certain weight of nails, so we want to know the number of atoms in a certain mass of atoms. Since atoms are too small to count, we use their mass.

Chemical Formulas and Chemical Composition: The chemical composition of compounds is important because it lets us determine how much of a particular element is contained within a particular compound. For example, an assessment of the threat to the Earth's ozone layer from chlorofluorocarbons (CFCs) requires knowing how much chlorine is in a particular CFC.

Empirical and Molecular Formulas from Laboratory Data: The first thing a chemist wants to know about an unknown compound is its chemical formula, because the formula reveals the compound's composition. Chemists often arrive at formulas by analyzing compounds in the laboratory—either by decomposing them or by synthesizing them—to determine the relative masses of the elements they contain.

CHEMICAL SKILLS

Converting between Moles and Number of Atoms (Section 3)

SORT
You are given moles of copper and asked to find the number of copper atoms.

STRATEGIZE
To convert between moles and number of atoms, use Avogadro's number, 6.022×10^{23} atoms = 1 mol, as a conversion factor.

EXAMPLES

EXAMPLE 13   Converting between Moles and Number of Atoms

Calculate the number of atoms in 4.8 mol of copper.

GIVEN: 4.8 mol Cu

FIND: Cu atoms

SOLUTION MAP

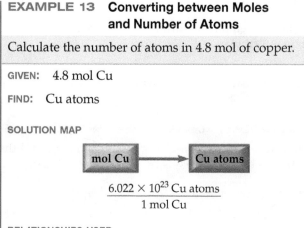

$$\frac{6.022 \times 10^{23} \text{ Cu atoms}}{1 \text{ mol Cu}}$$

RELATIONSHIPS USED
1 mol Cu = 6.022×10^{23} Cu atoms (Avogadro's number, from inside back cover)

SOLVE

Follow the solution map to solve the problem.

SOLUTION

$$4.8 \, \text{mol Cu} \times \frac{6.022 \times 10^{23} \, \text{Cu atoms}}{1 \, \text{mol Cu}} =$$

$$2.9 \times 10^{24} \, \text{Cu atoms}$$

CHECK

Check your answer. Are the units correct? Does the answer make physical sense?

The units, Cu atoms, are correct. The answer makes physical sense because the number is very large, as you would expect for nearly 5 moles of atoms.

Converting between Grams and Moles (Section 3)

EXAMPLE 14   Converting between Grams and Moles

Calculate the mass of aluminum (in grams) of 6.73 moles of aluminum.

GIVEN: 6.73 mol Al

FIND: g Al

SORT

You are given the number of moles of aluminum and asked to find the mass of aluminum in grams.

STRATEGIZE

Use the molar mass of aluminum to convert between moles and grams.

SOLUTION MAP

$$\frac{26.98 \, \text{g Al}}{1 \, \text{mol Al}}$$

RELATIONSHIPS USED

26.98 g Al = 1 mol Al (molar mass of Al from periodic table)

SOLVE

Follow the solution map to solve the problem.

SOLUTION

$$6.73 \, \text{mol Al} \times \frac{26.98 \, \text{g Al}}{1 \, \text{mol Al}} = 182 \, \text{g Al}$$

CHECK

Check your answer. Are the units correct? Does the answer make physical sense?

The units, g Al, are correct. The answer makes physical sense because each mole has a mass of about 27 g; therefore, nearly 7 moles should have a mass of nearly 190 g.

Converting between Grams and Number of Atoms or Molecules (Section 3)

EXAMPLE 15 Converting between Grams and Number of Atoms or Molecules

Determine the number of atoms in a 48.3-g sample of zinc.

GIVEN: 48.3 g Zn

FIND: Zn atoms

SOLUTION MAP

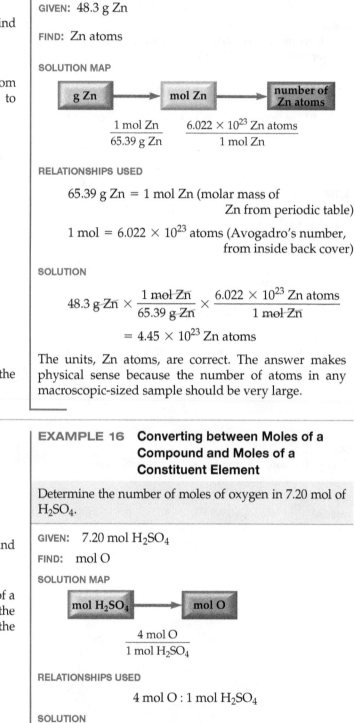

SORT

You are given the mass of a zinc sample and asked to find the number of Zn atoms that it contains.

STRATEGIZE

First use the molar mass of the element to convert from grams to moles, and then use Avogadro's number to convert moles to number of atoms.

RELATIONSHIPS USED

65.39 g Zn = 1 mol Zn (molar mass of Zn from periodic table)

$1 \text{ mol} = 6.022 \times 10^{23}$ atoms (Avogadro's number, from inside back cover)

SOLVE

Follow the solution map to solve the problem.

SOLUTION

$$48.3 \text{ g Zn} \times \frac{1 \text{ mol Zn}}{65.39 \text{ g Zn}} \times \frac{6.022 \times 10^{23} \text{ Zn atoms}}{1 \text{ mol Zn}}$$

$$= 4.45 \times 10^{23} \text{ Zn atoms}$$

CHECK

Check your answer. Are the units correct? Does the answer make physical sense?

The units, Zn atoms, are correct. The answer makes physical sense because the number of atoms in any macroscopic-sized sample should be very large.

Converting between Moles of a Compound and Moles of a Constituent Element (Section 5)

EXAMPLE 16 Converting between Moles of a Compound and Moles of a Constituent Element

Determine the number of moles of oxygen in 7.20 mol of H_2SO_4.

GIVEN: 7.20 mol H_2SO_4

FIND: mol O

SOLUTION MAP

```
mol H₂SO₄  ────────▶  mol O
```

$$\frac{4 \text{ mol O}}{1 \text{ mol } H_2SO_4}$$

SORT

You are given the number of moles of sulfuric acid and asked to find the number of moles of oxygen.

STRATEGIZE

To convert between moles of a compound and moles of a constituent element, use the chemical formula of the compound to determine a ratio between the moles of the element and the moles of the compound.

RELATIONSHIPS USED

4 mol O : 1 mol H_2SO_4

SOLVE

Follow the solution map to solve the problem.

SOLUTION

$$7.20 \text{ mol } H_2SO_4 \times \frac{4 \text{ mol O}}{1 \text{ mol } H_2SO_4} = 28.8 \text{ mol O}$$

CHECK

Check your answer. Are the units correct? Does the answer make physical sense?

The units, mol O, are correct. The answer makes physical sense because the number of moles of an element in a compound is equal to or greater than the number of moles of the compound itself.

Converting between Grams of a Compound and Grams of a Constituent Element (Section 5)

SORT

You are given the mass of iron (III) oxide and asked to find the mass of iron contained within it.

STRATEGIZE

Use the molar mass of the compound to convert from grams of the compound to moles of the compound. Then use the chemical formula to obtain a conversion factor to convert from moles of the compound to moles of the constituent element. Finally, use the molar mass of the constituent element to convert from moles of the element to grams of the element.

SOLVE

Follow the solution map to solve the problem.

CHECK

Check your answer. Are the units correct? Does the answer make physical sense?

EXAMPLE 17 Converting between Grams of a Compound and Grams of a Constituent Element

Find the grams of iron in 79.2 g of Fe_2O_3.

GIVEN: 79.2 g Fe_2O_3

FIND: g Fe

SOLUTION MAP

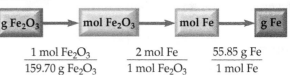

$$\frac{1 \text{ mol Fe}_2\text{O}_3}{159.70 \text{ g Fe}_2\text{O}_3} \qquad \frac{2 \text{ mol Fe}}{1 \text{ mol Fe}_2\text{O}_3} \qquad \frac{55.85 \text{ g Fe}}{1 \text{ mol Fe}}$$

RELATIONSHIPS USED

Molar mass Fe_2O_3

$$= 2(55.85) + 3(16.00)$$

$$= 159.70 \text{ g/mol}$$

2 mol Fe : 1 mol Fe_2O_3 (from given chemical formula)

SOLUTION

$$79.2 \text{ g Fe}_2\text{O}_3 \times \frac{1 \text{ mol Fe}_2\text{O}_3}{159.70 \text{ g Fe}_2\text{O}_3} \times \frac{2 \text{ mol Fe}}{1 \text{ mol Fe}_2\text{O}_3} \times$$

$$\frac{55.85 \text{ g Fe}}{1 \text{ mol Fe}} = 55.4 \text{ g Fe}$$

The units, g Fe, are correct. The answer makes physical sense because the mass of a constituent element within a compound should be less than the mass of the compound itself.

Using Mass Percent Composition as a Conversion Factor (Section 6)

EXAMPLE 18   Using Mass Percent Composition as a Conversion Factor

Determine the mass of titanium in 57.2 g of titanium(IV) oxide. The mass percent of titanium in titanium(IV) oxide is 59.9%.

SORT

You are given the mass of titanium(IV) oxide and the mass percent titanium in the oxide. You are asked to find the mass of titanium in the sample.

GIVEN: 57.2 g TiO_2

$$\frac{59 \text{ g Ti}}{100 \text{ g } TiO_2}$$

FIND: g Ti

STRATEGIZE

Use the percent composition as a conversion factor between grams of titanium(IV) oxide and grams of titanium.

SOLUTION MAP

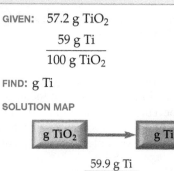

$$\frac{59.9 \text{ g Ti}}{100 \text{ g } TiO_2}$$

RELATIONSHIPS USED

59.9 g Ti : 100 g TiO_2

SOLVE

Follow the solution map to solve the problem.

SOLUTION

$$57.2 \text{ g } TiO_2 \times \frac{59.9 \text{ g Ti}}{100 \text{ g } TiO_2} = 34.3 \text{ g Ti}$$

CHECK

Check your answer. Are the units correct? Does the answer make physical sense?

The units, g Ti, are correct. The answer makes physical sense because the mass of an element within a compound should be less than the mass of the compound itself.

Determining Mass Percent Composition from a Chemical Formula (Section 7)

EXAMPLE 19   Determining Mass Percent Composition from a Chemical Formula

Calculate the mass percent composition of potassium in potassium oxide (K_2O).

GIVEN: K_2O

FIND: Mass % K

SORT

You are given the formula of potassium oxide and asked to determine the mass percent of potassium within it.

STRATEGIZE

The solution map shows how the information derived from the chemical formula can be substituted into the mass percent equation to yield the mass percent of the element.

SOLUTION MAP

$$\text{Mass \% K} = \frac{2 \times \text{Molar mass K}}{\text{Molar mass } K_2O} \times 100\%$$

RELATIONSHIPS USED

Mass percent of element X

$$= \frac{\text{Mass of element } X \text{ in 1 mol of compound}}{\text{Mass of 1 mol of compound}} \times 100\%$$

(mass percent equation, from Section 6)

SOLVE

Calculate the molar mass of potassium oxide and then follow the solution map to solve the problem.

SOLUTION

Molar mass $K_2O = 2(39.10) + 16.00$

$$= 94.20 \text{ g/mol}$$

$$\text{Mass \% K} = \frac{2(39.10 \text{ g K})}{94.20 \text{ g K}_2\text{O}} \times 100\% = 83.01\% \text{ K}$$

CHECK

Check your answer. Are the units correct? Does the answer make physical sense?

The units, % K, are correct. The answer makes physical sense because it should be below 100%.

Determining an Empirical Formula from Experimental Data (Section 8)

You must recognize this problem as one requiring a special procedure. Follow these steps to solve the problem.

EXAMPLE 20   Determining an Empirical Formula from Experimental Data

A laboratory analysis of vanillin, the flavoring agent in vanilla, determined the mass percent composition: C, 63.15%; H, 5.30%; O, 31.55%. Determine the empirical formula of vanillin.

GIVEN: 63.15 % C, 5.30 % H, and 31.55 % O.

FIND: empirical formula

1. Write down (or calculate) the masses of each element present in a sample of the compound. If you are given mass percent composition, assume a 100-g sample and calculate the masses of each element from the given percentages.

SOLUTION

In a 100 g sample:

63.15 g C

5.30 g H

31.55 g O

2. Convert each of the masses in Step 1 to moles by using the appropriate molar mass for each element as a conversion factor.

$$63.15 \text{ g C} \times \frac{1 \text{ mol C}}{12.01 \text{ g C}} = 5.258 \text{ mol C}$$

$$5.30 \text{ g H} \times \frac{1 \text{ mol H}}{1.01 \text{ g H}} = 5.25 \text{ mol H}$$

$$31.55 \text{ g O} \times \frac{1 \text{ mol O}}{16.00 \text{ g O}} = 1.972 \text{ mol O}$$

3. Write down a pseudoformula for the compound using the moles of each element (from Step 2) as subscripts.

$$C_{5.258}H_{5.25}O_{1.972}$$

4. Divide all the subscripts in the formula by the smallest subscript.

$$C_{\frac{5.258}{1.972}}H_{\frac{5.25}{1.972}}O_{\frac{1.972}{1.972}} \longrightarrow C_{2.67}H_{2.66}O_1$$

5. If the subscripts are not whole numbers, multiply all the subscripts by a small whole number to arrive at whole-number subscripts.

$$C_{2.67}H_{2.66}O_1 \times 3 \longrightarrow C_8H_8O_3$$

The correct empirical formula is $C_8H_8O_3$.

Calculating a Molecular Formula from an Empirical Formula and Molar Mass (Section 9)

EXAMPLE 21 **Calculating a Molecular Formula from an Empirical Formula and Molar Mass**

Acetylene, a gas often used in welding torches, has the empirical formula CH and a molar mass of 26.04 g/mol. Find its molecular formula.

GIVEN: empirical formula = CH

molar mass = 26.04 g/mol

FIND: molecular formula

SORT

You are given the empirical formula and molar mass of acetylene and asked to find the molecular formula.

STRATEGIZE

In the first step, use the molar mass (which is given) and the empirical formula molar mass (which you can calculate based on the empirical formula) to determine n (the integer by which you must multiply the empirical formula to arrive at the molecular formula).
In the second step, multiply the coefficients in the empirical formula by n to arrive at the molecular formula.

SOLUTION MAP

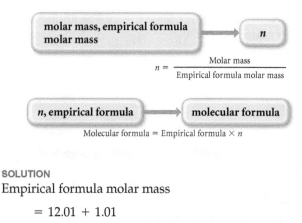

SOLVE

Follow the solution map to solve the problem. Calculate the empirical formula molar mass, which is the sum of the masses of all the atoms in the empirical formula.

SOLUTION

Empirical formula molar mass

$$= 12.01 + 1.01$$

$$= 13.02 \text{ g/mol}$$

Next, find n, the ratio of the molar mass to empirical mass.

$$n = \frac{\text{Molar mass}}{\text{Empirical formula molar mass}}$$

$$= \frac{26.04 \text{ g/mol}}{13.02 \text{ g/mol}} = 2$$

Finally, multiply the empirical formula by n to get the molecular formula.

$$\text{Molecular formula} = \text{CH} \times 2 \longrightarrow \text{C}_2\text{H}_2$$

CHECK

Check your answer. Does the answer make physical sense?

The answer makes physical sense because the formula subscripts are all integers. Any answer with fractional integers would be suspect.

KEY TERMS

Avogadro's number [**Section 3**]

empirical formula [**Section 8**]

empirical formula molar mass [**Section 9**]

mass percent (composition) [**Section 6**]

molar mass [**Section 3**]

mole (mol) [**Section 3**]

molecular formula [**Section 8**]

EXERCISES

QUESTIONS

1. Why is chemical composition important?
2. How can you determine the number of atoms in a sample of an element? Why is counting them not an option?
3. How many atoms are in 1 mol of atoms?
4. How many molecules are in 1 mol of molecules?
5. What is the mass of 1 mol of atoms for an element?
6. What is the mass of 1 mol of molecules for a compound?
7. What is the mass of 1 mol of atoms of each element?

   (a) P

   (b) Pt

   (c) C

   (d) Cr

8. What is the mass of 1 mol of molecules of each compound?

   (a) CO_2

   (b) CH_2Cl_2

   (c) $C_{12}H_{22}O_{11}$

   (d) SO_2

9. The subscripts in a chemical formula give relationships between moles of the constituent elements and moles of the compound. Explain why these subscripts *do not* give relationships between grams of the constituent elements and grams of the compound.

10. Write the conversion factors between moles of each constituent element and moles of the compound for $C_{12}H_{22}O_{11}$.
11. Mass percent composition can be used as a conversion factor between grams of a constituent element and grams of the compound. Write the conversion factor (including units) inherent in each mass percent composition.

    (a) Water is 11.19% hydrogen by mass.

    (b) Fructose, also known as fruit sugar, is 53.29% oxygen by mass.

    (c) Octane, a component of gasoline, is 84.12% carbon by mass.

    (d) Ethanol, the alcohol in alcoholic beverages, is 52.14% carbon by mass.

12. What is the mathematical formula for calculating mass percent composition from a chemical formula?
13. How are the empirical formula and the molecular formula of a compound related?
14. Why is it important to be able to calculate an empirical formula from experimental data?
15. What is the empirical formula mass of a compound?
16. How are the molar mass and empirical formula mass for a compound related?

PROBLEMS

THE MOLE CONCEPT

17. How many mercury atoms are in 5.8 mol of mercury?

18. How many moles of gold atoms do 3.45×10^{24} gold atoms constitute?

19. How many atoms are in each elemental sample?

    (a) 3.4 mol Cu

    (b) 9.7×10^{-3} mol C

    (c) 22.9 mol Hg

    (d) 0.215 mol Na

20. How many moles of atoms are in each elemental sample?

    (a) 4.6×10^{24} Pb atoms

    (b) 2.87×10^{22} He atoms

    (c) 7.91×10^{23} K atoms

    (d) 4.41×10^{21} Ca atoms

21. Complete the table:

Element	Moles	Number of Atoms
Ne	0.552	————
Ar	————	3.25×10^{24}
Xe	1.78	————
He	————	1.08×10^{20}

22. Complete the table:

Element	Moles	Number of Atoms
Cr	————	9.61×10^{23}
Fe	1.52×10^{-5}	————
Ti	0.0365	————
Hg	————	1.09×10^{23}

23. Consider these definitions.

    1 doz = 12

    1 gross = 144

    1 ream = 500

    1 mol = 6.022×10^{23}

    Suppose you have 872 sheets of paper. How many _____ of paper do you have?

    (a) dozens

    (b) gross

    (c) reams

    (d) moles

24. A pure copper penny contains approximately 3.0×10^{22} copper atoms. Use the definitions in the previous problem to determine how many _____ of copper atoms are in a penny.

    (a) dozens

    (b) gross

    (c) reams

    (d) moles

---

25. How many moles of tin atoms are in a pure tin cup with a mass of 38.1 g?

26. A lead fishing weight contains 0.12 mol of lead atoms. What is its mass?

---

27. A pure gold coin contains 0.145 mol of gold. What is its mass?

28. A helium balloon contains 0.46 g of helium. How many moles of helium does it contain?

---

29. How many moles of atoms are in each elemental sample?

    (a) 1.34 g Zn

    (b) 24.9 g Ar

    (c) 72.5 g Ta

    (d) 0.0223 g Li

30. What is the mass in grams of each elemental sample?

    (a) 6.64 mol W

    (b) 0.581 mol Ba

    (c) 68.1 mol Xe

    (d) 1.57 mol S

---

31. Complete the table:

Element	Moles	Mass
Ne	_____	22.5 g
Ar	0.117	_____
Xe	_____	1.00 kg
He	1.44×10^{-4}	_____

32. Complete the table:

Element	Moles	Mass
Cr	0.00442	_____
Fe	_____	73.5 mg
Ti	1.009×10^{-3}	_____
Hg	_____	1.78 kg

---

33. A pure silver ring contains 0.0134 mmol (millimol) Ag. How many silver atoms does it contain?

34. A pure gold ring contains 0.0102 mmol (millimol) Au. How many gold atoms does it contain?

---

35. How many aluminum atoms are in 3.78 g of aluminum?

36. What is the mass of 4.91×10^{21} platinum atoms?

---

37. How many atoms are in each elemental sample?

    (a) 16.9 g Sr

    (b) 26.1 g Fe

    (c) 8.55 g Bi

    (d) 38.2 g P

38. Calculate the mass in grams of each elemental sample:

    (a) 1.32×10^{20} uranium atoms

    (b) 2.55×10^{22} zinc atoms

    (c) 4.11×10^{23} lead atoms

    (d) 6.59×10^{24} silicon atoms

---

39. How many carbon atoms are in a diamond (pure carbon) with a mass of 38 mg?

40. How many helium atoms are in a helium blimp containing 495 kg of helium?

41. How many titanium atoms are in a pure titanium bicycle frame with a mass of 1.28 kg?

42. How many copper atoms are in a pure copper statue with a mass of 133 kg?

43. Complete the table:

Element	Mass	Moles	Number of Atoms
Na	38.5 mg	——	——
C	——	1.12	——
V	——	——	214
Hg	1.44 kg	——	——

44. Complete the table:

Element	Mass	Moles	Number of Atoms
Pt	——	0.0449	——
Fe	——	——	1.14×10^{25}
Ti	23.8 mg	——	——
Hg	——	2.05	——

45. Which sample contains the greatest number of atoms?
   (a) 27.2 g Cr
   (b) 55.1 g Ti
   (c) 205 g Pb

46. Which sample contains the greatest number of atoms?
   (a) 10.0 g He
   (b) 25.0 g Ne
   (c) 115 g Xe

47. Determine the number of moles of molecules (or formula units) in each sample.
   (a) 38.2 g sodium chloride
   (b) 36.5 g nitrogen monoxide
   (c) 4.25 kg carbon dioxide
   (d) 2.71 mg carbon tetrachloride

48. Determine the mass of each sample.
   (a) 1.32 mol carbon tetrafluoride
   (b) 0.555 mol magnesium fluoride
   (c) 1.29 mmol carbon disulfide
   (d) 1.89 kmol sulfur trioxide

49. Complete the table:

Compound	Mass	Moles	Number of molecules
H_2O	112 kg	——	——
N_2O	6.33 g	——	——
SO_2	——	2.44	——
CH_2Cl_2	——	0.0643	——

50. Complete the table:

Compound	Mass	Moles	Number of molecules
CO_2	——	0.0153	——
CO	——	0.0150	——
BrI	23.8 mg	——	——
CF_2Cl_2	1.02 kg	——	——

51. A mothball, composed of naphthalene ($C_{10}H_8$), has a mass of 1.32 g. How many naphthalene molecules does it contain?

52. Calculate the mass in grams of a single water molecule.

53. How many molecules are in each sample?
   (a) 3.5 g H_2O
   (b) 56.1 g N_2
   (c) 89 g CCl_4
   (d) 19 g $C_6H_{12}O_6$

54. Calculate the mass in grams of each sample.
   (a) 5.94×10^{20} H_2O_2 molecules
   (b) 2.8×10^{22} SO_2 molecules
   (c) 4.5×10^{25} O_3 molecules
   (d) 9.85×10^{19} CH_4 molecules

55. A sugar crystal contains approximately 1.8×10^{17} sucrose ($C_{12}H_{22}O_{11}$) molecules. What is its mass in milligrams?

56. A salt crystal has a mass of 0.12 mg. How many NaCl formula units does it contain?

57. How much money, in dollars, does one mole of pennies represent? If this amount of money were evenly distributed among the entire world's population (about 6.6 billion people), how much would each person get? Would each person be a millionaire? Billionaire? Trillionaire?

58. A typical dust particle has a diameter of about 10.0 μm. If 1.0 mol of dust particles were laid end to end along the equator, how many times would they encircle the planet? The circumference of the Earth at the equator is 40,076 km.

CHEMICAL FORMULAS AS CONVERSION FACTORS

59. Determine the number of moles of Cl in 2.7 mol $CaCl_2$.

60. How many moles of O are in 12.4 mol $Fe(NO_3)_3$?

61. Which sample contains the greatest number of moles of O?
  (a) 2.3 mol H_2O
  (b) 1.2 mol H_2O_2
  (c) 0.9 mol $NaNO_3$
  (d) 0.5 mol $Ca(NO_3)_2$

62. Which sample contains the greatest number of moles of Cl?
  (a) 3.8 mol HCl
  (b) 1.7 mol CH_2Cl_2
  (c) 4.2 mol $NaClO_3$
  (d) 2.2 mol $Mg(ClO_4)_2$

63. Determine the number of moles of C in each sample.
  (a) 2.5 mol CH_4
  (b) 0.115 mol C_2H_6
  (c) 5.67 mol C_4H_{10}
  (d) 25.1 mol C_8H_{18}

64. Determine the number of moles of H in each sample.
  (a) 4.67 mol H_2O
  (b) 8.39 mol NH_3
  (c) 0.117 mol N_2H_4
  (d) 35.8 mol $C_{10}H_{22}$

65. For each set of molecular models, write a relationship between moles of hydrogen and moles of molecules. Then determine the total number of hydrogen atoms present. (H—white; O—red; C—black; N—blue)

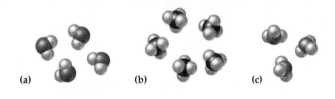

(a)   (b)   (c)

66. For each set of molecular models, write a relationship between moles of oxygen and moles of molecules. Then determine the total number of oxygen atoms present. (H—white; O—red; C—black; S—yellow)

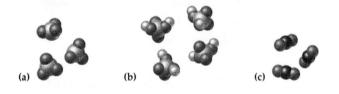

(a)   (b)   (c)

67. How many grams of Cl are in 38.0 g of each sample of chlorofluorocarbons (CFCs)?
  (a) CF_2Cl_2
  (b) $CFCl_3$
  (c) $C_2F_3Cl_3$
  (d) CF_3Cl

68. Calculate the number of grams of sodium in 1.00 g of each sodium-containing food additive.
  (a) NaCl (table salt)
  (b) Na_3PO_4 (sodium phosphate)
  (c) $NaC_7H_5O_2$ (sodium benzoate)
  (d) $Na_2C_6H_6O_7$ (sodium hydrogen citrate)

69. Iron is found in Earth's crust as several different iron compounds. Calculate the mass (in kg) of each compound that contains 1.0×10^3 kg of iron.
  (a) Fe_2O_3 (hematite)
  (b) Fe_3O_4 (magnetite)
  (c) $FeCO_3$ (siderite)

70. Lead is often found in Earth's crust as several lead compounds. Calculate the mass (in kg) of each compound that contains 1.0×10^3 kg of lead.
  (a) PbS (galena)
  (b) $PbCO_3$ (cerussite)
  (c) $PbSO_4$ (anglesite)

MASS PERCENT COMPOSITION

71. A 2.45-g sample of strontium completely reacts with oxygen to form 2.89 g of strontium oxide. Use this data to calculate the mass percent composition of strontium in strontium oxide.

72. A 4.78-g sample of aluminum completely reacts with oxygen to form 6.67 g of aluminum oxide. Use this data to calculate the mass percent composition of aluminum in aluminum oxide.

73. A 1.912-g sample of calcium chloride is decomposed into its constituent elements and found to contain 0.690 g Ca and 1.222 g Cl. Calculate the mass percent composition of Ca and Cl in calcium chloride.

74. A 0.45-g sample of aspirin is decomposed into its constituent elements and found to contain 0.27 g C, 0.020 g H, and 0.16 g O. Calculate the mass percent composition of C, H, and O in aspirin.

75. Copper(II) fluoride contains 37.42% F by mass. Use this percentage to calculate the mass of fluorine in grams contained in 28.5 g of copper(II) fluoride.

76. Silver chloride, often used in silver plating, contains 75.27% Ag. Calculate the mass of silver chloride in grams required to make 4.8 g of silver plating.

77. In small amounts, the fluoride ion (often consumed as NaF) prevents tooth decay. According to the American Dental Association, an adult female should consume 3.0 mg of fluorine per day. Calculate the amount of sodium fluoride (45.24% F) that a woman should consume to get the recommended amount of fluorine.

78. The iodide ion, usually consumed as potassium iodide, is a dietary mineral essential to good nutrition. In countries where potassium iodide is added to salt, iodine deficiency or goiter has been almost completely eliminated. The recommended daily allowance (RDA) for iodine is 150 μg/day. How much potassium iodide (76.45% I) should you consume to meet the RDA?

MASS PERCENT COMPOSITION FROM CHEMICAL FORMULA

79. Calculate the mass percent composition of nitrogen in each compound.
   - (a) N_2O
   - (b) NO
   - (c) NO_2
   - (d) N_2O_5

80. Calculate the mass percent composition of carbon in each compound.
   - (a) C_2H_2
   - (b) C_3H_6
   - (c) C_2H_6
   - (d) C_2H_6O

81. Calculate the mass percent composition of each element in each compound.
   - (a) $C_2H_4O_2$
   - (b) CH_2O_2
   - (c) C_3H_9N
   - (d) $C_4H_{12}N_2$

82. Calculate the mass percent composition of each element in each compound.
   - (a) $FeCl_3$
   - (b) TiO_2
   - (c) H_3PO_4
   - (d) HNO_3

83. Iron ores have different amounts of iron per kilogram of ore. Calculate the mass percent composition of iron for each iron ore: Fe_2O_3 (hematite), Fe_3O_4 (magnetite), $FeCO_3$ (siderite). Which ore has the highest iron content?

84. Plants need nitrogen to grow; so many fertilizers consist of nitrogen-containing compounds. Calculate the mass percent composition of nitrogen in each fertilizer: NH_3, $CO(NH_2)_2$, NH_4NO_3, $(NH_4)_2SO_4$. Which fertilizer has the highest nitrogen content?

CALCULATING EMPIRICAL FORMULAS

85. A compound containing nitrogen and oxygen is decomposed in the laboratory and produces 1.78 g of nitrogen and 4.05 g of oxygen. Calculate the empirical formula of the compound.

86. A compound containing selenium and fluorine is decomposed in the laboratory and produces 2.231 g of selenium and 3.221 g of fluorine. Calculate the empirical formula of the compound.

87. Samples of several compounds were decomposed, and the masses of their constituent elements were measured. Calculate the empirical formula for each compound.
    (a) 1.245 g Ni, 5.381 g I
    (b) 1.443 g Se, 5.841 g Br
    (c) 2.128 g Be, 7.557 g S, 15.107 g O

88. Samples of several compounds were decomposed, and the masses of their constituent elements were measured. Calculate the empirical formula for each compound.
    (a) 2.677 g Ba, 3.115 g Br
    (b) 1.651 g Ag, 0.1224 g O
    (c) 0.672 g Co, 0.569 g As, 0.486 g O

89. The rotten smell of a decaying animal carcass is partially due to a nitrogen-containing compound called putrescine. Elemental analysis of putrescine shows that it consists of 54.50% C, 13.73% H, and 31.77% N. Calculate the empirical formula of putrescine.

90. Citric acid, the compound responsible for the sour taste of lemons, has the elemental composition: C, 37.51%; H, 4.20%; O, 58.29%. Calculate the empirical formula of citric acid.

91. The compounds listed here are often found in many natural flavors and scents. Calculate the empirical formula for each compound.
    (a) ethyl butyrate (pineapple oil): C, 62.04%; H, 10.41%; O, 27.55%
    (b) methyl butyrate (apple flavor): C, 58.80%; H, 9.87%; O, 31.33%
    (c) benzyl acetate (oil of jasmine): C, 71.98%; H, 6.71%; O, 21.31%

92. The compounds listed here are all over-the-counter pain relievers. Calculate the empirical formula for each compound.
    (a) acetaminophen (Tylenol): C, 63.56%; H, 6.00%; N, 9.27%; O, 21.17%
    (b) naproxen (Aleve): C, 73.03%; H, 6.13%; O, 20.84%

93. A 1.45-g sample of phosphorus burns in air and forms 2.57 g of a phosphorus oxide. Calculate the empirical formula of the oxide.

94. A 2.241-g sample of nickel reacts with oxygen to form 2.852 g of the metal oxide. Calculate the empirical formula of the oxide.

95. A 0.77-mg sample of nitrogen reacts with chlorine to form 6.61 mg of the chloride. What is the empirical formula of the nitrogen chloride?

96. A 45.2-mg sample of phosphorus reacts with selenium to form 131.6 mg of the selenide. What is the empirical formula of the phosphorus selenide?

CALCULATING MOLECULAR FORMULAS

97. A compound containing carbon and hydrogen has a molar mass of 56.11 g/mol and an empirical formula of CH_2. Determine its molecular formula.

98. A compound containing phosphorus and oxygen has a molar mass of 219.9 g/mol and an empirical formula of P_2O_3. Determine its molecular formula.

99. The molar masses and empirical formulas of several compounds containing carbon and chlorine are as follows. Find the molecular formula of each compound.
    (a) 284.77 g/mol, CCl
    (b) 131.39 g/mol, C_2HCl_3
    (c) 181.44 g/mol, C_2HCl

100. The molar masses and empirical formulas of several compounds containing carbon and nitrogen are as follows. Find the molecular formula of each compound.
    (a) 163.26 g/mol, $C_{11}C_{17}N$
    (b) 186.24 g/mol, C_6C_7N
    (c) 312.29 g/mol, C_3C_2N

CUMULATIVE PROBLEMS

101. A pure copper cube has an edge length of 1.42 cm. How many copper atoms does it contain? (volume of a cube = (edge length)^3; density of copper = 8.96 g/cm^3)

102. A pure silver sphere has a radius of 0.886 cm. How many silver atoms does it contain? (volume of a sphere = $\frac{4}{3}\pi r^3$; density of silver = 10.5 g/cm^3)

103. A drop of water has a volume of approximately 0.05 mL. How many water molecules does it contain? (density of water = 1.0 g/cm^3)

104. Fingernail-polish remover is primarily acetone (C_3H_6O). How many acetone molecules are in a bottle of acetone with a volume of 325 mL? (density of acetone = 0.788 g/cm^3)

105. Complete the table:

Substance	Mass	Moles	Number of Particles (atoms or molecules)
Ar	———	4.5×10^{-4}	———
NO_2	———	———	1.09×10^{20}
K	22.4 mg	———	———
C_8H_{18}	3.76 kg	———	———

106. Complete the table:

Substance	Mass	Moles	Number of Particles (atoms or molecules)
$C_6H_{12}O_6$	15.8 g	———	———
Pb	———	———	9.04×10^{21}
CF_4	22.5 kg	———	———
C	———	0.0388	———

107. Determine the chemical formula of each compound and then refer to it to calculate the mass percent composition of each constituent element.

(a) copper(II) iodide

(b) sodium nitrate

(c) lead(II) sulfate

(d) calcium fluoride

108. Determine the chemical formula of each compound and then refer to it to calculate the mass percent composition of each constituent element.

(a) nitrogen triiodide

(b) xenon tetrafluoride

(c) phosphorus trichloride

(d) carbon monoxide

109. The rock in a particular iron ore deposit contains 78% Fe_2O_3 by mass. How many kilograms of the rock must be processed to obtain $1.0 \times 10^3 \text{ kg}$ of iron?

110. The rock in a lead ore deposit contains 84% PbS by mass. How many kilograms of the rock must be processed to obtain 1.0 kg of Pb?

111. A leak in the air conditioning system of an office building releases 12 kg of CHF_2Cl per month. If the leak continues, how many kilograms of Cl will be emitted into the atmosphere each year?

112. A leak in the air conditioning system of an older car releases 55 g of CF_2Cl_2 per month. How much Cl is emitted into the atmosphere each year by this car?

113. Hydrogen is a possible future fuel. However, elemental hydrogen is rare, so it must be obtained from a hydrogen-containing compound such as water. If hydrogen were obtained from water, how much hydrogen in grams could be obtained from 1.0 L of water? (density of water = 1.0 g/cm^3)

114. Hydrogen, a possible future fuel mentioned in Problem 113, can also be obtained from other compounds such as ethanol. Ethanol can be made from the fermentation of crops such as corn. How much hydrogen in grams can be obtained from 1.0 kg of ethanol (C_2H_5OH)?

115. Complete the table of compounds that contain only carbon and hydrogen.

Formula	Molar Mass	% C (by mass)	% H (by mass)
C_2H_4	———	———	———
———	58.12	82.66%	———
C_4H_8	———	———	———
———	44.09	———	18.29%

116. Complete the table of compounds that contain only chromium and oxygen.

Formula	Name	Molar Mass	% Cr (by mass)	% O (by mass)
———	Chromium (III) oxide	———	———	———
———	———	84.00	61.90%	———
———	———	100.00	———	48.00%

117. Butanedione, a component of butter and body odor, has a cheesy smell. Elemental analysis of butanedione gave the mass percent composition: C, 55.80%; H, 7.03%; O, 37.17%. The molar mass of butanedione is 86.09 g/mol. Determine the molecular formula of butanedione.

118. Caffeine, a stimulant found in coffee and soda, has the mass percent composition: C, 49.48%; H, 5.19%; N, 28.85%; O, 16.48%. The molar mass of caffeine is 194.19 g/mol. Find the molecular formula of caffeine.

119. Nicotine, a stimulant found in tobacco, has the mass percent composition: C, 74.03%; H, 8.70%; N, 17.27%. The molar mass of nicotine is 162.23 g/mol. Find the molecular formula of nicotine.

120. Estradiol is a female sexual hormone that causes maturation and maintenance of the female reproductive system. Elemental analysis of estradiol gave the mass percent composition: C, 79.37%; H, 8.88%; O, 11.75%. The molar mass of estradiol is 272.37 g/mol. Find the molecular formula of estradiol.

121. A sample contains both KBr and KI in unknown quantities. If the sample has a total mass of 5.00 g and contains 1.51 g K, what are the percentages of KBr and KI in the sample by mass?

122. A sample contains both CO_2 and Ne in unknown quantities. If the sample contains a combined total of 1.75 mol and has a total mass of 65.3 g, what are the percentages of CO_2 and Ne in the sample by mole?

123. Ethanethiol (C_2H_6S) is a compound with a disagreeable odor that can be used to impart an odor to natural gas. When ethanethiol is burned, the sulfur reacts with oxygen to form SO_2. What mass of SO_2 forms upon the complete combustion of 28.7 g of ethanethiol?

124. Methanethiol (CH_4S) has a disagreeable odor and is often a component of bad breath. When methanethiol is burned, the sulfur reacts with oxygen to form SO_2. What mass of SO_2 forms upon the complete combustion of 1.89 g of methanethiol?

125. An iron ore contains 38% Fe_2O_3 by mass. What is the maximum mass of iron that can be recovered from 10.0 kg of this ore?

126. Seawater contains approximately 3.5% NaCl by mass and has a density of 1.02 g/mL. What volume of seawater contains 1.0 g of sodium?

HIGHLIGHT PROBLEMS

127. You can use the concepts in this chapter to obtain an estimate of the number of atoms in the universe. These steps will guide you through this calculation.

    (a) Begin by calculating the number of atoms in the sun. Assume that the sun is pure hydrogen with a density of 1.4 g/cm^3. The radius of the sun is 7×10^8 m, and the volume of a sphere is $V = \frac{4}{3}\pi r^3$.

    (b) Since the sun is an average-sized star, and since stars are believed to compose most of the mass of the visible universe (planets are so small they can be ignored), we can estimate the number of atoms in a galaxy by assuming that every star in the galaxy has the same number of atoms as our sun. The Milky Way galaxy is believed to contain 1×10^{11} stars. Use your answer from part (a) to calculate the number of atoms in the Milky Way galaxy.

    (c) The universe is estimated to contain approximately 1×10^{11} galaxies. If each of these galaxies contains the same number of atoms as the Milky Way galaxy, what is the total number of atoms in the universe?

128. Because of increasing evidence of damage to the ozone layer, chlorofluorocarbon (CFC) production was banned in 1996. However, there are about 100 million auto air conditioners that still use CFC-12 (CF_2Cl_2). These air conditioners are recharged from stockpiled supplies of CFC-12. If each of the 100 million automobiles contains 1.1 kg of CFC-12 and leaks 25% of its CFC-12 into the atmosphere per year, how much Cl in kilograms is added to the atmosphere each year by auto air conditioners? (Assume two significant figures in your calculations.)

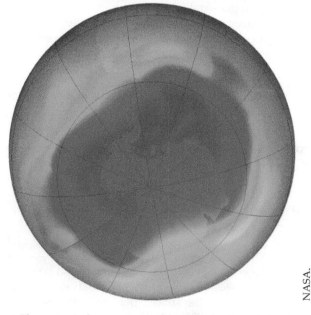

▲ The ozone hole over Antarctica on September 24, 2009. The dark blue and purple areas over the South Pole represent very depressed ozone concentrations.

NASA.

Getty Images.

Getty Images.

▲ Our sun is one of the 100 billion stars in the Milky Way galaxy. The universe is estimated to contain about 100 billion galaxies.

129. In 1996, the media reported that possible evidence of life on Mars was found on a meteorite called Allan Hills 84001 (AH 84001). The meteorite was discovered in Antarctica in 1984 and is believed to have originated on Mars. Elemental analysis of substances within its crevices revealed carbon-containing compounds that normally derive only from living organisms. Suppose that one of those compounds had a molar mass of 202.23 g/mol and the mass percent composition: C, 95.02%; H, 4.98%. What is the molecular formula for the carbon-containing compound?

NASA Johnson Space Center.

▲ The Allan Hills 84001 meteorite. Elemental analysis of the substances within the crevices of this meteorite revealed carbon-containing compounds that normally originate from living organisms.

▶ANSWERS TO SKILLBUILDER EXERCISES

Skillbuilder 1	5.32×10^{22} Au atoms	**Skillbuilder 8**	8.6 g Na
Skillbuilder 2	89.2 g S	**Skillbuilder 9**	53.28% O
Skillbuilder 3	8.17 g He	**Skillbuilder 10**	CH_2O
Skillbuilder 4	2.56×10^{-2} mol NO_2	**Skillbuilder 11**	$C_{13}H_{18}O_2$
Skillbuilder 5	1.22×10^{23} H_2O molecules	**Skillbuilder 12**	CuO
Skillbuilder 6	5.6 mol O	**Skillbuilder 13**	C_4H_{10}
Skillbuilder 7	3.3 g O	**Skillbuilder Plus 2**	$C_2H_8N_2$
Skillbuilder Plus 1	4.04 g O		

▶ANSWERS TO CONCEPTUAL CHECKPOINTS

1 (a) The mole is a counting unit; it represents a definite number (Avogadro's number, 6.022×10^{23}). Therefore, a given number of atoms always represents a precise number of moles, regardless of what atom is involved. Atoms of different elements have different masses, so if samples of different elements have the same mass, they *cannot* contain the same number of atoms or moles.

2 (b) Since carbon has lower molar mass than cobalt or lead, a one-gram sample of carbon contains more atoms than one gram of cobalt or lead.

3 (a) Sample A would have the greatest number of molecules. Since sample A has a lower molar mass than sample B, a given mass of sample A has more moles and therefore more molecules than the same mass of sample B.

4 (c) 1.0 mole of F_2 contains 2.0 mol of F atoms. The other two options each contain less than two moles of F atoms.

5 (b) This compound has the highest ratio of oxygen atoms to chromium atoms and so must have the greatest mass percent of oxygen.

ANSWERS TO ODD-NUMBERED EXERCISES

QUESTIONS

1. Chemical composition lets us determine how much of a particular element is contained within a particular compound.

3. There are 6.022×10^{23} atoms in 1 mole of atoms.

5. One mole of any element has a mass equal to its atomic mass in grams.

7. **a.** 30.97 g   **b.** 195.08 g
    c. 12.01 g   **d.** 52.00 g

9. Each element has a different atomic mass number. So, the subscripts that represent mole ratios cannot be used to represent the ratios of grams of a compound. The grams per mole of one element always differ from the grams per mole of a different element.

11. **a.** $11.19 \text{ g H} \equiv 100 \text{ g H}_2\text{O}$
   b. $53.29 \text{ g O} \equiv 100 \text{ g fructose}$
   c. $84.12 \text{ g C} \equiv 100 \text{ g octane}$
   d. $52.14 \text{ g C} \equiv 100 \text{ g ethanol}$

13. The empirical formula gives the smallest whole-number ratio of each type of atom. The molecular formula gives the specific number of each type of atom in the molecule. The molecular formula is always a multiple of the empirical formula.

15. The empirical formula mass of a compound is the sum of the masses of all the atoms in the empirical formula.

PROBLEMS

17. 3.5×10^{24} atoms

19. **a.** 2.0×10^{24} atoms   **b.** 5.8×10^{21} atoms.
   c. 1.38×10^{25} atoms   **d.** 1.29×10^{23} atoms

21.
Element	Moles	Number of Atoms
Ne	0.552	3.32×10^{23}
Ar	5.40	3.25×10^{24}
Xe	1.78	1.07×10^{24}
He	1.79×10^{-4}	1.08×10^{20}

23. **a.** 72.7 dozen   **b.** 6.06 gross
   c. 1.74 reams   **d.** 1.45×10^{-21} moles

25. 0.321 mol

27. 28.6 g

29. **a.** 2.05×10^{-2} mol   **b.** 0.623 mol
   c. 0.401 mol   **d.** 3.21×10^{-3} mol

31.
Element	Moles	Mass
Ne	1.11	22.5 g
Ar	0.117	4.67 g
Xe	7.62	1.00 kg
He	1.44×10^{-4}	5.76×10^{-4} g

33. 8.07×10^{18} atoms

35. 8.44×10^{22} atoms

37. **a.** 1.16×10^{23} atoms   **b.** 2.81×10^{23} atoms
   c. 2.46×10^{22} atoms   **d.** 7.43×10^{23} atoms

39. 1.9×10^{21} atoms

41. 1.61×10^{25} atoms

43.
Element	Mass	Moles	Number of Atoms
Na	38.5 mg	1.67×10^{-3}	1.01×10^{21}
C	13.5 g	1.12	6.74×10^{23}
V	1.81×10^{-20} g	3.55×10^{-22}	214
Hg	1.44 kg	7.18	4.32×10^{24}

45. **b**

47. **a.** 0.654 mol   **b.** 1.22 mol
   c. 96.6 mol   **d.** 1.76×10^{-5} mol

49.
Compound	Mass	Moles	Molecules
H_2O	112 kg	6.22×10^3	3.74×10^{27}
N_2O	6.33 g	0.144	8.66×10^{22}
SO_2	156	2.44	1.47×10^{24}
CH_2Cl_2	5.46	0.0643	3.87×10^{22}

51. 6.20×10^{21} molecules

53. **a.** 1.2×10^{23} molecules   **b.** 1.21×10^{24} molecules
   c. 3.5×10^{23} molecules   **d.** 6.4×10^{22} molecules

55. 0.10 mg

57. $\$6.022 \times 10^{21}$ total. $\$9.1 \times 10^{11}$ per person. Each person would be a billionaire.

59. 5.4 mol Cl

61. d, 3 mol O

63. **a.** 2.5 mol C   **b.** 0.230 mol C
   c. 22.7 mol C   **d.** 201 mol C

65. **a.** 2 moles H per mole of molecules; 8 H atoms present
   b. 4 moles H per mole of molecules; 20 H atoms present
   c. 3 moles H per mole of molecules; 9 H atoms present

67. **a.** 22.3 g   **b.** 29.4 g
   c. 21.6 g   **d.** 12.9 g

69. **a.** 1.4×10^3 kg   **b.** 1.4×10^3 kg
   c. 2.1×10^3 kg

71. 84.8% Sr

73. 36.1% Ca; 63.9% Cl

75. 10.7 g

77. 6.6 mg

79. **a.** 63.65%　　　**b.** 46.68%
　　c. 30.45%　　　**d.** 25.94%

81. **a.** 39.99% C; 6.73% H; 53.28% O
　　b. 26.09% C; 4.39% H; 69.52% O
　　c. 60.93% C; 15.37% H; 23.69% N
　　d. 54.48% C; 13.74% H; 31.78% N

83. Fe_3O_4, 72.36% Fe; Fe_2O_3, 69.94% Fe; $FeCO_3$, 48.20% Fe; magnetite

85. NO_2

87. **a.** NiI_2　　　**b.** $SeBr_4$
　　c. $BeSO_4$

89. C_2H_6N

91. **a.** C_3H_6O　　　**b.** $C_5H_{10}O_2$
　　c. $C_9H_{10}O_2$

93. P_2O_3

95. NCl_3

97. C_4H_8

99. **a.** C_6Cl_6　　　**b.** C_2HCl_3
　　c. $C_6H_3Cl_3$

101. 2.43×10^{23} atoms

103. 2×10^{21} molecules

105.

Substance	Mass	Moles	Number of Particles
Ar	0.018 g	4.5×10^{-4}	2.7×10^{20}
NO_2	8.33×10^{-3} g	1.81×10^{-4}	1.09×10^{20}
K	22.4 mg	5.73×10^{-4}	3.45×10^{20}
C_8H_{18}	3.76 kg	32.9	1.98×10^{25}

107. **a.** CuI_2: 20.03% Cu; 79.97% I
　　b. $NaNO_3$: 27.05% Na; 16.48% N; 56.47% O
　　c. $PbSO_4$: 68.32% Pb; 10.57% S; 21.10% O
　　d. CaF_2: 51.33% Ca; 48.67% F

109. 1.8×10^3 kg rock

111. 59 kg Cl

113. 1.1×10^2 g H

115.

Formula	Molar Mass	%C (by mass)	%H (by mass)
C_2H_4	28.06	85.60%	14.40%
C_4H_{10}	58.12	82.66%	17.34%
C_4H_8	56.12	85.60%	14.40%
C_3H_8	44.09	81.71%	18.29%

117. $C_4H_6O_2$

119. $C_{10}H_{14}N_2$

121. 70.4% KBr, 29.6% KI

123. 29.6 g SO_2

125. 2.66 kg Fe

127. **a.** 1×10^{57} atoms per star
　　b. 1×10^{68} atoms per galaxy
　　c. 1×10^{79} atoms in the universe

129. $C_{16}H_{10}$

Acids and Bases

From Chapter 14 of *Introductory Chemistry*, Fourth Edition, Nivaldo J. Tro. Copyright © 2011 by Pearson Education, Inc. Published by Pearson Prentice Hall. All rights reserved.

Acids and Bases

"The differences between the various acid–base concepts are not concerned with which is 'right,' but which is most convenient to use in a particular situation."

JAMES E. HUHEEY

1 Sour Patch Kids and International Spy Movies

Gummy candies have a sweet taste and chewy texture that both children and adults can enjoy. From the original classic gummy bear to the gummy worm to the gummy just-about-any-shape-you-can-imagine, these candies are incredibly popular. A common variation is the *sour* gummy candy, whose best-known incarnation is the Sour Patch Kid. Sour Patch Kids are gummy candies shaped like children and coated with a white powder. When you first put a Sour Patch Kid in your mouth, it tastes incredibly sour. The taste is caused by the white powder coating, a mixture of citric acid and tartaric acid. Like all acids, citric and tartaric acid taste sour.

A number of other foods contain acids as well. The taste of lemons and limes, the bite of sourdough bread, and the tang of a tomato are all caused by acids. Acids are substances that—by one definition that we will elaborate on later—produce H^+ ions in solution. When the citric and tartaric acids from a Sour Patch Kid combine with saliva in your mouth, they produce H^+ ions. Those H^+ ions react with protein molecules on your tongue. The protein molecules then change shape, sending an electrical signal to your brain that you experience as a sour taste (▶ Figure 1).

Acids have also been made famous by their use in spy movies. James Bond, for example, often carries an acid-filled gold pen. When Bond is captured and imprisoned—as inevitably happens at least one time in each movie—he squirts some acid out of his pen and onto the iron bars of his cell. The acid quickly dissolves the metal, allowing Bond to escape. Although acids do not dissolve iron bars with the ease depicted in the movies, they do dissolve metals. A small piece of aluminum placed in hydrochloric acid, for example, dissolves away in about

When we say that acids dissolve metals, we mean that acids react with metals in a way that causes them to go into solution as metal cations. Bond's pen is made of gold because gold is one of the few metals that is not dissolved by most acids.

◀ Acids are found in many common foods. The molecules shown here are citric acid (upper left), the acid found in lemon and limes; acetic acid (upper right), the acid present in vinegar; and tartaric acid (lower left), one of the acids used to coat sour gummy candies.

339

◄ **FIGURE 1** **Acids taste sour** When a person eats a sour food, H^+ ions from the acid in the food react with protein molecules in the taste cells of the tongue. This interaction causes the protein molecules to change shape, triggering a nerve impulse to the brain that the person experiences as a sour taste.

► **FIGURE 2** **Acids dissolve many metals** When aluminum is put into hydrochloric acid, the aluminum dissolves. **Question:** What happens to the aluminum atoms? Where do they go?

10 minutes (▲ Figure 2). With enough acid, it would be possible to dissolve the iron bars of a prison cell, but it would take more acid than the amount that fits in a pen.

2 Acids: Properties and Examples

▌ NEVER taste or touch laboratory chemicals.

▲ **FIGURE 3** **Acids turn blue litmus paper red.**

Acids have the following properties:

- Acids have a sour taste.
- Acids dissolve many metals.
- Acids turn blue litmus paper red.

We have just discussed examples of the sour taste of acids (Sour Patch Kids) and their ability to dissolve metals (spy movies). Acids also turn blue litmus paper red. Litmus paper contains a dye that turns red in acidic solutions (◄ Figure 3). In the laboratory, litmus paper is used routinely to test the acidity of solutions.

Some common acids are listed in Table 1. Hydrochloric acid is found in most chemistry laboratories. It is used in industry to clean metals, to prepare and process some foods, and to refine metal ores.

HCl

Hydrochloric acid

Hydrochloric acid is also the main component of stomach acid. In the stomach, hydrochloric acid helps break down food and kills harmful bacteria that might enter the body through food. The sour taste sometimes associated with

TABLE 1 Some Common Acids

Name	Uses
hydrochloric acid (HCl)	metal cleaning; food preparation; ore refining; main component of stomach acid
sulfuric acid (H$_2$SO$_4$)	fertilizer and explosive manufacturing; dye and glue production; automobile batteries
nitric acid (HNO$_3$)	fertilizer and explosive manufacturing; dye and glue production
acetic acid (HC$_2$H$_3$O$_2$)	plastic and rubber manufacturing; food preservation; active component of vinegar
carbonic acid (H$_2$CO$_3$)	found in carbonated beverages due to the reaction of carbon dioxide with water
hydrofluoric acid (HF)	metal cleaning; glass frosting and etching

indigestion is caused by the stomach's hydrochloric acid refluxing up into the esophagus (the tube that joins the stomach and the mouth) and throat.

Sulfuric acid—the most widely produced chemical in the United States—and nitric acid are commonly used in the laboratory. In addition, they are used in the manufacture of fertilizers, explosives, dyes, and glue. Sulfuric acid is contained in most automobile batteries.

Annual U.S. production of sulfuric acid exceeds 36 million tons.

H_2SO_4

Sulfuric acid

HNO_3

Nitric acid

Acetic acid is found in most people's homes as the active component of vinegar. It is also produced in improperly stored wines. The word *vinegar* originates from the French *vin aigre*, which means "sour wine." The presence of vinegar in wines is considered a serious fault, making the wine taste like salad dressing.

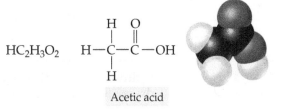

$HC_2H_3O_2$

Acetic acid

Acetic acid is an example of a **carboxylic acid**, an acid containing the grouping of atoms known as the carboxylic acid group.

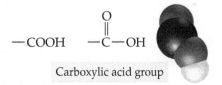

—COOH   —C—OH

Carboxylic acid group

We often find carboxylic acids, in substances derived from living organisms. Other carboxylic acids include citric acid, the main acid in lemons and limes, and malic acid, an acid found in apples, grapes, and wine.

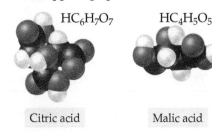

$HC_6H_7O_7$ $HC_4H_5O_5$

Citric acid   Malic acid

Ivaylo Ivanov/Shutterstock.

▲ Acetic acid is the active component in vinegar.

3 Bases: Properties and Examples

NEVER taste or touch laboratory chemicals.

Bases have the following properties:

- Bases have a bitter taste.
- Bases have a slippery feel.
- Bases turn red litmus paper blue.

Coffee is acidic overall, but bases present in coffee—such as caffeine—impart a bitter flavor.

▲ All these consumer products contain bases.

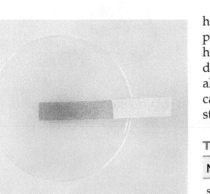

▲ FIGURE 4 **Bases turn red litmus paper blue.**

Bases are less common in foods than acids because of their bitter taste. A Sour Patch Kid coated with a base would never sell. Our aversion to the taste of bases is probably an adaptation to protect us against **alkaloids**, organic bases found in plants (see the Chemistry and Health box in Section 9). Alkaloids are often poisonous—the active component of hemlock, for example, is the alkaloid coniine—and their bitter taste warns us against eating them. Nonetheless, some foods, such as coffee, contain small amounts of base (caffeine is a base). Many people enjoy the bitterness, but only after acquiring the taste over time.

Bases feel slippery because they react with oils on your skin to form soaplike substances. Soap itself is basic, and its slippery feel is characteristic of bases. Some household cleaning solutions, such as ammonia, are also basic and have the typical slippery feel of a base. Bases turn red litmus paper blue (◄ Figure 4). In the laboratory, litmus paper is routinely used to test the basicity of solutions.

Table 2 lists some common bases. Sodium hydroxide and potassium hydroxide are found in most chemistry laboratories. They are also used in processing petroleum and cotton and in soap and plastic manufacturing. Sodium hydroxide is the active ingredient in products such as Drano that work to unclog drains. Sodium bicarbonate can be found in most homes as baking soda and is also an active ingredient in many antacids. When taken as an antacid, sodium bicarbonate neutralizes stomach acid (see Section 5), relieving heartburn and sour stomach.

TABLE 2 Some Common Bases

Name	Uses
sodium hydroxide (NaOH)	petroleum processing; soap and plastic manufacturing
potassium hydroxide (KOH)	cotton processing; electroplating; soap production
sodium bicarbonate (NaHCO$_3$)*	antacid; ingredient of baking soda; source of CO$_2$
ammonia (NH$_3$)	detergent; fertilizer and explosive manufacturing; synthetic fiber production

*Sodium bicarbonate is a salt whose anion (HCO$_3^-$) is the conjugate base of a weak acid (see Section 4) and acts as a base.

4 Molecular Definitions of Acids and Bases

We have just seen some of the properties of acids and bases. In this section we examine two different models that explain the molecular basis for acid and base behavior: the Arrhenius model and the Brønsted–Lowry model. The Arrhenius model, which was developed earlier, is more limited in its scope. The Brønsted–Lowry model was developed later and is more broadly applicable.

THE ARRHENIUS DEFINITION

In the 1880s, the Swedish chemist Svante Arrhenius proposed the following molecular definitions of acids and bases.

HCl

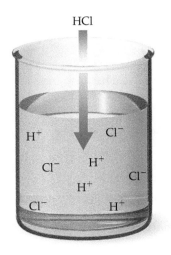

$$HCl(aq) \longrightarrow$$
$$H^+(aq) + Cl^-(aq)$$

▲ **FIGURE 5** **Arrhenius definition of an acid** The Arrhenius definition states that an acid is a substance that produces H^+ ions in solution. These H^+ ions associate with H_2O to form H_3O^+ ions.

NaOH

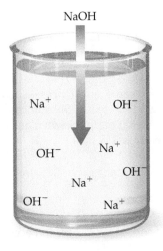

$$NaOH(aq) \longrightarrow$$
$$Na^+(aq) + OH^-(aq)$$

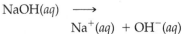

▲ **FIGURE 6** **Arrhenius definition of a base** The Arrhenius definition states that a base is a substance that produces OH^- ions in solution.

Ionic compounds such as NaOH are composed of positive and negative ions. In solution, soluble ionic compounds dissociate into their component ions. Molecular compounds containing an OH group, such as methanol CH_3OH, do not dissociate and therefore do not act as bases.

The Arrhenius definition

Acid—An acid produces H^+ ions in aqueous solution.
Base—A base produces OH^- ions in aqueous solution.

For example, according to the **Arrhenius definition**, HCl is an **Arrhenius acid** because it produces H^+ ions in solution (◄ Figure 5).

$$HCl(aq) \longrightarrow H^+(aq) + Cl^-(aq)$$

HCl is a covalent compound and does not contain ions. However, in water it **ionizes** to form $H^+(aq)$ ions and $Cl^-(aq)$ ions. The H^+ ions are highly reactive. In aqueous solution, they bond to water molecules according to the reaction.

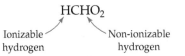

The H_3O^+ ion is the **hydronium ion**. In water, H^+ ions *always* associate with H_2O molecules. Chemists often use $H^+(aq)$ and $H_3O^+(aq)$ interchangeably, however, to refer to the same thing—a hydronium ion.

In the molecular formula for an acid, we often write the ionizable hydrogen first. For example, we write the formula for formic acid as follows:

$$HCHO_2$$

Ionizable hydrogen ⟋   ⟍ Non-ionizable hydrogen

The structure of formic acid, however, is not indicated by the molecular formula in the preceding figure. We represent the *structure* of formic acid with its structural formula:

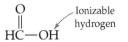

Notice that the structural formula indicates how the atoms are bonded together; the molecular formula, by contrast, simply indicates the number of each type of atom.

NaOH is an **Arrhenius base** because it produces OH^- ions in solution (◄ Figure 6).

$$NaOH(aq) \longrightarrow Na^+(aq) + OH^-(aq)$$

NaOH is an ionic compound and therefore contains Na^+ and OH^- ions. When NaOH is added to water, it **dissociates**, or breaks apart into its component ions.

Under the Arrhenius definition, acids and bases naturally combine to form water, neutralizing each other in the process.

$$H^+(aq) + OH^-(aq) \longrightarrow H_2O(l)$$

THE BRØNSTED–LOWRY DEFINITION

Although the Arrhenius definition of acids and bases works in many cases, it cannot easily explain why some substances act as bases even though they do not contain OH^-. The Arrhenius definition also does not apply to nonaqueous solvents. A second definition of acids and bases, called the **Brønsted–Lowry definition**, introduced in 1923, applies to a wider range of acid–base phenomena. This definition focuses on the *transfer* of H^+ ions in an acid–base reaction. Since an H^+ ion is a proton—a hydrogen atom with its electron taken away—this definition focuses on the idea of a proton donor and a proton acceptor.

Brønsted–Lowry definition

Acid—An acid is a proton (H^+ ion) *donor*.
Base—A base is a proton (H^+ ion) *acceptor*.

According to this definition, HCl is a **Brønsted–Lowry acid** because, in solution, it donates a proton to water.

$$HCl(aq) + H_2O(l) \longrightarrow H_3O^+(aq) + Cl^-(aq)$$

This definition more clearly accounts for what happens to the H^+ ion from an acid: it associates with a water molecule to form H_3O^+ (a hydronium ion). The Brønsted–Lowry definition also works well with bases (such as NH_3) that do not inherently contain OH^- ions but that still produce OH^- ions in solution. NH_3 is a **Brønsted–Lowry base** because it accepts a proton from water.

$$NH_3(aq) + H_2O(l) \rightleftharpoons NH_4^+(aq) + OH^-(aq)$$

In the Brønsted–Lowry definition, acids (proton donors) and bases (proton acceptors) always occur together. In the reaction between HCl and H_2O, HCl is the proton donor (acid), and H_2O is the proton acceptor (base).

$$\underset{\substack{\text{Acid} \\ \text{(Proton donor)}}}{HCl(aq)} + \underset{\substack{\text{Base} \\ \text{(Proton acceptor)}}}{H_2O(l)} \longrightarrow H_3O^+(aq) + Cl^-(aq)$$

In the reaction between NH_3 and H_2O, H_2O is the proton donor (acid) and NH_3 is the proton acceptor (base).

$$\underset{\substack{\text{Base} \\ \text{(Proton acceptor)}}}{NH_3(aq)} + \underset{\substack{\text{Acid} \\ \text{(Proton donor)}}}{H_2O(l)} \rightleftharpoons NH_4^+(aq) + OH^-(aq)$$

Notice that under the Brønsted–Lowry definition, some substances—such as water in the previous two equations—can act as acids *or* bases. Substances that can act as acids or bases are **amphoteric**. Notice also what happens when an equation representing Brønsted–Lowry acid–base behavior is reversed.

$$\underset{\substack{\text{Acid} \\ \text{(Proton donor)}}}{NH_4^+(aq)} + \underset{\substack{\text{Base} \\ \text{(Proton acceptor)}}}{OH^-(aq)} \rightleftharpoons NH_3(aq) + H_2O(l)$$

In this reaction, NH_4^+ is the proton donor (acid) and OH^- is the proton acceptor (base). What was the base (NH_3) has become the acid (NH_4^+), and vice versa. NH_4^+ and NH_3 are often referred to as a **conjugate acid–base pair**, two substances related to each other by the transfer of a proton (◀ Figure 7). Going back to the original forward reaction, we can identify the conjugate acid–base pairs as follows:

$$\underset{\text{Base}}{NH_3(aq)} + \underset{\text{Acid}}{H_2O(l)} \rightleftharpoons \underset{\substack{\text{Conjugate} \\ \text{acid}}}{NH_4^+(aq)} + \underset{\substack{\text{Conjugate} \\ \text{base}}}{OH^-(aq)}$$

In an acid–base reaction, a base accepts a proton and becomes a conjugate acid. An acid donates a proton and becomes a conjugate base.

Johannes Brønsted, working in Denmark, and Thomas Lowry, working in England, developed the concept of proton transfer in acid–base behavior independently and simultaneously.

The double arrows in this equation indicate that the reaction does not go to completion. We discuss this concept in more detail in Section 7.

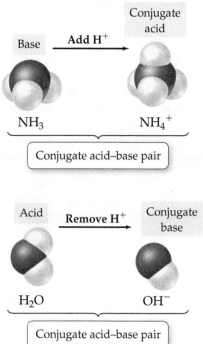

Base — **Add H⁺** → Conjugate acid

NH_3 NH_4^+

Conjugate acid–base pair

Acid — **Remove H⁺** → Conjugate base

H_2O OH^-

Conjugate acid–base pair

▲ FIGURE 7 **A conjugate acid–base pair** Any two substances related to each other by the transfer of a proton can be considered a conjugate acid–base pair.

EXAMPLE 1 Identifying Brønsted–Lowry Acids and Bases and Their Conjugates

In each reaction, identify the Brønsted–Lowry acid, the Brønsted–Lowry base, the conjugate acid, and the conjugate base.

(a) $H_2SO_4(aq) + H_2O(l) \longrightarrow H_3O^+(aq) + HSO_4^-(aq)$

(b) $HCO_3^-(aq) + H_2O(l) \rightleftharpoons H_2CO_3(aq) + OH^-(aq)$

SOLUTION

(a) Since H_2SO_4 donates a proton to H_2O in this reaction, it is the acid (the proton donor). After H_2SO_4 donates the proton, it becomes HSO_4^-, the conjugate base. Since H_2O accepts a proton, it is the base (the proton acceptor). After H_2O accepts the proton, it becomes H_3O^+, the conjugate acid.

$$H_2SO_4(aq) + H_2O(l) \longrightarrow HSO_4^-(aq) + H_3O^+(aq)$$

Acid   Base   Conjugate base   Conjugate acid

(b) Since H_2O donates a proton to HCO_3^- in this reaction, it is the acid (the proton donor). After H_2O donates the proton, it becomes OH^-, the conjugate base. Since HCO_3^- accepts a proton, it is the base (the proton acceptor). After HCO_3^- accepts the proton, it becomes H_2CO_3, the conjugate acid.

$$HCO_3^-(aq) + H_2O(l) \longrightarrow H_2CO_3(aq) + OH^-(aq)$$

Base   Acid   Conjugate acid   Conjugate base

▶SKILLBUILDER 1 Identifying Brønsted–Lowry Acids and Bases and Their Conjugates

In each reaction, identify the Brønsted–Lowry acid, the Brønsted–Lowry base, the conjugate acid, and the conjugate base.

(a) $C_5H_5N(aq) + H_2O(l) \rightleftharpoons C_5H_5NH^+(aq) + OH^-(aq)$

(b) $HNO_3(aq) + H_2O(l) \longrightarrow NO_3^-(aq) + H_3O^+(aq)$

▶**FOR MORE PRACTICE** Example 11; Problems 35, 36, 37, 38.

✔ CONCEPTUAL CHECKPOINT 1

Which species is the conjugate base of H_2SO_3?

(a) $H_3SO_3^+$ (b) HSO_3^- (c) SO_3^{2-}

---

5 Reactions of Acids and Bases

NEUTRALIZATION REACTIONS

| The reaction between HCl and KOH is also a double-displacement reaction.

One of the most important reactions of acids and bases is **neutralization**. When an acid and a base are mixed, the $H^+(aq)$ from the acid combines with the $OH^-(aq)$ from the base to form $H_2O(l)$. For example, consider the reaction between hydrochloric acid and potassium hydroxide.

$$HCl(aq) + KOH(aq) \longrightarrow H_2O(l) + KCl(aq)$$

Acid   Base   Water   Salt

Acid–base reactions generally form water and a **salt**—an ionic compound—that usually remains dissolved in the solution. The salt contains the cation from the base and the anion from the acid.

Ionic compound that contains the cation from the base and the anion from the acid

$$Acid + Base \longrightarrow Water + Salt$$

The net ionic equation for many neutralization reactions is:

$$H^+(aq) + OH^-(aq) \longrightarrow H_2O(l)$$

A slightly different but common type of neutralization reaction involves an acid reacting with carbonates or bicarbonates (compounds containing CO_3^{2-} or HCO_3^-). This type of neutralization reaction produces water, gaseous carbon dioxide, and a salt. As an example, consider the reaction of hydrochloric acid and sodium bicarbonate.

$$HCl(aq) + NaHCO_3(aq) \longrightarrow H_2O(l) + CO_2(g) + NaCl(aq)$$

Since this reaction produces gaseous CO_2, it is also called a *gas evolution reaction*.

$$HCl(aq) + NaHCO_3(aq) \longrightarrow$$

$$H_2O(l) + CO_2(g) + NaCl(aq)$$

▲ The reaction of carbonates or bicarbonates with acids produces water, gaseous carbon dioxide, and a salt.

EXAMPLE 2 Writing Equations for Neutralization Reactions

Write a molecular equation for the reaction between aqueous HCl and aqueous $Ca(OH)_2$.

SOLUTION	
First identify the acid and the base and write the skeletal reaction showing the production of water and the salt. The formulas for the ionic compounds in the equation must be charge neutral.	$HCl(aq) + Ca(OH)_2(aq) \longrightarrow H_2O(l) + CaCl_2(aq)$
Balance the equation. Notice that $Ca(OH)_2$ contains 2 mol of OH^- for every 1 mol of $Ca(OH)_2$ and will therefore require 2 mol of H^+ to neutralize it.	$2\,HCl(aq) + Ca(OH)_2(aq) \longrightarrow 2\,H_2O(l) + CaCl_2(aq)$

▶ **SKILLBUILDER 2 | Writing Equations for Neutralization Reactions**

Write a molecular equation for the reaction that occurs between aqueous H_3PO_4 and aqueous NaOH. *Hint:* H_3PO_4 is a triprotic acid, meaning that 1 mol of H_3PO_4 requires 3 mol of OH^- to completely react with it.

▶ **FOR MORE PRACTICE** Example 12; Problems 43, 44.

ACID REACTIONS

In Section 1, we learned that acids dissolve metals, or more precisely, that acids react with metals in a way that causes metals to go into solution. The reaction between an acid and a metal usually produces hydrogen gas and a dissolved salt containing the metal ion as the cation. For example, hydrochloric acid reacts with magnesium metal to form hydrogen gas and magnesium chloride.

$$\underset{\text{Acid}}{2\,HCl(aq)} + \underset{\text{Metal}}{Mg(s)} \longrightarrow \underset{\substack{\text{Hydrogen} \\ \text{gas}}}{H_2(g)} + \underset{\text{Salt}}{MgCl_2(aq)}$$

$$2\,HCl(aq) + Mg(s) \longrightarrow$$

$$H_2(g) + MgCl_2(aq)$$

▲ The reaction between an acid and a metal usually produces hydrogen gas and a dissolved salt containing the metal ion.

Similarly, sulfuric acid reacts with zinc to form hydrogen gas and zinc sulfate.

$$\underset{\text{Acid}}{H_2SO_4(aq)} + \underset{\text{Metal}}{Zn(s)} \longrightarrow \underset{\substack{\text{Hydrogen} \\ \text{gas}}}{H_2(g)} + \underset{\text{Salt}}{ZnSO_4(aq)}$$

It is through reactions such as these that the acid from James Bond's pen in our earlier example dissolves the metal bars that imprison him. For example, if the bars were made of iron and the acid in the pen were hydrochloric acid, the reaction would be:

$$\underset{\text{Acid}}{2\,HCl(aq)} + \underset{\text{Metal}}{Fe(s)} \longrightarrow \underset{\substack{\text{Hydrogen} \\ \text{gas}}}{H_2(g)} + \underset{\text{Salt}}{FeCl_2(aq)}$$

Some metals, however, do not readily react with acids. If the bars that imprisoned James Bond were made of gold, for example, a pen filled with hydrochloric acid would not dissolve the bars.

Acids also react with metal oxides to produce water and a dissolved salt. For example, hydrochloric acid reacts with potassium oxide to form water and potassium chloride.

$$\underset{\text{Acid}}{2\,HCl(aq)} + \underset{\text{Metal oxide}}{K_2O(s)} \longrightarrow \underset{\text{Water}}{H_2O(l)} + \underset{\text{Salt}}{2\,KCl(aq)}$$

Similarly, hydrobromic acid reacts with magnesium oxide to form water and magnesium bromide.

$$\underset{\text{Acid}}{2\,HBr(aq)} + \underset{\text{Metal oxide}}{MgO(s)} \longrightarrow \underset{\text{Water}}{H_2O(l)} + \underset{\text{Salt}}{MgBr_2(aq)}$$

EXAMPLE 3   Writing Equations for Acid Reactions

Write an equation for:

(a) The reaction of hydroiodic acid with potassium metal
(b) The reaction of hydrobromic acid with sodium oxide

SOLUTION

(a) The reaction of hydroiodic acid with potassium metal forms hydrogen gas and a salt. The salt contains the ionized form of the metal (K^+) as the cation and the anion of the acid (I^-). Write the skeletal equation and then balance it.

$$HI(aq) + K(s) \longrightarrow H_2(g) + KI(aq)$$

$$2\ HI(aq) + 2\ K(s) \longrightarrow H_2(g) + 2\ KI(aq)$$

(b) The reaction of hydrobromic acid with sodium oxide forms water and a salt. The salt contains the cation from the metal oxide (Na^+) and the anion of the acid (Br^-). Write the skeletal equation and then balance it.

$$HBr(aq) + Na_2O(s) \longrightarrow H_2O(l) + NaBr(aq)$$

$$2\ HBr(aq) + Na_2O(s) \longrightarrow H_2O(l) + 2\ NaBr(aq)$$

▶SKILLBUILDER 3 | Writing Equations for Acid Reactions

Write an equation for:

(a) The reaction of hydrochloric acid with strontium metal
(b) The reaction of hydroiodic acid with barium oxide

▶FOR MORE PRACTICE   Example 13; Problems 45, 46, 47, 48.

What Is in My Antacid?

Heartburn, a burning sensation in the lower throat and above the stomach, is caused by the reflux or backflow of stomach acid into the esophagus (the tube that joins the stomach to the throat). In most individuals, this occurs only occasionally, typically after large meals. Physical activity—such as bending, stooping, or lifting—after meals also aggravates heartburn. In some people, the flap between the esophagus and the stomach that normally prevents acid

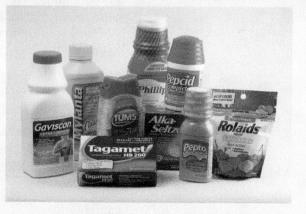

Maxwellartandphoto.com.

Drug Facts

Active ingredients (in each 5 mL teaspoon)   **Purposes**
Aluminum hydroxide (equivalent to dried gel, USP) 200 mg..........Antacid
Magnesium hydroxide 200 mg...Antacid
Simethicone 20 mg..Antigas

Use relieves:
■ heartburn   ■ acid indigestion   ■ sour stomach
■ upset stomach due to these symptoms   ■ overindulgence in food and drink

Warnings
Ask a doctor before use if you have kidney disease.
Ask a doctor or pharmacist if you are taking a prescription drug. Antacids may interact with certain prescription drugs.
Stop use and ask a doctor if symptoms last more than 2 weeks.
Keep out of reach of children.

Directions ■ shake well   ■ take 2-4 teaspoonfuls between meals, at bedtime, or as directed by a doctor   ■ do not take more than 24 teaspoonfuls in a 24-hour period, or use the maximum dosage for more than 2 weeks

Other information ■ does not meet USP requirements for preservative effectiveness   ■ do not use if breakaway band on plastic cap is broken or missing

reflux becomes damaged, in which case heartburn becomes a regular occurrence.

Drugstores carry many products that either reduce the secretion of stomach acid or neutralize the acid that is produced. Antacids such as Mylanta or Phillips' milk of magnesia contain bases that neutralize the refluxed stomach acid, alleviating heartburn.

CAN YOU ANSWER THIS?   *Look at the label of Mylanta shown in the photograph. Can you identify the bases responsible for the antacid action? Write chemical equations showing the reactions of these bases with stomach acid (HCl).*

BASE REACTIONS

The most important base reactions are those in which a base neutralizes an acid (see the beginning of this section). The only other kind of base reaction that we cover in this text is the reaction of sodium hydroxide with aluminum and water.

$$2 \, NaOH(aq) + 2 \, Al(s) + 6 \, H_2O(l) \longrightarrow 2 \, NaAl(OH)_4(aq) + 3 \, H_2(g)$$

Aluminum is one of the few metals that dissolves in a base. Consequently, it is safe to use NaOH (the main ingredient in many drain-opening products) to unclog your drain as long as your pipes are not made of aluminum, which is generally the case as the use of aluminum pipe is forbidden in most building codes.

6 Acid–Base Titration: A Way to Quantify the Amount of Acid or Base in a Solution

The principles on solution stoichiometry can be applied to a common laboratory procedure called a titration. In a **titration**, a substance in a solution of known concentration is reacted with another substance in a solution of unknown concentration. For example, consider the acid–base reaction between hydrochloric acid and sodium hydroxide:

$$HCl(aq) + NaOH(aq) \longrightarrow H_2O(l) + NaCl(aq)$$

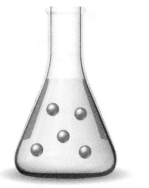

$\bullet$ H$^+$

The OH$^-$ solution also contains Na$^+$ cations that are not shown in this figure for clarity.

The net ionic equation for this reaction is:

$$H^+(aq) + OH^-(aq) \longrightarrow H_2O(l)$$

Suppose you have an HCl solution represented by the molecular diagram at left. (The Cl$^-$ ions and the H$_2$O molecules not involved in the reaction have been omitted from this representation for clarity.)

In titrating this sample, we slowly add a solution of known OH$^-$ concentration as represented by the following molecular diagrams.

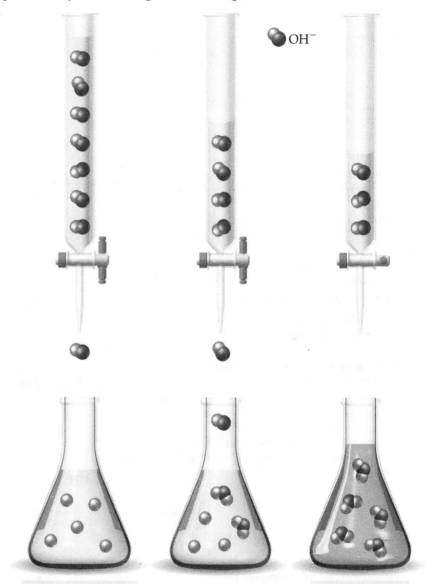

$\bullet$ OH$^-$

Beginning of titration   Equivalence point

At the equivalence point, neither reactant is present in excess, and both are limiting. The number of moles of the reactants are related by the reaction stoichiometry.

As the OH$^-$ is added, it reacts with and neutralizes the H$^+$, forming water. At the **equivalence point**—*the point in the titration when the number of moles of OH$^-$ added equals the number of moles of H$^+$ originally in solution*—the titration is complete. The equivalence point is usually signaled by an **indicator**, a dye whose color depends on the acidity of the solution (▶ Figure 8). In most laboratory titrations, the concentration of one of the reactant solutions is unknown, and the concentration of the other is precisely known. By carefully measuring the volume of each solution required to reach the equivalence point, the concentration of the unknown solution can be determined, as demonstrated in Example 4.

▶ FIGURE 8 Acid–base titration
In this titration, NaOH is added to an HCl solution. When the NaOH and HCl reach stoichiometric proportions (1 mol of OH^- for every 1 mol of H^+), the indicator (phenolphthalein) changes to pink, signaling the equivalence point of the titration. (Phenolphthalein is an indicator that is colorless in acidic solution and pink in basic solution.)

EXAMPLE 4 Acid–Base Titration

The titration of 10.00 mL of an HCl solution of unknown concentration requires 12.54 mL of a 0.100 M NaOH solution to reach the equivalence point. What is the concentration of the unknown HCl solution?

SORT You are given the volume of an unknown HCl solution and the volume of a known NaOH solution required to titrate the unknown solution. You are asked to find the concentration of the unknown solution.	**GIVEN:** 10.00 mL HCl solution 12.54 mL of a 0.100 M NaOH solution **FIND:** concentration of HCl solution (mol/L)

STRATEGIZE

You must first write the balanced chemical equation for the reaction between the acid and the base (see Example 2).

The solution map then has two parts. In the first part, use the volume of NaOH required to reach the equivalence point to calculate the number of moles of HCl in the solution. The final conversion factor comes from the balanced neutralization equation.

In the second part, use the number of moles of HCl and the volume of HCl solution to determine the molarity of the HCl solution.

SOLUTION MAP

$$HCl(aq) + NaOH(aq) \longrightarrow H_2O(l) + NaCl(aq)$$

mL NaOH	→	L NaOH	→	mol NaOH	→	mol HCl

$$\frac{1\ L}{1000\ mL} \qquad \frac{0.100\ mol\ NaOH}{1\ L\ NaOH} \qquad \frac{1\ mol\ HCl}{1\ mol\ NaOH}$$

mol HCl, volume HCl solution	→	molarity

$$M = \frac{mol}{L}$$

RELATIONSHIPS USED

1 mol HCl : 1 mol NaOH (from balanced chemical equation)

$$\text{Molarity (M)} = \frac{\text{mol solute}}{\text{L solution}} \text{ (definition of molarity, from Section 6)}$$

SOLVE

Calculate the moles of HCl in the unknown solution by following the first part of the solution map.

To get the concentration of the solution, divide the number of moles of HCl by the volume of the HCl solution in L. (Note that 10.00 mL is equivalent to 0.01000 L.)

The unknown HCl solution therefore has a concentration of 0.125 M.

SOLUTION

$$12.54\ \text{mL NaOH} \times \frac{1\ L}{1000\ mL} \times \frac{0.100\ mol\ NaOH}{1\ L\ NaOH} \times \frac{1\ mol\ HCl}{1\ mol\ NaOH}$$
$$= 1.25 \times 10^{-3}\ mol\ HCl$$

$$\text{Molarity} = \frac{1.25 \times 10^{-3}\ mol\ HCl}{0.01000\ L} = 0.125\ M$$

CHECK

Check your answer. Are the units correct? Does the answer make physical sense?

The units (M) are correct. The magnitude of the answer makes sense because the reaction has a one-to-one stoichiometry and the volumes of the two solutions are similar; therefore, their concentrations should also be similar.

▶SKILLBUILDER 4 | Acid–Base Titration

The titration of a 20.0-mL sample of an H_2SO_4 solution of unknown concentration requires 22.87 mL of a 0.158 M KOH solution to reach the equivalence point. What is the concentration of the unknown H_2SO_4 solution?

▶FOR MORE PRACTICE   Example 14; Problems 51, 52, 53, 54, 55, 56.

7   Strong and Weak Acids and Bases

STRONG ACIDS

Hydrochloric acid (HCl) and hydrofluoric acid (HF) appear to be similar, but there is an important difference between these two acids. HCl is an example of a **strong acid**, one that completely ionizes in solution.

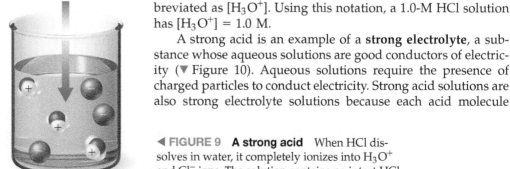

Single arrow indicates complete ionization

$$HCl(aq) + H_2O(l) \longrightarrow H_3O^+(aq) + Cl^-(aq)$$

‖ [X] means "molar concentration of X."

We show the *complete* ionization of HCl with a single arrow pointing to the right in the equation. An HCl solution contains almost no intact HCl; virtually all the HCl has reacted with water to form $H_3O^+(aq)$ and $Cl^-(aq)$ (◀ Figure 9). A 1.0 M HCl solution will therefore have an H_3O^+ concentration of 1.0 M. The concentration of H_3O^+ is often abbreviated as $[H_3O^+]$. Using this notation, a 1.0-M HCl solution has $[H_3O^+]$ = 1.0 M.

A strong acid is an example of a **strong electrolyte**, a substance whose aqueous solutions are good conductors of electricity (▼ Figure 10). Aqueous solutions require the presence of charged particles to conduct electricity. Strong acid solutions are also strong electrolyte solutions because each acid molecule

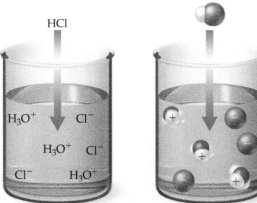

◀ FIGURE 9   **A strong acid**   When HCl dissolves in water, it completely ionizes into H_3O^+ and Cl^- ions. The solution contains no intact HCl.

Richard Megna/Fundamental Photographs.

(a) Pure water

(b) HCl solution

▲ FIGURE 10   **Conductivity of a strong electrolyte solution**   (a) Pure water will not conduct electricity. (b) The presence of ions in an HCl solution results in the conduction of electricity, causing the lightbulb to light. Solutions such as these are called strong electrolyte solutions.

ionizes into positive and negative ions. These mobile ions are good conductors of electricity. Pure water is not a good conductor of electricity because it has relatively few charged particles. The danger of using electrical devices—such as a hair dryer—while sitting in the bathtub is that water is seldom pure and often contains dissolved ions. If the device were to come in contact with the water, dangerously high levels of electricity could flow through the water and through your body.

> An ionizable proton is one that becomes an H^+ ion in solution.

Table 3 lists the six strong acids. The first five acids in the table are **monoprotic acids**, acids containing only one ionizable proton. Sulfuric acid is an example of a **diprotic acid**, an acid that contains two ionizable protons.

TABLE 3   **Strong Acids**

hydrochloric acid (HCl)	nitric acid (HNO_3)
hydrobromic acid (HBr)	perchloric acid ($HClO_4$)
hydroiodic acid (HI)	sulfuric acid (H_2SO_4) (diprotic)

WEAK ACIDS

> It is a common mistake to confuse the terms *strong* and *weak acids* with the terms *concentrated* and *dilute acids.* Can you state the difference between these terms?

In contrast to HCl, HF is a **weak acid**, one that does not completely ionize in solution.

Double arrow indicates partial ionization

$$HF(aq) + H_2O(l) \rightleftharpoons H_3O^+(aq) + F^-(aq)$$

> Calculating exact $[H_3O^+]$ for weak acids is beyond the scope of this text.

To show that HF does not completely ionize in solution, the equation for its ionization has two opposing arrows, indicating that the reverse reaction occurs to some degree. An HF solution contains a lot of intact HF; it also contains some $H_3O^+(aq)$ and $F^-(aq)$ (▼ Figure 11). In other words, a 1.0 M HF solution has $[H_3O^+] < 1.0$ M because only some of the HF molecules ionize to form H_3O^+.

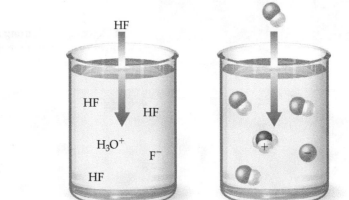

▶ **FIGURE 11   A weak acid**
When HF dissolves in water, only a fraction of the dissolved molecules ionize into H_3O^+ and F^- ions. The solution contains many intact HF molecules.

A weak acid is an example of a **weak electrolyte**, a substance whose aqueous solutions are poor conductors of electricity (▶ Figure 12). Weak acid solutions contain few charged particles because only a small fraction of the acid molecules ionize into positive and negative ions.

> Notice that the strength of a conjugate base is related to its attraction to H^+ in solution.

The degree to which an acid is strong or weak depends in part on the attraction between the anion of the acid (the conjugate base) and the hydrogen ion. Suppose HA is a generic formula for an acid. Then, the degree to which the following reaction proceeds in the forward direction depends in part on the strength of the attraction between H^+ and A^-.

$$\underset{\text{Acid}}{HA(aq)} + H_2O(l) \longrightarrow H_3O^+(aq) + \underset{\text{Conjugate base}}{A^-(aq)}$$

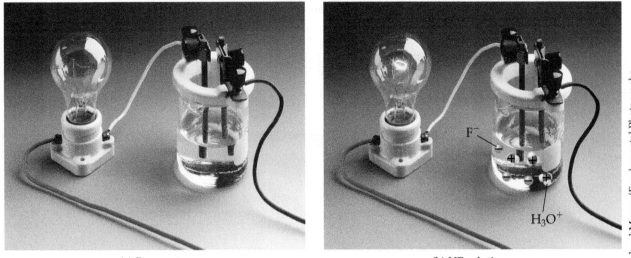

Richard Megna/Fundamental Photographs.

(a) Pure water   **(b)** HF solution

▲ FIGURE 12 **Conductivity of a weak electrolyte solution** **(a)** Pure water will not conduct electricity.
(b) An HF solution contains some ions, but most of the HF is intact. The light glows only dimly.
Solutions such as these are called weak electrolyte solutions.

Notice that the strength of a conjugate base is related to its attraction to H^+ in solution.

(a) Strong acid

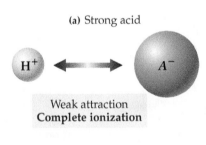

Weak attraction
Complete ionization

(b) Weak acid

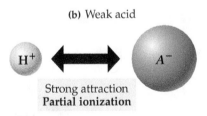

Strong attraction
Partial ionization

▲ FIGURE 13 **Strong and weak acids** **(a)** In a strong acid, the attraction between H^+ and A^- is low, resulting in complete ionization. **(b)** In a weak acid, the attraction between H^+ and A^- is high, resulting in partial ionization.

If the attraction between H^+ and A^- is *weak*, then the reaction favors the forward direction and the acid is *strong* (◄ Figure 13a). If the attraction between H^+ and A^- is *strong*, then the reaction favors the reverse direction and the acid is *weak* (Figure 13b).

For example, in HCl, the conjugate base (Cl^-) has a relatively weak attraction to H^+, meaning that the reverse reaction does not occur to any significant extent. In HF, on the other hand, the conjugate base (F^-) has a greater attraction to H^+, meaning that the reverse reaction occurs to a significant degree. *In general, the stronger the acid, the weaker the conjugate base and vice versa.* This means that if the forward reaction (that of the acid) has a high tendency to occur, then the reverse reaction (that of the conjugate base) has a low tendency to occur. Table 4 lists some common weak acids.

TABLE 4 Some Weak Acids

hydrofluoric acid (HF)	sulfurous acid (H_2SO_3) *(diprotic)*
acetic acid ($HC_2H_3O_2$)	carbonic acid (H_2CO_3) *(diprotic)*
formic acid ($HCHO_2$)	phosphoric acid (H_3PO_4) *(triprotic)*

Notice that two of the weak acids in Table 4 are diprotic (meaning they have two ionizable protons) and one is triprotic (meaning that it has three ionizable protons). Let us return to sulfuric acid for a moment. Sulfuric acid is a diprotic acid that is strong in its first ionizable proton:

$$H_2SO_4(aq) + H_2O(l) \longrightarrow H_3O^+(aq) + HSO_4^-(aq)$$

but weak in its second ionizable proton.

$$HSO_4^-(aq) + H_2O(l) \rightleftharpoons H_3O^+(aq) + SO_4^{2-}(aq)$$

Sulfurous acid and carbonic acid are weak in both of their ionizable protons, and phosphoric acid is weak in all three of its ionizable protons.

EXAMPLE 5 Determining [H₃O⁺] in Acid Solutions

What is the H_3O^+ concentration in each solution?

(a) 1.5 M HCl
(b) 3.0 M HC₂H₃O₂
(c) 2.5 M HNO₃

SOLUTION

(a) Since HCl is a strong acid, it completely ionizes. The concentration of H_3O^+ will be 1.5 M.

$$[H_3O^+] = 1.5 \text{ M}$$

(b) Since HC₂H₃O₂ is a weak acid, it partially ionizes. The calculation of the exact concentration of H_3O^+ is beyond the scope of this text, but we know that it will be less than 3.0 M.

$$[H_3O^+] < 3.0 \text{ M}$$

(c) Since HNO₃ is a strong acid, it completely ionizes. The concentration of H_3O^+ will be 2.5 M.

$$[H_3O^+] = 2.5 \text{ M}$$

▶**SKILLBUILDER 5 | Determining [H₃O⁺] in Acid Solutions**

What is the H_3O^+ concentration in each solution?

(a) 0.50 M HCHO₂
(b) 1.25 M HI
(c) 0.75 M HF

▶**FOR MORE PRACTICE** Example 15; Problems 59, 60.

✔ CONCEPTUAL CHECKPOINT 2

Examine the molecular views of three different acid solutions shown here. Based on these views, which one of these acids is a weak acid?

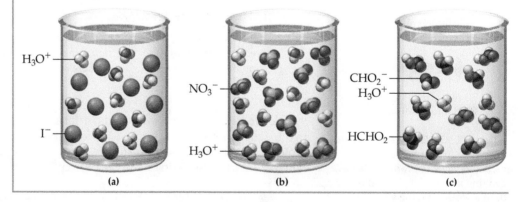

(a) (b) (c)

STRONG BASES

In analogy to the definition of a strong acid, a **strong base** is one that completely dissociates in solution. NaOH, for example, is a strong base.

$$NaOH(aq) \longrightarrow Na^+(aq) + OH^-(aq)$$

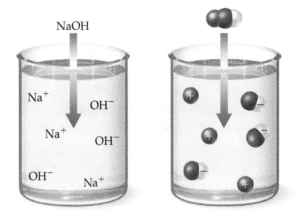

▶ FIGURE 14 **A strong base**
When NaOH dissolves in water, it completely dissociates into Na^+ and OH^-. Question: The solution contains no intact NaOH. Is NaOH a strong or weak electrolyte?

An NaOH solution contains no intact NaOH—it has all dissociated to form $Na^+(aq)$ and $OH^-(aq)$ (▲ Figure 14), and a 1.0 M NaOH solution has $[OH^-]$ = 1.0 M and $[Na^+]$ = 1.0 M. Some common strong bases are listed in Table 5.

TABLE 5 Strong Bases

lithium hydroxide (LiOH)	strontium hydroxide (Sr(OH)$_2$)
sodium hydroxide (NaOH)	calcium hydroxide (Ca(OH)$_2$)
potassium hydroxide (KOH)	barium hydroxide (Ba(OH)$_2$)

Unlike diprotic acids, which ionize in two steps, bases containing 2 OH^- ions dissociate in one step.

Some strong bases, such as $Sr(OH)_2$, contain two OH^- ions. These bases completely dissociate, producing two moles of OH^- per mole of base. For example, $Sr(OH)_2$ dissociates as follows:

$$Sr(OH)_2(aq) \longrightarrow Sr^{2+}(aq) + 2\ OH^-(aq)$$

WEAK BASES

A **weak base** is analogous to a weak acid. Unlike strong bases that contain OH^- and dissociate in water, the most common weak bases produce OH^- by accepting a proton from water, ionizing water to form OH^-.

$$B(aq) + H_2O(l) \rightleftharpoons BH^+(aq) + OH^-(aq)$$

In this equation, B is generic for a weak base. Ammonia, for example, ionizes water according to the reaction:

Calculating exact $[OH^-]$ for weak bases is beyond the scope of this text.

$$NH_3(aq) + H_2O(l) \rightleftharpoons NH_4^+(aq) + OH^-(aq)$$

The double arrow indicates that the ionization is not complete. An NH_3 solution contains NH_3, NH_4^+, and OH^- (◀ Figure 15). A 1.0 M NH_3 solution has $[OH^-]$ < 1.0 M. Table 6 lists some common weak bases.

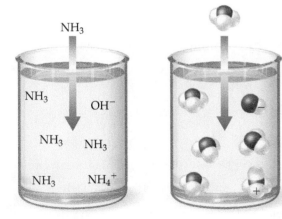

◀ FIGURE 15 **A weak base** When NH_3 dissolves in water, it partially ionizes to form NH_4^+ and OH^-. However, only a fraction of the molecules ionize. Most NH_3 molecules remain as NH_3. Question: Is NH_3 a strong or weak electrolyte?

TABLE 6 Some Weak Bases

Base	Ionization Reaction
ammonia (NH_3)	$NH_3(aq) + H_2O(l) \rightleftharpoons NH_4^+(aq) + OH^-(aq)$
pyridine (C_5H_5N)	$C_5H_5N(aq) + H_2O(l) \rightleftharpoons C_5H_5NH^+(aq) + OH^-(aq)$
methylamine (CH_3NH_2)	$CH_3NH_2(aq) + H_2O(l) \rightleftharpoons CH_3NH_3^+(aq) + OH^-(aq)$
ethylamine ($C_2H_5NH_2$)	$C_2H_5NH_2(aq) + H_2O(l) \rightleftharpoons C_2H_5NH_3^+(aq) + OH^-(aq)$
bicarbonate ion (HCO_3^-)*	$HCO_3^-(aq) + H_2O(l) \rightleftharpoons H_2CO_3(aq) + OH^-(aq)$

*The bicarbonate ion must occur with a positively charged ion such as Na^+ that serves to balance the charge but does not have any part in the ionization reaction. It is the bicarbonate ion that makes sodium bicarbonate ($NaHCO_3$) basic.

EXAMPLE 6   Determining [OH⁻] in Base Solutions

What is the OH^- concentration in each solution?

(a) 2.25 M KOH
(b) 0.35 M CH_3NH_2
(c) 0.025 M $Sr(OH)_2$

SOLUTION

(a) Since KOH is a strong base, it completely dissociates into K^+ and OH^- in solution. The concentration of OH^- is 2.25 M.

$$[OH^-] = 2.25 \text{ M}$$

(b) Since CH_3NH_2 is a weak base, it only partially ionizes water. We cannot calculate the exact concentration of OH^-, but we know it is less than 0.35 M.

$$[OH^-] < 0.35 \text{ M}$$

(c) Since $Sr(OH)_2$ is a strong base, it completely dissociates into $Sr^{2+}(aq)$ and $2\,OH^-(aq)$. $Sr(OH)_2$ forms 2 mol of OH^- for every 1 mol of $Sr(OH)_2$. Consequently, the concentration of OH^- is twice the concentration of $Sr(OH)_2$.

$$[OH^-] = 2(0.025 \text{ M}) = 0.050 \text{ M}$$

▶**SKILLBUILDER 6 | Determining [OH⁻] in Base Solutions**

What is the OH^- concentration in each solution?

(a) 0.055 M $Ba(OH)_2$
(b) 1.05 M C_5H_5N
(c) 0.45 M NaOH

▶**FOR MORE PRACTICE**   Example 16; Problems 63, 64.

---

8   Water: Acid and Base in One

We saw earlier that water acts as a base when it reacts with HCl and as an acid when it reacts with NH_3.

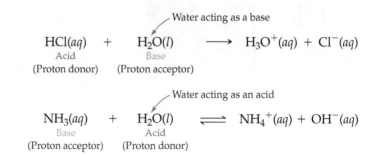

Water acting as a base

$$HCl(aq) \quad + \quad H_2O(l) \quad \longrightarrow \quad H_3O^+(aq) + Cl^-(aq)$$
Acid   Base
(Proton donor)   (Proton acceptor)

Water acting as an acid

$$NH_3(aq) \quad + \quad H_2O(l) \quad \rightleftharpoons \quad NH_4^+(aq) + OH^-(aq)$$
Base   Acid
(Proton acceptor)   (Proton donor)

Water is *amphoteric*; it can act as either an acid or a base. Even in pure water, water acts as an acid and a base with itself, a process called self-ionization.

Water acting as both an acid and a base

$$H_2O(l) \quad + \quad H_2O(l) \quad \rightleftharpoons \quad H_3O^+(aq) + OH^-(aq)$$

Acid   Base
(Proton donor)   (Proton acceptor)

In pure water, at 25 °C, the preceding reaction occurs only to a very small extent, resulting in equal and small concentrations of H_3O^+ and OH^-.

$$[H_3O^+] = [OH^-] = 1.0 \times 10^{-7}\ M \quad \text{(in pure water at 25 °C)}$$

where $[H_3O^+]$ = the concentration of H_3O^+ in M

and $[OH^-]$ = the concentration of OH^- in M

So all samples of water contain some hydronium ions and some hydroxide ions. The *product* of the concentration of these two ions in aqueous solutions is called the **ion product constant for water (K_w)**.

$$K_w = [H_3O^+][OH^-]$$

| The units of K_w are normally dropped.

We can find the value of K_w at 25 °C by multiplying the hydronium and hydroxide concentrations for pure water listed earlier.

$$K_w = [H_3O^+][OH^-]$$

$$= (1.0 \times 10^{-7})(1.0 \times 10^{-7})$$

$$= (1.0 \times 10^{-7})^2$$

$$= 1.0 \times 10^{-14}$$

The preceding equation holds true for all aqueous solutions at 25 °C. The concentration of H_3O^+ times the concentration of OH^- will be 1.0×10^{-14}. In pure water, since H_2O is the only source of these ions, there is one H_3O^+ ion for every OH^- ion. Consequently, the concentrations of H_3O^+ and OH^- are equal. Such a solution is a **neutral solution**.

| In a neutral solution, $[H_3O^+] = [OH^-]$.

$$[H_3O^+] = [OH^-] = \sqrt{K_w} = 1.0 \times 10^{-7}\ M \text{ (in pure water)}$$

An **acidic solution** contains an acid that creates additional H_3O^+ ions, causing $[H_3O^+]$ to increase. However, the *ion product constant still applies*.

$$[H_3O^+][OH^-] = K_w = 1.0 \times 10^{-14}$$

| In an acidic solution, $[H_3O^+] > [OH^-]$.

If $[H_3O^+]$ increases, then $[OH^-]$ must decrease for the ion product to remain 1.0×10^{-14}. For example, suppose $[H_3O^+] = 1.0 \times 10^{-3}$ M; then $[OH^-]$ can be found by solving the ion product expression for $[OH^-]$.

$$(1.0 \times 10^{-3})[OH^-] = 1.0 \times 10^{-14}$$

$$[OH^-] = \frac{1.0 \times 10^{-14}}{1.0 \times 10^{-3}} = 1.0 \times 10^{-11}\ M$$

In an acidic solution, $[H_3O^+]$ is greater than 1.0×10^{-7} M, and $[OH^-]$ is less than 1.0×10^{-7} M.

In a basic solution, $[H_3O^+] < [OH^-]$.

A **basic solution** contains a base that creates additional OH^- ions, causing the $[OH^-]$ to increase and the $[H_3O^+]$ to decrease. For example, suppose $[OH^-] = 1.0 \times 10^{-2}$ M; then $[H_3O^+]$ can be found by solving the ion product expression for $[H_3O^+]$.

$$[H_3O^+](1.0 \times 10^{-2}) = 1.0 \times 10^{-14}$$

$$[H_3O^+] = \frac{1.0 \times 10^{-14}}{1.0 \times 10^{-2}} = 1.0 \times 10^{-12} \text{ M}$$

In a basic solution, $[OH^-]$ is greater than 1.0×10^{-7} M and $[H_3O^+]$ is less than 1.0×10^{-7} M.

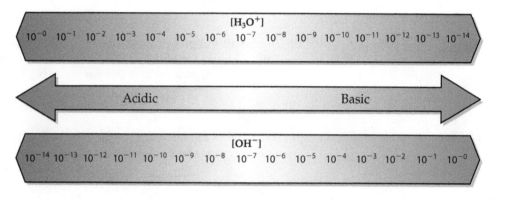

▶ FIGURE 16 **Acidic and basic solutions**

To summarize, at 25 °C (see ▲ Figure 16):

- In a neutral solution, $[H_3O^+] = [OH^-] = 1.0 \times 10^{-7}$ M
- In an acidic solution, $[H_3O^+] > 1.0 \times 10^{-7}$ M $[OH^-] < 1.0 \times 10^{-7}$ M
- In a basic solution, $[H_3O^+] < 1.0 \times 10^{-7}$ M $[OH^-] > 1.0 \times 10^{-7}$ M
- In all aqueous solutions, $[H_3O^+][OH^-] = K_w = 1.0 \times 10^{-14}$

EXAMPLE 7   Using K_w in Calculations

Calculate $[OH^-]$ in each solution and determine whether the solution is acidic, basic, or neutral.

(a) $[H_3O^+] = 7.5 \times 10^{-5}$ M
(b) $[H_3O^+] = 1.5 \times 10^{-9}$ M
(c) $[H_3O^+] = 1.0 \times 10^{-7}$ M

To find $[OH^-]$ use the ion product constant, K_w. Substitute the given value for $[H_3O^+]$ and solve the equation for $[OH^-]$. Since $[H_3O^+] > 1.0 \times 10^{-7}$ M and $[OH^-] < 1.0 \times 10^{-7}$ M, the solution is acidic.	**SOLUTION** **(a)** $[H_3O^+][OH^-] = K_w = 1.0 \times 10^{-14}$ $[7.5 \times 10^{-5}][OH^-] = K_w = 1.0 \times 10^{-14}$ $[OH^-] = \dfrac{1.0 \times 10^{-14}}{7.5 \times 10^{-5}} = 1.3 \times 10^{-10}$ M acidic solution
Substitute the given value for $[H_3O^+]$ into the ion product constant equation and solve the equation for $[OH^-]$. Since $[H_3O^+] < 1.0 \times 10^{-7}$ M and $[OH^-] > 1.0 \times 10^{-7}$ M, the solution is basic.	**(b)** $[H_3O^+][OH^-] = K_w = 1.0 \times 10^{-14}$ $[1.5 \times 10^{-9}][OH^-] = 1.0 \times 10^{-14}$ $[OH^-] = \dfrac{1.0 \times 10^{-14}}{1.5 \times 10^{-9}} = 6.7 \times 10^{-6}$ M basic solution

Substitute the given value for $[H_3O^+]$ into the ion product constant equation and solve the equation for $[OH^-]$. Since $[H_3O^+] = 1.0 \times 10^{-7}$ M and $[OH^-] = 1.0 \times 10^{-7}$ M, the solution is neutral.

(c) $[H_3O^+][OH^-] = K_w = 1.0 \times 10^{-14}$

$[1.0 \times 10^{-7}][OH^-] = 1.0 \times 10^{-14}$

$$[OH^-] = \frac{1.0 \times 10^{-14}}{1.0 \times 10^{-7}} = 1.0 \times 10^{-7} \text{ M}$$

neutral solution

▶**SKILLBUILDER 7** | Using K_w in Calculations

Calculate $[H_3O^+]$ in each solution and determine whether the solution is acidic, basic, or neutral.

(a) $[OH^-] = 1.5 \times 10^{-2}$ M
(b) $[OH^-] = 1.0 \times 10^{-7}$ M
(c) $[OH^-] = 8.2 \times 10^{-10}$ M

▶**FOR MORE PRACTICE** Example 17; Problems 67, 68, 69, 70.

✓ **CONCEPTUAL CHECKPOINT 3**

Which substance would be least likely to act as a base?

(a) H_2O

(b) OH^-

(c) NH_3

(d) NH_4^+

9 The pH and pOH Scales: Ways to Express Acidity and Basicity

TABLE 7 The pH of Some Common Substances

Substance	pH
gastric (human stomach) acid	1.0–3.0
limes	1.8–2.0
lemons	2.2–2.4
soft drinks	2.0–4.0
plums	2.8–3.0
wine	2.8–3.8
apples	2.9–3.3
peaches	3.4–3.6
cherries	3.2–4.0
beer	4.0–5.0
rainwater (unpolluted)	5.6
human blood	7.3–7.4
egg whites	7.6–8.0
milk of magnesia	10.5
household ammonia	10.5–11.5
4% NaOH solution	14

Notice that an increase of 1 in pH corresponds to a tenfold *decrease* in $[H_3O^+]$.

Chemists have devised a scale based on the hydrogen ion concentration to compactly express the acidity or basicity of solutions. The scale is called the **pH** scale and at 25 °C has these general characteristics:

- pH < 7   *acidic* solution
- pH > 7   *basic* solution
- pH = 7   *neutral* solution

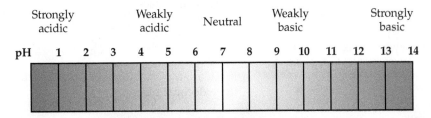

Table 7 lists the pH of some common substances. Notice that, as we discussed in Section 1, many foods, especially fruits, are acidic and therefore have low pH values. The foods with the lowest pH values are limes and lemons, and they are among the sourest. Relatively few foods, however, are basic.

The pH scale is a **logarithmic scale**; therefore, a change of 1 pH unit corresponds to a tenfold change in H_3O^+ concentration. For example, a lime with a pH of 2.0 is 10 times more acidic than a plum with a pH of 3.0 and 100 times more acidic than a cherry with a pH of 4.0. Each change of 1 in pH scale corresponds to a change of 10 in $[H_3O^+]$ (▶ Figure 17).

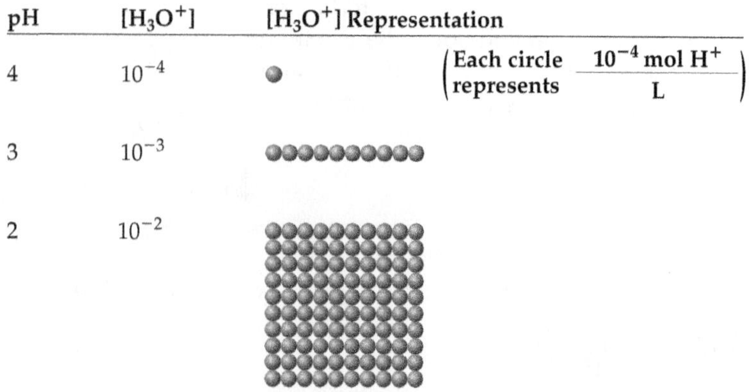

pH	$[H_3O^+]$	$[H_3O^+]$ Representation	
4	10^{-4}	●	$\left(\begin{array}{l}\text{Each circle} \\ \text{represents}\end{array}\ \dfrac{10^{-4}\ \text{mol H}^+}{\text{L}}\right)$
3	10^{-3}	●●●●●●●●●●	
2	10^{-2}		

▶ FIGURE 17 **The pH scale is a logarithmic scale** A *decrease* of 1 unit on the pH scale corresponds to an *increase* in $[H_3O^+]$ concentration by a factor of 10. Each circle stands for 10^{-4} mol H$^+$/L, or 6.022×10^{19} H$^+$ ions per liter. Question: How much of an increase in H_3O^+ concentration corresponds to a decrease of 2 pH units?

CALCULATING pH FROM [H₃O⁺]

The pH of a solution is defined as the negative of the log of the hydronium ion concentration:

$$pH = -\log[H_3O^+]$$

To calculate pH, you must be able to calculate logarithms. Recall that the log of a number is the exponent to which 10 must be raised to obtain that number, as shown in these examples:

$$\log 10^1 = 1;\ \log 10^2 = 2;\ \log 10^3 = 3$$

$$\log 10^{-1} = -1;\ \log 10^{-2} = -2;\ \log 10^{-3} = -3$$

Note that pH is defined using the log function (base ten), which is different from the natural log (abbreviated ln).

In the next example, we calculate the log of 1.5×10^{-7}. A solution having an $[H_3O^+] = 1.5 \times 10^{-7}$ M (acidic) has a pH of:

$$\begin{aligned} pH &= -\log[H_3O^+] \\ &= -\log(1.5 \times 10^{-7}) \\ &= -(-6.82) \\ &= 6.82 \end{aligned}$$

Notice that the pH is reported to two decimal places here. This is because only the numbers to the right of the decimal place are significant in a log. Since our original value for the concentration had two significant figures, the log of that number has two decimal places.

When you take the log of a quantity, the result should have the same number of decimal places as the number of significant figures in the original quantity.

$$\log 1.0 \times 10^{-3} = 3.\overset{\text{2 decimal places}}{00}$$

If the original number had three significant figures, the log would be reported to three decimal places:

$$-\log 1.00 \times 10^{-3} = 3.\overset{\text{3 decimal places}}{000}$$

A solution having $[H_3O^+] = 1.0 \times 10^{-7}$ M (neutral) has a pH of:

$$\begin{aligned} pH &= -\log[H_3O^+] \\ &= -\log 1.0 \times 10^{-7} \\ &= -(-7.00) \\ &= 7.00 \end{aligned}$$

EXAMPLE 8 Calculating pH from [H₃O⁺]

Calculate the pH of each solution and indicate whether the solution is acidic or basic.

(a) $[H_3O^+] = 1.8 \times 10^{-4}$ M

(b) $[H_3O^+] = 7.2 \times 10^{-9}$ M

SOLUTION

To calculate pH, substitute the given $[H_3O^+]$ into the pH equation.	(a) $\begin{aligned} pH &= -\log[H_3O^+] \\ &= -\log 1.8 \times 10^{-4} \\ &= -(-3.74) \\ &= 3.74 \end{aligned}$
Since the pH < 7, this solution is acidic.	
Again, substitute the given $[H_3O^+]$ into the pH equation.	(b) $\begin{aligned} pH &= -\log[H_3O^+] \\ &= -\log(7.2 \times 10^{-9}) \\ &= -(-8.14) \\ &= 8.14 \end{aligned}$
Since the pH > 7, this solution is basic.	

▶ **SKILLBUILDER 8 | Calculating pH from [H₃O⁺]**

Calculate the pH of each solution and indicate whether the solution is acidic or basic.

(a) $[H_3O^+] = 9.5 \times 10^{-9}$ M

(b) $[H_3O^+] = 6.1 \times 10^{-3}$ M

▶ **SKILLBUILDER PLUS 1**

Calculate the pH of a solution with $[OH^-] = 1.3 \times 10^{-2}$ M and indicate whether the solution is acidic or basic. *Hint:* Begin by using K_w to find $[H_3O^+]$.

▶ **FOR MORE PRACTICE** Example 18; Problems 73, 74.

CALCULATING [H₃O⁺] FROM pH

Ten raised to the log of a number is equal to that number: $10^{\log x} = x$.

To calculate $[H_3O^+]$ from a pH value, you must *undo* the log. The log can be undone using the inverse log function *(Method 1)* on most calculators or using the 10^x key *(Method 2)*. Both methods do the same thing; the one you use depends on your calculator.

Method 1: Inverse Log Function	Method 2: 10^x Function
$pH = -\log[H_3O^+]$	$pH = -\log[H_3O^+]$
$-pH = \log[H_3O^+]$	$-pH = \log[H_3O^+]$
$invlog(-pH) = invlog(\log[H_3O^+])$	$10^{-pH} = 10^{\log[H_3O^+]}$
$invlog(-pH) = [H_3O^+]$	$10^{-pH} = [H_3O^+]$

The invlog function "undoes" log: $invlog(\log x) = x$.

The inverse log is sometimes called the antilog.

So, to calculate $[H_3O^+]$ from a pH value, take the inverse log of the negative of the pH value *(Method 1)* or raise 10 to the negative of the pH value *(Method 2)*.

EXAMPLE 9 Calculating $[H_3O^+]$ from pH

Calculate the H_3O^+ concentration for a solution with a pH of 4.80.

SOLUTION

To find the $[H_3O^+]$ from pH, we must undo the log function. Use either Method 1 or Method 2.

The number of significant figures in the inverse log of a number is equal to the number of decimal places in the number.

Method 1: Inverse Log Function	Method 2: 10^x function
$pH = -\log[H_3O^+]$	$pH = -\log[H_3O^+]$
$4.80 = -\log[H_3O^+]$	$4.80 = -\log[H_3O^+]$
$-4.80 = \log[H_3O^+]$	$-4.80 = \log[H_3O^+]$
$\text{invlog}(-4.80) = \text{invlog}(\log[H_3O^+])$	$10^{-4.80} = 10^{\log[H_3O^+]}$
$\text{invlog}(-4.80) = [H_3O^+]$	$10^{-4.80} = [H_3O^+]$
$[H_3O^+] = 1.6 \times 10^{-5}$ M	$[H_3O^+] = 1.6 \times 10^{-5}$ M

▶**SKILLBUILDER 9 | Calculating $[H_3O^+]$ from pH**

Calculate the H_3O^+ concentration for a solution with a pH of 8.37.

▶**SKILLBUILDER PLUS 2**

Calculate the OH^- concentration for a solution with a pH of 3.66.

▶**FOR MORE PRACTICE** Example 19; Problems 75, 76.

CONCEPTUAL CHECKPOINT 4

Solution A has a pH of 13. Solution B has a pH of 10. The concentration of H_3O^+ in solution B is ______ times that in solution A.

(a) 0.001

(b) $\frac{1}{3}$

(c) 3

(d) 1000

THE pOH SCALE

The **pOH** scale is analogous to the pH scale, but is defined with respect to $[OH^-]$ instead of $[H_3O^+]$.

Notice that *p* is the mathematical function −log; thus, $pX = -\log X$.

$$pOH = -\log [OH^-]$$

A solution having an $[OH^-]$ of 1.0×10^{-3} M (basic) has a pOH of 3.00. On the pOH scale, a pOH less than 7 is basic and a pOH greater than 7 is acidic. A pOH of 7 is neutral. The $[OH^-]$ concentration can be found from the pOH just as the $[H_3O^+]$ concentration is found from the pH, as shown in the following example.

EXAMPLE 10 Calculating $[OH^-]$ from pOH

Calculate the $[OH^-]$ concentration for a solution with a pOH of 8.55.

SOLUTION

To find the $[OH^-]$ from pOH, we must undo the log function. Use either Method 1 or Method 2.

Method 1: Inverse Log Function	Method 2: 10^x function
$pOH = -\log[OH^-]$	$pOH = -\log[OH^-]$
$8.55 = -\log[OH^-]$	$8.55 = -\log[OH^-]$
$-8.55 = \log[OH^-]$	$-8.55 = \log[OH^-]$
$invlog(-8.55) = invlog(\log[OH^-])$	$10^{-8.55} = 10^{\log[OH^-]}$
$invlog(-8.55) = [OH^-]$	$10^{-8.55} = [OH^-]$
$[OH^-] = 2.8 \times 10^{-9}$ M	$[OH^-] = 2.8 \times 10^{-9}$ M

▶**SKILLBUILDER 10 | Calculating OH⁻ from pOH**

Calculate the OH^- concentration for a solution with a pOH of 4.25.

▶**SKILLBUILDER PLUS 3**

Calculate the H_3O^+ concentration for a solution with a pOH of 5.68.

▶**FOR MORE PRACTICE** Problems 83, 84, 85, 86.

We can derive a relationship between pH and pOH at 25 °C from the expression for K_w.

$$[H_3O^+][OH^-] = 1.0 \times 10^{-14}$$

| $\log (AB) = \log A + \log B$

Taking the log of both sides, we get

$$\log \{[H_3O^+][OH^-]\} = \log (1.0 \times 10^{-14})$$
$$\log[H_3O^+] + \log[OH^-] = -14.00$$
$$-\log[H_3O^+] - \log[OH^-] = 14.00$$
$$pH + pOH = 14.00$$

The sum of pH and pOH is always equal to 00 at 25 °C. Therefore, a solution with a pH of 3 has a pOH of 11.

CONCEPTUAL CHECKPOINT 5

A solution has a pH of 5. What is the pOH of the solution?

(a) 5   **(b)** 10   **(c)** 14   **(d)** 9

10 Buffers: Solutions That Resist pH Change

Most solutions rapidly become more acidic (lower pH) upon addition of an acid or more basic (higher pH) upon addition of a base. A **buffer**, however, resists pH change by neutralizing added acid or added base. Human blood, for example, is a buffer. Acid or base that is added to blood gets neutralized by components within blood, resulting in a nearly constant pH. In healthy individuals, blood pH is between 7.36 and 7.40. If blood pH were to drop below 7.0 or rise above 7.8, death would result.

How does blood maintain such a narrow pH range? Like all buffers, blood contains *significant* amounts of *both a weak acid and its conjugate base*. When additional base is added to blood, the weak acid reacts with the base, neutralizing it. When additional acid is added to blood, the conjugate base reacts with the acid, neutralizing it. In this way, blood maintains a constant pH.

| Buffers can also be composed of a weak base and its conjugate acid.

CHEMISTRY AND HEALTH

Alkaloids

Alkaloids are organic bases that occur naturally in many plants (see Section 3) that often have medicinal qualities. Morphine, for example, is a powerful alkaloid drug that occurs in the opium poppy (▶ Figure 18) and is used to relieve severe pain. Morphine is an example of a *narcotic*, a drug that dulls the senses and induces sleep. It produces relief from and indifference to pain. Morphine can also produce feelings of euphoria and contentment, which leads to its abuse. Morphine is highly addictive, both psychologically and physically. A person who abuses morphine over long periods of time becomes physically dependent on the drug and suffers severe withdrawal symptoms upon termination of use.

▲ **FIGURE 18** **Opium poppy** The opium poppy contains the alkaloids morphine and codeine.

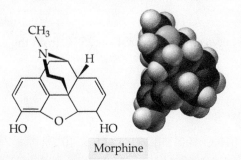

Morphine

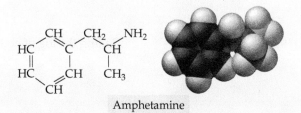

Amphetamine

Amphetamine is another powerful drug related to the alkaloid ephedrine. Whereas morphine slows down nerve signal transmissions, amphetamine enhances them. Amphetamine is an example of a *stimulant*, a drug that increases alertness and wakefulness. Amphetamine is widely used to treat Attention-Deficit Hyperactivity Disorder (ADHD) and is prescribed under the trade name Adderall. Patients suffering from ADHD find that amphetamine helps them to focus and concentrate more effectively. However, because amphetamine produces alertness and increased stamina, it, too, is often abused.

Other common alkaloids include caffeine and nicotine, both of which are stimulants. Caffeine is found in the coffee bean, and nicotine is found in tobacco. Although both have some addictive qualities, nicotine is by far the most addictive. A nicotine addiction is among the most difficult to break, as any smoker can attest.

CAN YOU ANSWER THIS? *What part of the amphetamine and morphine molecules makes them bases?*

A simple buffer can be made by mixing both acetic acid ($HC_2H_3O_2$) and its conjugate base, sodium acetate ($NaC_2H_3O_2$) in water (▶ Figure 19). (The sodium in sodium acetate is just a spectator ion and does not contribute to buffering action.) Since $HC_2H_3O_2$ is a weak acid and since $C_2H_3O_2^-$ is its conjugate base, a solution containing both of these is a buffer. Note that a weak acid by itself, even though it partially ionizes to form some of its conjugate base, does not contain sufficient base to be a buffer. A buffer must contain *significant* amounts of *both* a weak acid and its conjugate base. Suppose that we add more base, in the form of NaOH, to the buffer solution containing acetic acid and sodium acetate. The acetic acid would neutralize the base according to the reaction:

$$\underset{\text{Base}}{NaOH(aq)} + \underset{\text{Acid}}{HC_2H_3O_2(aq)} \longrightarrow H_2O(l) + NaC_2H_3O_2(aq)$$

Added H$^+$ is neutralized by the conjugate base. Added OH$^-$ is neutralized by the weak acid.

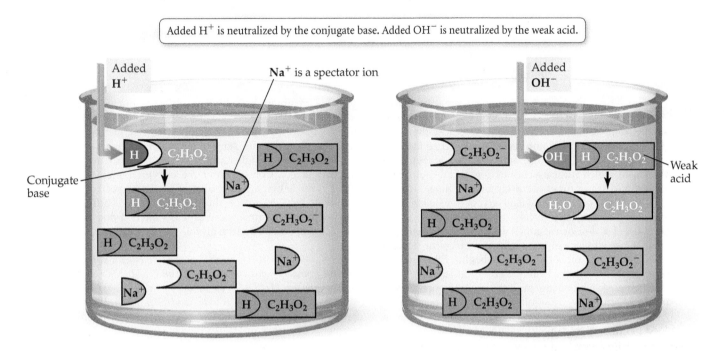

▲ FIGURE 19 **Buffers** A buffer contains significant amounts of a weak acid and its conjugate base. The acid consumes any added base, and the base consumes any added acid. In this way, a buffer resists pH change.

As long as the amount of NaOH that we add is less than the amount of HC$_2$H$_3$O$_2$ in solution, the solution neutralizes the NaOH, and the resulting pH change is small. Suppose, on the other hand, that we add more acid, in the form of HCl, to the solution. Then the conjugate base, NaC$_2$H$_3$O$_2$, neutralizes the added HCl according to the reaction:

$$\underset{\text{Acid}}{\text{HCl}(aq)} + \underset{\text{Base}}{\text{NaC}_2\text{H}_3\text{O}_2(aq)} \longrightarrow \text{HC}_2\text{H}_3\text{O}_2(aq) + \text{NaCl}(aq)$$

As long as the amount of HCl that we add is less than the amount of NaC$_2$H$_3$O$_2$ in solution, the solution will neutralize the HCl and the resulting pH change is small.

To summarize:

- Buffers resist pH change.
- Buffers contain significant amounts of both a weak acid and its conjugate base.
- The weak acid neutralizes added base.
- The conjugate base neutralizes added acid.

✓ CONCEPTUAL CHECKPOINT 6

Which of the following is a buffer solution?

(a) H$_2$SO$_4$(aq) and H$_2$SO$_3$(aq)

(b) HF(aq) and NaF(aq)

(c) HCl(aq) and NaCl(aq)

(d) NaCl(aq) and NaOH(aq)

CHEMISTRY AND HEALTH

The Danger of Antifreeze

Most types of antifreeze used in cars are solutions of ethylene glycol. Every year, thousands of dogs and cats die from ethylene glycol poisoning because they consume improperly stored antifreeze or antifreeze that has leaked out of a radiator. The antifreeze has a somewhat sweet taste, which attracts a curious dog or cat. Young children are also at risk for ethylene glycol poisoning.

The first stage of ethylene glycol poisoning is a drunken state. Ethylene glycol is an alcohol, and it affects the brain of a dog or cat much as an alcoholic beverage would. Once ethylene glycol begins to metabolize, however, the second and more deadly stage begins. Ethylene glycol is metabolized in the liver into glycolic acid ($HC_2H_3O_3$), which enters the bloodstream. If the original quantities of consumed antifreeze are significant, the glycolic acid overwhelms the blood's natural buffering system, causing blood pH to drop to dangerously low levels. At this point, the cat or dog may begin hyperventilating in an effort to overcome the acidic blood's reduced ability to carry oxygen. If no treatment is administered, the animal will eventually go into a coma and die.

One treatment for ethylene glycol poisoning is the administration of ethyl alcohol (the alcohol found in alcoholic beverages). The liver enzyme that metabolizes ethylene glycol is the same one that metabolizes ethyl alcohol, but it has a higher affinity for ethyl alcohol than for ethylene glycol. Consequently, the enzyme preferentially metabolizes ethyl alcohol, allowing the unmetabolized ethylene glycol to escape through the urine. If administered early, this treatment can save the life of a dog or cat that has consumed ethylene glycol.

CAN YOU ANSWER THIS? *One of the main buffering systems found in blood consists of carbonic acid (H_2CO_3) and bicarbonate ion (HCO_3^-). Write an equation showing how this buffering system could neutralize glycolic acid ($HC_2H_3O_3$) that might enter the blood from ethylene glycol poisoning. Suppose a cat has 0.15 mol of HCO_3^- and 0.15 mol of H_2CO_3 in its bloodstream. How many grams of $HC_2H_3O_3$ could be neutralized before the buffering system in the cat's blood is overwhelmed?*

---

11 Acid Rain: An Environmental Problem Related to Fossil Fuel Combustion

About 90% of U.S. energy comes from fossil fuel combustion. Fossil fuels include petroleum, natural gas, and coal. Some fossil fuels, especially coal, contain significant amounts of sulfur impurities. During combustion, these impurities react with oxygen to form SO_2. In addition, during combustion of any fossil fuel, nitrogen from the air reacts with oxygen to form NO_2. The SO_2 and NO_2 emitted from fossil fuel combustion react with water in the atmosphere to form sulfuric acid and nitric acid.

These equations represent simplified versions of the reactions that actually occur.

$$2\ SO_2 + O_2 + 2\ H_2O \longrightarrow 2\ H_2SO_4$$

$$4\ NO_2 + O_2 + 2\ H_2O \longrightarrow 4\ HNO_3$$

These acids combine with rain to form **acid rain**. In the United States, the problem is greatest in the northeastern portion of the country because many midwestern power plants burn coal. The sulfur and nitrogen oxides produced from coal combustion in the Midwest are carried toward the Northeast by natural air currents, making rain in that portion of the country significantly acidic.

Rain is naturally somewhat acidic because of atmospheric carbon dioxide. Carbon dioxide combines with rainwater to form carbonic acid.

$$CO_2 + H_2O \longrightarrow H_2CO_3$$

However, carbonic acid is a relatively weak acid. Even rain that is saturated with CO_2 has a pH of only about 5.6, which is mildly acidic. However, when nitric acid and sulfuric acid mix with rain, the pH of the rain can fall as low as 4.4 (▶ Figure 20). Remember that, because of the logarithmic nature of the pH scale, rain with a pH of 4.4 has an $[H_3O^+]$ about 16 times greater than that of rain with a pH of 5.6. Rain that is this acidic has negative consequences for the environment.

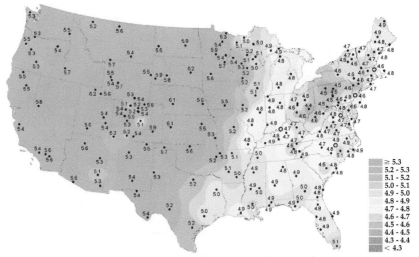

≥ 5.3	
5.2 - 5.3	
5.1 - 5.2	
5.0 - 5.1	
4.9 - 5.0	
4.8 - 4.9	
4.7 - 4.8	
4.6 - 4.7	
4.5 - 4.6	
4.4 - 4.5	
4.3 - 4.4	
< 4.3	

▶ FIGURE 20 **Acid rain in the United States** Average pH of precipitation in the United States for 2008.

National Atmospheric Deposition Program/National Trends Network
http://nadp.sws.uiuc.edu

ACID RAIN DAMAGE

Because acids dissolve metals, acid rain damages metal structures. Bridges, railroads, and even automobiles can be damaged by acid rain. Since acids also react with carbonates (CO_3^{2-}), acid rain damages building materials that contain carbonates, including marble, cement, and limestone. Statues, buildings, and pathways in the Northeast show significant signs of acid rain damage (▼ Figure 21).

Acid rain can also accumulate in lakes and rivers and affect aquatic life. In the northeastern United States, more than 2000 lakes and streams have increased acidity levels due to acid rain. Aquatic plants, frogs, salamanders, and some species of fish are sensitive to acid levels and cannot live in the acidified lakes. Trees can also be affected by acid rain because the acid removes nutrients from the soil, making it more difficult for trees to survive.

▶ FIGURE 21 **Acid rain damage** Many monuments and statues, such as this one of George Washington in New York's Washington Square Park, have suffered severe deterioration caused by acid rain. The photo at left was taken in 1935, the one at right some 60 years later. (The statue has recently undergone restoration.)

NYC Parks Photo Archive/Fundamental Photographs.

Spencer Platt/Getty Images.

ACID RAIN LEGISLATION

The Clean Air Act, and its 1990 amendments, have provisions that target acid rain. These provisions force electrical utilities—which are the most significant source of SO_2—to lower their SO_2 emissions gradually over time (▶ Figure 22). The decrease in SO_2 emissions has been significant, and the acidity of rain in the Northeast has already stabilized and should decrease in the coming years. Scientists expect most lakes, streams, and forests to recover once the pH of the rain returns to normal levels.

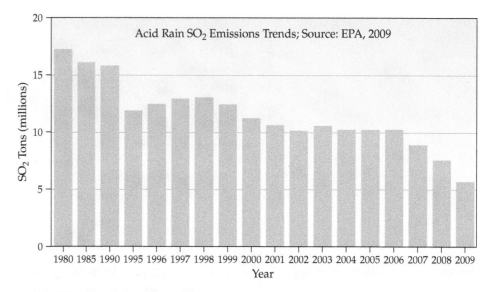

▲ FIGURE 22 **Emissions of SO₂ from 1980 to 2009** The height of each bar represents annual SO₂ emissions for the year noted. Under the Clean Air Act and its amendments, SO₂ emissions have been decreasing significantly in the last 30 years.

CHAPTER IN REVIEW

CHEMICAL PRINCIPLES

RELEVANCE

Acid Properties:

- Acids have a sour taste.
- Acids dissolve many metals.
- Acids turn blue litmus paper red.

Acid Properties: Acids are responsible for the sour taste in many foods such as lemons, limes, and vinegar. They are also often used in the laboratory and in industry.

Base Properties:

- Bases have a bitter taste.
- Bases have a slippery feel.
- Bases turn red litmus paper blue.

Base Properties: Bases are less common in foods, but their presence in some foods—such as coffee and beer—is enjoyed by many as an acquired taste. Bases also have widespread use in the laboratory and in industry.

Molecular Definitions of Acids and Bases:
Arrhenius definition

Acid—substance that produces H^+ ions in solution

Base—substance that produces OH^- ions in solution

Brønsted–Lowry definition

Acid—proton donor

Base—proton acceptor

Molecular Definitions of Acids and Bases: The Arrhenius definition is simpler and easier to use. It also shows how an acid and a base neutralize each other to form water ($H^+ + OH^- \longrightarrow H_2O$). The more generally applicable Brønsted–Lowry definition helps us see that, in water, H^+ ions usually associate with water molecules to form H_3O^+. It also shows how bases that do not contain OH^- ions can still act as bases by accepting a proton from water.

Reactions of Acids and Bases:

Neutralization Reactions In a neutralization reaction, an acid and a base react to form water and a salt.

$$\text{HCl}(aq) + \text{KOH}(aq) \longrightarrow \text{H}_2\text{O}(l) + \text{KCl}(aq)$$
$$\underset{\text{Acid}}{} \quad \underset{\text{Base}}{} \qquad \underset{\text{Water}}{} \quad \underset{\text{Salt}}{}$$

Acid–Metal Reactions Acids react with many metals to form hydrogen gas and a salt.

$$2\,\text{HCl}(aq) + \text{Mg}(s) \longrightarrow \text{H}_2(g) + \text{MgCl}_2(aq)$$
$$\underset{\text{Acid}}{} \quad \underset{\text{Metal}}{} \qquad \underset{\text{Hydrogen gas}}{} \quad \underset{\text{Salt}}{}$$

Acid–Metal Oxide Reactions Acids react with many metal oxides to form water and a salt.

$$2\,\text{HCl}(aq) + \text{K}_2\text{O}(s) \longrightarrow \text{H}_2\text{O}(l) + 2\,\text{KCl}(aq)$$
$$\underset{\text{Acid}}{} \quad \underset{\text{Metal oxide}}{} \qquad \underset{\text{Water}}{} \quad \underset{\text{Salt}}{}$$

Reactions of Acids and Bases: Neutralization reactions are common in our everyday lives. Antacids, for example, are bases that react with acids from the stomach to alleviate heartburn and sour stomach.

Acid–metal and acid–metal oxide reactions show the corrosive nature of acids. In both of these reactions, the acid dissolves the metal or the metal oxide. Some of the effects of these kinds of reactions can be seen in the damage to building materials caused by acid rain. Since acids dissolve metals and metal oxides, any building materials composed of these substances are susceptible to acid rain.

Acid–Base Titration: In an acid–base titration, an acid (or base) of known concentration is added to a base (or acid) of unknown concentration. The two reactants are combined until they are in exact stoichiometric proportions (moles of H^+ = moles of OH^-), which marks the equivalence point of the titration. In titration, since you know the moles of H^+ (or OH^-) that you added, you can determine the moles of OH^- (or H^+) in the unknown solution.

Acid–Base Titration: An acid–base titration is a laboratory procedure often used to determine the unknown concentration of an acid or a base.

Strong and Weak Acids and Bases: Strong acids completely ionize, and strong bases completely dissociate in aqueous solutions. For example:

$$\text{HCl}(aq) + \text{H}_2\text{O}(l) \longrightarrow \text{H}_3\text{O}^+(aq) + \text{Cl}^-(aq)$$

$$\text{NaOH}(aq) \longrightarrow \text{Na}^+(aq) + \text{OH}^-(aq)$$

A 1 M HCl solution has $[\text{H}_3\text{O}^+] = 1$ M and a 1 M NaOH solution has $[\text{OH}^-] = 1$ M.

Weak acids only partially ionize in solution. Most weak bases partially ionize water in solution. For example:

$$\text{HF}(aq) + \text{H}_2\text{O}(l) \rightleftharpoons \text{H}_3\text{O}^+(aq) + \text{F}^-(aq)$$

$$\text{NH}_3(aq) + \text{H}_2\text{O}(l) \rightleftharpoons \text{NH}_4^+(aq) + \text{OH}^-(aq)$$

A 1 M HF solution has $[\text{H}_3\text{O}^+] < 1$ M, and a 1 M NH$_3$ solution has $[\text{OH}^-] < 1$ M.

Strong and Weak Acids and Bases: Whether an acid is strong or weak depends on the conjugate base: The stronger the conjugate base, the weaker the acid. Since the acidity or basicity of a solution depends on $[\text{H}_3\text{O}^+]$ and $[\text{OH}^-]$, we must know whether an acid is strong or weak to know the degree of acidity or basicity.

Self-Ionization of Water: Water can act as both an acid and a base with itself.

$$\text{H}_2\text{O}(l) + \text{H}_2\text{O}(l) \rightleftharpoons \text{H}_3\text{O}^+(aq) + \text{OH}^-(aq)$$
$$\underset{\text{Acid}}{} \qquad \underset{\text{Base}}{}$$

The product of $[\text{H}_3\text{O}^+]$ and $[\text{OH}^-]$ in aqueous solutions will always be equal to the ion product constant, $K_w(10^{-14})$.

$$[\text{H}_3\text{O}^+][\text{OH}^-] = K_w = 1.0 \times 10^{-14}$$

Self-Ionization of Water: The self-ionization of water occurs because aqueous solutions always contain some H_3O^+ and some OH^-. In a neutral solution, the concentrations of these are equal (1.0×10^{-7} M). When an acid is added to water, $[\text{H}_3\text{O}^+]$ increases and $[\text{OH}^-]$ decreases. When a base is added to water, the opposite happens. The ion product constant, however, still equals 1.0×10^{-14}, allowing us to calculate $[\text{H}_3\text{O}^+]$ given $[\text{OH}^-]$ and vice versa.

pH and pOH Scales:

$$pH = -\log[H_3O^+]$$
$$pH > 7\,(\text{basic})$$
$$pH < 7\,(\text{acidic})$$
$$pH = 7\,(\text{neutral})$$
$$pOH = -\log[OH^-]$$

pH and pOH Scales: pH is a convenient way to specify acidity or basicity. Since the pH scale is logarithmic, a change of one on the pH scale corresponds to a tenfold change in the $[H_3O^+]$. The pOH scale, defined with respect to $[OH^-]$ instead of $[H_3O^+]$, is less commonly used.

Buffers: Buffers are solutions containing significant amounts of both a weak acid and its conjugate base. Buffers resist pH change by neutralizing added acid or base.

Buffers: Buffers are important in blood chemistry because blood must stay within a narrow pH range in order to carry oxygen.

Acid Rain: Acid rain is the result of sulfur oxides and nitrogen oxides emitted by fossil fuel combustion. These oxides react with water to form sulfuric acid and nitric acid, which then fall as acid rain.

Acid Rain: Since acids are corrosive, acid rain damages building materials. Because many aquatic plants and animals cannot survive in acidic water, acid rain also affects lakes and rivers, making them too acidic for the survival of some species.

CHEMICAL SKILLS

EXAMPLES

Identifying Brønsted–Lowry Acids and Bases and Their Conjugates (Section 4)

The substance that donates the proton is the acid (proton donor) and becomes the conjugate base (as a product). The substance that accepts the proton (proton acceptor) is the base and becomes the conjugate acid (as a product).

EXAMPLE 11   Identifying Brønsted–Lowry Acids and Bases and Their Conjugates

Identify the Brønsted–Lowry acid, the Brønsted–Lowry base, the conjugate acid, and the conjugate base in this reaction:

$$HNO_3(aq) + H_2O(l) \longrightarrow H_3O^+(aq) + NO_3^-(aq)$$

SOLUTION

$$\underset{\text{Acid}}{HNO_3(aq)} + \underset{\text{Base}}{H_2O(l)} \longrightarrow \underset{\text{Conjugate acid}}{H_3O^+(aq)} + \underset{\text{Conjugate base}}{NO_3^-(aq)}$$

Writing Equations for Neutralization Reactions (Section 5)

In a neutralization reaction, an acid and a base usually react to form water and a salt (ionic compound).

$$\text{Acid} + \text{Base} \longrightarrow \text{Water} + \text{Salt}$$

Write the skeletal equation first, making sure to write the formula of the salt so that it is charge-neutral. Then balance the equation.

EXAMPLE 12   Writing Equations for Neutralization Reactions

Write a molecular equation for the reaction between aqueous HBr and aqueous $Ca(OH)_2$.

SOLUTION
Skeletal equation:

$$HBr(aq) + Ca(OH)_2(aq) \longrightarrow H_2O(l) + CaBr_2(aq)$$

Balanced equation:

$$2\,HBr(aq) + Ca(OH)_2(aq) \longrightarrow 2\,H_2O(l) + CaBr_2(aq)$$

Writing Equations for the Reactions of Acids with Metals and with Metal Oxides (Section 5)

Acids react with many metals to form hydrogen gas and a salt.

$$\text{Acid} + \text{Metal} \longrightarrow \text{Hydrogen gas} + \text{Salt}$$

Write the skeletal equation first, making sure to write the formula of the salt so that it is charge-neutral. Then balance the equation.

Acids react with many metal oxides to form water and a salt.

$$\text{Acid} + \text{Metal oxide} \longrightarrow \text{Water} + \text{Salt}$$

Write the skeletal equation first, making sure to write the formula of the salt so that it is charge-neutral. Then balance the equation.

EXAMPLE 13 Writing Equations for the Reactions of Acids with Metals and with Metal Oxides

Write equations for the reaction of hydrobromic acid with calcium metal and for the reaction of hydrobromic acid with calcium oxide.

SOLUTION

Skeletal equation:

$$HBr(aq) + Ca(s) \longrightarrow H_2(g) + CaBr_2(aq)$$

Balanced equation:

$$2\,HBr(aq) + Ca(s) \longrightarrow H_2(g) + CaBr_2(aq)$$

Skeletal equation:

$$HBr(aq) + CaO(s) \longrightarrow H_2O(l) + CaBr_2(aq)$$

Balanced equation:

$$2\,HBr(aq) + CaO(s) \longrightarrow H_2O(l) + CaBr_2(aq)$$

Acid–Base Titrations (Section 6)

EXAMPLE 14 Acid–Base Titrations

A 15.00-mL sample of a NaOH solution of unknown concentration requires 17.88 mL of a 0.1053 M H_2SO_4 solution to reach the equivalence point in a titration. What is the concentration of the NaOH solution?

GIVEN: 15.00-mL NaOH

17.88 mL of a 0.1053 M H_2SO_4 solution

FIND: concentration of NaOH solution mol/L

SORT

You are given the volume of a sodium hydroxide solution and the volume and concentration of the sulfuric acid solution required for its titration. You are asked to find the concentration of the sodium hydroxide solution.

STRATEGIZE

Begin by writing the balanced equation for the neutralization reaction (see Example 12).

Next draw a solution map. Use the volume and concentration of the known reactant to determine moles of the known reactant. (You have to convert from milliliters to liters first.) Then use the stoichiometric ratio from the balanced equation to get moles of the unknown reactant.

Then add a second part to the solution map indicating how moles and volume can be used to determine molarity.

SOLUTION MAP

$$H_2SO_4(aq) + 2\,NaOH(aq) \longrightarrow$$
$$2\,H_2O(l) + Na_2SO_4(aq)$$

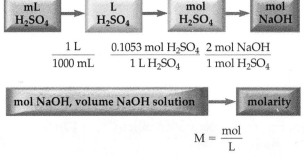

$$\frac{1\,L}{1000\,mL} \qquad \frac{0.1053\,\text{mol }H_2SO_4}{1\,L\,H_2SO_4} \qquad \frac{2\,\text{mol NaOH}}{1\,\text{mol }H_2SO_4}$$

mol NaOH, volume NaOH solution → molarity

$$M = \frac{\text{mol}}{L}$$

RELATIONSHIPS USED

2 mol NaOH : 1 mol H_2SO_4 (from balanced equation)

$$\text{Molarity(M)} = \frac{\text{mol solute}}{\text{L solution}}$$

SOLVE

Follow the solution map to solve the problem. The first part of the solution gives you moles of the unknown reactant. In the second part of the solution, divide the moles from the first part by the volume to obtain molarity.

CHECK

Check your answer. Are the units correct? Does the answer make physical sense?

SOLUTION

$$17.88 \text{ mL H}_2\text{SO}_4 \times \frac{1 \text{ L}}{1000 \text{ mL}} \times \frac{0.1053 \text{ mol H}_2\text{SO}_4}{\text{L H}_2\text{SO}_4}$$

$$\times \frac{2 \text{ mol NaOH}}{1 \text{ mol H}_2\text{SO}_4} = 3.7655 \times 10^{-3} \text{ mol NaOH}$$

$$M = \frac{\text{mol}}{\text{L}} = \frac{3.7655 \times 10^{-3} \text{ mol NaOH}}{0.01500 \text{ L NaOH}} = 0.2510 \text{ M}$$

The unknown NaOH solution has a concentration of 0.2510 M.

The units (M) are correct. The magnitude of the answer makes sense because the reaction has a two-to-one stoichiometry and the volumes of the two solutions are similar; therefore, the concentration of the NaOH solution must be approximately twice the concentration of the H_2SO_4 solution.

Determining $[H_3O^+]$ in Acid Solutions (Section 7)

In a strong acid, $[H_3O^+]$ will be equal to the concentration of the acid. In a weak acid, $[H_3O^+]$ will be less than the concentration of the acid.

EXAMPLE 15 Determining $[H_3O^+]$ in Acid Solutions

What is the H_3O^+ concentration in a 0.25 M HCl solution and in a 0.25 M HF solution?

SOLUTION

In the 0.25 M HCl solution (strong acid), $[H_3O^+] = $ 0.25 M. In the 0.25 M HF solution (weak acid), $[H_3O^+] < 0.25$ M.

Determining $[OH^-]$ in Base Solutions (Section 7)

In a strong base, $[OH^-]$ is equal to the concentration of the base times the number of hydroxide ions in the base. In a weak base, $[OH^-]$ is less than the concentration of the base.

EXAMPLE 16 Determining $[OH^-]$ in Base Solutions

What is the OH^- concentration in a 0.25 M NaOH solution, in a 0.25 M $Sr(OH)_2$ solution, and in a 0.25 M NH_3 solution?

SOLUTION

In the 0.25 M NaOH solution (strong base), $[OH^-] = $ 0.25 M. In the 0.25 M $Sr(OH)_2$ solution (strong base),

$[OH^-] = 0.50$ M. In the 0.25 M NH_3 solution (weak base),

$[OH^-] < 0.25$ M.

Finding the Concentration of $[H_3O^+]$ or $[OH^-]$ from K_w (Section 8)

To find $[H_3O^+]$ or $[OH^-]$, use the ion product constant expression.

$$[H_3O^+][OH^-] = 1.0 \times 10^{-14}$$

Substitute the known quantity into the equation ($[H_3O^+]$ or $[OH^-]$) and solve for the unknown quantity.

EXAMPLE 17 Finding the Concentration of $[H_3O^+]$ or $[OH^-]$ from K_w

Calculate $[OH^-]$ in a solution with

$$[H_3O^+] = 1.5 \times 10^{-4} \text{ M}.$$

SOLUTION

$$[H_3O^+][OH^-] = 1.0 \times 10^{-14}$$
$$[1.5 \times 10^{-4}][OH^-] = 1.0 \times 10^{-14}$$
$$[OH^-] = \frac{1.0 \times 10^{-14}}{1.5 \times 10^{-4}} = 6.7 \times 10^{-11} \text{ M}$$

Calculating pH from $[H_3O^+]$ (Section 9)

To calculate the pH of a solution from $[H_3O^+]$, simply take the negative log of $[H_3O^+]$.

$$pH = -\log[H_3O^+]$$

EXAMPLE 18   Calculating pH from $[H_3O^+]$

Calculate the pH of a solution with $[H_3O^+] = 2.4 \times 10^{-5}$ M.

SOLUTION

$$
\begin{aligned}
pH &= -\log[H_3O^+] \\
&= -\log(2.4 \times 10^{-5}) \\
&= -(-4.62) \\
&= 4.62
\end{aligned}
$$

Calculating $[H_3O^+]$ from pH (Section 9)

You can calculate $[H_3O^+]$ from pH by taking the inverse log of the negative of the pH value (Method 1):

$$[H_3O^+] = \text{invlog}(-pH)$$

You can also calculate $[H_3O^+]$ from pH by raising 10 to the negative of the pH (Method 2):

$$[H_3O^+] = 10^{-pH}$$

EXAMPLE 19   Calculating $[H_3O^+]$ from pH

Calculate the $[H_3O^+]$ for a solution with a pH of 6.22.

SOLUTION

Method 1: Inverse Log Function

$$
\begin{aligned}
[H_3O^+] &= \text{invlog}(-pH) \\
&= \text{invlog}(-6.22) \\
&= 6.0 \times 10^{-7}
\end{aligned}
$$

Method 2: 10^x Function

$$
\begin{aligned}
[H_3O^+] &= 10^{-pH} \\
&= 10^{-6.22} \\
&= 6.0 \times 10^{-7}
\end{aligned}
$$

KEY TERMS

acid [**Section 2**]
acid rain [**Section 11**]
acidic solution [**Section 8**]
alkaloid [**Section 3**]
amphoteric [**Section 4**]
Arrhenius acid [**Section 4**]
Arrhenius base [**Section 4**]
Arrhenius definition [**Section 4**]
base [**Section 3**]
basic solution [**Section 8**]

Brønsted–Lowry acid [**Section 4**]
Brønsted–Lowry base [**Section 4**]
Brønsted–Lowry definition [**Section 4**]
buffer [**Section 10**]
carboxylic acid [**Section 2**]
conjugate acid–base pair [**Section 4**]
diprotic acid [**Section 7**]

dissociation [**Section 4**]
equivalence point [**Section 6**]
hydronium ion [**Section 4**]
indicator [**Section 6**]
ion product constant for water (K_w) [**Section 8**]
ionize [**Section 4**]
logarithmic scale [**Section 9**]
monoprotic acid [**Section 7**]
neutral solution [**Section 8**]

neutralization [**Section 5**]
pH [**Section 9**]
pOH [**Section 9**]
salt [**Section 5**]
strong acid [**Section 7**]
strong base [**Section 7**]
strong electrolyte [**Section 7**]
titration [**Section 6**]
weak acid [**Section 7**]
weak base [**Section 7**]
weak electrolyte [**Section 7**]

EXERCISES

QUESTIONS

1. What makes tart gummy candies, such as Sour Patch Kids, sour?
2. What are the properties of acids? List some examples of foods that contain acids.
3. What is the main component of stomach acid? Why do we have stomach acid?
4. What are organic acids? List two examples of organic acids.
5. What are the properties of bases? Provide some examples of common substances that contain bases.

6. What are alkaloids?
7. Give the Arrhenius definition of an acid and demonstrate the definition with a chemical equation.
8. Give the Arrhenius definition of a base and demonstrate the definition with a chemical equation.
9. Give the Brønsted–Lowry definitions of acids and bases and demonstrate each with a chemical equation.
10. According to the Brønsted–Lowry definition of acids and bases, what is a conjugate acid–base pair? Provide an example.

11. What is an acid–base neutralization reaction? Provide an example.

12. Provide an example of a reaction between an acid and a metal.

13. List an example of a reaction between an acid and a metal oxide.

14. Name a metal that dissolves in a base and write an equation for the reaction.

15. What is a titration? What is the equivalence point?

16. If a solution contains 0.85 mol of OH^-, how many moles of H^+ would be required to reach the equivalence point in a titration?

17. What is the difference between a strong acid and a weak acid?

18. How is the strength of an acid related to the strength of its conjugate base?

19. What are monoprotic and diprotic acids?

20. What is the difference between a strong base and a weak base?

21. Does pure water contain any H_3O^+ ions? Explain.

22. What happens to $[OH^-]$ in an aqueous solution when $[H_3O^+]$ increases?

23. Give a possible value of $[OH^-]$ and $[H_3O^+]$ in a solution that is:

   (a) acidic   (b) basic   (c) neutral

24. How is pH defined? A change of 1.0 pH unit corresponds to how much of a change in $[H_3O^+]$?

25. How is pOH defined? A change of 2.0 pOH units corresponds to how much of a change in $[OH^-]$?

26. In any aqueous solution at 25 °C, the sum of pH and pOH is 14.0. Explain why this is so.

27. What is a buffer?

28. What are the main components in a buffer?

29. What is the cause of acid rain?

30. Write equations for the chemical reactions by which acid rain forms in the atmosphere.

31. What are the effects of acid rain?

32. How is the problem of acid rain being addressed in the United States?

PROBLEMS

ACID AND BASE DEFINITIONS

33. Identify each substance as an acid or a base and write a chemical equation showing how it is an acid or a base according to the Arrhenius definition.

   (a) $H_2SO_4(aq)$

   (b) $Sr(OH)_2(aq)$

   (c) $HBr(aq)$

   (d) $NaOH(aq)$

34. Identify each substance as an acid or a base and write a chemical equation showing how it is an acid or a base according to the Arrhenius definition.

   (a) $Ca(OH)_2(aq)$

   (b) $HC_2H_3O_2(aq)$

   (c) $KOH(aq)$

   (d) $HNO_3(aq)$

35. For each reaction, identify the Brønsted–Lowry acid, the Brønsted–Lowry base, the conjugate acid, and the conjugate base.

   (a) $HBr(aq) + H_2O(l) \longrightarrow H_3O^+(aq) + Br^-(aq)$

   (b) $NH_3(aq) + H_2O(l) \rightleftharpoons NH_4^+(aq) + OH^-(aq)$

   (c) $HNO_3(aq) + H_2O(l) \longrightarrow$
   $\qquad H_3O^+(aq) + NO_3^-(aq)$

   (d) $C_5H_5N(aq) + H_2O(l) \rightleftharpoons$
   $\qquad C_5H_5NH^+(aq) + OH^-(aq)$

36. For each reaction, identify the Brønsted–Lowry acid, the Brønsted–Lowry base, the conjugate acid, and the conjugate base.

   (a) $HI(aq) + H_2O(l) \longrightarrow H_3O^+(aq) + I^-(aq)$

   (b) $CH_3NH_2(aq) + H_2O(l) \rightleftharpoons$
   $\qquad CH_3NH_3^+(aq) + OH^-(aq)$

   (c) $CO_3^{2-}(aq) + H_2O(l) \rightleftharpoons$
   $\qquad HCO_3^-(aq) + OH^-(aq)$

   (d) $H_2CO_3(aq) + H_2O(l) \rightleftharpoons$
   $\qquad H_3O^+(aq) + HCO_3^-(aq)$

37. Determine whether each pair is a conjugate acid–base pair.

   (a) NH_3, NH_4^+

   (b) HCl, HBr

   (c) $C_2H_3O_2^-$, $HC_2H_3O_2$

   (d) HCO_3^-, NO_3^-

38. Determine whether each pair is a conjugate acid–base pair

   (a) HI, I^-

   (b) $HCHO_2$, SO_4^{2-}

   (c) PO_4^{3-}, HPO_4^{2-}

   (d) CO_3^{2-}, HCl

39. Write the formula for the conjugate base of each acid.

   (a) HCl (b) H_2SO_3

   (c) $HCHO_2$ (d) HF

40. Write the formula for the conjugate base of each acid.

   (a) HBr (b) H_2CO_3

   (c) $HClO_4$ (d) $HC_2H_3O_2$

41. Write the formula for the conjugate acid of each base.
    (a) NH_3
    (b) ClO_4^-
    (c) HSO_4^-
    (d) CO_3^{2-}

42. Write the formula for the conjugate acid of each base.
    (a) CH_3NH_2
    (b) C_5H_5N
    (c) Cl^-
    (d) F^-

ACID–BASE REACTIONS

43. Write a neutralization reaction for each acid and base pair.
    (a) $HI(aq)$ and $NaOH(aq)$
    (b) $HBr(aq)$ and $KOH(aq)$
    (c) $HNO_3(aq)$ and $Ba(OH)_2(aq)$
    (d) $HClO_4(aq)$ and $Sr(OH)_2(aq)$

44. Write a neutralization reaction for each acid and base pair.
    (a) $HF(aq)$ and $Ba(OH)_2(aq)$
    (b) $HClO_4(aq)$ and $NaOH(aq)$
    (c) $HBr(aq)$ and $Ca(OH)_2(aq)$
    (d) $HCl(aq)$ and $KOH(aq)$

45. Write a balanced chemical equation showing how each metal reacts with HBr.
    (a) Rb
    (b) Mg
    (c) Ba
    (d) Al

46. Write a balanced chemical equation showing how each metal reacts with HCl.
    (a) K
    (b) Ca
    (c) Na
    (d) Sr

47. Write a balanced chemical equation showing how each metal oxide reacts with HI.
    (a) MgO
    (b) K_2O
    (c) Rb_2O
    (d) CaO

48. Write a balanced chemical equation showing how each metal oxide reacts with HCl.
    (a) SrO
    (b) Na_2O
    (c) Li_2O
    (d) BaO

49. Predict the products of each reaction:
    (a) $HClO_4(aq) + Fe_2O_3(s) \longrightarrow$
    (b) $H_2SO_4(aq) + Sr(s) \longrightarrow$
    (c) $H_3PO_4(aq) + KOH(aq) \longrightarrow$

50. Predict the products of each reaction:
    (a) $HI(aq) + Al(s) \longrightarrow$
    (b) $H_2SO_4(aq) + TiO_2(s) \longrightarrow$
    (c) $H_2CO_3(aq) + LiOH(aq) \longrightarrow$

ACID–BASE TITRATIONS

51. Four solutions of unknown HCl concentration are titrated with solutions of NaOH. The following table lists the volume of each unknown HCl solution, the volume of NaOH solution required to reach the equivalence point, and the concentration of each NaOH solution. Calculate the concentration (in M) of the unknown HCl solution in each case.

HCl Volume (mL)	NaOH Volume (mL)	[NaOH] (M)
(a) 25.00 mL	28.44 mL	0.1231 M
(b) 15.00 mL	21.22 mL	0.0972 M
(c) 20.00 mL	14.88 mL	0.1178 M
(d) 5.00 mL	6.88 mL	0.1325 M

52. Four solutions of unknown NaOH concentration are titrated with solutions of HCl. The following table lists the volume of each unknown NaOH solution, the volume of HCl solution required to reach the equivalence point, and the concentration of each HCl solution. Calculate the concentration (in M) of the unknown NaOH solution in each case.

NaOH Volume (mL)	HCl Volume (mL)	[HCl] (M)
(a) 5.00 mL	9.77 mL	0.1599 M
(b) 15.00 mL	11.34 mL	0.1311 M
(c) 10.00 mL	10.55 mL	0.0889 M
(d) 30.00 mL	36.18 mL	0.1021 M

53. A 25.00-mL sample of an H_2SO_4 solution of unknown concentration is titrated with a 0.1322 M KOH solution. A volume of 41.22 mL of KOH was required to reach the equivalence point. What is the concentration of the unknown H_2SO_4 solution?

54. A 5.00-mL sample of an H_3PO_4 solution of unknown concentration is titrated with a 0.1090 M NaOH solution. A volume of 7.12 mL of the NaOH solution was required to reach the equivalence point. What is the concentration of the unknown H_3PO_4 solution?

55. What volume in milliliters of a 0.121 M sodium hydroxide solution is required to reach the equivalence point in the complete titration of a 10.0-mL sample of 0.102 M sulfuric acid?

56. What volume in milliliters of 0.0985 M sodium hydroxide solution is required to reach the equivalence point in the complete titration of a 15.0-mL sample of 0.124 M phosphoric acid?

STRONG AND WEAK ACIDS AND BASES

57. Classify each acid as strong or weak.
    (a) HCl
    (b) HF
    (c) HBr
    (d) H_2SO_3

58. Classify each acid as strong or weak.
    (a) $HCHO_2$
    (b) H_2SO_4
    (c) HNO_3
    (d) H_2CO_3

59. Determine $[H_3O^+]$ in each acid solution. If the acid is weak, indicate the value that $[H_3O^+]$ is less than.
    (a) 1.7 M HBr
    (b) 1.5 M HNO_3
    (c) 0.38 M H_2CO_3
    (d) 1.75 M $HCHO_2$

60. Determine $[H_3O^+]$ in each acid solution. If the acid is weak, indicate the value that $[H_3O^+]$ is less than.
    (a) 0.125 M $HClO_2$
    (b) 1.25 M H_3PO_4
    (c) 2.77 M HCl
    (d) 0.95 M H_2SO_3

61. Classify each base as strong or weak.
    (a) LiOH
    (b) NH_4OH
    (c) $Ca(OH)_2$
    (d) NH_3

62. Classify each base as strong or weak.
    (a) C_5H_5N
    (b) NaOH
    (c) $Ba(OH)_2$
    (d) KOH

63. Determine $[OH^-]$ in each base solution. If the acid is weak, indicate the value that $[OH^-]$ is less than.
    (a) 0.25 M NaOH
    (b) 0.25 M NH_3
    (c) 0.25 M $Sr(OH)_2$
    (d) 1.25 M KOH

64. Determine $[OH^-]$ in each base solution. If the acid is weak, indicate the value that $[OH^-]$ is less than.
    (a) 2.5 M KOH
    (b) 1.95 M NH_3
    (c) 0.225 M $Ba(OH)_2$
    (d) 1.8 M C_5H_5N

ACIDITY, BASICITY, AND K_W

65. Determine whether each solution is acidic, basic, or neutral.
    (a) $[H_3O^+] = 1 \times 10^{-5}$ M; $[OH^-] = 1 \times 10^{-9}$ M
    (b) $[H_3O^+] = 1 \times 10^{-6}$ M; $[OH^-] = 1 \times 10^{-8}$ M
    (c) $[H_3O^+] = 1 \times 10^{-7}$ M; $[OH^-] = 1 \times 10^{-7}$ M
    (d) $[H_3O^+] = 1 \times 10^{-8}$ M; $[OH^-] = 1 \times 10^{-6}$ M

66. Determine whether each solution is acidic, basic, or neutral.
    (a) $[H_3O^+] = 1 \times 10^{-9}$ M; $[OH^-] = 1 \times 10^{-5}$ M
    (b) $[H_3O^+] = 1 \times 10^{-10}$ M; $[OH^-] = 1 \times 10^{-4}$ M
    (c) $[H_3O^+] = 1 \times 10^{-2}$ M; $[OH^-] = 1 \times 10^{-12}$ M
    (d) $[H_3O^+] = 1 \times 10^{-13}$ M; $[OH^-] = 1 \times 10^{-1}$ M

67. Calculate $[OH^-]$ given $[H_3O^+]$ in each aqueous solution and classify the solution as acidic or basic.
    (a) $[H_3O^+] = 1.5 \times 10^{-9}$ M
    (b) $[H_3O^+] = 9.3 \times 10^{-9}$ M
    (c) $[H_3O^+] = 2.2 \times 10^{-6}$ M
    (d) $[H_3O^+] = 7.4 \times 10^{-4}$ M

68. Calculate $[OH^-]$ given $[H_3O^+]$ in each aqueous solution and classify the solution as acidic or basic.
    (a) $[H_3O^+] = 1.3 \times 10^{-3}$ M
    (b) $[H_3O^+] = 9.1 \times 10^{-12}$ M
    (c) $[H_3O^+] = 5.2 \times 10^{-4}$ M
    (d) $[H_3O^+] = 6.1 \times 10^{-9}$ M

69. Calculate $[H_3O^+]$ given $[OH^-]$ in each aqueous solution and classify each solution as acidic or basic.
    (a) $[OH^-] = 2.7 \times 10^{-12}$ M
    (b) $[OH^-] = 2.5 \times 10^{-2}$ M
    (c) $[OH^-] = 1.1 \times 10^{-10}$ M
    (d) $[OH^-] = 3.3 \times 10^{-4}$ M

70. Calculate $[H_3O^+]$ given $[OH^-]$ in each aqueous solution and classify each solution as acidic or basic.
    (a) $[OH^-] = 2.1 \times 10^{-11}$ M
    (b) $[OH^-] = 7.5 \times 10^{-9}$ M
    (c) $[OH^-] = 2.1 \times 10^{-4}$ M
    (d) $[OH^-] = 1.0 \times 10^{-2}$ M

pH

71. Classify each solution as acidic, basic, or neutral according to its pH value.
    (a) pH = 8.0
    (b) pH = 7.0
    (c) pH = 3.5
    (d) pH = 6.1

72. Classify each solution as acidic, basic, or neutral according to its pH value.
    (a) pH = 4.0
    (b) pH = 3.5
    (c) pH = 13.0
    (d) pH = 0.85

73. Calculate the pH of each solution.
    (a) $[H_3O^+] = 1.7 \times 10^{-8}$ M
    (b) $[H_3O^+] = 1.0 \times 10^{-7}$ M
    (c) $[H_3O^+] = 2.2 \times 10^{-6}$ M
    (d) $[H_3O^+] = 7.4 \times 10^{-4}$ M

74. Calculate the pH of each solution.
    (a) $[H_3O^+] = 2.4 \times 10^{-10}$ M
    (b) $[H_3O^+] = 7.6 \times 10^{-2}$ M
    (c) $[H_3O^+] = 9.2 \times 10^{-13}$ M
    (d) $[H_3O^+] = 3.4 \times 10^{-5}$ M

75. Calculate $[H_3O^+]$ for each solution.
    (a) pH = 8.55
    (b) pH = 11.23
    (c) pH = 2.87
    (d) pH = 1.22

76. Calculate $[H_3O^+]$ for each solution.
    (a) pH = 1.76
    (b) pH = 3.88
    (c) pH = 8.43
    (d) pH = 12.32

77. Calculate the pH of each solution.
    (a) $[OH^-] = 1.9 \times 10^{-7}$ M
    (b) $[OH^-] = 2.6 \times 10^{-8}$ M
    (c) $[OH^-] = 7.2 \times 10^{-11}$ M
    (d) $[OH^-] = 9.5 \times 10^{-2}$ M

78. Calculate the pH of each solution.
    (a) $[OH^-] = 2.8 \times 10^{-11}$ M
    (b) $[OH^-] = 9.6 \times 10^{-3}$ M
    (c) $[OH^-] = 3.8 \times 10^{-12}$ M
    (d) $[OH^-] = 6.4 \times 10^{-4}$ M

79. Calculate $[OH^-]$ for each solution.
    (a) pH = 4.25
    (b) pH = 12.53
    (c) pH = 1.50
    (d) pH = 8.25

80. Calculate $[OH^-]$ for each solution.
    (a) pH = 1.82
    (b) pH = 13.28
    (c) pH = 8.29
    (d) pH = 2.32

81. Calculate the pH of each solution:
    (a) 0.0155 M HBr
    (b) 1.28×10^{-3} M KOH
    (c) 1.89×10^{-3} M HNO_3
    (d) 1.54×10^{-4} M $Sr(OH)_2$

82. Calculate the pH of each solution:
    (a) 1.34×10^{-3} M $HClO_4$
    (b) 0.0211 M NaOH
    (c) 0.0109 M HBr
    (d) 7.02×10^{-5} M $Ba(OH)_2$

pOH

83. Detemine the pOH of each solution and classify it as acidic, basic, or neutral.
    (a) $[OH^-] = 1.5 \times 10^{-9}$ M
    (b) $[OH^-] = 7.0 \times 10^{-5}$ M
    (c) $[OH^-] = 1.0 \times 10^{-7}$ M
    (d) $[OH^-] = 8.8 \times 10^{-3}$ M

84. Detemine the pOH of each solution and classify it as acidic, basic, or neutral.
    (a) $[OH^-] = 4.5 \times 10^{-2}$ M
    (b) $[OH^-] = 3.1 \times 10^{-12}$ M
    (c) $[OH^-] = 5.4 \times 10^{-5}$ M
    (d) $[OH^-] = 1.2 \times 10^{-2}$ M

85. Determine the pOH of each solution.
    (a) $[H_3O^+] = 1.2 \times 10^{-8}$ M
    (b) $[H_3O^+] = 5.5 \times 10^{-2}$ M
    (c) $[H_3O^+] = 3.9 \times 10^{-9}$ M
    (d) $[OH^-] = 1.88 \times 10^{-13}$ M

86. Determine the pOH of each solution.
    (a) $[H_3O^+] = 8.3 \times 10^{-10}$ M
    (b) $[H_3O^+] = 1.6 \times 10^{-7}$ M
    (c) $[H_3O^+] = 7.3 \times 10^{-2}$ M
    (d) $[OH^-] = 4.32 \times 10^{-4}$ M

87. Determine the pH of each solution and classify it as acidic, basic, or neutral.
    (a) pOH = 8.5
    (b) pOH = 4.2
    (c) pOH = 1.7
    (d) pOH = 7.0

88. Determine the pH of each solution and classify it as acidic, basic, or neutral.
    (a) pOH = 12.5
    (b) pOH = 5.5
    (c) pOH = 0.55
    (d) pOH = 7.98

BUFFERS AND ACID RAIN

89. Determine your location on the map in Figure 20. What is the pH of rain where you live? What is the $[H_3O^+]$?

90. Identify the area of the United States with the most acidic rainfall on the map in Figure 20. What is the pH of the rain? What is the $[H_3O^+]$?

91. Determine whether or not each mixture is a buffer.
    (a) HCl and HF
    (b) NaOH and NH_3
    (c) HF and NaF
    (d) $HC_2H_3O_2$ and $KC_2H_3O_2$

92. Determine whether or not each mixture is a buffer.
    (a) HBr and NaCl
    (b) $HCHO_2$ and $NaCHO_2$
    (c) HCl and HBr
    (d) KOH and NH_3

93. Write reactions showing how each of the buffers in Problem 91 would neutralize added HCl.

94. Write reactions showing how each of the buffers in Problem 92 would neutralize added NaOH.

95. What substance could you add to each solution to make it a buffer solution?
    (a) 0.100 M $NaC_2H_3O_2$
    (b) 0.500 M H_3PO_4
    (c) 0.200 M $HCHO_2$

96. What substance could you add to each solution to make it a buffer solution?
    (a) 0.050 M $NaHSO_3$
    (b) 0.150 M HF
    (c) 0.200 M $KCHO_2$

CUMULATIVE PROBLEMS

97. How much 0.100 M HCl is required to completely neutralize 20.0 mL of 0.250 M NaOH?

98. How much 0.200 M KOH is required to completely neutralize 25.0 mL of 0.150 M $HClO_4$?

99. What is the minimum volume of 5.0 M HCl required to completely dissolve 10.0 g of magnesium metal?

100. What is the minimum volume of 3.0 M HBr required to completely dissolve 15.0 g of potassium metal?

101. When 18.5 g of $K_2O(s)$ is completely dissolved by $HI(aq)$, how many grams of $KI(aq)$ are formed in solution?

102. When 5.88 g of $CaO(s)$ is completely dissolved by $HBr(aq)$, how many grams of $CaBr_2(aq)$ are formed in solution?

103. A 0.125-g sample of a monoprotic acid of unknown molar mass is dissolved in water and titrated with 0.1003 M NaOH. The equivalence point is reached after adding 20.77 mL of base. What is the molar mass of the unknown acid?

104. A 0.105-g sample of a diprotic acid of unknown molar mass is dissolved in water and titrated with 0.1288 M NaOH. The equivalence point is reached after adding 15.2 mL of base. What is the molar mass of the unknown acid?

105. Antacids, such as milk of magnesia, are often taken to reduce the discomfort of acid stomach or heartburn. The recommended dose of milk of magnesia is 1 teaspoon, which contains 400 mg of $Mg(OH)_2$. What volume of HCl solution with a pH of 1.1 can be neutralized by 1 dose of milk of magnesia? (Assume two significant figures in your calculations.)

106. An antacid tablet requires 25.82 mL of 0.200 M HCl to titrate to its equivalence point. What volume in milliliters of stomach acid can be neutralized by the antacid tablet? Assume that stomach acid has a pH of 1.1. (Assume two significant figures in your calculations.)

107. For each $[H_3O^+]$, determine the pH and state whether the solution is acidic or basic.
   (a) $[H_3O^+] = 0.0025$ M
   (b) $[H_3O^+] = 1.8 \times 10^{-12}$ M
   (c) $[H_3O^+] = 9.6 \times 10^{-9}$ M
   (d) $[H_3O^+] = 0.0195$ M

108. For each $[OH^-]$, determine the pH and state whether the solution is acidic or basic.
   (a) $[OH^-] = 1.8 \times 10^{-5}$ M
   (b) $[OH^-] = 8.9 \times 10^{-12}$ M
   (c) $[OH^-] = 3.1 \times 10^{-2}$ M
   (d) $[OH^-] = 1.96 \times 10^{-9}$ M

109. Complete the table. (The first row is completed for you.)

$[H_3O^+]$	$[OH^-]$	pOH	pH	Acidic or Basic
1.0×10^{-4}	1.0×10^{-10}	10.00	4.00	acidic
5.5×10^{-3}	___	___	___	___
___	3.2×10^{-6}	___	___	___
4.8×10^{-9}	___	___	___	___
___	___	___	7.55	___

110. Complete the table. (The first row is completed for you.)

$[H_3O^+]$	$[OH^-]$	pOH	pH	Acidic or Basic
1.0×10^{-8}	1.0×10^{-6}	6.00	8.00	basic
___	___	___	3.55	___
1.7×10^{-9}	___	___	___	___
___	___	___	13.5	___
___	8.6×10^{-11}	___	___	___

111. For each strong acid solution, determine $[H_3O^+]$, $[OH^-]$, and pH.
   (a) 0.0088 M $HClO_4$
   (b) 1.5×10^{-3} M HBr
   (c) 9.77×10^{-4} M HI
   (d) 0.0878 M HNO_3

112. For each strong acid solution, determine $[H_3O^+]$, $[OH^-]$, and pH.
   (a) 0.0150 M HCl
   (b) 1.9×10^{-4} M HI
   (c) 0.0226 M HBr
   (d) 1.7×10^{-3} M HNO_3

113. For each strong base solution, determine $[OH^-]$, $[H_3O^+]$, pH, and pOH.

    (a) 0.15 M NaOH

    (b) 1.5×10^{-3} M Ca(OH)$_2$

    (c) 4.8×10^{-4} M Sr(OH)$_2$

    (d) 8.7×10^{-5} M KOH

114. For each strong base solution, determine $[OH^-]$, $[H_3O^+]$, pH, and pOH.

    (a) 8.77×10^{-3} M LiOH

    (b) 0.0112 M Ba(OH)$_2$

    (c) 1.9×10^{-4} M KOH

    (d) 5.0×10^{-4} M Ca(OH)$_2$

115. As described in Section 1, jailed spies on the big screen often use acid stored in a pen to dissolve jail bars and escape. What minimum volume of 12.0 M hydrochloric acid would be required to completely dissolve a 500.0-g iron bar? Would this amount of acid fit into a pen?

116. A popular classroom demonstration consists of filing notches into a new penny and soaking the penny in hydrochloric acid overnight. Since new pennies are made of zinc coated with copper, and since hydrochloric acid dissolves zinc and not copper, the inside of the penny is dissolved by the acid, while the outer copper shell remains. Suppose the penny contains 2.5 g of zinc and is soaked in 20.0 mL of 6.0 M HCl. Calculate the concentration of the HCl solution after all of the zinc has dissolved. *Hint:* The Zn from the penny is oxidized to Zn^{2+}.

117. What is the pH of a solution formed by mixing 125.0 mL of 0.0250 M HCl with 75.0 mL of 0.0500 M NaOH?

118. What is the pH of a solution formed by mixing 175.0 mL of 0.0880 M HI with 125.0 mL of 0.0570 M KOH?

119. How many H^+ (or H_3O^+) ions are present in one drop (0.050 mL) of pure water at 25 °C?

120. Calculate the number of H^+ (or H_3O^+) ions and OH^- ions in 1.0 mL of 0.100 M HCl.

121. A 4.00-L base solution contains 0.100 mol total of NaOH and Sr(OH)$_2$. The pOH of the solution is 1.51. Determine the amounts (in moles) of NaOH and Sr(OH)$_2$ in the solution.

122. A 1.50-L acid solution contains 0.35 g total of HCl and HBr. The pH of the solution is 2.40. What are the masses of HCl and HBr in the solution?

HIGHLIGHT PROBLEMS

123. Based on the molecular view of each acid solution, determine whether the acid is weak or strong.

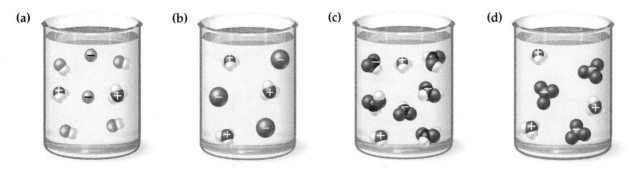

    (a)   **(b)**   **(c)**   **(d)**

124. Lakes that have been acidified by acid rain can be neutralized by liming, the addition of limestone (CaCO$_3$). How much limestone in kilograms is required to completely neutralize a 3.8×10^9 L lake with a pH of 5.5?

125. Acid rain over the Great Lakes has a pH of about 4.5. Calculate the $[H_3O^+]$ of this rain and compare that value to the $[H_3O^+]$ of rain over the West Coast that has a pH of 5.4. How many times more concentrated is the acid in rain over the Great Lakes?

►ANSWERS TO SKILLBUILDER EXERCISES

Skillbuilder 1

(a) $C_5H_5N(aq) + H_2O(l) \rightleftharpoons$
   Base   Acid

$\qquad C_5H_5NH^+(aq) + OH^-(aq)$
   Conjugate acid   Conjugate base

(b) $HNO_3(aq) + H_2O(l) \longrightarrow H_3O^+(aq) + NO_3^-(aq)$
   Acid   Base   Conjugate acid   Conjugate base

Skillbuilder 2

$H_3PO_4(aq) + 3\,NaOH(aq) \longrightarrow 3\,H_2O(l) + Na_3PO_4(aq)$

Skillbuilder 3

(a) $2\,HCl(aq) + Sr(s) \longrightarrow H_2(g) + SrCl_2(aq)$

(b) $2\,HI(aq) + BaO(s) \longrightarrow H_2O(l) + BaI_2(aq)$

Skillbuilder 4 $\qquad 9.03 \times 10^{-2}$ M H_2SO_4

Skillbuilder 5

(a) $[H_3O^+] < 0.50$ M

(b) $[H_3O^+] = 1.25$ M

(c) $[H_3O^+] < 0.75$ M

Skillbuilder 6

(a) $[OH^-] = 0.11$ M

(b) $[OH^-] < 1.05$ M

(c) $[OH^-] = 0.45$ M

Skillbuilder 7

(a) $[H_3O^+] = 6.7 \times 10^{-13}$ M; basic

(b) $[H_3O^+] = 1.0 \times 10^{-7}$ M; neutral

(c) $[H_3O^+] = 1.2 \times 10^{-5}$ M; acidic

Skillbuilder 8

(a) pH = 8.02; basic

(b) pH = 2.21 acidic

Skillbuilder Plus 1 pH = 12.11; basic

Skillbuilder 9 4.3×10^{-9} M

Skillbuilder Plus 2 4.6×10^{-11} M

Skillbuilder 10 5.6×10^{-5} M

Skillbuilder Plus 3 4.8×10^{-9} M

►ANSWERS TO CONCEPTUAL CHECKPOINTS

1 (b) The conjugate base of an acid always has one fewer proton and is one charge unit lower (more negative) than the acid.

2 (c) Both (a) and (b) show complete ionization and are therefore strong acids. Only the acid depicted in (c) undergoes partial ionization and is therefore a weak acid.

3 (d) Each of the others can accept a proton and thus acts as a base. NH_4^+, however, is the conjugate acid of NH_3 and therefore acts as an acid and not as a base.

4 (d) Because pH is the *negative* log of the H_3O^+ concentration, a higher pH corresponds to a lower $[H_3O^+]$, and each unit of pH represents a tenfold change in concentration.

5 (d) Since the pH is 5, the pOH = 14 − 5 = 9.

6 (b) A buffer solution consists of a weak acid and its conjugate base. Of the compounds listed, HF is the only weak acid, and F^- (from NaF in solution) is its conjugate base.

ANSWERS TO ODD-NUMBERED EXERCISES

QUESTIONS

1. Sour gummy candies are coated with a white powder that is a mixture of citric acid and tartaric acid. The combination of these two acids creates the sour taste.

3. The main component of stomach acid is hydrochloric acid. Its purpose is to help break down food and kill harmful bacteria.

5. The properties of bases are bitter taste, slippery feel, and the ability to turn red litmus paper blue. Some common substances that contain bases are ammonia, Drano, baking soda, and antacids.

7. The Arrhenius definition of an acid is a substance that produces H^+ ions in aqueous solution. An example:

$$HCl(aq) \longrightarrow H^+(aq) + Cl^-(aq)$$

9. The Brønsted–Lowry definition states that an acid is a proton donor and a base is a proton acceptor. The following is an example of a chemical equation demonstrating this definition:

$$\underset{\text{acid}}{HCl(aq)} + \underset{\text{base}}{H_2O(l)} \longrightarrow H_3O^+(aq) + Cl^-(aq)$$

11. An acid–base neutralization reaction occurs when an acid and a base are mixed and the $H^+(aq)$ from the acid combines with the $OH^-(aq)$ from the base to form $H_2O(l)$. An example follows.

$$HCl(aq) + KOH(aq) \longrightarrow H_2O(l) + KCl(aq)$$

13. $2\,HCl(aq) + K_2O(s) \longrightarrow H_2O(l) + 2\,KCl(aq)$

15. A titration is a laboratory procedure in which a reactant in a solution of known concentration is reacted with another reactant in a solution of unknown concentration until the reaction has reached the equivalence point. The equivalence point is the point at which the reactants are in exact stoichiometric proportions.

17. A strong acid is one that will completely dissociate in solution, while a weak acid does not completely dissociate in solution.

19. Monoprotic acids (such as HCl) contain only one hydrogen ion that will dissociate in solution, while diprotic acids (such as H_2SO_4) contain two hydrogen ions that will dissociate in solution.

21. Yes, pure water contains H_3O^+ ions. Through self-ionization, water acts as an acid and a base with itself; water is amphoteric.

23. **a.** $[H_3O^+] > 1.0 \times 10^{-7}$ M; $[OH^-] < 1.0 \times 10^{-7}$ M
    b. $[H_3O^+] < 1.0 \times 10^{-7}$ M; $[OH^-] > 1.0 \times 10^{-7}$ M
    c. $[H_3O^+] = 1.0 \times 10^{-7}$ M; $[OH^-] = 1.0 \times 10^{-7}$ M

25. The pOH of a solution is the negative base-10 logarithm of the concentration of OH^- ions ($-\log[OH^-]$). A change of 2.0 pOH units corresponds to a 100-fold change in $[OH^-]$.

27. A buffer is a solution that resists pH change by neutralizing added acid or added base.

29. The cause of acid rain is the formation of SO_2, NO, and NO_2 during the combustion of fossil fuels.

31. Acid rain damages structures made out of metal, marble, cement, and limestone, as well as harming and possibly killing aquatic life and trees.

PROBLEMS

33. **a.** acid; $H_2SO_4(aq) \longrightarrow H^+(aq) + HSO_4^-(aq)$
    b. base; $Sr(OH)_2(aq) \longrightarrow Sr^{2+}(aq) + 2\,OH^-(aq)$
    c. acid; $HBr(aq) \longrightarrow H^+(aq) + Br^-(aq)$
    d. base; $NaOH(aq) \longrightarrow Na^+(aq) + OH^-(aq)$

35.

B-L Acid	B-L Base	Conjugate Acid	Conjugate Base
a. HBr	H_2O	H_3O^+	Br^-
b. H_2O	NH_3	NH_4^+	OH^-
c. HNO_3	H_2O	H_3O^+	NO_3^-
d. H_2O	C_5H_5N	$C_5H_5NH^+$	OH^-

37. a, c

39. **a.** Cl^- **b.** HSO_3^-
    c. CHO_2^- **d.** F^-

41. **a.** NH_4^+ **b.** $HClO_4$
    c. H_2SO_4 **d.** HCO_3^-

43. **a.** $HI(aq) + NaOH(aq) \longrightarrow H_2O(l) + NaI(aq)$
    b. $HBr(aq) + KOH(aq) \longrightarrow H_2O(l) + KBr(aq)$
    c. $2\,HNO_3(aq) + Ba(OH)_2(aq) \longrightarrow$
    $$2\,H_2O(l) + Ba(NO_3)_2(aq)$$
    d. $2\,HClO_4(aq) + Sr(OH)_2(aq) \longrightarrow$
    $$2\,H_2O(l) + Sr(ClO_4)_2(aq)$$

45. **a.** $2\,HBr(aq) + 2\,Rb(s) \longrightarrow 2\,RbBr(aq) + H_2(g)$
    b. $2\,HBr(aq) + Mg(s) \longrightarrow MgBr_2(aq) + H_2(g)$
    c. $2\,HBr(aq) + 2\,Ba(s) \longrightarrow 2\,BaBr(aq) + H_2(g)$
    d. $6\,HBr(aq) + 2\,Al(s) \longrightarrow 2\,AlBr_3(aq) + 3\,H_2(g)$

47. **a.** $MgO(aq) + 2\,HI(aq) \longrightarrow H_2O(l) + MgI_2(aq)$
    b. $K_2O(aq) + 2\,HI(aq) \longrightarrow H_2O(l) + 2\,KI(aq)$
    c. $Rb_2O(aq) + 2\,HI(aq) \longrightarrow H_2O(l) + 2\,RbI(aq)$
    d. $CaO(aq) + 2\,HI(aq) \longrightarrow H_2O(l) + CaI_2(aq)$

49. **a.** $6\,HClO_4(aq) + Fe_2O_3(s) \longrightarrow$
    $$2\,Fe(ClO_4)_3(aq) + 3\,H_2O(l)$$
    b. $H_2SO_4(aq) + Sr(s) \longrightarrow SrSO_4(aq) + H_2(g)$
    c. $H_3PO_4(aq) + 3\,KOH(aq) \longrightarrow 3\,H_2O(l) + K_3PO_4(aq)$

51. **a.** 0.1400 M **b.** 0.138 M
    c. 0.08764 M **d.** 0.182 M

53. 0.1090 M H_2SO_4

55. 16.9 mL

57. a. strong   **b.** weak

    c. strong   **d.** weak

59. a. $[H_3O^+] = 1.7$ M   **b.** $[H_3O^+] = 1.5$ M

    c. $[H_3O^+] < 0.38$ M   **d.** $[H_3O^+] < 1.75$ M

61. a. strong   **b.** weak

    c. strong   **d.** weak

63. a. $[OH^-] = 0.25$ M   **b.** $[OH^-] < 0.25$ M

    c. $[OH^-] = 0.50$ M   **d.** $[OH^-] = 1.25$ M

65. a. acidic   **b.** acidic

    c. neutral   **d.** basic

67. a. 6.7×10^{-6} M, basic   **b.** 1.1×10^{-6} M, basic

    c. 4.5×10^{-9} M, acidic   **d.** 1.4×10^{-11} M, acidic

69. a. 3.7×10^{-3} M, acidic   **b.** 4.0×10^{-13} M, basic

    c. 9.1×10^{-5} M, acidic   **d.** 3.0×10^{-11} M, basic

71. a. basic   **b.** neutral

    c. acidic   **d.** acidic

73. a. 7.77   **b.** 7.00

    c. 5.66   **d.** 3.13

75. a. 2.8×10^{-9} M   **b.** 5.9×10^{-12} M

    c. 1.3×10^{-3} M   **d.** 6.0×10^{-2} M

77. a. 7.28   **b.** 6.42

    c. 3.86   **d.** 12.98

79. a. 1.8×10^{-10} M   **b.** 3.4×10^{-2} M

    c. 3.2×10^{-13} M   **d.** 1.8×10^{-6} M

81. a. 1.810   **b.** 11.107

    c. 2.724   **d.** 10.489

83. a. pOH = 8.82, acidic   **b.** pOH = 4.15, basic

    c. pOH = 7.00, neutral   **d.** pOH = 2.06, basic

85. a. pOH = 6.08, basic   **b.** pOH = 12.74, acidic

    c. pOH = 5.59, basic   **d.** pOH = 1.274, basic

87. a. pH = 5.5, acidic   **b.** pH = 9.8, basic

    c. pH = 12.3, basic   **d.** pH = 7.0, neutral

89. various answers

91. c and d are buffers

93. $HCl(aq) + NaF(aq) \longrightarrow HF(aq) + NaCl(aq)$

    $HCl(aq) + KC_2H_3O_2(aq) \longrightarrow HC_2H_3O_2(aq) + KCl(aq)$

95. a. $HC_2H_3O_2$ **b.** NaH_2PO_4

    c. $NaCHOO$

97. 50.0 mL

99. 0.16 L

101. 65.2 g

103. 60.0 g/mol

105. 0.17 L

107. a. 2.60, acidic

    b. 11.75, basic

    c. 8.02, basic

    d. 1.710, acidic

109.

$[H_3O^+]$	$[OH^-]$	pH	Acidic or Basic
1.0×10^{-4}	1.0×10^{-10}	4.00	acidic
5.5×10^{-3}	1.8×10^{-12}	2.26	acidic
3.1×10^{-9}	3.2×10^{-6}	8.50	basic
4.8×10^{-9}	2.1×10^{-6}	8.32	basic
2.8×10^{-8}	3.5×10^{-7}	7.55	basic

111. a. $[H_3O^+] = 0.0088$ M

    $[OH^-] = 1.1 \times 10^{-12}$ M

    pH = 2.06

    b. $[H_3O^+] = 1.5 \times 10^{-3}$ M

    $[OH^-] = 6.7 \times 10^{-12}$ M

    pH = 2.82

    c. $[H_3O^+] = 9.77 \times 10^{-4}$ M

    $[OH^-] = 1.02 \times 10^{-11}$ M

    pH = 3.010

    d. $[H_3O^+] = 0.0878$ M

    $[OH^-] = 1.14 \times 10^{-13}$ M

    pH = 1.057

113. a. $[OH^-] = 0.15$ M

    $[H_3O^+] = 6.7 \times 10^{-14}$ M

    pH = 13.18

    b. $[OH^-] = 3.0 \times 10^{-3}$ M

    $[H_3O^+] = 3.3 \times 10^{-12}$ M

    pH = 11.48

    c. $[OH^-] = 9.6 \times 10^{-4}$ M

    $[H_3O^+] = 1.0 \times 10^{-11}$ M

    pH = 10.98

    d. $[OH^-] = 8.7 \times 10^{-5}$ M

    $[H_3O^+] = 1.1 \times 10^{-10}$ M

    pH = 9.94

115. 1.49 L

117. 11.495

119. 3.0×10^{12} H^+ ions

121. 0.024 mol $Sr(OH)_2$, 0.076 mol NaOH

123. a. weak

    b. strong

    c. weak

    d. strong

125. approximately 8 times more concentrated

Chemical Reactions

From Chapter 7 of *Introductory Chemistry*, Fourth Edition, Nivaldo J. Tro. Copyright © 2011 by Pearson Education, Inc. Published by Pearson Prentice Hall. All rights reserved.

Chemical Reactions

"Chemistry . . . is one of the broadest branches of science if for no other reason than, when we think about it, everything is chemistry."

LUCIANO CAGLIOTI (1933–)

1 Kindergarten Volcanoes, Automobiles, and Laundry Detergents

Did you ever make a clay volcano in kindergarten that erupted when filled with vinegar, baking soda, and red food coloring for effect? Have you pushed the gas pedal of a car and felt the acceleration as the car moved forward? Have you wondered why laundry detergents work better than normal soap to clean your clothes? Each of these processes involves a *chemical reaction*—the transformation of one or more substances into different substances.

In the classic kindergarten volcano, the baking soda (which is sodium bicarbonate) reacts with acetic acid in the vinegar to form carbon dioxide gas, water, and sodium acetate. The newly formed carbon dioxide bubbles out of the mixture, causing the eruption. Reactions that occur in liquids and form a gas are *gas evolution reactions*. A similar reaction causes the fizzing of antacids such as Alka-Seltzer™.

When you drive a car, hydrocarbons such as octane (in gasoline) react with oxygen from the air to form carbon dioxide gas and water (▶ Figure 1). This reaction produces heat, which expands the gases in the car's cylinders, accelerating it forward. Reactions such as this one—in which a substance reacts with oxygen, emitting heat and forming one or more oxygen-containing compounds—are *combustion reactions*. Combustion reactions are a subcategory of *oxidation–reduction reactions*, in which electrons are transferred from one substance to another. The formation of rust and the dulling of automobile paint are other examples of oxidation–reduction reactions.

Laundry detergent works better than soap to wash clothes because it contains substances that soften hard water. Hard water contains dissolved calcium (Ca^{2+}) and magnesium (Mg^{2+}) ions. These ions interfere with the action of soap by reacting

◀ In the space shuttle's main engines, hydrogen molecules, H_2 (white), and oxygen molecules, O_2 (red), which are stored in the central fuel tank, react violently to form water molecules, H_2O. The reaction emits the energy that helps propel the shuttle into space.

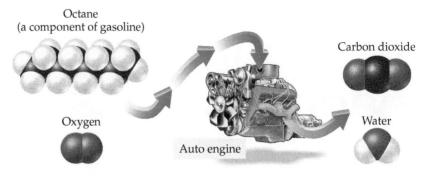

Octane
(a component of gasoline)

Oxygen

Auto engine

Carbon dioxide

Water

▲ FIGURE 1   **A combustion reaction**   In an automobile engine, hydrocarbons such as octane (C_8H_{18}) from gasoline combine with oxygen from the air and react to form carbon dioxide and water.

Soap in pure water	Soap in hard water

▲ FIGURE 2   **Soap and water**
Soap forms suds with pure water (left), but reacts with the ions in hard water (right) to form a gray residue that adheres to clothes.

with it to form a gray, slimy substance called *curd* or *soap scum* (◀ Figure 2). If you have ever washed your clothes in ordinary soap, you may have noticed gray soap scum residue on your clothes.

Laundry detergents inhibit curd formation because they contain substances such as sodium carbonate (Na_2CO_3) that remove calcium and magnesium ions from the water. When sodium carbonate dissolves in water, it *dissociates*, or separates into sodium ions (Na^+) and carbonate ions (CO_3^{2-}). The dissolved carbonate ions react with calcium and magnesium ions in the hard water to form solid calcium carbonate ($CaCO_3$) and solid magnesium carbonate ($MgCO_3$). These solids simply settle to the bottom of the laundry mixture, resulting in the removal of the ions from the water. In other words, laundry detergents contain substances that react with the ions in hard water to immobilize them. Reactions such as these—that form solid substances in water—are *precipitation reactions*. Precipitation reactions are also used to remove dissolved toxic metals in industrial wastes.

Chemical reactions take place all around us and even inside us. They are involved in many of the products we use daily and in many of our experiences. Chemical reactions can be relatively simple, like the combination of hydrogen and oxygen to form water, or they can be complex, like the synthesis of a protein molecule from thousands of simpler molecules. In some cases, such as the neutralization reaction that occurs in a swimming pool when acid is added to adjust the water's acidity level, chemical reactions are not noticeable to the naked eye. In other cases, such as the combustion reaction that produces a pillar of smoke and fire under the space shuttle during liftoff, chemical reactions are very obvious. In all cases, however, chemical reactions produce changes in the arrangements of the molecules and atoms that compose matter. Often, these molecular changes cause macroscopic changes that we can directly experience.

2   Evidence of a Chemical Reaction

If we could see the atoms and molecules that compose matter, we could easily identify a chemical reaction. Do atoms combine with other atoms to form compounds? Do new molecules form? Do the original molecules decompose? Do atoms in one molecule change places with atoms in another? If the answer to one or more of these questions is yes, a chemical reaction has occurred. Of course, we are not normally able to see atoms and molecules, so we need other ways to identify a chemical reaction.

Although we can't see atoms, many chemical reactions do produce easily detectable changes as they occur. For example, when the color-causing molecules in a brightly colored shirt decompose with repeated exposure to sunlight, the color of the shirt fades. Similarly, when the molecules embedded in the plastic of a child's temperature-sensitive spoon transform upon warming, the color of the spoon changes. These *color changes* are evidence that a chemical reaction has occurred.

Solid formation

Richard Megna/Fundamental Photographs.

▲ **FIGURE 3** **A precipitation reaction** The formation of a solid in a previously clear solution is evidence of a chemical reaction.

Gas formation

Charles D. Winters/Photo Researchers.

▲ **FIGURE 4** **A gas evolution reaction** The formation of a gas is evidence of a chemical reaction.

Other changes that identify chemical reactions include the *formation of a solid* (▶ Figure 3) or *the formation of a gas* (▶ Figure 4). Dropping Alka-Seltzer tablets into water or combining baking soda and vinegar (as in our opening example of the kindergarten volcano) are both good examples of chemical reactions that produce a gas—the gas is visible as bubbles in the liquid.

Heat absorption or *emission*, as well as *light emission*, are also evidence of reactions. For example, a natural gas flame produces heat and light. A chemical cold pack becomes cold when the plastic barrier separating two substances is broken. Both of these changes suggest that a chemical reaction is occurring.

Recall that a reaction that emits heat is an *exothermic* reaction and one that absorbs heat is an *endothermic* reaction.

Color change

Maxwellartandphoto.com.

▲ A child's temperature-sensitive spoon changes color upon warming due to a reaction induced by the higher temperature.

Heat absorption

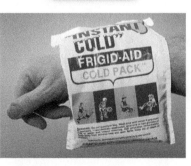

Tom Bochsler/Pearson Education/PH College.

▲ A change in temperature due to absorption or emission of heat is evidence of a chemical reaction. This chemical cold pack becomes cold when the barrier separating two substances is broken.

▲ FIGURE 5 **Boiling: a physical change** When water boils, bubbles are formed and a gas is evolved. However, no chemical change has occurred because the gas, like the liquid water, is also composed of water molecules.

While these changes provide evidence of a chemical reaction, they are not *definitive* evidence. Only chemical analysis showing that the initial substances have changed into other substances conclusively proves that a chemical reaction has occurred. We can be fooled. For example, when water boils, bubbles form, but no chemical reaction has occurred. Boiling water forms gaseous steam, but both water and steam are composed of water molecules—no chemical change has occurred (◄ Figure 5). On the other hand, chemical reactions may occur without any obvious signs, yet chemical analysis may show that a reaction has indeed occurred. The changes occurring at the atomic and molecular level determine whether a chemical reaction has occurred.

In summary, each of the following provides *evidence of a chemical reaction*.

• a *color change*

• the *formation of a solid* in a previously clear solution

• the *formation of a gas* when you add a substance to a solution

• the *emission of light*

• the *emission* or *absorption of heat*

EXAMPLE 1   **Evidence of a Chemical Reaction**

Which changes involve a chemical reaction? Explain your answers.

(a) ice melting upon warming
(b) an electric current passing through water, resulting in the formation of hydrogen and oxygen gas that appear as bubbles rising in the water
(c) iron rusting
(d) bubbles forming when a soda can is opened

SOLUTION

(a) not a chemical reaction; melting ice forms water, but both the ice and water are composed of water molecules.
(b) chemical reaction; water decomposes into hydrogen and oxygen, as evidenced by the bubbling.
(c) chemical reaction; iron changes into iron oxide, changing color in the process.
(d) not a chemical reaction; even though there is bubbling, it is just carbon dioxide coming out of the liquid.

▶SKILLBUILDER 1 | **Evidence of a Chemical Reaction**

Which changes involve a chemical reaction? Explain your answers.

(a) butane burning in a butane lighter
(b) butane evaporating out of a butane lighter
(c) wood burning
(d) dry ice subliming

▶FOR MORE PRACTICE   Example 16; Problems 25, 26, 27, 28, 29, 30.

✔ CONCEPTUAL CHECKPOINT 1

These images portray molecular views of one substance before and after a change. Determine whether a chemical reaction has occurred in each case.

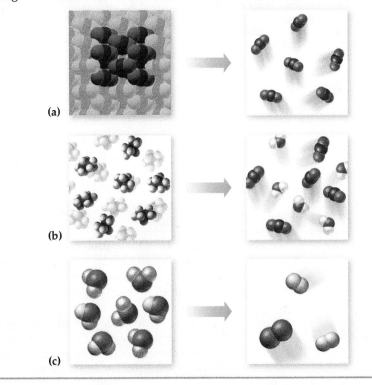

(a)

(b)

(c)

3   The Chemical Equation

We represent chemical reactions with *chemical equations*. For example, the reaction occurring in a natural-gas flame, such as the flame on a kitchen stove, is methane (CH_4) reacting with oxygen (O_2) to form carbon dioxide (CO_2) and water (H_2O). We represent this reaction with the equation:

$$CH_4 + O_2 \longrightarrow CO_2 + H_2O$$

reactants   products

The substances on the left side of the equation are the *reactants*, and the substances on the right side are the *products*. We often specify the state of each reactant or product in parentheses next to the formula. If we add states to our equation, it becomes:

$$CH_4(g) + O_2(g) \longrightarrow CO_2(g) + H_2O(g)$$

The (g) indicates that these substances are gases in the reaction. Table 1 summarizes the common states of reactants and products and their symbols used in chemical reactions.

Let's look more closely at the equation for the burning of natural gas. How many oxygen atoms are on each side of the equation?

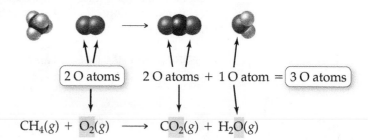

$$CH_4(g) + O_2(g) \longrightarrow CO_2(g) + H_2O(g)$$

TABLE 1   Abbreviations Indicating the States of Reactants and Products in Chemical Equations

Abbreviation	State
(g)	gas
(l)	liquid
(s)	solid
(aq)	aqueous (water solution)*

*The (aq) designation stands for *aqueous*, which indicates that a substance is dissolved in water. When a substance dissolves in water, the mixture is called a *solution* (see Section 5).

In chemical equations, atoms cannot change from one type to another—hydrogen atoms cannot change into oxygen atoms, for example. Nor can atoms disappear (recall the law of conservation of mass.

The left side of the equation has two oxygen atoms, and the right side has three. Since chemical equations represent real chemical reactions, atoms cannot simply appear or disappear in chemical equations because, as we know, atoms don't simply appear or disappear in nature. We must account for the atoms on both sides of the equation. Notice also that the left side of the equation has four hydrogen atoms and the right side only two.

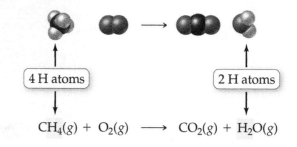

$$CH_4(g) + O_2(g) \longrightarrow CO_2(g) + H_2O(g)$$

To correct these problems, we must create a **balanced equation**, one in which the numbers of each type of atom on both sides of the equation are equal. To balance an equation, we insert coefficients—not subscripts—in front of the chemical formulas as needed to make the number of each type of atom in the reactants equal to the number of each type of atom in the products. New atoms do not form during a reaction, nor do atoms vanish—matter must be conserved.

When we balance chemical equations by inserting coefficients as needed in front of the formulas of the reactants and products, it changes the number of molecules in the equation, but it does not change the *kinds* of molecules. To balance the preceding equation, for example, we put the coefficient 2 before O_2 in the reactants, and the coefficient 2 before H_2O in the products.

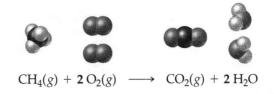

$$CH_4(g) + 2\,O_2(g) \longrightarrow CO_2(g) + 2\,H_2O$$

The equation is now balanced because the numbers of each type of atom on both sides of the equation are equal. We can verify this by summing the number of each type of atom.

> The number of a particular type of atom within a chemical formula embedded in an equation is obtained by multiplying the subscript for the atom by the coefficient for the chemical formula.

If there is no coefficient or subscript, a 1 is implied. So, the balanced equation for the combustion of natural gas is:

$$CH_4(g) + 2\,O_2(g) \longrightarrow CO_2(g) + 2\,H_2O(g)$$

Reactants	Products
1 C atom ($1 \times \underline{C}H_4$)	1 C atom ($1 \times \underline{C}O_2$)
4 H atoms ($1 \times C\underline{H}_4$)	4 H atoms ($2 \times \underline{H}_2O$)
4 O atoms ($2 \times \underline{O}_2$)	4 O atoms ($1 \times C\underline{O}_2 + 2 \times H_2\underline{O}$)

The numbers of each type of atom on both sides of the equation are equal—the equation is balanced.

$$CH_4(g) + 2\,O_2(g) \longrightarrow CO_2(g) + 2\,H_2O(g)$$

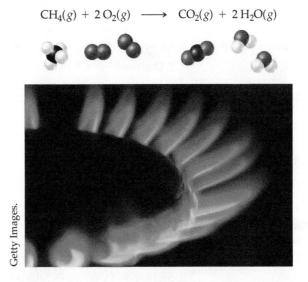

▶ A balanced chemical equation represents a chemical reaction. In this image, methane molecules combine with oxygen to form carbon dioxide and water.

Getty Images.

✔ CONCEPTUAL CHECKPOINT 2

In photosynthesis, plants make the sugar glucose, $C_6H_{12}O_6$, from carbon dioxide and water. The equation for the reaction is

$$6\,CO_2 + 6\,H_2O \longrightarrow C_6H_{12}O_6 + x\,O_2$$

In order for this equation to be balanced, the coefficient x must be

(a) 3   **(b)** 6   **(c)** 9   **(d)** 12

4 How to Write Balanced Chemical Equations

The following procedure box details the steps for writing balanced chemical equations. As in other procedures, we show the steps in the left column and examples of applying each step in the center and right columns. Remember, change only the *coefficients* to balance a chemical equation; *never change the subscripts*.

Writing Balanced Chemical Equations	**EXAMPLE 2** Write a balanced equation for the reaction between solid silicon dioxide and solid carbon to produce solid silicon carbide and carbon monoxide gas.	**EXAMPLE 3** Write a balanced equation for the combustion of liquid octane (C_8H_{18}), a component of gasoline, in which it combines with gaseous oxygen to form gaseous carbon dioxide and gaseous water.
1. Write a skeletal equation by writing chemical formulas for each of the reactants and products. Review nomenclature rules. (If a skeletal equation is provided, skip this step and go to Step 2.)	**SOLUTION** $$SiO_2(s) + C(s) \longrightarrow SiC(s) + CO(g)$$	**SOLUTION** $$C_8H_{18}(l) + O_2(g) \longrightarrow$$ $$CO_2(g) + H_2O(g)$$
2. If an element occurs in only one compound on both sides of the equation, balance it first. If there is more than one such element, balance metals before nonmetals.	**Begin with Si** $$SiO_2(s) + C(s) \longrightarrow SiC(s) + CO(g)$$ **1 Si atom $\longrightarrow$ 1 Si atom** Si is already balanced. **Balance O next** $$SiO_2(s) + C(s) \longrightarrow SiC(s) + CO(g)$$ **2 O atoms $\longrightarrow$ 1 O atom** To balance O, put a 2 before CO(g). $$SiO_2(s) + C(s) \longrightarrow SiC(s) + \mathbf{2}\,CO(g)$$ **2 O atoms $\longrightarrow$ 2 O atoms**	**Begin with C** $$C_8H_{18}(l) + O_2(g) \longrightarrow$$ $$CO_2(g) + H_2O(g)$$ **8 C atoms $\longrightarrow$ 1 C atom** To balance C, put an 8 before $CO_2(g)$. $$C_8H_{18}(l) + O_2(g) \longrightarrow$$ $$8\,CO_2(g) + H_2O(g)$$ **8 C atoms $\longrightarrow$ 8 C atoms** **Balance H next** $$C_8H_{18}(l) + O_2(g) \longrightarrow$$ $$8\,CO_2(g) + H_2O(g)$$ **18 H atoms $\longrightarrow$ 2 H atoms** To balance H, put a 9 before $H_2O(g)$. $$C_8H_{18}(l) + O_2(g) \longrightarrow$$ $$8\,CO_2(g) + \mathbf{9}\,H_2O(g)$$ **18 H atoms $\longrightarrow$ 18 H atoms**
3. If an element occurs as a free element on either side of the chemical equation, balance it last. Always balance free elements by adjusting the coefficient *on the free element*.	**Balance C** $$SiO_2(s) + C(s) \longrightarrow SiC(s) + 2\,CO(g)$$ **1 C atom $\longrightarrow$ 1 C + 2 C = 3 C atoms** To balance C, put a 3 before C(s). $$SiO_2(s) + \mathbf{3}\,C(s) \longrightarrow SiC(s) + 2\,CO(g)$$ **3 C atoms $\longrightarrow$ 1 C + 2 C = 3 C atoms**	**Balance O** $$C_8H_{18}(l) + O_2(g) \longrightarrow$$ $$8\,CO_2(g) + 9\,H_2O(g)$$ **2 O atoms $\longrightarrow$ 16 O + 9 O = 25 O atoms** To balance O, put a $\frac{25}{2}$ before $O_2(g)$. $$C_8H_{18}(l) + \frac{25}{2}\,O_2(g) \longrightarrow$$ $$8\,CO_2(g) + 9\,H_2O(g)$$ **25 O atoms $\longrightarrow$ 16 O + 9 O = 25 O atoms**
4. If the balanced equation contains coefficient fractions, change these into whole numbers by multiplying the entire equation by the appropriate factor.	This step is not necessary in this example. Proceed to Step 5.	$$[C_8H_{18}(l) + \frac{25}{2}\,O_2(g) \longrightarrow$$ $$8\,CO_2(g) + 9\,H_2O(g)] \times 2$$ $$2\,C_8H_{18}(l) + 25\,O_2(g) \longrightarrow$$ $$16\,CO_2(g) + 18\,H_2O(g)$$

5. Check to make certain the equation is balanced by summing the total number of each type of atom on both sides of the equation.

$$SiO_2(s) + 3\,C(s) \longrightarrow SiC(s) + 2\,CO(g)$$

Reactants		Products
1 Si atom	$\longrightarrow$	1 Si atom
2 O atoms	$\longrightarrow$	2 O atoms
3 C atoms	$\longrightarrow$	3 C atoms

The equation is balanced.

$$2\,C_8H_{18}(l) + 25\,O_2(g) \longrightarrow$$
$$16\,CO_2(g) + 18\,H_2O(g)$$

Reactants		Products
16 C atoms	$\longrightarrow$	16 C atoms
36 H atoms	$\longrightarrow$	36 H atoms
50 O atoms	$\longrightarrow$	50 O atoms

The equation is balanced.

▶**SKILLBUILDER 2**

Write a balanced equation for the reaction between solid chromium(III) oxide and solid carbon to produce solid chromium and carbon dioxide gas.

▶**SKILLBUILDER 3**

Write a balanced equation for the combustion of gaseous C_4H_{10} in which it combines with gaseous oxygen to form gaseous carbon dioxide and gaseous water.

▶**FOR MORE PRACTICE** Example 17; Problems 33, 34, 35, 36, 37, 38.

EXAMPLE 4 Balancing Chemical Equations

Write a balanced equation for the reaction of solid aluminum with aqueous sulfuric acid to form aqueous aluminum sulfate and hydrogen gas.

Use your knowledge of chemical nomenclature to write a skeletal equation containing formulas for each of the reactants and products. The formulas for each compound MUST BE CORRECT before you begin to balance the equation.	**SOLUTION** $$Al(s) + H_2SO_4(aq) \longrightarrow Al_2(SO_4)_3(aq) + H_2(g)$$
Since both aluminum and hydrogen occur as pure elements, balance those last. Sulfur and oxygen occur in only one compound on each side of the equation, so balance these first. Sulfur and oxygen are also part of a polyatomic ion that stays intact on both sides of the equation. *Balance polyatomic ions such as these as a unit.* There are $3\,SO_4{}^{2-}$ ions on the right side of the equation, so put a 3 in front of H_2SO_4.	$$Al(s) + \mathbf{3}\,H_2SO_4(aq) \longrightarrow Al_2(SO_4)_3(aq) + H_2(g)$$
Balance Al next. Since there are 2 Al atoms on the right side of the equation, place a 2 in front of Al on the left side of the equation.	$$\mathbf{2}\,Al(s) + 3\,H_2SO_4(aq) \longrightarrow Al_2(SO_4)_3(aq) + H_2(g)$$
Balance H next. Since there are 6 H atoms on the left side, place a 3 in front of $H_2(g)$ on the right side.	$$2\,Al(s) + 3\,H_2SO_4(aq) \longrightarrow Al_2(SO_4)_3(aq) + \mathbf{3}\,H_2(g)$$
Finally, sum the number of atoms on each side to make sure that the equation is balanced.	$$2\,Al(s) + 3\,H_2SO_4(aq) \longrightarrow Al_2(SO_4)_3(aq) + 3\,H_2(g)$$ **Reactants** / **Products** 2 Al atoms $\longrightarrow$ 2 Al atoms 6 H atoms $\longrightarrow$ 6 H atoms 3 S atoms $\longrightarrow$ 3 S atoms 12 O atoms $\longrightarrow$ 12 O atoms

▶**SKILLBUILDER 4 | Balancing Chemical Equations**

Write a balanced equation for the reaction of aqueous lead(II) acetate with aqueous potassium iodide to form solid lead(II) iodide and aqueous potassium acetate.

▶**FOR MORE PRACTICE** Problems 39, 40, 41, 42, 43, 44.

EXAMPLE 5   Balancing Chemical Equations

Balance this chemical equation.

$$Fe(s) + HCl(aq) \longrightarrow FeCl_3(aq) + H_2(g)$$

Since Cl occurs in only one compound on each side of the equation, balance it first. There is 1 Cl atom on the left side of the equation and 3 Cl atoms on the right side. To balance Cl, place a 3 in front of HCl.	**SOLUTION** $Fe(s) + \mathbf{3}\, HCl(aq) \longrightarrow FeCl_3(aq) + H_2(g)$
Since H and Fe occur as free elements, balance them last. There is 1 Fe atom on the left side of the equation and 1 Fe atom on the right, so Fe is balanced. There are 3 H atoms on the left and 2 H atoms on the right. Balance H by placing a $\frac{3}{2}$ in front of H_2. (That way you don't alter other elements that are already balanced.)	$Fe(s) + 3\, HCl(aq) \longrightarrow FeCl_3(aq) + \frac{3}{2}\, H_2(g)$
Since the equation now contains a coefficient fraction, clear it by multiplying the entire equation (both sides) by 2.	$[Fe(s) + 3\, HCl(aq) \longrightarrow FeCl_3(aq) + \frac{3}{2}\, H_2(g)] \times 2$ $2\, Fe(s) + 6\, HCl(aq) \longrightarrow 2\, FeCl_3(aq) + 3\, H_2(g)$
Finally, sum the number of atoms on each side to check that the equation is balanced.	$2\, Fe(s) + 6\, HCl(aq) \longrightarrow 2\, FeCl_3(aq) + 3\, H_2(g)$

Reactants		Products
2 Fe atoms	$\longrightarrow$	2 Fe atoms
6 Cl atoms	$\longrightarrow$	6 Cl atoms
6 H atoms	$\longrightarrow$	6 H atoms

▶**SKILLBUILDER 5 | Balancing Chemical Equations**

Balance this chemical equation.

$$HCl(g) + O_2(g) \longrightarrow H_2O(l) + Cl_2(g)$$

▶**FOR MORE PRACTICE**   Problems 45, 46, 47, 48, 49, 50.

 CONCEPTUAL CHECKPOINT 3

Which quantity must always be the same on both sides of a balanced chemical equation?

(a) the number of each type of atom

(b) the number of each type of molecule

(c) the sum of all of the coefficients

5   Aqueous Solutions and Solubility: Compounds Dissolved in Water

Reactions occurring in aqueous solution are among the most common and important. An **aqueous solution** is a homogeneous mixture of a substance with water. For example, a sodium chloride (NaCl) solution, also called a saline solution, is composed of sodium chloride dissolved in water. Sodium chloride

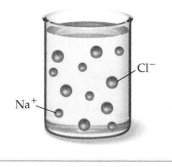

A sodium chloride solution contains independent **Na⁺** and **Cl⁻** ions.

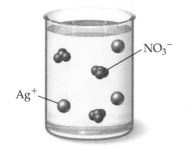

A silver nitrate solution contains independent **Ag⁺** and **NO₃⁻** ions.

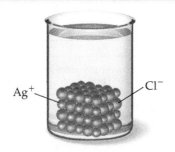

When silver chloride is added to water, it remains as solid AgCl—it does not dissolve into independent ions.

solutions are common both in the oceans and in living cells. You can form a sodium chloride solution yourself by adding table salt to water. As you stir the salt into the water, it seems to disappear. However, you know the salt is still there because if you taste the water, it has a salty flavor. How does sodium chloride dissolve in water?

When ionic compounds such as NaCl dissolve in water, they usually dissociate into their component ions. A sodium chloride solution, represented as NaCl(*aq*), does not contain any NaCl units; only dissolved Na⁺ ions and Cl⁻ ions are present.

We know that NaCl is present as independent sodium and chloride ions in solution because sodium chloride solutions conduct electricity, which requires the presence of freely moving charged particles. Substances (such as NaCl) that completely dissociate into ions in solution are called *strong electrolytes* and the resultant solutions are called **strong electrolyte solutions** (▼ Figure 6). Similarly, a silver nitrate solution, represented as AgNO₃(*aq*), does not contain any AgNO₃ units, but only dissolved Ag⁺ ions and NO₃⁻ ions. It, too, is a strong electrolyte solution. When compounds containing polyatomic ions such as NO₃⁻ dissolve, the polyatomic ions dissolve as intact units.

Not all ionic compounds, however, dissolve in water. AgCl, for example, does not. If we add AgCl to water, it remains as solid AgCl and appears as a white solid at the bottom of the beaker.

▲ FIGURE 6 **Ions as conductors** **(a)** Pure water does not conduct electricity. **(b)** Ions in a sodium chloride solution conduct electricity, causing the bulb to light. Solutions such as NaCl are called strong electrolyte solutions.

SOLUBILITY

A compound is **soluble** in a particular liquid if it dissolves in that liquid; a compound is **insoluble** if it does not dissolve in the liquid. NaCl, for example, is soluble in water. If we mix solid sodium chloride into water, it dissolves and forms a strong electrolyte solution. AgCl, on the other hand, is insoluble in water. If we mix solid silver chloride into water, it remains as a solid within the liquid water.

There is no easy way to tell whether a particular compound will be soluble or insoluble in water. For ionic compounds, however, empirical rules have been deduced from observations of many compounds. These **solubility rules** are summarized in Table 2 and ▼ Figure 7. For example, the solubility rules indicate that compounds containing the lithium ion are *soluble*. That means that compounds such as $LiBr$, $LiNO_3$, Li_2SO_4, $LiOH$, and Li_2CO_3 all dissolve in water to form strong electrolyte solutions. If a compound contains Li^+, it is soluble. Similarly, the solubility rules state that compounds containing the NO_3^- ion are soluble. Therefore, compounds such as $AgNO_3$, $Pb(NO_3)_2$, $NaNO_3$, $Ca(NO_3)_2$ and $Sr(NO_3)_2$ all dissolve in water to form strong electrolyte solutions.

The solubility rules also state that, with some exceptions, compounds containing the CO_3^{2-} ion are *insoluble*. Therefore, compounds such as $CuCO_3$, $CaCO_3$, $SrCO_3$, and $FeCO_3$ do not dissolve in water. Note that the solubility rules contain many exceptions. For example, compounds containing CO_3^{2-} are *soluble when paired with* Li^+, Na^+, K^+, or NH_4^+. Thus Li_2CO_3, Na_2CO_3, K_2CO_3, and $(NH_4)_2CO_3$ are all soluble.

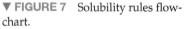

The solubility rules apply only to the solubility of the compounds in water.

▼ **FIGURE 7**   Solubility rules flowchart.

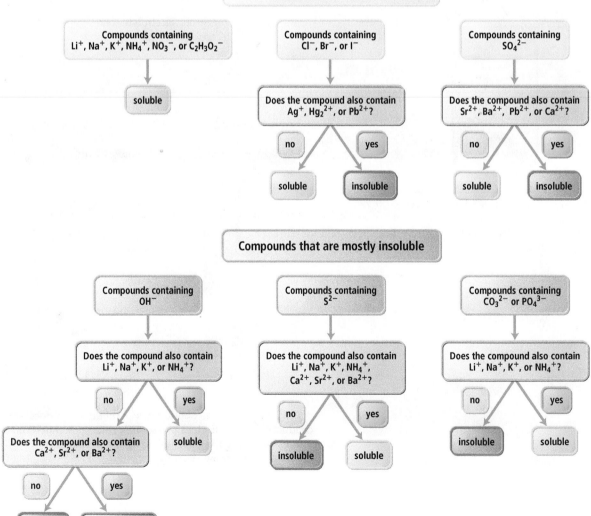

TABLE 2 Solubility Rules

Compounds Containing the Following Ions Are Mostly Soluble	Exceptions
Li^+, Na^+, K^+, NH_4^+	None
NO_3^-, $C_2H_3O_2^-$	None
Cl^-, Br^-, I^-	When any of these ions pairs with Ag^+, Hg_2^{2+}, or Pb^{2+}, the compound is insoluble.
SO_4^{2-}	When SO_4^{2-} pairs with Sr^{2+}, Ba^{2+}, Pb^{2+}, or Ca^{2+}, the compound is insoluble.

Compounds Containing the Following Ions Are Mostly Insoluble	Exceptions
OH^-, S^{2-}	When either of these ions pairs with Li^+, Na^+, K^+, or NH_4^+ the compound is soluble. When S^{2-} pairs with Ca^{2+}, Sr^{2+}, or Ba^{2+}, the compound is soluble. When OH^- pairs with Ca^{2+}, Sr^{2+}, or Ba^{2+}, the compound is slightly soluble.*
CO_3^{2-}, PO_4^{3-}	When either of these ions pairs with Li^+, Na^+, K^+, or NH_4^+, the compound is soluble.

*For many purposes these can be considered insoluble.

EXAMPLE 6 Determining Whether a Compound Is Soluble

Determine whether each compound is soluble or insoluble.

(a) AgBr (b) $CaCl_2$ (c) $Pb(NO_3)_2$ (d) $PbSO_4$

SOLUTION

(a) Insoluble; compounds containing Br^- are normally soluble, but Ag^+ is an exception.
(b) Soluble; compounds containing Cl^- are normally soluble, and Ca^{2+} is not an exception.
(c) Soluble; compounds containing NO_3^- are always soluble.
(d) Insoluble; compounds containing SO_4^{2-} are normally soluble, but Pb^{2+} is an exception.

▶SKILLBUILDER 6 | Determining Whether a Compound Is Soluble

Determine whether each compound is soluble or insoluble.
(a) CuS (b) $FeSO_4$ (c) $PbCO_3$ (d) NH_4Cl

▶FOR MORE PRACTICE Example 18; Problems 57, 58, 59, 60, 61, 62.

✔ CONCEPTUAL CHECKPOINT 4

Which image best depicts a mixture of $BaCl_2$ and water?

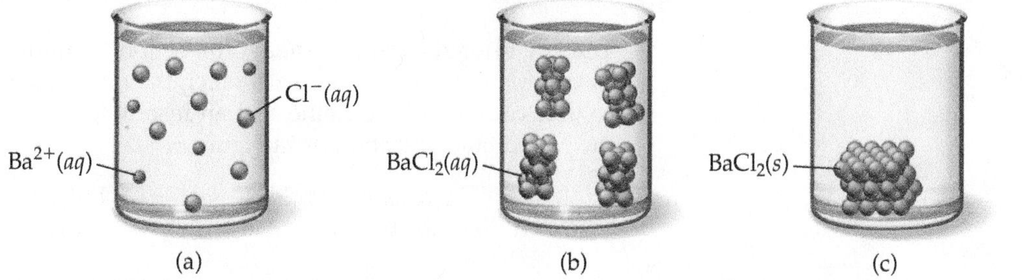

$Cl^-(aq)$

$Ba^{2+}(aq)$

$BaCl_2(aq)$

$BaCl_2(s)$

(a)   (b)   (c)

6 Precipitation Reactions: Reactions in Aqueous Solution That Form a Solid

Recall from Section 1 that sodium carbonate in laundry detergent reacts with dissolved Mg^{2+} and Ca^{2+} ions to form solids that precipitate (or come out of) solution. These reactions are examples of **precipitation reactions**—reactions that form a solid, called a **precipitate**, upon mixing two aqueous solutions.

Precipitation reactions are common in chemistry. Potassium iodide and lead nitrate, for example, both form colorless, strong electrolyte solutions when dissolved in water (see the solubility rules). When the two solutions are combined, however, a brilliant yellow precipitate forms (▼ Figure 8). We can describe this precipitation reaction with the chemical equation:

$$2\ KI(aq) + Pb(NO_3)_2(aq) \longrightarrow PbI_2(s) + 2\ KNO_3(aq)$$

Precipitation reactions do not always occur when mixing two aqueous solutions. For example, when solutions of $KI(aq)$ and $NaCl(aq)$ are combined, nothing happens (▼ Figure 9).

$$KI(aq) + NaCl(aq) \longrightarrow NO\ REACTION$$

$$2\ KI(aq) + Pb(NO_3)_2(aq) \longrightarrow PbI_2(s) + 2\ KNO_3(aq)$$

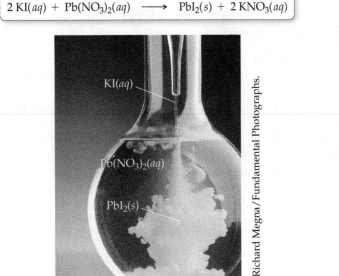

▲ FIGURE 8 **Precipitation** When a potassium iodide solution is mixed with a lead(II) nitrate solution, a brilliant yellow precipitate of $PbI_2(s)$ forms.

Richard Megna/Fundamental Photographs.

$$KI(aq) + NaCl(aq) \longrightarrow NO\ REACTION$$

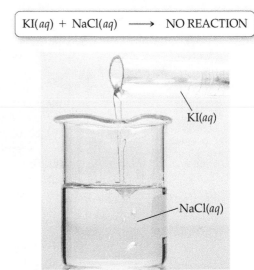

▲ FIGURE 9 **No reaction** When a potassium iodide solution is mixed with a sodium chloride solution, no reaction occurs.

PREDICTING PRECIPITATION REACTIONS

The key to predicting precipitation reactions is understanding that *only insoluble compounds form precipitates*. In a precipitation reaction, two solutions containing soluble compounds combine and an insoluble compound precipitates. Consider the precipitation reaction from Figure 8.

$$2\ KI(aq) + Pb(NO_3)_2(aq) \longrightarrow PbI_2(s) + 2\ KNO_3(aq)$$
soluble   soluble   insoluble   soluble

KI and $Pb(NO_3)_2$ are both soluble, but the precipitate, PbI_2, is *insoluble*. Before mixing, $KI(aq)$ and $Pb(NO_3)_2(aq)$ are both dissociated in their respective solutions.

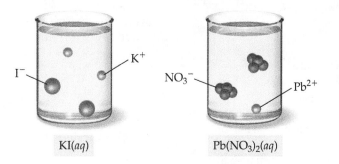

KI(*aq*)   Pb(NO_3)_2(*aq*)

The instant that the solutions are mixed, all four ions are present.

KI(*aq*) and Pb(NO_3)_2(*aq*)

However, new compounds—potentially insoluble ones—are now possible. Specifically, the cation from one compound can now pair with the anion from the other compound to form new (and potentially insoluble) products.

Original compounds	*Potentially insoluble products*
K I (*aq*)	KNO$_3$
Pb (NO$_3$)$_2$(*aq*)	PbI$_2$

If the *potentially insoluble* products are both *soluble*, then no reaction occurs. If, on the other hand, one or both of the potentially insoluble products are *indeed insoluble*, a precipitation reaction occurs. In this case, KNO_3 is soluble, but PbI_2 is insoluble. Consequently, PbI_2 precipitates.

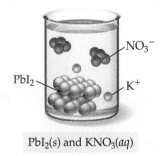

PbI$_2$(*s*) and KNO$_3$(*aq*)

To predict whether a precipitation reaction will occur when two solutions are mixed and to write an equation for the reaction, follow the steps in the procedure box. As usual, the steps are shown in the left column, and two examples of applying the procedure are shown in the center and right columns.

Writing Equations for Precipitation Reactions	**EXAMPLE 7** Write an equation for the precipitation reaction that occurs (if any) when solutions of sodium carbonate and copper(II) chloride are mixed.	**EXAMPLE 8** Write an equation for the precipitation reaction that occurs (if any) when solutions of lithium nitrate and sodium sulfate are mixed.
1. Write the formulas of the two compounds being mixed as reactants in a chemical equation.	SOLUTION $Na_2CO_3(aq) + CuCl_2(aq) \longrightarrow$	SOLUTION $LiNO_3(aq) + Na_2SO_4(aq) \longrightarrow$
2. Below the equation, write the formulas of the potentially insoluble products that could form from the reactants. Obtain these by combining the cation from one reactant with the anion from the other. Make sure to write correct (charge neutral) formulas for these ionic compounds.	$Na_2CO_3(aq) + CuCl_2(aq) \longrightarrow$ **Potentially Insoluble Products** NaCl $CuCO_3$	$LiNO_3(aq) + Na_2SO_4(aq) \longrightarrow$ **Potentially Insoluble Products** $NaNO_3$ Li_2SO_4
3. Use the solubility rules to determine whether any of the potential new products are indeed insoluble.	NaCl is *soluble* (compounds containing Cl^- are usually soluble, and Na^+ is not an exception). $CuCO_3$ is *insoluble* (compounds containing CO_3^{2-} are usually insoluble, and Cu^{2+} is not an exception).	$NaNO_3$ is *soluble* (compounds containing NO_3^- are soluble and Na^+ is not an exception). Li_2SO_4 is *soluble* (compounds containing SO_4^{2-} are soluble and Li^+ is not an exception).
4. If all of the potentially insoluble products are soluble, there will be no precipitate. Write NO REACTION next to the arrow.	Since this example has an insoluble product, proceed to the next step.	$LiNO_3(aq) + Na_2SO_4(aq) \longrightarrow$ NO REACTION
5. If one or both of the potentially insoluble products are insoluble, write their formula(s) as the product(s) of the reaction, using (s) to indicate solid. Write any soluble products with (aq) to indicate aqueous.	$Na_2CO_3(aq) + CuCl_2(aq) \longrightarrow$ $CuCO_3(s) + NaCl(aq)$	
6. Balance the equation. Remember to adjust only coefficients, not subscripts.	$Na_2CO_3(aq) + CuCl_2(aq) \longrightarrow$ $CuCO_3(s) + \textbf{2}\,NaCl(aq)$	
	▶**SKILLBUILDER 7** Write an equation for the precipitation reaction that occurs (if any) when solutions of potassium hydroxide and nickel(II) bromide are mixed.	▶**SKILLBUILDER 8** Write an equation for the precipitation reaction that occurs (if any) when solutions of ammonium chloride and iron(III) nitrate are mixed. ▶**FOR MORE PRACTICE** Example 19; Problems 63, 64, 65, 66.

EXAMPLE 9   Predicting and Writing Equations for Precipitation Reactions

Write an equation for the precipitation reaction (if any) that occurs when solutions of lead(II) acetate and sodium sulfate are mixed. If no reaction occurs, write *NO REACTION*.

1. Write the formulas of the two compounds being mixed as reactants in a chemical equation.	SOLUTION $Pb(C_2H_3O_2)_2(aq) + Na_2SO_4(aq) \longrightarrow$
2. Below the equation, write the formulas of the potentially insoluble products that could form from the reactants. These are obtained by combining the cation from one reactant with the anion from the other. Make sure to adjust the subscripts so that all formulas are charge-neutral.	$Pb(C_2H_3O_2)_2(aq) + Na_2SO_4(aq) \longrightarrow$ **Potentially insoluble products** $NaC_2H_3O_2$ $PbSO_4$
3. Use the solubility rules to determine whether any of the potentially insoluble products are indeed insoluble.	$NaC_2H_3O_2$ is *soluble* (compounds containing Na^+ are always soluble). $PbSO_4$ is *insoluble* (compounds containing SO_4^{2-} are normally soluble, but Pb^{2+} is an exception).
4. If all of the potentially insoluble products are soluble, there will be no precipitate. Write *NO REACTION* next to the arrow.	Since this reaction has an insoluble product, proceed to the next step.
5. If one or both of the potentially insoluble products are indeed insoluble, write their formula(s) as the product(s) of the reaction, using (s) to indicate solid. Write any soluble products with (aq) to indicate aqueous.	$Pb(C_2H_3O_2)_2(aq) + Na_2SO_4(aq) \longrightarrow PbSO_4(s) + NaC_2H_3O_2(aq)$
6. Balance the equation.	$Pb(C_2H_3O_2)_2(aq) + Na_2SO_4(aq) \longrightarrow PbSO_4(s) + 2\,NaC_2H_3O_2(aq)$

▶**SKILLBUILDER 9 | Predicting and Writing Equations for Precipitation Reactions**

Write an equation for the precipitation reaction (if any) that occurs when solutions of potassium sulfate and strontium nitrate are mixed. If no reaction occurs, write *NO REACTION*.

▶**FOR MORE PRACTICE**   Problems 67, 68.

CONCEPTUAL CHECKPOINT 5

Which of these reactions would result in the formation of a precipitate?

(a) $NaNO_3(aq) + CaS(aq)$

(b) $MgSO_4(aq) + CaS(aq)$

(c) $NaNO_3(aq) + MgSO_4(aq)$

7   Writing Chemical Equations for Reactions in Solution: Molecular, Complete Ionic, and Net Ionic Equations

Consider the following equation for a precipitation reaction.

$$AgNO_3(aq) + NaCl(aq) \longrightarrow AgCl(s) + NaNO_3(aq)$$

This equation is written as a **molecular equation**, an equation showing the complete neutral formulas for every compound in the reaction. Equations for reactions occurring in aqueous solution may also be written to show that aqueous ionic compounds normally dissociate in solution. For example, the previous equation can be written as:

$$Ag^+(aq) + NO_3^-(aq) + Na^+(aq) + Cl^-(aq) \longrightarrow AgCl(s) + Na^+(aq) + NO_3^-(aq)$$

> When writing complete ionic equations, separate only aqueous ionic compounds into their constituent ions. Do NOT separate solid, liquid, or gaseous compounds.

Equations such as this one, showing the reactants and products as they are actually present in solution, are called **complete ionic equations**.

Notice that in the complete ionic equation, some of the ions in solution appear unchanged on both sides of the equation. These ions are called **spectator ions** because they do not participate in the reaction.

$$Ag^+(aq) + NO_3^-(aq) + Na^+(aq) + Cl^-(aq) \longrightarrow AgCl(s) + Na^+(aq) + NO_3^-(aq)$$

Spectator ions

To simplify the equation, and to more clearly show what is happening, spectator ions can be omitted.

$$Ag^+(aq) + Cl^-(aq) \longrightarrow AgCl(s)$$

> Species refers to a kind or sort of thing. In this case, the species are all the different molecules and ions that are present during the reaction.

Equations such as this one, which show only the *species* that actually participate in the reaction, are called **net ionic equations**.

As another example, consider the reaction between HCl(*aq*) and NaOH(*aq*).

$$HCl(aq) + NaOH(aq) \longrightarrow H_2O(l) + NaCl(aq)$$

HCl, NaOH, and NaCl exist in solution as independent ions. The *complete ionic equation* for this reaction is:

$$H^+(aq) + Cl^-(aq) + Na^+(aq) + OH^-(aq) \longrightarrow H_2O(l) + Na^+(aq) + Cl^-(aq)$$

To write the *net ionic equation*, we remove the spectator ions, those that are unchanged on both sides of the equation.

$$H^+(aq) + Cl^-(aq) + Na^+(aq) + OH^-(aq) \longrightarrow H_2O(l) + Na^+(aq) + Cl^-(aq)$$

Spectator ions

The net ionic equation is $H^+(aq) + OH^-(aq) \longrightarrow H_2O(l)$

To summarize:

- A molecular equation is a chemical equation showing the complete, neutral formulas for every compound in a reaction.
- A complete ionic equation is a chemical equation showing all of the species as they are actually present in solution.
- A net ionic equation is an equation showing only the species that actually participate in the reaction.

EXAMPLE 10   Writing Complete Ionic and Net Ionic Equations

Consider this precipitation reaction occurring in aqueous solution.

$$Pb(NO_3)_2(aq) + 2\,LiCl(aq) \longrightarrow PbCl_2(s) + 2\,LiNO_3(aq)$$

Write a complete ionic equation and a net ionic equation for the reaction.

| Write the complete ionic equation by separating aqueous ionic compounds into their constituent ions. The $PbCl_2(s)$ remains as one unit. | **SOLUTION**

Complete ionic equation

$Pb^{2+}(aq) + 2\,NO_3^-(aq) + 2\,Li^+(aq) + 2\,Cl^-(aq) \longrightarrow$
$\qquad\qquad\qquad PbCl_2(s) + 2\,Li^+(aq) + 2\,NO_3^-(aq)$ |
| Write the net ionic equation by eliminating the spectator ions, those that do not change during the reaction. | **Net ionic equation**

$Pb^{2+}(aq) + 2\,Cl^-(aq) \longrightarrow PbCl_2(s)$ |

▶**SKILLBUILDER 10** | **Writing Complete Ionic and Net Ionic Equations**

Consider this reaction occurring in aqueous solution.

$$2\,HBr(aq) + Ca(OH)_2(aq) \longrightarrow 2\,H_2O(l) + CaBr_2(aq)$$

Write a complete ionic equation and net ionic equation for the reaction.

▶**FOR MORE PRACTICE**   Example 20; Problems 69, 70, 71, 72.

8   Acid–Base and Gas Evolution Reactions

Two other kinds of reactions that occur in solution are **acid–base reactions**—reactions that form water upon mixing of an acid and a base—and **gas evolution reactions**—reactions that evolve a gas. Like precipitation reactions, these reactions occur when the cation of one reactant combines with the anion of another. As we will see in the next section, many gas evolution reactions also happen to be acid–base reactions.

ACID–BASE (NEUTRALIZATION) REACTIONS

An acid is a compound characterized by its sour taste, its ability to dissolve some metals, and its tendency to form H^+ ions in solution. A base is a compound characterized by its bitter taste, its slippery feel, and its tendency to form OH^- ions in solution. Some common acids and bases are listed in Table 3. Acids and bases are also found in many everyday substances. Foods such as lemons, limes, and vinegar contain acids. Soap, coffee, and milk of magnesia all contain bases.

When an acid and base are mixed, the $H^+(aq)$ from the acid combines with the $OH^-(aq)$ from the base to form $H_2O(l)$. Consider the reaction between hydrochloric acid and sodium hydroxide mentioned earlier.

$$\underset{\text{Acid}}{HCl(aq)} + \underset{\text{Base}}{NaOH(aq)} \longrightarrow \underset{\text{Water}}{H_2O(l)} + \underset{\text{Salt}}{NaCl(aq)}$$

Basic

Maxwellartandphoto.com.

▲ Milk of magnesia is basic and tastes bitter.

Even though coffee itself is acidic overall, it contains some naturally occurring bases (such as caffeine) that give it a bitter taste.

TABLE 3   Some Common Acids and Bases

Acid	Formula	Base	Formula
hydrochloric acid	HCl	sodium hydroxide	NaOH
hydrobromic acid	HBr	lithium hydroxide	LiOH
nitric acid	HNO_3	potassium hydroxide	KOH
sulfuric acid	H_2SO_4	calcium hydroxide	$Ca(OH)_2$
perchloric acid	$HClO_4$	barium hydroxide	$Ba(OH)_2$
acetic acid	$HC_2H_3O_2$		

Acidic

▲ Common foods and everyday sub-stances such as oranges, lemons, vinegar, and vitamin C contain acids.

Acid–base reactions (also called **neutralization reactions**) generally form water and an ionic compound—called a **salt**—that usually remains dissolved in the solution. The net ionic equation for many acid–base reactions is:

$$H^+(aq) + OH^-(aq) \longrightarrow H_2O(l)$$

Another example of an acid–base reaction is the reaction that occurs between sulfuric acid and potassium hydroxide.

$$\underset{\text{acid}}{H_2SO_4(aq)} + \underset{\text{base}}{2\,KOH} \longrightarrow \underset{\text{water}}{2\,H_2O(l)} + \underset{\text{salt}}{K_2SO_4(aq)}$$

Notice the pattern of acid and base reacting to form water and a salt.

$$\text{Acid} + \text{Base} \longrightarrow \text{Water} + \text{Salt} \qquad \text{(acid–base reactions)}$$

When writing equations for acid–base reactions, write the formula of the salt using the procedure for writing formulas of ionic compounds given in Section 5.5.

EXAMPLE 11 **Writing Equations for Acid–Base Reactions**

Write a molecular and net ionic equation for the reaction between aqueous HNO_3 and aqueous $Ca(OH)_2$.

You must recognize these substances as an acid and a base. Write the skeletal reaction following the general pattern of acid plus base goes to water plus salt.	**SOLUTION** $$\underset{\text{acid}}{HNO_3(aq)} + \underset{\text{base}}{Ca(OH)_2(aq)} \longrightarrow \underset{\text{water}}{H_2O(l)} + \underset{\text{salt}}{Ca(NO_3)_2(aq)}$$
Next, balance the equation.	$$2\,HNO_3(aq) + Ca(OH)_2(aq) \longrightarrow 2\,H_2O(l) + Ca(NO_3)_2(aq)$$
Write the net ionic equation by eliminating those ions that remain the same on both sides of the equation.	$$2\,H^+(aq) + 2\,OH^-(aq) \longrightarrow 2\,H_2O(l)$$ or simply $$H^+(aq) + OH^-(aq) \longrightarrow H_2O(l)$$

▶**SKILLBUILDER 11** | **Writing Equations for Acid–Base Reactions**

Write a molecular and net ionic equation for the reaction that occurs between aqueous H_2SO_4 and aqueous KOH.

▶**FOR MORE PRACTICE**   Example 21; Problems 77, 78, 79, 80.

GAS EVOLUTION REACTIONS

Some aqueous reactions form a gas as a product. These reactions, as we learned in the opening section of this chapter, are called gas evolution reactions. Some gas evolution reactions form a gaseous product directly when the cation of one reac-tant reacts with the anion of the other. For example, when sulfuric acid reacts with lithium sulfide, dihydrogen sulfide gas is formed.

$$H_2SO_4(aq) + Li_2S(aq) \longrightarrow \underset{\text{Gas}}{H_2S(g)} + Li_2SO_4(aq)$$

Many gas evolution reactions such as this one are also acid–base reactions.

Other gas evolution reactions form an intermediate product that then decomposes into a gas. For example, when aqueous hydrochloric acid is mixed with aqueous sodium bicarbonate, the following reaction occurs.

$$HCl(aq) + NaHCO_3(aq) \longrightarrow H_2CO_3(aq) + NaCl(aq) \longrightarrow H_2O(l) + CO_2(g) + NaCl(aq)$$
Gas

Gas evolution reaction

The intermediate product, H_2CO_3, is not stable and decomposes to form H_2O and gaseous CO_2. This reaction is almost identical to the reaction in the kindergarten volcano of Section 1, which involves the mixing of acetic acid and sodium bicarbonate.

$$HC_2H_3O_2(aq) + NaHCO_3(aq) \longrightarrow H_2CO_3(aq) + NaC_2H_3O_2(aq) \longrightarrow$$
$$H_2O(l) + CO_2(g) + NaC_2H_3O_2(aq)$$

The bubbling is caused by the newly formed carbon dioxide gas. Other important gas evolution reactions form either H_2SO_3 or NH_4OH as intermediate products.

$$HCl(aq) + NaHSO_3(aq) \longrightarrow H_2SO_3(aq) + NaCl(aq) \longrightarrow$$
$$H_2O(l) + SO_2(g) + NaCl(aq)$$

$$NH_4Cl(aq) + NaOH(aq) \longrightarrow NH_4OH(aq) + NaCl(aq) \longrightarrow$$
$$H_2O(l) + NH_3(g) + NaCl(aq)$$

▲ In this gas evolution reaction, vinegar (a dilute solution of acetic acid) and baking soda (sodium bicarbonate) produce carbon dioxide.

The main types of compounds that form gases in aqueous reactions, as well as the gases that they form, are listed in Table 4.

TABLE 4   Types of Compounds That Undergo Gas Evolution Reactions

Reactant Type	Intermediate Product	Gas Evolved	Example
sulfides	none	H_2S	$2\,HCl(aq) + K_2S(aq) \longrightarrow H_2S(g) + 2\,KCl(aq)$
carbonates and bicarbonates	H_2CO_3	CO_2	$2\,HCl(aq) + K_2CO_3(aq) \longrightarrow H_2O(l) + CO_2(g) + 2\,KCl(aq)$
sulfites and bisulfites	H_2SO_3	SO_2	$2\,HCl(aq) + K_2SO_3(aq) \longrightarrow H_2O(l) + SO_2(g) + 2\,KCl(aq)$
ammonium	NH_4OH	NH_3	$NH_4Cl(aq) + KOH(aq) \longrightarrow H_2O(l) + NH_3(g) + KCl(aq)$

EXAMPLE 12   Writing Equations for Gas Evolution Reactions

Write a molecular equation for the gas evolution reaction that occurs when you mix aqueous nitric acid and aqueous sodium carbonate.

Begin by writing a skeletal equation that includes the reactants and products that form when the cation of each reactant combines with the anion of the other.	SOLUTION $$HNO_3(aq) + Na_2CO_3(aq) \longrightarrow H_2CO_3(aq) + NaNO_3(aq)$$
You must recognize that $H_2CO_3(aq)$ decomposes into $H_2O(l)$ and $CO_2(g)$ and write the corresponding equation.	$$HNO_3(aq) + Na_2CO_3(aq) \longrightarrow H_2O(l) + CO_2(g) + NaNO_3(aq)$$
Finally, balance the equation.	$$2\,HNO_3(aq) + Na_2CO_3(aq) \longrightarrow H_2O(l) + CO_2(g) + 2\,NaNO_3(aq)$$

▶**SKILLBUILDER 12 | Writing Equations for Gas Evolution Reactions**

Write a molecular equation for the gas evolution reaction that occurs when you mix aqueous hydrobromic acid and aqueous potassium sulfite.

▶**SKILLBUILDER PLUS 1**

Write a net ionic equation for the previous reaction.

▶**FOR MORE PRACTICE**   Example 22; Problems 81, 82.

Neutralizing Excess Stomach Acid

Your stomach normally contains acids that are involved in food digestion. Certain foods and stress, however, can increase the acidity of your stomach to uncomfortable levels, causing acid stomach or heartburn. Antacids are over-the-counter medicines that work by reacting with and neutralizing stomach acid. Antacids employ different bases as neutralizing agents. Tums™, for example, contains $CaCO_3$; milk of magnesia contains $Mg(OH)_2$; and Mylanta™ contains $Al(OH)_3$. They all, however, have the same effect of neutralizing stomach acid and relieving heartburn.

CAN YOU ANSWER THIS? *Assume that stomach acid is HCl and write equations showing how each of these antacids neutralizes stomach acid.*

▲ Antacids contain bases such $Mg(OH)_2$, $Al(OH)_3$, and $NaHCO_3$.

Renn SMinkey/Creative Digital Visions/Pearson.

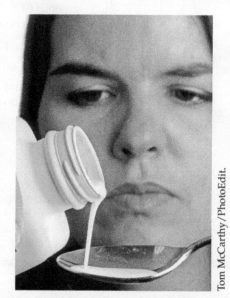

▲ The base in an antacid neutralizes excess stomach acid, relieving heartburn and acid stomach.

Tom McCarthy/PhotoEdit.

9 Oxidation–Reduction Reactions

Reactions involving the transfer of electrons are called **oxidation–reduction reactions** or **redox reactions**. Redox reactions are responsible for the rusting of iron, the bleaching of hair, and the production of electricity in batteries. Many redox reactions involve the reaction of a substance with oxygen.

$$2 H_2(g) + O_2(g) \longrightarrow 2 H_2O(g)$$
(reaction that powers the space shuttle)

$$4 Fe(s) + 3 O_2(g) \longrightarrow 2 Fe_2O_3(s)$$
(rusting of iron)

$$CH_4(g) + 2 O_2(g) \longrightarrow CO_2(g) + 2 H_2O(g)$$
(combustion of natural gas)

However, redox reactions need not involve oxygen. Consider, for example, the reaction between sodium and chlorine to form table salt (NaCl).

$$2 Na(s) + Cl_2(g) \longrightarrow 2 NaCl(s)$$

This reaction is similar to the reaction between sodium and oxygen which can form sodium oxide.

The reaction between sodium and oxygen also forms other oxides besides Na_2O.

$$4 Na(s) + O_2(g) \longrightarrow 2 Na_2O(s)$$

What do these two reactions have in common? In both cases, sodium (a metal with a tendency to lose electrons) reacts with a nonmetal (that has a tendency to gain electrons). In both cases, sodium atoms lose electrons to nonmetal atoms. A fundamental definition of oxidation is *the loss of electrons*, and a fundamental definition of reduction is *the gain of electrons*.

Notice that oxidation and reduction must occur together. If one substance loses electrons (oxidation), then another substance must gain electrons (reduction). For now, you simply need to be able to identify redox reactions.

Redox reactions are those in which:

A reaction can be classified as a redox reaction if it meets any one of these requirements.

- A substance reacts with elemental oxygen.
- A metal reacts with a nonmetal.
- More generally, one substance transfers electrons to another substance.

EXAMPLE 13 **Identifying Redox Reactions**

Which of these are redox reactions?

(a) $2 Mg(s) + O_2(g) \longrightarrow 2 MgO(s)$
(b) $2 HBr(aq) + Ca(OH)_2(aq) \longrightarrow 2 H_2O(l) + CaBr_2(aq)$
(c) $Ca(s) + Cl_2(g) \longrightarrow CaCl_2(s)$
(d) $Zn(s) + Fe^{2+}(aq) \longrightarrow Zn^{2+}(aq) + Fe(s)$

SOLUTION

(a) Redox reaction; Mg reacts with elemental oxygen.
(b) Not a redox reaction; it is an acid–base reaction.
(c) Redox reaction; a metal reacts with a nonmetal.
(d) Redox reaction; Zn transfers two electrons to Fe^{2+}.

▶**SKILLBUILDER 13** | Identifying Redox Reactions

Which of these are redox reactions?

(a) $2 Li(s) + Cl_2(g) \longrightarrow 2 LiCl(s)$
(b) $2 Al(s) + 3 Sn^{2+}(aq) \longrightarrow 2 Al^{3+}(aq) + 3 Sn(s)$
(c) $Pb(NO_3)_2(aq) + 2 LiCl(aq) \longrightarrow PbCl_2(s) + 2 LiNO_3(aq)$
(d) $C(s) + O_2(g) \longrightarrow CO_2(g)$

▶**FOR MORE PRACTICE** Example 23; Problems 83, 84.

COMBUSTION REACTIONS

Combustion reactions are a type of redox reaction. They are important to us because most of our society's energy is derived from combustion reactions. Combustion reactions are characterized by the reaction of a substance with O_2 to form one or more oxygen-containing compounds, often including water. Combustion reactions are exothermic (they emit heat). For example, as we saw in Section 3, natural gas (CH_4) reacts with oxygen to form carbon dioxide and water.

The water formed in combustion reactions may be gaseous (g) or liquid (l) depending on the reaction conditions.

$$CH_4(g) + 2 O_2(g) \longrightarrow CO_2(g) + 2 H_2O(g)$$

As mentioned in the opening section of this chapter, combustion reactions power automobiles. For example, octane, a component of gasoline, reacts with oxygen to form carbon dioxide and water.

$$2 C_8H_{18}(l) + 25 O_2(g) \longrightarrow 16 CO_2(g) + 18 H_2O(g)$$

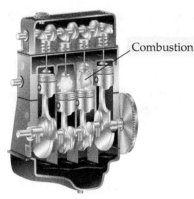

▲ Combustion of octane occurs in the cylinders of an automobile engine.

Ethanol, the alcohol in alcoholic beverages, also reacts with oxygen in a combustion reaction to form carbon dioxide and water.

$$C_2H_5OH(l) + 3\,O_2(g) \longrightarrow 2\,CO_2(g) + 3\,H_2O(g)$$

Compounds containing carbon and hydrogen—or carbon, hydrogen, and oxygen—always form carbon dioxide and water upon combustion. Other combustion reactions include the reaction of carbon with oxygen to form carbon dioxide:

$$C(s) + O_2(g) \longrightarrow CO_2(g)$$

and the reaction of hydrogen with oxygen to form water:

$$2\,H_2(g) + O_2(g) \longrightarrow 2\,H_2O(g)$$

EXAMPLE 14   Writing Combustion Reactions

Write a balanced equation for the combustion of liquid methyl alcohol (CH_3OH).

Begin by writing a skeletal equation showing the reaction of CH_3OH with O_2 to form CO_2 and H_2O.	**SOLUTION** $$CH_3OH(l) + O_2(g) \longrightarrow CO_2(g) + H_2O(g)$$
Balance the skeletal equation using the rules in Section 4.	$$2\,CH_3OH(l) + 3\,O_2(g) \longrightarrow 2\,CO_2(g) + 4\,H_2O(g)$$

▶ SKILLBUILDER 14 | Writing Combustion Reactions

Write a balanced equation for the combustion of liquid pentane (C_5H_{12}), a component of gasoline.

▶ SKILLBUILDER PLUS 2

Write a balanced equation for the combustion of liquid propanol (C_3H_7OH).

▶ FOR MORE PRACTICE   Example 24; Problems 85, 86.

10   Classifying Chemical Reactions

Throughout this chapter, we have examined different types of chemical reactions. We have seen examples of precipitation reactions, acid–base reactions, gas evolution reactions, oxidation–reduction reactions, and combustion reactions. We can organize these different types of reactions with the following flowchart.

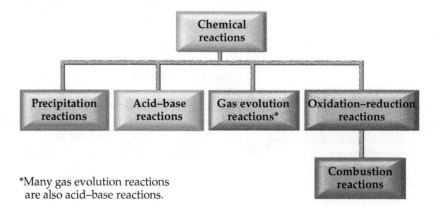

*Many gas evolution reactions are also acid–base reactions.

This classification scheme focuses on the type of chemistry or phenomenon that is occurring during the reaction (such as the formation of a precipitate or the transfer of electrons). However, an alternative way to classify chemical reactions is by what atoms or groups of atoms do during the reaction.

CLASSIFYING CHEMICAL REACTIONS
BY WHAT ATOMS DO

In this alternative way of classifying reactions, we focus on the pattern of the reaction by classifying it into one of the following four categories. In this classification scheme, the letters (A, B, C, D) represent atoms or groups of atoms.

Type of Reaction	Generic Equation
synthesis or combination	$A + B \longrightarrow AB$
decomposition	$AB \longrightarrow A + B$
displacement	$A + BC \longrightarrow AC + B$
double-displacement	$AB + CD \longrightarrow AD + CB$

SYNTHESIS OR COMBINATION REACTIONS. In a **synthesis** or **combination reaction**, simpler substances combine to form more complex substances. The simpler substances may be elements, such as sodium and chlorine combining to form sodium chloride.

$$2\,Na(s) + Cl_2(g) \longrightarrow 2\,NaCl(s)$$

The simpler substances may also be compounds, such as calcium oxide and carbon dioxide combining to form calcium carbonate.

$$CaO(s) + CO_2(g) \longrightarrow CaCO_3(s)$$

In either case, a synthesis reaction follows the general equation:

$$A + B \longrightarrow AB$$

$$2\,Na(s) + Cl_2(g) \longrightarrow 2\,NaCl(s)$$

▲ In a synthesis reaction, two simpler substances combine to make a more complex substance. In this series of photographs we see sodium metal and chlorine gas. When they combine, a chemical reaction occurs that forms sodium chloride.

Richard Megna/Fundamental Photographs.

411

Richard Megna/Fundamental Photographs.

Note that the first two of these reactions are also redox reactions.

Other examples of synthesis reactions include:

$$2\,H_2(g) + O_2(g) \longrightarrow 2\,H_2O(l)$$
$$2\,Mg(s) + O_2(g) \longrightarrow 2\,MgO(s)$$
$$SO_3(g) + H_2O(l) \longrightarrow H_2SO_4(aq)$$

DECOMPOSITION REACTIONS. In a **decomposition reaction**, a complex substance decomposes to form simpler substances. The simpler substances may be elements, such as the hydrogen and oxygen gases that form upon the decomposition of water when electrical current passes through it.

$$2\,H_2O(l) \xrightarrow[\text{electrical current}]{} 2\,H_2(g) + O_2(g)$$

The simpler substances may also be compounds, such as the calcium oxide and carbon dioxide that form upon heating calcium carbonate.

$$CaCO_3(s) \xrightarrow[\text{heat}]{} CaO(s) + CO_2(g)$$

In either case, a decomposition reaction follows the general equation:

$$AB \longrightarrow A + B$$

Other examples of decomposition reactions include:

$$2\,HgO(s) \xrightarrow[\text{heat}]{} 2\,Hg(l) + O_2(g)$$
$$2\,KClO_3(s) \xrightarrow[\text{heat}]{} 2\,KCl(s) + 3\,O_2(g)$$
$$CH_3I(g) \xrightarrow[\text{light}]{} CH_3(g) + I(g)$$

Notice that these decomposition reactions require energy in the form of heat, electrical current, or light to make them happen. This is because compounds are normally stable and energy is required to decompose them. A number of decomposition reactions require *ultraviolet* or *UV light*, which is light in the ultraviolet region of the spectrum. UV light carries more energy than visible light and can therefore initiate the decomposition of many compounds.

DISPLACEMENT REACTIONS. In a **displacement** or **single-displacement reaction**, one element displaces another in a compound. For example, when metallic zinc is added to a solution of copper(II) chloride, the zinc replaces the copper.

$$Zn(s) + CuCl_2(aq) \longrightarrow ZnCl_2(aq) + Cu(s)$$

A displacement reaction follows the general equation:

$$A + BC \longrightarrow AC + B$$

Other examples of displacement reactions include:

$$Mg(s) + 2\,HCl(aq) \longrightarrow MgCl_2(aq) + H_2(g)$$
$$2\,Na(s) + 2\,H_2O(l) \longrightarrow 2\,NaOH(aq) + H_2(g)$$

The last reaction can be identified more easily as a displacement reaction if we write water as HOH(l).

$$2\,Na(s) + 2\,HOH(l) \longrightarrow 2\,NaOH(aq) + H_2(g)$$

$O_2(g)$ — $H_2(g)$ — $H_2O(l)$ — Alkaline

$$2\,H_2O(l) \longrightarrow 2\,H_2(g) + O_2(g)$$

▲ When electrical current is passed through water, the water undergoes a decomposition reaction to form hydrogen gas and oxygen gas.

▶ In a single-displacement reaction, one element displaces another in a compound. When zinc metal is immersed in a copper(II) chloride solution, the zinc atoms displace the copper ions in solution.

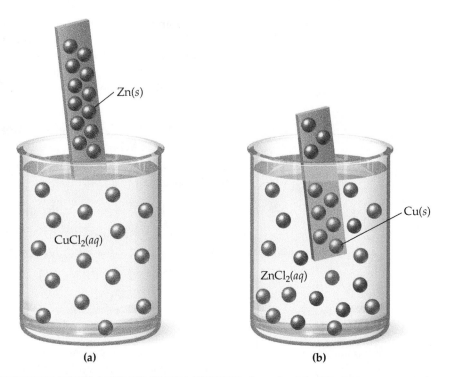

Zn(s)

CuCl₂(aq)

Cu(s)

ZnCl₂(aq)

(a)   (b)

DOUBLE-DISPLACEMENT REACTIONS. In a **double-displacement reaction**, two elements or groups of elements in two different compounds exchange places to form two new compounds. For example, in aqueous solution, the silver in silver nitrate changes places with the sodium in sodium chloride to form solid silver chloride and aqueous sodium nitrate.

This double-displacement reaction is also a precipitation reaction.

$$AgNO_3(aq) + NaCl(aq) \longrightarrow AgCl(s) + NaNO_3(aq)$$

A double-displacement reaction follows the general form:

$$AB + CD \longrightarrow AD + CB$$

Other examples of double-displacement reactions include:

These double-displacement reactions are also acid–base reactions.

$$HCl(aq) + NaOH(aq) \longrightarrow H_2O(l) + NaCl(aq)$$
$$2\,HCl(aq) + Na_2CO_3(aq) \longrightarrow H_2CO_3(aq) + 2\,NaCl(aq)$$

As we learned in Section 8, $H_2CO_3(aq)$ is not stable and decomposes to form $H_2O(l) + CO_2(g)$, so the overall equation is:

This double-displacement reacton is also a gas evolution reaction and an acid–base reaction.

$$2\,HCl(aq) + Na_2CO_3(aq) \longrightarrow H_2O(l) + CO_2(g) + 2\,NaCl(aq)$$

CLASSIFICATION FLOWCHART

A flowchart for this classification scheme of chemical reactions is as follows:

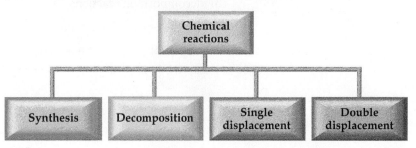

Chemical reactions

Synthesis | Decomposition | Single displacement | Double displacement

413

Of course, no single classification scheme is perfect because all chemical reactions are unique in some sense. However, both classification schemes—one that focuses on the type of chemistry occurring and the other that focuses on what atoms or groups of atoms are doing—are helpful because they help us see differences and similarities among chemical reactions.

EXAMPLE 15   Classifying Chemical Reactions According to What Atoms Do

Classify each reaction as a synthesis, decomposition, single-displacement, or double-displacement reaction.

(a) $Na_2O(s) + H_2O(l) \longrightarrow 2\,NaOH(aq)$

(b) $Ba(NO_3)_2(aq) + K_2SO_4(aq) \longrightarrow BaSO_4(s) + 2\,KNO_3(aq)$

(c) $2\,Al(s) + Fe_2O_3(s) \longrightarrow Al_2O_3(s) + 2\,Fe(l)$

(d) $2\,H_2O_2(aq) \longrightarrow 2\,H_2O(l) + O_2(g)$

(e) $Ca(s) + Cl_2(g) \longrightarrow CaCl_2(s)$

SOLUTION

(a) Synthesis; a more complex substance forms from two simpler ones.
(b) Double-displacment; Ba and K switch places to form two new compounds.
(c) Single-displacement; Al displaces Fe in Fe_2O_3.
(d) Decomposition; a complex substance decomposes into simpler ones.
(e) Synthesis; a more complex substance forms from two simpler ones.

▶**SKILLBUILDER 15 | Classifying Chemical Reactions According to What Atoms Do**

Classify each reaction as a synthesis, decomposition, single-displacement, or double-displacement reaction.

(a) $2\,Al(s) + 2\,H_3PO_4(aq) \longrightarrow 2\,AlPO_4(aq) + 3\,H_2(g)$

(b) $CuSO_4(aq) + 2\,KOH(aq) \longrightarrow Cu(OH)_2(s) + K_2SO_4(aq)$

(c) $2\,K(s) + Br_2(l) \longrightarrow 2\,KBr(s)$

(d) $CuCl_2(aq) \xrightarrow[\text{electrical current}]{} Cu(s) + Cl_2(g)$

▶**FOR MORE PRACTICE**   Example 25; Problems 89, 90, 91, 92.

✓ **CONCEPTUAL CHECKPOINT 6**

Precipitation reactions and acid–base reactions can both also be classified as:

(a) synthesis reactions

(b) decomposition reactions

(c) single-displacement reactions

(d) double-displacement reactions

CHEMISTRY IN THE ENVIRONMENT
The Reactions Involved in Ozone Depletion

Chlorine atoms from chlorofluorocarbons deplete the ozone layer, which normally protects life on Earth from harmful ultraviolet light. Through research, chemists have discovered the reactions by which this depletion occurs.

Ozone normally forms in the upper atmosphere according to this reaction.

(a) $O_2(g) + O(g) \longrightarrow O_3(g)$

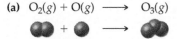

When chlorofluorocarbons drift to the upper atmosphere, they are exposed to ultraviolet light and undergo the reaction.

(b) $CF_2Cl_2(g) \xrightarrow{\text{UV light}} CF_2Cl(g) + Cl(g)$

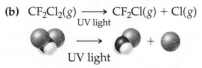

Atomic chlorine then reacts with and depletes ozone according to this cycle of reactions.

(c) $Cl(g) + O_3(g) \longrightarrow ClO(g) + O_2(g)$

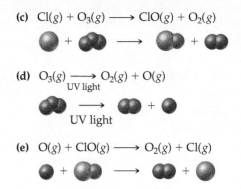

(d) $O_3(g) \xrightarrow{\text{UV light}} O_2(g) + O(g)$

(e) $O(g) + ClO(g) \longrightarrow O_2(g) + Cl(g)$

Notice that in the final reaction, atomic chlorine is regenerated and can go through the cycle again to deplete more ozone. Through this cycle of reactions, a single chlorofluorocarbon molecule can deplete thousands of ozone molecules.

CAN YOU ANSWER THIS? *Classify each of these reactions (a–e) as a synthesis, decomposition, single-displacement, or double-displacement reaction.*

CHAPTER IN REVIEW

CHEMICAL PRINCIPLES

RELEVANCE

Chemical Reactions: In a chemical reaction, one or more substances—either elements or compounds—changes into a different substance.

Chemical Reactions: Chemical reactions are central to many processes, including transportation, energy generation, manufacture of household products, vision, and life itself.

Evidence of a Chemical Reaction: The only absolute evidence for a chemical reaction is chemical analysis showing that one or more substances has changed into another substance. However, one or more of the following often accompanies a chemical reaction: a color change; the formation of a solid or precipitate; the formation of a gas; the emission of light; and the emission or absorption of heat.

Evidence of a Chemical Reaction: We can often perceive the changes that accompany chemical reactions. In fact, we often employ chemical reactions for the changes they produce. For example, we use the heat emitted by the combustion of fossil fuels to heat our homes, drive our cars, and generate electricity.

Chemical Equations: Chemical equations represent chemical reactions. They include formulas for the reactants (the substances present before the reaction) and for the products (the new substances formed by the reaction). Chemical equations must be balanced to reflect the conservation of matter in nature; atoms do not spontaneously appear or disappear.

Chemical Equations: Chemical equations allow us to represent and understand chemical reactions. For example, the equations for the combustion reactions of fossil fuels let us see that carbon dioxide, a gas that contributes to global warming, is one of the products of these reactions.

Aqueous Solutions and Solubility: Aqueous solutions are mixtures of a substance dissolved in water. If a substance dissolves in water it is soluble. Otherwise, it is insoluble.

Aqueous Solutions and Solubility: Aqueous solutions are common. Oceans, lakes, and most of the fluids in our bodies are aqueous solutions.

Some Specific Types of Reactions:

Precipitation reaction: A solid or precipitate forms upon mixing two aqueous solutions.

Acid–base reaction: Water forms upon mixing an acid and a base.

Gas evolution reaction: A gas forms upon mixing two aqueous solutions.

Redox reaction: Electrons are transferred from one substance to another.

Combustion reaction: A substance reacts with oxygen, emitting heat, and forming an oxygen-containing compound and, in many cases, water.

Some Specific Types of Reactions: Many of the specific types of reactions discussed in this chapter occur in aqueous solutions and are therefore important to living organisms. Acid–base reactions, for example, constantly occur in the blood of living organisms to maintain constant blood acidity levels. In humans, a small change in blood acidity levels would result in death, so the body carries out chemical reactions to prevent this. Combustion reactions are important because they are the main energy source for our society.

Classifying Chemical Reactions: Many chemical reactions can be classified into one of the following four categories according to what atoms or groups of atoms do:

· synthesis: $(A + B \longrightarrow AB)$

· decomposition: $(AB \longrightarrow A + B)$

· single-displacement: $(A + BC \longrightarrow AC + B)$

· double-displacement: $(AB + CD \longrightarrow AD + CB)$

Classifying Chemical Reactions: We classify chemical reactions to better understand them and to recognize similarities and differences among reactions.

CHEMICAL SKILLS

EXAMPLES

Identifying a Chemical Reaction (Section 2)

EXAMPLE 16   Identifying a Chemical Reaction

Which of these are chemical reactions?

(a) Copper turns green on exposure to air.
(b) When sodium bicarbonate is combined with hydrochloric acid, bubbling is observed.
(c) Liquid water freezes to form solid ice.
(d) A pure copper penny forms bubbles of a dark brown gas when dropped into nitric acid. The nitric acid solution turns blue.

To identify a chemical reaction, determine whether one or more of the initial substances changed into a different substance. If so, a chemical reaction occurred. One or more of the following often accompanies a chemical reaction: a color change; the formation of a solid or precipitate; the formation of a gas; the emission of light; and the emission or absorption of heat.

SOLUTION

(a) Chemical reaction, as evidenced by the color change.
(b) Chemical reaction, as evidenced by the evolution of a gas.
(c) Not a chemical reaction; solid ice is still water.
(d) Chemical reaction, as evidenced by the evolution of a gas and by a color change.

Writing Balanced Chemical Equations (Sections 3, 4)

To write balanced chemical equations, follow these steps.

1. Write a skeletal equation by writing chemical formulas for each of the reactants and products. (If a skeletal equation is provided, proceed to Step 2.)

2. If an element occurs in only one compound on both sides of the equation, balance that element first. If there is more than one such element, and the equation contains both metals and nonmetals, balance metals before nonmetals.

3. If an element occurs as a free element on either side of the chemical equation, balance that element last.

4. If the balanced equation contains coefficient fractions, clear these by multiplying the entire equation by the appropriate factor.

5. Check to make certain the equation is balanced by summing the total number of each type of atom on both sides of the equation.

Reminders

- Change only the *coefficients* to balance a chemical equation, *never the subscripts*. Changing the subscripts would change the compound itself.

- If the equation contains polyatomic ions that stay intact on both sides of the equation, balance the polyatomic ions as a group.

EXAMPLE 17 Writing Balanced Chemical Equations

Write a balanced chemical equation for the reaction of solid vanadium(V) oxide with hydrogen gas to form solid vanadium(III) oxide and liquid water.

$$V_2O_5(s) + H_2(g) \longrightarrow V_2O_3(s) + H_2O(l)$$

SOLUTION

Skeletal equation is given. Proceed to Step 2.

Vanadium occurs in only one compound on both sides of the equation. However, it is balanced, so you can proceed and balance oxygen by placing a 2 in front of H_2O on the right side.

$$V_2O_5(s) + H_2(g) \longrightarrow V_2O_3(s) + \mathbf{2}\,H_2O(l)$$

Hydrogen occurs as a free element, so balance it last by placing a 2 in front of H_2 on the left side.

$$V_2O_5(s) + \mathbf{2}\,H_2(g) \longrightarrow V_2O_3(s) + 2\,H_2O(l)$$

Equation does not contain coefficient fractions. Proceed to Step 5.

Check the equation.

$$V_2O_5(s) + \mathbf{2}\,H_2(g) \longrightarrow V_2O_3(s) + \mathbf{2}\,H_2O(l)$$

Reactants		Products
2 V atoms	$\longrightarrow$	2 V atoms
5 O atoms	$\longrightarrow$	5 O atoms
4 H atoms	$\longrightarrow$	4 H atoms

Determining Whether a Compound Is Soluble (Section 5)

To determine whether a compound is soluble, refer to the solubility rules in Table 2. It is easiest to begin by looking for those ions that always form soluble compounds (Li^+, Na^+, K^+, NH_4^+, NO_3^-, and $C_2H_3O_2^-$). If a compound contains one of those, it is soluble. If it does not, look at the anion and determine whether it is mostly soluble (Cl^-, Br^-, I^-, or SO_4^{2-}) or mostly insoluble (OH^-, S^{2-}, CO_3^{2-}, or PO_4^{3-}). Look also at the cation to determine whether it is one of the exceptions.

EXAMPLE 18 Determining Whether a Compound Is Soluble

Determine whether each compound is soluble.

(a) $CuCO_3$
(b) $BaSO_4$
(c) $Fe(NO_3)_3$

SOLUTION

(a) Insoluble; compounds containing CO_3^{2-} are insoluble, and Cu^{2+} is not an exception.
(b) Insoluble; compounds containing SO_4^{2-} are usually soluble, but Ba^{2+} is an exception.
(c) Soluble; all compounds containing NO_3^- are soluble.

Predicting Precipitation Reactions (Section 6)

To predict whether a precipitation reaction occurs when two solutions are mixed and to write an equation for the reaction, follow these steps.

1. Write the formulas of the two compounds being mixed as reactants in a chemical equation.
2. Below the equation, write the formulas of the potentially insoluble products that could form from the reactants. These are obtained by combining the cation from one reactant with the anion from the other. Make sure to adjust the subscripts so that all formulas are charge-neutral.
3. Use the solubility rules to determine whether any of the potentially insoluble products are indeed insoluble.
4. If all of the potentially insoluble products are soluble, there will be no precipitate. Write *NO REACTION* next to the arrow.
5. If one or both of the potentially insoluble products are insoluble, write their formula(s) as the product(s) of the reaction using (s) to indicate *solid*. Write any soluble products with (aq) to indicate *aqueous*.
6. Balance the equation.

EXAMPLE 19 Predicting Precipitation Reactions

Write an equation for the precipitation reaction that occurs, if any, when solutions of sodium phosphate and cobalt(II) chloride are mixed.

SOLUTION

$$Na_3PO_4(aq) + CoCl_2(aq) \longrightarrow$$

Potentially Insoluble Products:

$$NaCl \qquad Co_3(PO_4)_2$$

NaCl is soluble.
$Co_3(PO_4)_2$ is insoluble.
   Reaction contains an insoluble product; proceed to Step 5.

$$Na_3PO_4(aq) + CoCl_2(aq) \longrightarrow Co_3(PO_4)_2(s) + NaCl(aq)$$

$$2\,Na_3PO_4(aq) + 3\,CoCl_2(aq) \longrightarrow$$
$$CO_3(PO_4)_2(s) + 6\,NaCl(aq)$$

Writing Complete Ionic and Net Ionic Equations (Section 7)

To write a complete ionic equation from a molecular equation, separate all aqueous ionic compounds into independent ions. Do not separate solid, liquid, or gaseous compounds.

   To write a net ionic equation from a complete ionic equation, eliminate all species that do not change (spectator ions) in the course of the reaction.

EXAMPLE 20 Writing Complete Ionic and Net Ionic Equations

Write a complete ionic and net ionic equation for the reaction.

$$2\,NH_4Cl(aq) + Hg_2(NO_3)_2(aq) \longrightarrow$$
$$Hg_2Cl_2(s) + 2\,NH_4NO_3(aq)$$

SOLUTION

Complete ionic equation:

$$2\,NH_4^+(aq) + 2\,Cl^-(aq) + Hg_2^{2+}(aq) + 2\,NO_3^-(aq) \longrightarrow$$
$$Hg_2Cl_2(s) + 2\,NH_4^+(aq) + 2\,NO_3^-(aq)$$

Net ionic equation:

$$2\,Cl^-(aq) + Hg_2^{2+}(aq) \longrightarrow Hg_2Cl_2(s)$$

Writing Equations for Acid–Base Reactions (Section 8)

When you see an acid and a base (see Table 3) as reactants in an equation, write a reaction in which the acid and the base react to form water and a salt.

EXAMPLE 21 Writing Equations for Acid–Base Reactions

Write an equation for the reaction that occurs when aqueous hydroiodic acid is mixed with aqueous barium hydroxide.

SOLUTION

$$\underset{\text{acid}}{2\,HI(aq)} + \underset{\text{base}}{Ba(OH)_2(aq)} \longrightarrow \underset{\text{water}}{2\,H_2O(l)} + \underset{\text{salt}}{BaI_2(aq)}$$

Writing Equations for Gas Evolution Reactions (Section 8)

See Table 4 to identify gas evolution reactions.

EXAMPLE 22   Writing Equations for Gas Evolution Reactions

Write an equation for the reaction that occurs when aqueous hydrobromic acid is mixed with aqueous potassium bisulfite.

SOLUTION

$$HBr(aq) + KHSO_3(aq) \longrightarrow H_2SO_3(aq) + KBr(aq) \longrightarrow$$
$$H_2O(l) + SO_2(g) + KBr(aq)$$

Identifying Redox Reactions (Section 9)

Redox reactions are those in which any of the following occurs:

- a substance reacts with elemental oxygen
- a metal reacts with a nonmetal
- one substance transfers electrons to another substance

EXAMPLE 23   Identifying Redox Reactions

Which of these reactions is a redox reaction?

(a) $4 Fe(s) + 3 O_2(g) \longrightarrow 2 Fe_2O_3(s)$
(b) $CaO(s) + CO_2(g) \longrightarrow CaCO_3(s)$
(c) $AgNO_3(aq) + NaCl(aq) \longrightarrow AgCl(s) + NaNO_3(aq)$

SOLUTION
Only **(a)** is a redox reaction.

Writing Equations for Combustion Reactions (Section 9)

In a combustion reaction, a substance reacts with O_2 to form one or more oxygen-containing compounds and, in many cases, water.

EXAMPLE 24   Writing Equations for Combustion Reactions

Write a balanced equation for the combustion of gaseous ethane (C_2H_6), a minority component of natural gas.

SOLUTION
The skeletal equation is:

$$C_2H_6(g) + O_2(g) \longrightarrow CO_2(g) + H_2O(g)$$

The balanced equation is:

$$2 C_2H_6(g) + 7 O_2(g) \longrightarrow 4 CO_2(g) + 6 H_2O(g)$$

Classifying Chemical Reactions (Section 10)

Chemical reactions can be classified by inspection. The four major categories are:
Synthesis or combination

$$A + B \longrightarrow AB$$

Decomposition

$$AB \longrightarrow A + B$$

Single-displacement

$$A + BC \longrightarrow AC + B$$

Double-displacement

$$AB + CD \longrightarrow AD + CB$$

EXAMPLE 25   Classifying Chemical Reactions

Classify each chemical reaction as a synthesis, decomposition, single-displacement, or double-displacement reaction.

(a) $2 K(s) + Br_2(g) \longrightarrow 2 KBr(s)$
(b) $Fe(s) + 2 AgNO_3(aq) \longrightarrow Fe(NO_3)_2(aq) + 2 Ag(s)$
(c) $CaSO_3(s) \longrightarrow CaO(s) + SO_2(g)$
(d) $CaCl_2(aq) + Li_2SO_4(aq) \longrightarrow CaSO_4(s) + 2 LiCl(aq)$

SOLUTION

(a) Synthesis; KBr, a more complex substance, is formed from simpler substances.
(b) Single-displacement; Fe displaces Ag in $AgNO_3$.
(c) Decomposition; $CaSO_3$ decomposes into simpler substances.
(d) Double-displacement; Ca and Li switch places to form new compounds.

KEY TERMS

acid–base reaction **[Section 8]**

aqueous solution **[Section 5]**

balanced equation **[Section 3]**

combination reaction **[Section 10]**

combustion reaction **[Section 9]**

complete ionic equation **[Section 7]**

decomposition reaction **[Section 10]**

displacement reaction **[Section 10]**

double-displacement reaction **[Section 10]**

gas evolution reaction **[Section 8]**

insoluble **[Section 5]**

molecular equation **[Section 7]**

net ionic equation **[Section 7]**

neutralization reaction **[Section 8]**

oxidation–reduction (redox) reaction **[Section 9]**

precipitate **[Section 6]**

precipitation reaction **[Section 6]**

salt **[Section 8]**

single-displacement reaction **[Section 10]**

solubility rules **[Section 5]**

soluble **[Section 5]**

spectator ion **[Section 7]**

strong electrolyte solution **[Section 5]**

synthesis reaction **[Section 10]**

EXERCISES

QUESTIONS

1. What is a chemical reaction? List some examples.
2. If you could observe atoms and molecules, what would you look for as conclusive evidence of a chemical reaction?
3. What are the main indications that a chemical reaction has occurred?
4. What is a chemical equation? Provide an example and identify the reactants and products.
5. What does each abbreviation, often used in chemical equations, represent?
   (a) (g) (b) (l) (c) (s) (d) (aq)
6. To balance a chemical equation, adjust the _____ as necessary to make the numbers of each type of atom on both sides of the equation equal. Never adjust the _____ to balance a chemical equation.
7. List the number of each type of atom on both sides of each equation. Are the equations balanced?
   (a) $2 \, Ag_2O(s) + C(s) \longrightarrow CO_2(g) + 4 \, Ag(s)$
   (b) $Pb(NO_3)_2(aq) + 2 \, NaCl(aq) \longrightarrow$
   $PbCl_2(s) + 2 \, NaNO_3(aq)$
   (c) $C_3H_8(g) + O_2(g) \longrightarrow 3 \, CO_2(g) + 4 \, H_2O(g)$
8. What is an aqueous solution? List two examples.
9. What does it mean for a compound to be soluble? Insoluble?
10. Explain what happens to an ionic substance when it dissolves in water.

11. Do polyatomic ions dissociate when they dissolve in water, or do they remain intact?
12. What is a strong electrolyte solution?
13. What are the solubility rules, and how are they useful?
14. What is a precipitation reaction? Provide an example and identify the precipitate.
15. Will the precipitate in a precipitation reaction always be a compound that is soluble or insoluble? Explain.
16. Describe the differences between a molecular equation, a complete ionic equation, and net ionic equation. Give an example of each to illustrate the differences.
17. What is an acid–base reaction? List an example and identify the acid and the base.
18. What are the properties of acids and bases?
19. What is a gas evolution reaction? Give an example.
20. What is a redox reaction? Give an example.
21. What is a combustion reaction? Give an example.
22. What are two different ways to classify chemical reactions presented in Section 10? Explain the differences between them.
23. Explain the difference between a synthesis reaction and a decomposition reaction and give an example of each.
24. Explain the difference between a single-displacement reaction and a double-displacement reaction and give an example of each.

PROBLEMS

EVIDENCE OF CHEMICAL REACTIONS

25. Which observation is consistent with a chemical reaction occurring? Why?
    (a) Solid copper deposits on a piece of aluminum foil when the foil is placed in a blue copper nitrate solution. The blue color of the solution fades.
    (b) Liquid ethyl alcohol turns into a solid when placed in a low-temperature freezer.
    (c) A white precipitate forms when solutions of barium nitrate and sodium sulfate are mixed.
    (d) A mixture of sugar and water bubbles when yeasts are added. After several days, the sugar is gone and ethyl alcohol is found in the water.

26. Which observation is consistent with a chemical reaction occurring? Why?
    (a) Propane forms a flame and emits heat as it burns.
    (b) Acetone feels cold as it evaporates from the skin.
    (c) Bubbling is observed when potassium carbonate and hydrochloric acid solutions are mixed.
    (d) Heat is felt when a warm object is placed in your hand.

27. Vinegar forms bubbles when it is poured onto the calcium deposits on a faucet, and some of the calcium dissolves. Has a chemical reaction occurred? Explain your answer.

28. When a chemical drain opener is added to a clogged sink, bubbles form and the water in the sink gets warmer. Has a chemical reaction occurred? Explain your answer.

29. When a commercial hair bleaching mixture is applied to brown hair, the hair turns blond. Has a chemical reaction occurred? Explain your answer.

30. When water is boiled in a pot, it bubbles. Has a chemical reaction occurred? Explain your answer.

WRITING AND BALANCING CHEMICAL EQUATIONS

31. Consider the unbalanced chemical equation:

$$H_2O(l) \xrightarrow{\text{electrical current}} H_2(g) + O_2(g)$$

A chemistry student tries to balance the equation by placing the subscript 2 after the oxygen atom in H_2O. Explain why this is not correct. What is the correct balanced equation?

32. Consider the unbalanced chemical equation:

$$Al(s) + Cl_2(g) \longrightarrow AlCl_3(s)$$

A student tries to balance the equation by changing the subscript 2 on Cl to a 3. Explain why this is not correct. What is the correct balanced equation?

33. Write a balanced chemical equation for each chemical reaction:
   (a) Solid lead(II) sulfide reacts with aqueous hydrochloric acid to form solid lead(II) chloride and dihydrogen sulfide gas.
   (b) Gaseous carbon monoxide reacts with hydrogen gas to form gaseous methane (CH_4) and liquid water.
   (c) Solid iron(III) oxide reacts with hydrogen gas to form solid iron and liquid water.
   (d) Gaseous ammonia (NH_3) reacts with gaseous oxygen to form gaseous nitrogen monoxide and gaseous water.

34. Write a balanced chemical equation for each chemical reaction:
   (a) Solid copper reacts with solid sulfur to form solid copper(I) sulfide.
   (b) Sulfur dioxide gas reacts with oxygen gas to form sulfur trioxide gas.
   (c) Aqueous hydrochloric acid reacts with solid manganese(IV) oxide to form aqueous manganese(II) chloride, liquid water, and chlorine gas.
   (d) Liquid benzene (C_6H_6) reacts with gaseous oxygen to form carbon dioxide and liquid water.

35. Write a balanced chemical equation for each chemical reaction:
   (a) Solid magnesium reacts with aqueous copper(I) nitrate to form aqueous magnesium nitrate and solid copper.
   (b) Gaseous dinitrogen pentoxide decomposes to form nitrogen dioxide and oxygen gas.
   (c) Solid calcium reacts with aqueous nitric acid to form aqueous calcium nitrate and hydrogen gas.
   (d) Liquid methanol (CH_3OH) reacts with oxygen gas to form gaseous carbon dioxide and gaseous water.

36. Write a balanced chemical equation for each chemical reaction:
   (a) Gaseous acetylene (C_2H_2) reacts with oxygen gas to form gaseous carbon dioxide and gaseous water.
   (b) Chlorine gas reacts with aqueous potassium iodide to form solid iodine and aqueous potassium chloride.
   (c) Solid lithium oxide reacts with liquid water to form aqueous lithium hydroxide.
   (d) Gaseous carbon monoxide reacts with oxygen gas to form carbon dioxide gas.

37. Hydrogen has been widely proposed as a potential fuel to replace fossil fuels. Some scientists are trying to anticipate any potential problems that might be associated with a hydrogen-based economy. One group of scientists has calculated that the amount of atmospheric hydrogen could increase by a factor of four due to leaks in hydrogen transport and storage. Upper atmospheric hydrogen gas reacts with oxygen gas to form liquid water. An increase in upper atmospheric water would enhance processes that release atmospheric chlorine atoms. The gaseous chlorine atoms would then react with gaseous ozone (O_3) to form gaseous chlorine monoxide and gaseous oxygen, resulting in the depletion of ozone. Write balanced chemical equations for the two reactions described in this problem.

38. Waste water from certain industrial chemical processes contains aqueous Hg_2^{2+} ions. Since the mercury ion is toxic, it is removed from the waste water by reaction with aqueous sodium sulfide. The products of the reaction are solid mercury(I) sulfide and aqueous sodium ions. Write a balanced equation for this reaction.

39. When solid sodium is added to liquid water, it reacts with the water to produce hydrogen gas and aqueous sodium hydroxide. Write a balanced chemical equation for this reaction.

40. When iron rusts, solid iron reacts with gaseous oxygen to form solid iron(III) oxide. Write a balanced chemical equation for this reaction.

41. Sulfuric acid in acid rain forms when gaseous sulfur dioxide pollutant reacts with gaseous oxygen and liquid water to form aqueous sulfuric acid. Write a balanced chemical equation for this reaction.

42. Nitric acid in acid rain forms when gaseous nitrogen dioxide pollutant reacts with gaseous oxygen and liquid water to form aqueous nitric acid. Write a balanced chemical equation for this reaction.

43. Write a balanced chemical equation for the reaction of solid vanadium(V) oxide with hydrogen gas to form solid vanadium(III) oxide and liquid water.

44. Write a balanced chemical equation for the reaction of gaseous nitrogen dioxide with hydrogen gas to form gaseous ammonia and liquid water.

45. Write a balanced chemical equation for the fermentation of sugar ($C_{12}H_{22}O_{11}$) by yeasts in which the aqueous sugar reacts with water to form aqueous ethyl alcohol (C_2H_5OH) and carbon dioxide gas.

46. Write a balanced chemical equation for the photosynthesis reaction in which gaseous carbon dioxide and liquid water react in the presence of chlorophyll to produce aqueous glucose ($C_6H_{12}O_6$) and oxygen gas.

47. Balance each chemical equation.

(a) $Na_2S(aq) + Cu(NO_3)_2(aq) \longrightarrow$
$$NaNO_3(aq) + CuS(s)$$

(b) $HCl(aq) + O_2(g) \longrightarrow H_2O(l) + Cl_2(g)$

(c) $H_2(g) + O_2(g) \longrightarrow H_2O(l)$

(d) $FeS(s) + HCl(aq) \longrightarrow FeCl_2(aq) + H_2S(g)$

48. Balance each chemical equation.

(a) $N_2H_4(l) \longrightarrow NH_3(g) + N_2(g)$

(b) $H_2(g) + N_2(g) \longrightarrow NH_3(g)$

(c) $Cu_2O(s) + C(s) \longrightarrow Cu(s) + CO(g)$

(d) $H_2(g) + Cl_2(g) \longrightarrow HCl(g)$

49. Balance each chemical equation.

(a) $BaO_2(s) + H_2SO_4(aq) \longrightarrow$
$$BaSO_4(s) + H_2O_2(aq)$$

(b) $Co(NO_3)_3(aq) + (NH_4)_2S(aq) \longrightarrow$
$$Co_2S_3(s) + NH_4NO_3(aq)$$

(c) $Li_2O(s) + H_2O(l) \longrightarrow LiOH(aq)$

(d) $Hg_2(C_2H_3O_2)_2(aq) + KCl(aq) \longrightarrow$
$$Hg_2Cl_2(s) + KC_2H_3O_2(aq)$$

50. Balance each chemical equation.

(a) $MnO_2(s) + HCl(aq) \longrightarrow$
$$Cl_2(g) + MnCl_2(aq) + H_2O(l)$$

(b) $CO_2(g) + CaSiO_3(s) + H_2O(l) \longrightarrow$
$$SiO_2(s) + Ca(HCO_3)_2(aq)$$

(c) $Fe(s) + S(l) \longrightarrow Fe_2S_3(s)$

(d) $NO_2(g) + H_2O(l) \longrightarrow HNO_3(aq) + NO(g)$

51. Determine whether each chemical equation is correctly balanced. If not, correct it.

(a) $Rb(s) + H_2O(l) \longrightarrow RbOH(aq) + H_2(g)$

(b) $2 N_2H_4(g) + N_2O_4(g) \longrightarrow 3 N_2(g) + 4 H_2O(g)$

(c) $NiS(s) + O_2(g) \longrightarrow NiO(s) + SO_2(g)$

(d) $PbO(s) + 2 NH_3(g) \longrightarrow$
$$Pb(s) + N_2(g) + H_2O(l)$$

52. Determine whether each chemical equation is correctly balanced. If not, correct it.

(a) $SiO_2(s) + 4 HF(aq) \longrightarrow SiF_4(g) + 2 H_2O(l)$

(b) $2 Cr(s) + 3 O_2(g) \longrightarrow Cr_2O_3(s)$

(c) $Al_2S_3(s) + H_2O(l) \longrightarrow 2 Al(OH)_3(s) + 3 H_2S(g)$

(d) $Fe_2O_3(s) + CO(g) \longrightarrow 2 Fe(s) + CO_2(g)$

53. Human cells obtain energy from a reaction called cellular respiration. Balance the skeletal equation for cellular respiration.

$$C_6H_{12}O_6(aq) + O_2(g) \longrightarrow CO_2(g) + H_2O(l)$$

54. Propane camping stoves produce heat by the combustion of gaseous propane (C_3H_8). Balance the skeletal equation for the combustion of propane.

$$C_3H_8(g) + O_2(g) \longrightarrow CO_2(g) + H_2O(g)$$

55. Catalytic converters work to remove nitrogen oxides and carbon monoxide from exhaust. Balance the skeletal equation for one of the reactions that occurs in a catalytic converter.

$$NO(g) + CO(g) \longrightarrow N_2(g) + CO_2(g)$$

56. Billions of pounds of urea are produced annually for use as a fertilizer. Balance the skeletal equation for the synthesis of urea.

$$NH_3(g) + CO_2(g) \longrightarrow CO(NH_2)_2(s) + H_2O(l)$$

SOLUBILITY

57. Determine whether each compound is soluble or insoluble. For the soluble compounds, identify the ions present in solution.

(a) $NaC_2H_3O_2$

(b) $Sn(NO_3)_2$

(c) AgI

(d) $Na_3(PO_4)$

58. Determine whether each compound is soluble or insoluble. For the soluble compounds, identify the ions present in solution.

(a) $(NH_4)_2S$

(b) $CuCO_3$

(c) ZnS

(d) $Pb(C_2H_3O_2)_2$

59. Pair each cation on the left with an anion on the right that will form an *insoluble* compound with it and write a formula for the insoluble compound. Use each anion only once.

Ag^+	SO_4^{2-}
Ba^{2+}	Cl^-
Cu^{2+}	CO_3^{2-}
Fe^{3+}	S^{2-}

60. Pair each cation on the left with an anion on the right that will form a *soluble* compound with it and write a formula for the soluble compound. Use each anion only once.

Na^+	NO_3^-
Sr^{2+}	SO_4^{2-}
Co^{2+}	S^{2-}
Pb^{2+}	CO_3^{2-}

61. Determine whether each compound is in the correct column. Move any misplaced compounds to the correct column.

Soluble	Insoluble
K_2S	K_2SO_4
$PbSO_4$	Hg_2I_2
BaS	$Cu_3(PO_4)_2$
$PbCl_2$	MgS
Hg_2Cl_2	$CaSO_4$
NH_4Cl	SrS
Na_2CO_3	Li_2S

62. Determine whether each compound is in the correct column. Move any misplaced compounds to the correct column.

Soluble	Insoluble
$LiOH$	$CaCl_2$
Na_2CO_3	$Cu(OH)_2$
$AgCl$	$Ca(C_2H_3O_2)_2$
K_3PO_4	$SrSO_4$
CuI_2	Hg_2Br_2
$Pb(NO_3)_2$	$PbBr_2$
$CoCO_3$	PbI_2

PRECIPITATION REACTIONS

63. Complete and balance each equation. If no reaction occurs, write *NO REACTION*.

(a) $KI(aq) + BaS(aq) \longrightarrow$

(b) $K_2SO_4(aq) + BaBr_2(aq) \longrightarrow$

(c) $NaCl(aq) + Hg_2(C_2H_3O_2)_2(aq) \longrightarrow$

(d) $NaC_2H_3O_2(aq) + Pb(NO_3)_2(aq) \longrightarrow$

64. Complete and balance each equation. If no reaction occurs, write *NO REACTION*.

(a) $NaOH(aq) + FeBr_3(aq) \longrightarrow$

(b) $BaCl_2(aq) + AgNO_3(aq) \longrightarrow$

(c) $Na_2CO_3(aq) + CoCl_2(aq) \longrightarrow$

(d) $K_2S(aq) + BaCl_2(aq) \longrightarrow$

65. Write a molecular equation for the precipitation reaction that occurs (if any) when each pair of solutions is mixed. If no reaction occurs, write *NO REACTION*.

(a) sodium carbonate and lead(II) nitrate

(b) potassium sulfate and lead(II) acetate

(c) copper(II) nitrate and barium sulfide

(d) calcium nitrate and sodium iodide

66. Write a molecular equation for the precipitation reaction that occurs (if any) when each pair of solutions is mixed. If no reaction occurs, write *NO REACTION*.

(a) potassium chloride and lead(II) acetate

(b) lithium sulfate and strontium chloride

(c) potassium bromide and calcium sulfide

(d) chromium(III) nitrate and potassium phosphate

67. Determine whether each equation for a precipitation reaction is correct. Correct any incorrect equations. If no reaction occurs, write *NO REACTION*.

(a) $Ba(NO_3)_2(aq) + (NH_4)_2SO_4(aq) \longrightarrow$
$$BaSO_4(s) + 2\,NH_4NO_3(aq)$$

(b) $BaS(aq) + 2\,KCl(aq) \longrightarrow BaCl_2(s) + K_2S(aq)$

(c) $2\,KI(aq) + Pb(NO_3)_2(aq) \longrightarrow$
$$PbI_2(s) + 2\,KNO_3(aq)$$

(d) $Pb(NO_3)_2(aq) + 2\,LiCl(aq) \longrightarrow$
$$2\,LiNO_3(s) + PbCl_2(aq)$$

68. Determine whether each equation for a precipitation reaction is correct. Correct any incorrect equations. If no reaction occurs, write *NO REACTION*.

(a) $AgNO_3(aq) + NaCl(aq) \longrightarrow$
$$NaCl(s) + AgNO_3(aq)$$

(b) $K_2SO_4(aq) + Co(NO_3)_2(aq) \longrightarrow$
$$CoSO_4(s) + 2\,KNO_3(aq)$$

(c) $Cu(NO_3)_2(aq) + (NH_4)_2S(aq) \longrightarrow$
$$CuS(s) + 2\,NH_4NO_3(aq)$$

(d) $Hg_2(NO_3)_2(aq) + 2\,LiCl(aq) \longrightarrow$
$$Hg_2Cl_2(s) + 2\,LiNO_3(aq)$$

IONIC AND NET IONIC EQUATIONS

69. Identify the spectator ions in the complete ionic equation.

$2\,K^+(aq) + S^{2-}(aq) + Pb^{2+}(aq) + 2\,NO_3^-(aq) \longrightarrow$
$$PbS(s) + 2\,K^+(aq) + 2\,NO_3^-(aq)$$

70. Identify the spectator ions in the complete ionic equation.

$Ba^{2+}(aq) + 2\,I^-(aq) + 2\,Na^+(aq) + SO_4^{2-}(aq) \longrightarrow$
$$BaSO_4(s) + 2\,I^-(aq) + 2\,Na^+(aq)$$

71. Write balanced complete ionic and net ionic equations for each reaction.

(a) $AgNO_3(aq) + KCl(aq) \longrightarrow$
$$AgCl(s) + KNO_3(aq)$$

(b) $CaS(aq) + CuCl_2(aq) \longrightarrow CuS(s) + CaCl_2(aq)$

(c) $NaOH(aq) + HNO_3(aq) \longrightarrow$
$$H_2O(l) + NaNO_3(aq)$$

(d) $2\,K_3PO_4(aq) + 3\,NiCl_2(aq) \longrightarrow$
$$Ni_3(PO_4)_2(s) + 6\,KCl(aq)$$

72. Write balanced complete ionic and net ionic equations for each reaction.

(a) $HI(aq) + KOH(aq) \longrightarrow H_2O(l) + KI(aq)$

(b) $Na_2SO_4(aq) + CaI_2(aq) \longrightarrow$
$$CaSO_4(s) + 2\,NaI(aq)$$

(c) $2\,HC_2H_3O_2(aq) + Na_2CO_3(aq) \longrightarrow$
$$H_2O(l) + CO_2(g) + 2\,NaC_2H_3O_2(aq)$$

(d) $NH_4Cl(aq) + NaOH(aq) \longrightarrow$
$$H_2O(l) + NH_3(g) + NaCl(aq)$$

73. Mercury(I) ions (Hg_2^{2+}) can be removed from solution by precipitation with Cl^-. Suppose a solution contains aqueous $Hg_2(NO_3)_2$. Write complete ionic and net ionic equations to show the reaction of aqueous $Hg_2(NO_3)_2$ with aqueous sodium chloride to form solid Hg_2Cl_2 and aqueous sodium nitrate.

74. Lead ions can be removed from solution by precipitation with sulfate ions. Suppose a solution contains lead(II) nitrate. Write a complete ionic and net ionic equation to show the reaction of aqueous lead(II) nitrate with aqueous potassium sulfate to form solid lead(II) sulfate and aqueous potassium nitrate.

75. Write complete ionic and net ionic equations for each of the reactions in Problem 65.

76. Write complete ionic and net ionic equations for each of the reactions in Problem 66.

ACID–BASE AND GAS EVOLUTION REACTIONS

77. When a hydrochloric acid solution is combined with a potassium hydroxide solution, an acid–base reaction occurs. Write a balanced molecular equation and a net ionic equation for this reaction.

78. A beaker of nitric acid is neutralized with calcium hydroxide. Write a balanced molecular equation and a net ionic equation for this reaction.

79. Complete and balance each acid–base reaction.

(a) $HCl(aq) + Ba(OH)_2(aq) \longrightarrow$

(b) $H_2SO_4(aq) + KOH(aq) \longrightarrow$

(c) $HClO_4(aq) + NaOH(aq) \longrightarrow$

80. Complete and balance each acid–base reaction.

(a) $HC_2H_3O_2(aq) + Ca(OH)_2(aq) \longrightarrow$

(b) $HBr(aq) + LiOH(aq) \longrightarrow$

(c) $H_2SO_4(aq) + Ba(OH)_2(aq) \longrightarrow$

81. Complete and balance each gas evolution reaction.

(a) $HBr(aq) + NaHCO_3(aq) \longrightarrow$

(b) $NH_4I(aq) + KOH(aq) \longrightarrow$

(c) $HNO_3(aq) + K_2SO_3(aq) \longrightarrow$

(d) $HI(aq) + Li_2S(aq) \longrightarrow$

82. Complete and balance each gas evolution reaction.

(a) $HClO_4(aq) + K_2CO_3(aq) \longrightarrow$

(b) $HC_2H_3O_2(aq) + LiHSO_3(aq) \longrightarrow$

(c) $(NH_4)_2SO_4(aq) + Ca(OH)_2(aq) \longrightarrow$

(d) $HCl(aq) + ZnS(s) \longrightarrow$

OXIDATION–REDUCTION AND COMBUSTION

83. Which reactions are redox reactions?

(a) $Ba(NO_3)_2(aq) + K_2SO_4(aq) \longrightarrow$
$BaSO_4(s) + 2\,KNO_3(aq)$

(b) $Ca(s) + Cl_2(g) \longrightarrow CaCl_2(s)$

(c) $HCl(aq) + NaOH(aq) \longrightarrow H_2O(l) + NaCl(aq)$

(d) $Zn(s) + Fe^{2+}(aq) \longrightarrow Zn^{2+}(aq) + Fe(s)$

84. Which reactions are redox reactions?

(a) $Al(s) + 3\,Ag^+(aq) \longrightarrow Al^{3+}(aq) + 3\,Ag(s)$

(b) $4\,K(s) + O_2(g) \longrightarrow 2\,K_2O(s)$

(c) $SO_3(g) + H_2O(l) \longrightarrow H_2SO_4(aq)$

(d) $Mg(s) + Br_2(l) \longrightarrow MgBr_2(s)$

85. Complete and balance each combustion reaction.

(a) $C_2H_6(g) + O_2(g) \longrightarrow$

(b) $Ca(s) + O_2(g) \longrightarrow$

(c) $C_3H_8O(l) + O_2(g) \longrightarrow$

(d) $C_4H_{10}S(l) + O_2(g) \longrightarrow$

86. Complete and balance each combustion reaction.

(a) $S(s) + O_2(g) \longrightarrow$

(b) $C_7H_{16}(l) + O_2(g) \longrightarrow$

(c) $C_4H_{10}O(l) + O_2(g) \longrightarrow$

(d) $CS_2(l) + O_2(g) \longrightarrow$

87. Write a balanced chemical equation for the synthesis reaction of $Br_2(g)$ with each metal:

(a) $Ag(s)$

(b) $K(s)$

(c) $Al(s)$

(d) $Ca(s)$

88. Write a balanced chemical equation for the synthesis reaction of $Cl_2(g)$ with each metal:

(a) $Zn(s)$

(b) $Ga(s)$

(c) $Rb(s)$

(d) $Mg(s)$

CLASSIFYING CHEMICAL REACTIONS BY WHAT ATOMS DO

89. Classify each chemical reaction as a synthesis, decomposition, single-displacement, or double-displacement reaction.

(a) $K_2S(aq) + Co(NO_3)_2(aq) \longrightarrow$
$2\,KNO_3(aq) + CoS(s)$

(b) $3\,H_2(g) + N_2(g) \longrightarrow 2\,NH_3(g)$

(c) $Zn(s) + CoCl_2(aq) \longrightarrow ZnCl_2(aq) + Co(s)$

(d) $CH_3Br(g) \xrightarrow{\text{UV light}} CH_3(g) + Br(g)$

90. Classify each chemical reaction as a synthesis, decomposition, single-displacement, or double-displacement reaction.

(a) $CaSO_4(s) \xrightarrow{\text{heat}} CaO(s) + SO_3(g)$

(b) $2\,Na(s) + O_2(g) \longrightarrow Na_2O_2(s)$

(c) $Pb(s) + 2\,AgNO_3(aq) \longrightarrow$
$Pb(NO_3)_2(aq) + 2\,Ag(s)$

(d) $HI(aq) + NaOH(aq) \longrightarrow H_2O(l) + NaI(aq)$

91. NO is a pollutant emitted by motor vehicles. It is formed by the reaction:

(a) $N_2(g) + O_2(g) \longrightarrow 2\,NO(g)$

Once in the atmosphere, NO (through a series of reactions) adds one oxygen atom to form NO_2. NO_2 then interacts with UV light according to the reaction:

(b) $NO_2(g) \xrightarrow[\text{UV light}]{} NO(g) + O(g)$

These freshly formed oxygen atoms then react with O_2 in the air to form ozone (O_3), a main component of smog:

(c) $O(g) + O_2(g) \longrightarrow O_3(g)$

Classify each of the preceding reactions as a synthesis, decomposition, single-displacement, or double-displacement reaction.

92. A main source of sulfur oxide pollutants are smelters where sulfide ores are converted into metals. The first step in this process is the reaction of the sulfide ore with oxygen in reactions such as:

(a) $2\,PbS(s) + 3\,O_2(g) \longrightarrow 2\,PbO(s) + 2\,SO_2(g)$

Sulfur dioxide can then react with oxygen in air to form sulfur trioxide:

(b) $2\,SO_2(g) + O_2(g) \longrightarrow 2\,SO_3(g)$

Sulfur trioxide can then react with water from rain to form sulfuric acid that falls as acid rain:

(c) $SO_3(g) + H_2O(l) \longrightarrow H_2SO_4(aq)$

Classify each of the preceding reactions as a synthesis, decomposition, single-displacement, or double-displacement reaction.

CUMULATIVE PROBLEMS

93. Predict the products of each reaction and write balanced complete ionic and net ionic equations for each. If no reaction occurs, write *NO REACTION*.

(a) $NaI(aq) + Hg_2(NO_3)_2(aq) \longrightarrow$

(b) $HClO_4(aq) + Ba(OH)_2(aq) \longrightarrow$

(c) $Li_2CO_3(aq) + NaCl(aq) \longrightarrow$

(d) $HCl(aq) + Li_2CO_3(aq) \longrightarrow$

94. Predict the products of each reaction and write balanced complete ionic and net ionic equations for each. If no reaction occurs, write *NO REACTION*.

(a) $LiCl(aq) + AgNO_3(aq) \longrightarrow$

(b) $H_2SO_4(aq) + Li_2SO_3(aq) \longrightarrow$

(c) $HC_2H_3O_2(aq) + Ca(OH)_2(aq) \longrightarrow$

(d) $HCl(aq) + KBr(aq) \longrightarrow$

95. Predict the products of each reaction and write balanced complete ionic and net ionic equations for each. If no reaction occurs, write *NO REACTION*.

(a) $BaS(aq) + NH_4Cl(aq) \longrightarrow$

(b) $NaC_2H_3O_2(aq) + KCl(aq) \longrightarrow$

(c) $KHSO_3(aq) + HNO_3(aq) \longrightarrow$

(d) $MnCl_3(aq) + K_3PO_4(aq) \longrightarrow$

96. Predict the products of each reaction and write balanced complete ionic and net ionic equations for each. If no reaction occurs, write *NO REACTION*.

(a) $H_2SO_4(aq) + HNO_3(aq) \longrightarrow$

(b) $NaOH(aq) + LiOH(aq) \longrightarrow$

(c) $Cr(NO_3)_3(aq) + LiOH(aq) \longrightarrow$

(d) $HCl(aq) + Hg_2(NO_3)_2(aq) \longrightarrow$

97. Predict the type of reaction (if any) that occurs between each pair of substances. Write balanced molecular equations for each. If no reaction occurs, write *NO REACTION*.

(a) aqueous potassium hydroxide and aqueous acetic acid

(b) aqueous hydrobromic acid and aqueous potassium carbonate

(c) gaseous hydrogen and gaseous oxygen

(d) aqueous ammonium chloride and aqueous lead(II) nitrate

98. Predict the type of reaction (if any) that occurs between each pair of substances. Write balanced molecular equations for each. If no reaction occurs, write *NO REACTION*.

(a) aqueous hydrochloric acid and aqueous copper(II) nitrate

(b) liquid pentanol ($C_5H_{12}O$) and gaseous oxygen

(c) aqueous ammonium chloride and aqueous calcium hydroxide

(d) aqueous strontium sulfide and aqueous copper(II) sulfate

99. Classify each reaction in as many ways as possible.

(a) $2 \, Al(s) + 3 \, Cu(NO_3)_2(aq) \longrightarrow$
$$2 \, Al(NO_3)_3(aq) + 3 \, Cu(s)$$

(b) $HBr(aq) + KHSO_3(aq) \longrightarrow$
$$H_2O(l) + SO_2(g) + NaBr(aq)$$

(c) $2 \, HI(aq) + Na_2S(aq) \longrightarrow H_2S(g) + 2 \, NaI(aq)$

(d) $K_2CO_3(aq) + FeBr_2(aq) \longrightarrow$
$$FeCO_3(s) + 2 \, KBr(aq)$$

100. Classify each reaction in as many ways as possible.

(a) $NaCl(aq) + AgNO_3(aq) \longrightarrow$
$$AgCl(s) + NaNO_3(aq)$$

(b) $2 \, Rb(s) + Br_2(g) \longrightarrow 2 \, RbBr(s)$

(c) $Zn(s) + NiBr_2(aq) \longrightarrow Ni(s) + ZnBr_2(aq)$

(d) $Ca(s) + 2 \, H_2O(l) \longrightarrow Ca(OH)_2(aq) + H_2(g)$

101. Hard water often contains dissolved Ca^{2+} and Mg^{2+} ions. One way to soften water is to add phosphates. The phosphate ion forms insoluble precipitates with calcium and magnesium ions, removing them from solution. Suppose that a solution contains aqueous calcium chloride and aqueous magnesium nitrate. Write molecular, complete ionic, and net ionic equations showing how the addition of sodium phosphate precipitates the calcium and magnesium ions.

102. Lakes that have been acidified by acid rain (HNO_3 and H_2SO_4) can be neutralized by a process called *liming*, in which limestone ($CaCO_3$) is added to the acidified water. Write ionic and net ionic equations to show how limestone reacts with HNO_3 and H_2SO_4 to neutralize them. How would you be able to tell if the neutralization process was working?

103. What solution can you add to each cation mixture to precipitate one cation while keeping the other cation in solution? Write a net ionic equation for the precipitation reaction that occurs.

(a) $Fe^{2+}(aq)$ and $Pb^{2+}(aq)$

(b) $K^+(aq)$ and $Ca^{2+}(aq)$

(c) $Ag^+(aq)$ and $Ba^{2+}(aq)$

(d) $Cu^{2+}(aq)$ and $Hg_2^{2+}(aq)$

104. What solution can you add to each cation mixture to precipitate one cation while keeping the other cation in solution? Write a net ionic equation for the precipitation reaction that occurs.

(a) $Sr^{2+}(aq)$ and $Hg_2^{2+}(aq)$

(b) $NH_4^+(aq)$ and $Ca^{2+}(aq)$

(c) $Ba^{2+}(aq)$ and $Mg^{2+}(aq)$

(d) $Ag^+(aq)$ and $Zn^{2+}(aq)$

105. A solution contains one or more of the following ions: Ag^+, Ca^{2+}, and Cu^{2+}. When sodium chloride is added to the solution, no precipitate occurs. When sodium sulfate is added to the solution, a white precipitate occurs. The precipitate is filtered off and sodium carbonate is added to the remaining solution, producing a precipitate. Which ions were present in the original solution? Write net ionic equations for the formation of each of the precipitates observed.

106. A solution contains one or more of the following ions: Hg_2^{2+}, Ba^{2+}, and Fe^{2+}. When potassium chloride is added to the solution, a precipitate forms. The precipitate is filtered off and potassium sulfate is added to the remaining solution, producing no precipitate. When potassium carbonate is added to the remaining solution, a precipitate occurs. Which ions were present in the original solution? Write net ionic equations for the formation of each of the precipitates observed.

107. A solution contains an unknown amount of dissolved calcium. Addition of 0.112 mol of K_3PO_4 causes complete precipitation of all of the calcium. How many moles of calcium were dissolved in the solution? What mass of calcium was dissolved in the solution?

108. A solution contains an unknown amount of dissolved magnesium. Addition of 0.0877 mol of Na_2CO_3 causes complete precipitation of all of the magnesium. What mass of magnesium was dissolved in the solution?

109. A solution contains 0.133 g of dissolved lead. How many moles of sodium chloride must be added to the solution to completely precipitate all of the dissolved lead? What mass of sodium chloride must be added?

110. A solution contains 1.77 g of dissolved silver. How many moles of potassium chloride must be added to the solution to completely precipitate all of the silver? What mass of potassium chloride must be added?

HIGHLIGHT PROBLEMS

111. The following are molecular views of two different possible mechanisms by which an automobile air bag might function. One of these mechanisms involves a chemical reaction and the other does not. By looking at the molecular views, can you tell which mechanism operates via a chemical reaction?

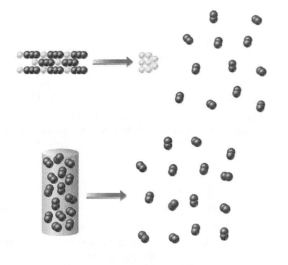

▲ When an airbag is detonated, the bag inflates. These figures show two possible ways in which the inflation may happen.

112. Precipitation reactions often produce brilliant colors. Look at the photographs of each precipitation reaction and write molecular, complete ionic, and net ionic equations for each one.

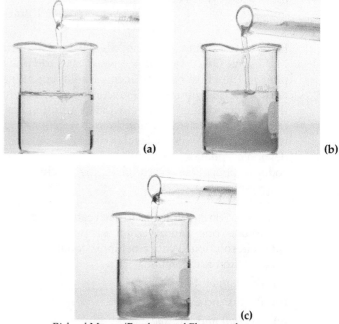

Richard Megna/Fundamental Photographs.

▲ (a) The precipitation reaction that occurs when aqueous iron(III) nitrate is added to aqueous sodium hydroxide. (b) The precipitation reaction that occurs when aqueous cobalt(II) chloride is added to aqueous potassium hydroxide. (c) The precipitation reaction that occurs when aqueous $AgNO_3$ is added to aqueous sodium iodide.

▶ANSWERS TO SKILLBUILDER EXERCISES

Skillbuilder 1 (a) Chemical reaction; heat and light are emitted. (b) Not a chemical reaction; gaseous and liquid butane are both butane. (c) Chemical reaction; heat and light are emitted. (d) Not a chemical reaction; solid dry ice is made of carbon dioxide, which sublimes (evaporates) as carbon dioxide gas.

Skillbuilder 2
$$2\,Cr_2O_3(s) + 3\,C(s) \longrightarrow 4\,Cr(s) + 3\,CO_2(g)$$

Skillbuilder 3
$$2\,C_4H_{10}(g) + 13\,O_2(g) \longrightarrow 8\,CO_2(g) + 10\,H_2O(g)$$

Skillbuilder 4
$$Pb(C_2H_3O_2)_2(aq) + 2\,KI(aq) \longrightarrow PbI_2(s) + 2\,KC_2H_3O_2(aq)$$

Skillbuilder 5 $\quad 4\,HCl(g) + O_2(g) \longrightarrow 2\,H_2O(l) + 2\,Cl_2(g)$

Skillbuilder 6 (a) insoluble (b) soluble (c) insoluble (d) soluble

Skillbuilder 7
$$2\,KOH(aq) + NiBr_2(aq) \longrightarrow Ni(OH)_2(s) + 2\,KBr(aq)$$

Skillbuilder 8
$$NH_4Cl(aq) + Fe(NO_3)_3(aq) \longrightarrow \text{NO REACTION}$$

Skillbuilder 9
$$K_2SO_4(aq) + Sr(NO_3)_2(aq) \longrightarrow SrSO_4(s) + 2\,KNO_3(aq)$$

Skillbuilder 10 Complete ionic equation:
$$2\,H^+(aq) + 2\,Br^-(aq) + Ca^{2+}(aq) + 2\,OH^-(aq) \longrightarrow$$
$$2\,H_2O(l) + Ca^{2+}(aq) + 2\,Br^-(aq)$$

Net ionic equation:
$$2\,H^+(aq) + 2\,OH^-(aq) \longrightarrow 2\,H_2O(l), \text{ or simply}$$
$$H^+(aq) + OH^-(aq) \longrightarrow H_2O(l)$$

Skillbuilder 11   Molecular equation:

$H_2SO_4(aq) + 2\,KOH(aq) \longrightarrow 2\,H_2O(l) + K_2SO_4(aq)$

Net ionic equation:

$2\,H^+(aq) + 2\,OH^-(aq) \longrightarrow 2\,H_2O(l)$

Skillbuilder 12

$2\,HBr(aq) + K_2SO_3(aq) \longrightarrow H_2O(l) + SO_2(g) + 2\,KBr(aq)$

Skillbuilder Plus 1

$2\,H^+(aq) + SO_3^{2-}(aq) \longrightarrow H_2O(l) + SO_2(g)$

Skillbuilder 13   (a), (b), and (d) are all redox reactions; (c) is a precipitation reaction.

Skillbuilder 14

$C_5H_{12}(l) + 8\,O_2(g) \longrightarrow 5\,CO_2(g) + 6\,H_2O(g)$

Skillbuilder Plus 2

$2\,C_3H_7OH(l) + 9\,O_2(g) \longrightarrow 6\,CO_2(g) + 8\,H_2O(g)$

Skillbuilder 15   (a) single-displacement (b) double-displacement (c) synthesis (d) decomposition

▶ANSWERS TO CONCEPTUAL CHECKPOINTS

1 (a) No reaction occurred. The molecules are the same before and after the change.
   (b) A reaction occurred; the molecules have changed.
   (c) A reaction occurred; the molecules have changed.

2 (b) There are 18 oxygen atoms on the left side of the equation, so the same number is needed on the right: 6 + 6(2) = 18.

3 (a) (a) The number of each type of atom must be the same on both sides of a balanced chemical equation. Since molecules change during a chemical reaction, their number is not the same on both sides (b), nor is the sum of all of the coefficients the same (c).

4 (a) Since chlorides are soluble, and since Ba^{2+} is not an exception, $BaCl_2$ is soluble and will dissolve in water. When it dissolves, it dissociates into its component ions, as shown in (a).

5 (b) Both of the possible products, MgS and $CaSO_4$, are insoluble. The possible products of the other reactions—Na_2S, $Ca(NO_3)_2$, Na_2SO_4, and $Mg(NO_3)_2$—are all soluble.

6 (d) In a precipitation reaction, cations and anions "exchange partners" to produce at least one insoluble product. In an acid–base reaction, H^+ and OH^- combine to form water, and their partners pair off to form a salt.

ANSWERS TO ODD-NUMBERED EXERCISES

QUESTIONS

1. A chemical reaction is the change of one or more substances into different substances, for example, burning wood, rusting iron, and protein synthesis.

3. The main evidence of a chemical reaction includes a color change, the formation of a solid, the formation of a gas, the emission of light, and the emission or absorption of heat.

5. **a.** gas   **b.** liquid
   c. solid   **d.** aqueous

7. **a.** reactants: 4 Ag, 2 O, 1 C products: 4 Ag, 2 O, 1 C balanced: yes
   b. reactants: 1 Pb, 2 N, 6 O, 2 Na, 2 Cl products: 1 Pb, 2 N, 6 O, 2 Na, 2 Cl balanced: yes
   c. reactants: 3 C, 8 H, 2 O products: 3 C, 8 H, 10 O balanced: no

9. If a compound dissolves in water, then it is soluble. If it does not dissolve in water, it is insoluble.

11. When ionic compounds containing polyatomic ions dissolve in water, the polyatomic ions usually dissolve as intact units.

13. The solubility rules are a set of empirical rules for ionic compounds that were deduced from observations on many compounds. The rules help us determine whether particular compounds will be soluble or insoluble.

15. The precipitate will always be insoluble; it is the solid that forms upon mixing two aqueous solutions.

17. Acid–base reactions involve an acid and a base reacting to form water and an ionic compound. An example is the reaction between hydrobromic acid and sodium hydroxide: $HBr + NaOH \longrightarrow H_2O + NaBr$

19. Gas evolution reactions are reactions that evolve a gas. An example is the reaction between hydrochloric acid and sodium bicarbonate: $HCl + NaHCO_3 \longrightarrow H_2O + CO_2 + NaCl$

21. Combustion reactions are a type of redox reaction and are characterized by the exothermic reaction of a substance with O_2. An example is the reaction between methane and oxygen: $CH_4 + 2 O_2 \longrightarrow CO_2 + 2 H_2O$

23. A synthesis reaction combines simpler substances to form more complex substances. An example is the reaction between elemental potassium and chloride: $2 K + Cl_2 \longrightarrow 2 KCl$. A decomposition decomposes a more complex substance into simpler substances. An example is the decomposition of water: $2 H_2O \longrightarrow 2 H_2 + O_2$

PROBLEMS

25. **a.** Yes; there is a color change showing a chemical reaction

b. No; the state of the compound changes, but no chemical reaction takes place.

c. Yes; there is a formation of a solid in a previously clear solution.

d. Yes; there is a formation of a gas when the yeast was added to the solution.

27. Yes; a chemical reaction has occurred, for the presence of the bubbles is evidence for the formation of a gas.

29. Yes; a chemical reaction has occurred. We know this due to the color change of the hair.

31. Placing a subscript 2 after H_2O would change the compound from water to hydrogen peroxide (H_2O_2). To balance chemical reactions, one must add coefficients, not subscripts.
$$2 H_2O(l) \longrightarrow 2 H_2(g) + O_2(g)$$

33. **a.** $PbS + 2 HCl \longrightarrow PbCl_2 + H_2S$
   b. $CO + 3 H_2 \longrightarrow CH_4 + H_2O$
   c. $Fe_2O_3 + 3 H_2 \longrightarrow 2 Fe + 3 H_2O$
   d. $4 NH_3 + 5 O_2 \longrightarrow 4 NO + 6 H_2O$

35. **a.** $Mg(s) + 2 CuNO_3(aq) \longrightarrow 2 Cu(s) + Mg(NO_3)_2(aq)$
   b. $2 N_2O_5(g) \longrightarrow 4 NO_2(g) + O_2(g)$
   c. $Ca(s) + 2 HNO_3(aq) \longrightarrow H_2(g) + Ca(NO_3)_2(aq)$
   d. $2 CH_3OH(l) + 3 O_2(g) \longrightarrow 2 CO_2(g) + 4 H_2O(g)$

37. $2 H_2(g) + O_2(g) \longrightarrow 2 H_2O(l)$;
   $Cl(g) + O_3(g) \longrightarrow ClO(g) + O_2(g)$

39. $2 Na(s) + 2 H_2O(l) \longrightarrow H_2(g) + 2 NaOH(aq)$

41. $2 SO_2(g) + O_2(g) + 2 H_2O(l) \longrightarrow 2 H_2SO_4(aq)$

43. $V_2O_5(s) + 2 H_2(g) \longrightarrow V_2O_3(s) + 2 H_2O(l)$

45. $C_{12}H_{22}O_{11}(aq) + H_2O(l) \longrightarrow 4 CO_2(g) + 4 C_2H_5OH(aq)$

47. **a.** $Na_2S(aq) + Cu(NO_3)_2(aq) \longrightarrow$
   $$2 NaNO_3(aq) + CuS(s)$$
   b. $4 HCl(aq) + O_2(g) \longrightarrow 2 H_2O(l) + 2 Cl_2(g)$
   c. $2 H_2(g) + O_2(g) \longrightarrow 2 H_2O(l)$
   d. $FeS(s) + 2 HCl(aq) \longrightarrow FeCl_2(aq) + H_2S(g)$

49. **a.** $BaO_2(s) + H_2SO_4(aq) \longrightarrow BaSO_4(s) + H_2O_2(aq)$
   b. $2 Co(NO_3)_3(aq) + 3 (NH_4)_2S(aq) \longrightarrow$
   $$Co_2S_3(s) + 6 NH_4NO_3(aq)$$
   c. $Li_2O(s) + H_2O(l) \longrightarrow 2 LiOH(aq)$
   d. $Hg_2(C_2H_3O_2)_2(aq) + 2 KCl(aq) \longrightarrow$
   $$Hg_2Cl_2(s) + 2 KC_2H_3O_2(aq)$$

51. **a.** $2 Rb(s) + 2 H_2O(l) \longrightarrow 2 RbOH(aq) + H_2(g)$
   b. Equation is balanced
   c. $2 NiS(s) + 3 O_2(g) \longrightarrow 2 NiO(s) + 2 SO_2(g)$
   d. $3 PbO(s) + 2 NH_3(g) \longrightarrow 3 Pb(s) + N_2(g) + 3 H_2O(l)$

53. $C_6H_{12}O_6(aq) + 6 O_2(g) \longrightarrow 6 CO_2(g) + 6 H_2O(l)$

55. $2 NO(g) + 2 CO(g) \longrightarrow N_2(g) + 2 CO_2(g)$

57. a. soluble; Na^+, $C_2H_3O_2^-$

   b. soluble; Sn^{2+}, NO_3^-

   c. insoluble

   d. soluble; Na^+, PO_4^{3-}

59. $AgCl$; $BaSO_4$; $CuCO_3$; Fe_2S_3

61.

Soluble	Insoluble
K_2S	Hg_2I_2
BaS	$Cu_3(PO_4)_2$
NH_4Cl	MgS
Na_2CO_3	$CaSO_4$
K_2SO_4	$PbSO_4$
SrS	$PbCl_2$
Li_2S	Hg_2Cl_2

63. a. NO REACTION

   b. $K_2SO_4(aq) + BaBr_2(aq) \longrightarrow BaSO_4(s) + 2 KBr(aq)$

   c. $2 NaCl(aq) + Hg_2(C_2H_3O_2)_2(aq) \longrightarrow$
$$Hg_2Cl_2(s) + 2 NaC_2H_3O_2(aq)$$

   d. NO REACTION

65. a. $Na_2CO_3(aq) + Pb(NO_3)_2(aq) \longrightarrow$
$$PbCO_3(s) + 2 NaNO_3(aq)$$

   b. $K_2SO_4(aq) + Pb(CH_3CO_2)_2(aq) \longrightarrow$
$$PbSO_4(s) + 2 KC_2H_3O_2$$

   c. $Cu(NO_3)_2(aq) + BaS(aq) \longrightarrow CuS(s) + Ba(NO_3)_2(aq)$

   d. NO REACTION

67. a. correct

   b. NO REACTION

   c. correct

   d. $Pb(NO_3)_2(aq) + 2 LiCl(aq) \longrightarrow$
$$PbCl_2(s) + 2 LiNO_3(aq)$$

69. K^+, NO_3^-

71. a. $Ag^+(aq) + NO_3^-(aq) + K^+(aq) + Cl^-(aq) \longrightarrow$
$$AgCl(s) + K^+(aq) + NO_3^-(aq)$$
$$Ag^+(aq) + Cl^-(aq) \longrightarrow AgCl(s)$$

   b. $Ca^{2+}(aq) + S^{2-}(aq) + Cu^{2+}(aq) + 2 Cl^-(aq) \longrightarrow$
$$CuS(s) + Ca^{2+}(aq) + 2 Cl^-(aq)$$
$$Cu^{2+}(aq) + S^{2-}(aq) \longrightarrow CuS(s)$$

   c. $Na^+(aq) + OH^-(aq) + H^+(aq) + NO_3^-(aq) \longrightarrow$
$$H_2O(l) + Na^+(aq) + NO_3^-(aq)$$
$$H^+(aq) + OH^-(aq) \longrightarrow H_2O(l)$$

   d. $6 K^+(aq) + 2 PO_4^{3-}(aq) + 3 Ni^{2+}(aq) + 6 Cl^-(aq) \longrightarrow$
$$Ni_3(PO_4)_2(s) + 6 K^+(aq) + 6 Cl^-(aq)$$
$$3 Ni^{2+}(aq) + 2 PO_4^{3-}(aq) \longrightarrow Ni_3(PO_4)_2(s)$$

73. $Hg_2^{2+}(aq) + 2 NO_3^-(aq) + 2 Na^+(aq) + 2 Cl^-(aq) \longrightarrow$
$$Hg_2Cl_2(s) + 2 Na^+(aq) + 2 NO_3^-(aq)$$
$$Hg_2^{2+}(aq) + 2 Cl^-(aq) \longrightarrow Hg_2Cl_2(s)$$

75. a. $2 Na^+(aq) + CO_3^{2-}(aq) + Pb^{2+}(aq) + 2 NO_3^-(aq)$
$$\longrightarrow PbCO_3(s) + 2 Na^+(aq) + 2 NO_3^-(aq)$$
$$Pb^{2+}(aq) + CO_3^{2-}(aq) \longrightarrow PbCO_3(s)$$

   b. $2 K^+(aq) + SO_4^{2-}(aq) + Pb^{2+}(aq) + 2 CH_3CO_2^-(aq)$
$$\longrightarrow PbSO_4(s) + 2 K^+(aq) + 2 CH_3CO_2^-(aq)$$
$$Pb^{2+}(aq) + SO_4^{2-}(aq) \longrightarrow PbSO_4(s)$$

   c. $Cu^{2+}(aq) + 2 NO_3^-(aq) + Ba^{2+}(aq) + S^{2-}(aq) \longrightarrow$
$$CuS(s) + Ba^{2+}(aq) + 2 NO_3^-(aq)$$
$$Cu^{2+}(aq) + S^{2-}(aq) \longrightarrow CuS(s)$$

   d. NO REACTION

77. $HCl(aq) + KOH(aq) \longrightarrow H_2O(l) + KCl(aq)$
$$H^+(aq) + OH^-(aq) \longrightarrow H_2O(l)$$

79. a. $2 HCl(aq) + Ba(OH)_2(aq) \longrightarrow 2 H_2O(l) + BaCl_2(aq)$

   b. $H_2SO_4(aq) + 2 KOH(aq) \longrightarrow 2 H_2O(l) + K_2SO_4(aq)$

   c. $HClO_4(aq) + NaOH(aq) \longrightarrow H_2O(l) + NaClO_4(aq)$

81. a. $HBr(aq) + NaHCO_3(aq) \longrightarrow$
$$H_2O(l) + CO_2(g) + NaBr(aq)$$

   b. $NH_4I(aq) + KOH(aq) \longrightarrow H_2O(l) + NH_3(g) + KI(aq)$

   c. $2 HNO_3(aq) + K_2SO_3(aq) \longrightarrow$
$$H_2O(l) + SO_2(g) + 2 KNO_3(aq)$$

   d. $2 HI(aq) + Li_2S(aq) \longrightarrow H_2S(g) + 2 LiI(aq)$

83. b and d are redox reactions; a and c are not.

85. a. $2 C_2H_6(g) + 7 O_2(g) \longrightarrow 4 CO_2(g) + 6 H_2O(g)$

   b. $2 Ca(s) + O_2(g) \longrightarrow 2 CaO(s)$

   c. $2 C_3H_8O(l) + 9 O_2(g) \longrightarrow 6 CO_2(g) + 8 H_2O(g)$

   d. $2 C_4H_{10}S(l) + 15 O_2(g) \longrightarrow$
$$8 CO_2(g) + 10 H_2O(g) + 2 SO_2(g)$$

87. a. $2 Ag(s) + Br_2(g) \longrightarrow 2 AgBr(s)$

   b. $2 K(s) + Br_2(g) \longrightarrow 2 KBr(s)$

   c. $2 Al(s) + 3 Br_2(g) \longrightarrow 2 AlBr_3(s)$

   d. $Ca(s) + Br_2(g) \longrightarrow CaBr_2(s)$

89. a. double displacement

   b. synthesis or combination

   c. single displacement

   d. decomposition

91. a. synthesis

   b. decomposition

   c. synthesis

93. a. $2 Na^+(aq) + 2 I^-(aq) + Hg_2^+(aq) + 2 NO_3^-(aq)$
$$\longrightarrow Hg_2I_2(s) + 2 Na^+(aq) + 2 NO_3^-(aq)$$

   b. $2 H^+(aq) + 2 ClO_4^-(aq) + Ba^{2+}(aq) + 2 OH^-(aq)$
$$\longrightarrow 2 H_2O(l) + Ba^{2+}(aq) + 2 ClO_4^-(aq)$$
$$H^+(aq) + OH^-(aq) \longrightarrow H_2O(s)$$

   c. NO REACTION

   d. $2 H^+(aq) + 2 Cl^-(aq) + 2 Li^+(aq) + CO_3^{2-}(aq) \longrightarrow$
$$H_2O(l) + CO_2(g) + 2 Li^+(aq) + 2 Cl^-(aq)$$
$$2 H^+(aq) + CO_3^{2-}(aq) \longrightarrow H_2O(l) + CO_2(g)$$

95. a. NO REACTION

   b. NO REACTION

   c. $K^+(aq) + HSO_3^-(aq) + H^+(aq) + NO_3^-(aq) \longrightarrow$
$$H_2O(l) + SO_2(g) + K^+(aq) + NO_3^-(aq)$$
$$H^+(aq) + HSO_3^-(aq) \longrightarrow H_2O(l) + SO_2(g)$$

d. $Mn^{3+}(aq) + 3\,Cl^-(aq) + 3\,K^+(aq) + PO_4^{3-}(aq) \longrightarrow$
$$MnPO_4(s) + 3\,K^+(aq) + 3\,Cl^-(aq)$$

$$Mn^{3+}(aq) + PO_4^{3-}(aq) \longrightarrow MnPO_4(s)$$

97. a. acid–base; $KOH(aq) + HC_2H_3O_2(aq) \longrightarrow$
$$H_2O(l) + KC_2H_3O_2(aq)$$

b. gas evolution; $2\,HBr(aq) + K_2CO_3(aq) \longrightarrow$
$$H_2O(l) + CO_2(g) + 2\,KBr(aq)$$

c. synthesis; $2\,H_2(g) + O_2(g) \longrightarrow 2\,H_2O(l)$

d. precipitation; $2\,NH_4Cl(aq) + Pb(NO_3)_2(aq) \longrightarrow$
$$PbCl_2(s) + 2\,NH_4NO_3(aq)$$

99. a. oxidation–reduction; single displacement

b. gas evolution; acid–base

c. gas evolution; double displacement

d. precipitation; double displacement

101. $3\,CaCl_2(aq) + 2\,Na_3PO_4(aq) \longrightarrow$
$$Ca_3(PO_4)_2(s) + 6\,NaCl(aq)$$

$3\,Ca^{2+}(aq) + 6\,Cl^-(aq) + 6\,Na^+(aq) + 2\,PO_4^{3-}(aq)$
$$\longrightarrow Ca_3(PO_4)_2(s) + 6\,Na^+(aq) + 6\,Cl^-(aq)$$

$3\,Ca^{2+}(aq) + 2\,PO_4^{3-}(aq) \longrightarrow Ca_3(PO_4)_2(s)$

$3\,Mg(NO_3)_2(aq) + 2\,Na_3PO_4(aq) \longrightarrow$
$$Mg_3(PO_4)_2(s) + 6\,NaNO_3(aq)$$

$3\,Mg^{2+}(aq) + 6\,NO_3^-(aq) + 6\,Na^+(aq) + 2\,PO_4^{3-}(aq)$
$$\longrightarrow Mg_3(PO_4)_2(s) + 6\,Na^+(aq) + 6\,NO_3^-(aq)$$

$3\,Mg^{2+}(aq) + 2\,PO_4^{3-}(aq) \longrightarrow Mg_3(PO_4)_2(s)$

103. *Correct answers may vary; representative correct answers are:

a. addition of a solution containing SO_4^{2-};
$Pb^{2+}(aq) + SO_4^{2-}(aq) \longrightarrow PbSO_4(s)$

b. addition of a solution containing SO_4^{2-};
$Ca^{2+}(aq) + SO_4^{2-}(aq) \longrightarrow CaSO_4(s)$

c. addition of a solution containing SO_4^{2-};
$Ba^{2+}(aq) + SO_4^{2-}(aq) \longrightarrow BaSO_4(s)$

d. addition of a solution containing Cl^-;
$Hg_2^{2+}(aq) + 2\,Cl^-(aq) \longrightarrow Hg_2Cl_2(s)$

105. Ca^{2+} and Cu^{2+} were present in the original solution.

1st: $Ca^{2+}(aq) + SO_4^{2-}(aq) \longrightarrow CaSO_4(s)$

2nd: $Cu^{2+}(aq) + CO_3^{2-}(aq) \longrightarrow CuCO_3(s)$

107. 0.168 mol Ca; 6.73 g Ca

109. 0.00128 mol NaCl, 0.0750 g NaCl

111. a. chemical

b. physical

Quantities in Chemical Reactions

From Chapter 8 of *Introductory Chemistry,* Fourth Edition, Nivaldo J. Tro. Copyright © 2011 by Pearson Education, Inc. Published by Pearson Prentice Hall. All rights reserved.

Quantities in Chemical Reactions

"Man masters nature not by force but by understanding. That is why science has succeeded where magic failed: because it has looked for no spell to cast."

JACOB BRONOWSKI (1908–1974)

1 Global Warming: Too Much Carbon Dioxide

Outgoing heat is trapped by atmospheric greenhouse gases.

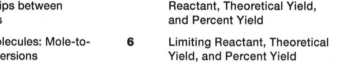

Heat

Visible sunlight

Greenhouse gases

Earth

▲ **FIGURE 1 The greenhouse effect** Greenhouse gases act like glass in a greenhouse, allowing visible-light energy to enter the atmosphere but preventing heat energy from escaping.

◄ The combustion of fossil fuels such as octane (shown here) produces water and carbon dioxide as products. Carbon dioxide is a greenhouse gas that is believed to be responsible for global warming.

Average global temperatures depend on the balance between incoming sunlight, which warms Earth, and outgoing heat lost to space, which cools it. Certain gases in Earth's atmosphere, called **greenhouse gases**, affect that balance by acting like glass in a greenhouse. They allow sunlight into the atmosphere to warm Earth but prevent heat from escaping (◄ Figure 1). Without greenhouse gases, more heat would escape, and Earth's average temperature would be about 60 °F (15 °C) colder. Caribbean tourists would freeze at an icy 21 °F, instead of baking at a tropical 81 °F. On the other hand, if the concentration of greenhouse gases in the atmosphere were to increase, Earth's average temperature would rise.

In recent years scientists have become concerned because the atmospheric concentration of carbon dioxide (CO_2)—Earth's most significant greenhouse gas in terms of its contribution to climate—is rising. This rise in CO_2 concentration enhances the atmosphere's ability to hold heat and may therefore lead to **global warming**, an increase in Earth's average temperature. Since 1860, atmospheric CO_2 levels have risen by 25%, and Earth's average temperature has increased by 0.6 °C (about 1.1 °F) (► Figure 2 on the next page).

The primary cause of rising atmospheric CO_2 concentration is the burning of fossil fuels. Fossil fuels—natural gas, petroleum, and coal—provide approximately 90% of our society's energy. Combustion of fossil fuels, however, produces CO_2. As an example, consider the combustion of octane (C_8H_{18}), a component of gasoline.

$$2\,C_8H_{18}(l) + 25\,O_2(g) \longrightarrow 16\,CO_2(g) + 18\,H_2O(g)$$

The balanced chemical equation shows that 16 mol of CO_2 are produced for every 2 mol of octane burned. Since we know the world's annual fossil fuel consumption, we can estimate the world's annual CO_2 production. A simple calculation shows that the world's annual CO_2 production—from fossil fuel

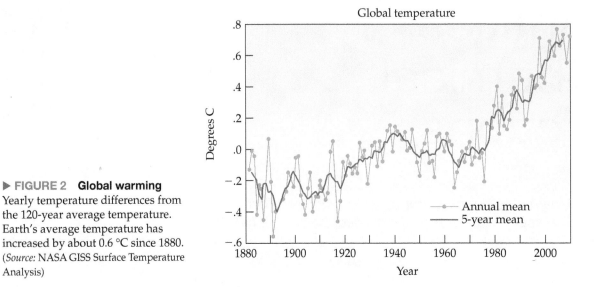

▶ FIGURE 2 **Global warming**
Yearly temperature differences from
the 120-year average temperature.
Earth's average temperature has
increased by about 0.6 °C since 1880.
(*Source:* NASA GISS Surface Temperature
Analysis)

combustion—matches the measured annual atmospheric CO_2 increase, imply-
ing that fossil fuel combustion is indeed responsible for increased atmospheric
CO_2 levels.

The numerical relationship between chemical quantities in a balanced chemical equation is called reaction **stoichiometry**. Stoichiometry allows us to predict
the amounts of products that form in a chemical reaction based on the amounts of
reactants. Stoichiometry also allows us to predict how much of the reactants are
necessary to form a given amount of product, or how much of one reactant is
required to completely react with another reactant. These calculations are central
to chemistry, allowing chemists to plan and carry out chemical reactions to obtain
products in the desired quantities.

2 Making Pancakes: Relationships between Ingredients

The concepts of stoichiometry are similar to the concepts we use in following a
cooking recipe. Calculating the amount of carbon dioxide produced by the combustion of a given amount of a fossil fuel is similar to calculating the number of
pancakes that can be made from a given number of eggs. For example, suppose
you use the following pancake recipe.

For the sake of simplicity, this recipe omits
liquid ingredients.

$$1 \text{ cup flour} + 2 \text{ eggs} + \tfrac{1}{2} \text{ tsp baking powder} \longrightarrow 5 \text{ pancakes}$$

1 cup flour   2 eggs $\frac{1}{2}$ tsp baking powder   5 pancakes

▲ A recipe gives numerical relationships between the ingredients and
the number of pancakes.

The recipe shows the numerical relationships between the pancake ingredients. It
says that if we have 2 eggs—and enough of everything else—we can make 5 pancakes. We can write this relationship as a ratio.

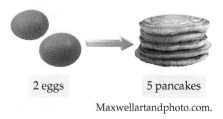

| 2 eggs | 5 pancakes |

Maxwellartandphoto.com.

2 eggs : 5 pancakes

What if we have 8 eggs? Assuming that we have enough of everything else, how many pancakes can we make? Using the preceding ratio as a conversion factor, we can determine that 8 eggs are sufficient to make 20 pancakes.

| 8 eggs | 20 pancakes |

Maxwellartandphoto.com.

$$8 \text{ eggs} \times \frac{5 \text{ pancakes}}{2 \text{ eggs}} = 20 \text{ pancakes}$$

The pancake recipe contains numerical conversion factors between the pancake ingredients and the number of pancakes. Other conversion factors from this recipe include:

1 cup flour : 5 pancakes

$\frac{1}{2}$ tsp baking powder : 5 pancakes

The recipe also gives us relationships among the ingredients themselves. For example, how much baking powder is required to go with 3 cups of flour? From the recipe:

1 cup flour : $\frac{1}{2}$ tsp baking powder

With this ratio, we can form the conversion factor to calculate the appropriate amount of baking powder.

$$3 \text{ cups flour} \times \frac{\frac{1}{2} \text{ tsp baking powder}}{1 \text{ cup flour}} = \frac{3}{2} \text{ tsp baking powder}$$

3 Making Molecules: Mole-to-Mole Conversions

In a balanced chemical equation, we have a "recipe" for how reactants combine to form products. For example, the following equation shows how hydrogen and nitrogen combine to form ammonia (NH_3).

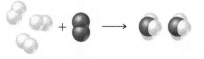

$$3 H_2(g) + N_2(g) \longrightarrow 2 NH_3(g)$$

The balanced equation shows that 3 H_2 molecules react with 1 N_2 molecule to form 2 NH_3 molecules. We can express these relationships as the following ratios.

3 H_2 molecules : 1 N_2 molecule : 2 NH_3 molecules

Since we do not ordinarily deal with individual molecules, we can express the same ratios in moles.

$$3 \text{ mol } H_2 : 1 \text{ mol } N_2 : 2 \text{ mol } NH_3$$

If we have 3 mol of N_2, and more than enough H_2, how much NH_3 can we make? We first sort the information in the problem.

GIVEN: 3 mol N_2

FIND: mol NH_3

SOLUTION MAP

We then strategize by drawing a solution map that begins with mol N_2 and ends with mol NH_3. The conversion factor comes from the balanced chemical equation.

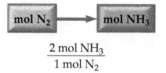

$$\frac{2 \text{ mol } NH_3}{1 \text{ mol } N_2}$$

RELATIONSHIPS USED

1 mol N_2 : 2 mol NH_3 (from balanced equation)

SOLUTION

We can then do the conversion.

$$3 \text{ mol } N_2 \times \frac{2 \text{ mol } NH_3}{1 \text{ mol } N_2} = 6 \text{ mol } NH_3$$

We have enough N_2 to make 6 mol of NH_3.

EXAMPLE 1   Mole-to-Mole Conversions

Sodium chloride, NaCl, forms by this reaction between sodium and chlorine.

$$2 \text{ Na}(s) + Cl_2(g) \longrightarrow 2 \text{ NaCl}(s)$$

How many moles of NaCl result from the complete reaction of 3.4 mol of Cl_2? Assume that there is more than enough Na.

SORT	
You are given the number of moles of a reactant (Cl_2) and asked to find the number of moles of product (NaCl) that will form if the reactant completely reacts.	**GIVEN:** 3.4 mol Cl_2 **FIND:** mol NaCl

STRATEGIZE	
Draw the solution map beginning with moles of chlorine and using the stoichiometric conversion factor to calculate moles of sodium chloride. The conversion factor comes from the balanced chemical equation.	**SOLUTION MAP** mol Cl_2 ⟶ mol NaCl $\dfrac{2 \text{ mol NaCl}}{1 \text{ mol } Cl_2}$ **RELATIONSHIPS USED** 1 mol Cl_2 : 2 mol NaCl (from balanced chemical equation)

SOLVE	
Follow the solution map to solve the problem. There is enough Cl_2 to produce 6.8 mol of NaCl.	**SOLUTION** $3.4 \text{ mol } Cl_2 \times \dfrac{2 \text{ mol NaCl}}{1 \text{ mol } Cl_2} = 6.8 \text{ mol NaCl}$

CHECK	
Check your answer. Are the units correct? Does the answer make physical sense?	The answer has the correct units, moles. The answer is reasonable because each mole of Cl_2 makes two moles of NaCl.

▶**SKILLBUILDER 1 | Mole-to-Mole Conversions**

Water is formed when hydrogen gas reacts explosively with oxygen gas according to the balanced equation:

$$O_2(g) + 2\,H_2(g) \longrightarrow 2\,H_2O(g)$$

How many moles of H_2O result from the complete reaction of 24.6 mol of O_2? Assume that there is more than enough H_2.

▶**FOR MORE PRACTICE**   Example 8; Problems 15, 16, 17, 18.

CONCEPTUAL CHECKPOINT 1

Methane (CH_4) undergoes combustion according to the reaction:

$$CH_4(g) + 2\,O_2(g) \longrightarrow CO_2(g) + 2\,H_2O(g)$$

If the figure at left represents the amount of oxygen available to react, which of the following best represents the amount of CH_4 required to completely react with all of the oxygen?

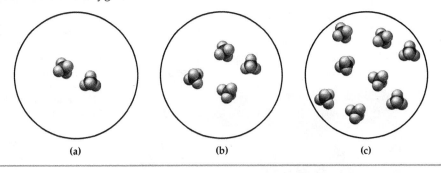

| (a) | (b) | (c) |

4   Making Molecules: Mass-to-Mass Conversions

A chemical *formula* contains conversion factors for converting between moles of a compound and moles of its constituent elements. In this chapter, we have seen how a chemical *equation* contains conversion factors between moles of reactants and moles of products. However, we are often interested in relationships between *mass* of reactants and *mass* of products. For example, we might want to know the mass of carbon dioxide emitted by an automobile per kilogram of gasoline used. Or we might want to know the mass of each reactant required to obtain a certain mass of a product in a synthesis reaction. These calculations are similar to calculations you may have seen previously, where we converted between mass of a compound and mass of a constituent element. The general outline for these types of calculations is:

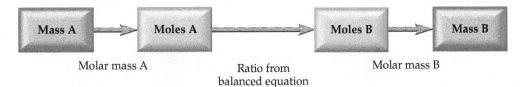

where A and B are two different substances involved in the reaction. We use the molar mass of A to convert from mass of A to moles of A. We use the ratio from the balanced equation to convert from moles of A to moles of B, and we use the molar mass of B to convert moles of B to mass of B. For example, suppose we want to calculate the mass of CO_2 emitted upon the combustion of 5.0×10^2 g of pure octane. The balanced chemical equation for octane combustion is:

$$2\,C_8H_{18}(l) + 25\,O_2(g) \longrightarrow 16\,CO_2(g) + 18\,H_2O(g)$$

CHEMISTRY IN THE MEDIA
The Controversy over Oxygenated Fuels

We have seen that the balanced chemical equation for the combustion of octane, a component of gasoline, is:

$$2\,C_8H_{18}(l) + 25\,O_2(g) \longrightarrow 16\,CO_2(g) + 18\,H_2O(g)$$

We have also learned how balanced chemical equations give numerical relationships between reactants. The preceding equation shows that 25 mol of O_2 are required to completely react with 2 mol of C_8H_{18}. What if there were not enough O_2 in the cylinders of an automobile engine to fully react with the amount of octane flowing into them? For many reactions, a shortage of one reactant simply means that less product forms, something we will learn more about later in this chapter. However, for some reactions, a shortage of one reactant causes other reactions—called *side reactions*—to occur along with the desired reaction. In the case of octane and the other major components of gasoline, those side reactions result in pollutants such as carbon monoxide (CO) and ozone (O_3).

In 1990, the U.S. Congress, in efforts to lower air pollution, passed amendments to the Clean Air Act requiring oil companies to add substances to gasoline that prevent these side reactions. Since these additives have the effect of increasing the amount of oxygen during combustion, the resulting gasoline is called oxygenated fuel. The additive of choice among oil companies used to be a compound called MTBE (methyl tertiary butyl ether). The immediate results were positive. Carbon monoxide and ozone levels in many major cities decreased significantly.

Over time, however, MTBE—a compound that does not readily biodegrade—began to appear in drinking-water supplies across the nation. MTBE made its way into drinking water through gasoline spills at gas stations, from boat motors, and from leaking underground storage tanks. The consequences have been significant. MTBE, even at low levels, imparts a turpentine-like odor and foul taste to drinking water. It is also a suspected carcinogen.

Public response was swift and dramatic. Several multimillion dollar class-action lawsuits were filed and settled against the manufacturers of MTBE, against gas stations suspected of leaking it, and against the oil companies that put MTBE into gasoline. Most states have completely banned MTBE from gasoline. Ethanol, made from the fermentation of grains, has been used as a substitute for MTBE because it has many of the same pollution-reducing effects without the associated health hazards. Oil companies did not use ethanol originally because it was more expensive than MTBE, but now ethanol has become the additive of choice.

CAN YOU ANSWER THIS? *How many moles of oxygen (O_2) are required to completely react with 425 mol of octane (approximate capacity of a 15-gal automobile gasoline tank)?*

▲ The 1990 amendments to the Clean Air Act required oil companies to put additives in gasoline that increased its oxygen content.

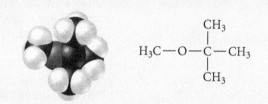

▲ MTBE was the additive of choice.

We begin by sorting the information in the problem.

GIVEN: 5.0×10^2 g C_8H_{18}

FIND: g CO_2

Notice that we are given g C_8H_{18} and asked to find g CO_2. The balanced chemical equation, however, gives us a relationship between moles of C_8H_{18} and moles of CO_2. Consequently, before using that relationship, we must convert from grams to moles.

The solution map uses the general outline

Mass A $\longrightarrow$ Moles A $\longrightarrow$ Moles B $\longrightarrow$ Mass B

where A is octane and B is carbon dioxide.

SOLUTION MAP

We strategize by drawing the solution map, which begins with mass of octane and ends with mass of carbon dioxide.

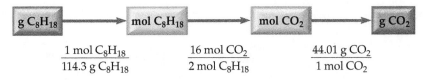

$$\boxed{\text{g } C_8H_{18}} \longrightarrow \boxed{\text{mol } C_8H_{18}} \longrightarrow \boxed{\text{mol } CO_2} \longrightarrow \boxed{\text{g } CO_2}$$

$$\dfrac{1 \text{ mol } C_8H_{18}}{114.3 \text{ g } C_8H_{18}} \qquad \dfrac{16 \text{ mol } CO_2}{2 \text{ mol } C_8H_{18}} \qquad \dfrac{44.01 \text{ g } CO_2}{1 \text{ mol } CO_2}$$

RELATIONSHIPS USED

2 mol $C_8H_{18} \equiv$ 16 mol CO_2 (from chemical equation)

Molar mass C_8H_{18} = 114.3 g/mol

Molar mass CO_2 = 44.01 g/mol

SOLUTION

We then follow the solution map to solve the problem, beginning with g C_8H_{18} and canceling units to arrive at g CO_2.

$$5.0 \times 10^2 \text{ g } C_8H_{18} \times \frac{1 \text{ mol } C_8H_{18}}{114.3 \text{ g } C_8H_{18}} \times \frac{16 \text{ mol } CO_2}{2 \text{ mol } C_8H_{18}} \times \frac{44.01 \text{ g } CO_2}{1 \text{ mol } CO_2} = 1.5 \times 10^3 \text{ g } CO_2$$

Upon combustion, 5.0×10^2 g of octane produces 1.5×10^3 g of carbon dioxide.

EXAMPLE 2 Mass-to-Mass Conversions

In photosynthesis, plants convert carbon dioxide and water into glucose ($C_6H_{12}O_6$) according to the reaction:

$$6 \text{ CO}_2(g) + 6 \text{ H}_2\text{O}(l) \xrightarrow[\text{sunlight}]{} 6 \text{ O}_2(g) + C_6H_{12}O_6(aq)$$

How many grams of glucose can be synthesized from 58.5 g of CO_2? Assume that there is more than enough water present to react with all of the CO_2.

SORT You are given the mass of carbon dioxide and asked to find the mass of glucose that can form if the carbon dioxide completely reacts.	**GIVEN:** 58.5 g CO_2 **FIND:** g $C_6H_{12}O_6$
STRATEGIZE The solution map uses the general outline Mass A $\longrightarrow$ Moles A $\longrightarrow$ Moles B $\longrightarrow$ Mass B where A is carbon dioxide and B is glucose. The main conversion factor is the stoichiometric relationship between moles of carbon dioxide and moles of glucose. This conversion factor comes from the balanced equation. The other conversion factors are simply the molar masses of carbon dioxide and glucose.	**SOLUTION MAP** 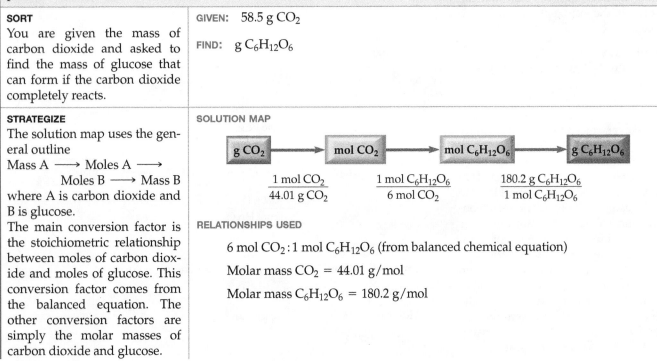 $\boxed{\text{g } CO_2} \longrightarrow \boxed{\text{mol } CO_2} \longrightarrow \boxed{\text{mol } C_6H_{12}O_6} \longrightarrow \boxed{\text{g } C_6H_{12}O_6}$ $\dfrac{1 \text{ mol } CO_2}{44.01 \text{ g } CO_2} \quad \dfrac{1 \text{ mol } C_6H_{12}O_6}{6 \text{ mol } CO_2} \quad \dfrac{180.2 \text{ g } C_6H_{12}O_6}{1 \text{ mol } C_6H_{12}O_6}$ **RELATIONSHIPS USED** 6 mol CO_2 : 1 mol $C_6H_{12}O_6$ (from balanced chemical equation) Molar mass CO_2 = 44.01 g/mol Molar mass $C_6H_{12}O_6$ = 180.2 g/mol

SOLVE	SOLUTION
Follow the solution map to solve the problem. Begin with grams of carbon dioxide and multiply by the appropriate factors to arrive at grams of glucose.	$58.5 \text{ g } CO_2 \times \dfrac{1 \text{ mol } CO_2}{44.01 \text{ g } CO_2} \times \dfrac{1 \text{ mol } C_6H_{12}O_6}{6 \text{ mol } CO_2} \times \dfrac{180.2 \text{ g } C_6H_{12}O_6}{1 \text{ mol } C_6H_{12}O_6} = 39.9 \text{ g } C_6H_{12}O_6$

CHECK	
Are the units correct? Does the answer make physical sense?	The units, g $C_6H_{12}O_6$, are correct. The magnitude of the answer seems reasonable because it is of the same order of magnitude as the given mass of carbon dioxide. An answer that is orders of magnitude different would immediately be suspect.

▶SKILLBUILDER 2 | Mass-to-Mass Conversions

Magnesium hydroxide, the active ingredient in milk of magnesia, neutralizes stomach acid, primarily HCl, according to the reaction:

$$Mg(OH)_2(aq) + 2 HCl(aq) \longrightarrow 2 H_2O(l) + MgCl_2(aq)$$

How much HCl in grams can be neutralized by 5.50 g of $Mg(OH)_2$?

▶FOR MORE PRACTICE   Example 9; Problems 31, 32, 33, 34.

EXAMPLE 3   Mass-to-Mass Conversions

One of the components of acid rain is nitric acid, which forms when NO_2, a pollutant, reacts with oxygen and rainwater according to the following simplified reaction.

$$4 NO_2(g) + O_2(g) + 2 H_2O(l) \longrightarrow 4 HNO_3(aq)$$

Assuming that there is more than enough O_2 and H_2O, how much HNO_3 in kilograms forms from 1.5×10^3 kg of NO_2 pollutant?

SORT	
You are given the mass of nitrogen dioxide (a reactant) and asked to find the mass of nitric acid that can form if the nitrogen dioxide completely reacts.	GIVEN: 1.5×10^3 kg NO_2 FIND: kg HNO_3

STRATEGIZE	SOLUTION MAP
The solution map follows the general format of: Mass $\longrightarrow$ Moles $\longrightarrow$ Moles $\longrightarrow$ Mass However, since the original quantity of NO_2 is given in kilograms, you must first convert to grams. Since the final quantity is requested in kilograms, you must convert back to kilograms at the end. The main conversion factor is the stoichiometric relationship between moles of nitrogen dioxide and moles of nitric acid. This conversion factor comes from the balanced equation. The other conversion factors are simply the molar masses of nitrogen dioxide and nitric acid and the relationship between kilograms and grams.	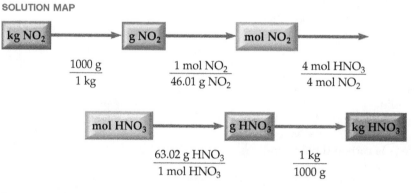 RELATIONSHIPS USED 4 mol NO_2 : 4 mol HNO_3 (from balanced chemical equation) Molar mass NO_2 = 46.01 g/mol Molar mass HNO_3 = 63.02 g/mol 1 kg = 1000 g

SOLVE

Follow the solution map to solve the problem. Begin with kilograms of nitrogen dioxide and multiply by the appropriate conversion factors to arrive at kilograms of nitric acid.

SOLUTION

$$1.5 \times 10^3 \text{ kg NO}_2 \times \frac{1000 \text{ g}}{1 \text{ kg}} \times \frac{1 \text{ mol NO}_2}{46.01 \text{ g NO}_2} \times \frac{4 \text{ mol HNO}_3}{4 \text{ mol NO}_2} \times$$

$$\frac{63.02 \text{ g HNO}_3}{1 \text{ mol HNO}_3} \times \frac{1 \text{ kg}}{1000 \text{ g}} = 2.1 \times 10^3 \text{ kg HNO}_3$$

CHECK

Are the units correct? Does the answer make physical sense?

The units, kg HNO_3 are correct. The magnitude of the answer seems reasonable because it is of the same order of magnitude as the given mass of nitrogen dioxide. An answer that is orders of magnitude different would immediately be suspect.

▶**SKILLBUILDER 3 | Mass-to-Mass Conversions**

Another component of acid rain is sulfuric acid, which forms when SO_2, also a pollutant, reacts with oxygen and rainwater according to the following reaction.

$$2 \text{ SO}_2(g) + \text{O}_2(g) + 2 \text{ H}_2\text{O}(l) \longrightarrow 2 \text{ H}_2\text{SO}_4(aq)$$

Assuming that there is more than enough O_2 and H_2O, how much H_2SO_4 in kilograms forms from 2.6×10^3 kg of SO_2?

▶**FOR MORE PRACTICE**   Problems 35, 36, 37, 38.

5 More Pancakes: Limiting Reactant, Theoretical Yield, and Percent Yield

Let's return to our pancake analogy to understand two more concepts important in reaction stoichiometry: limiting reactant and percent yield. Recall our pancake recipe:

$$1 \text{ cup flour} + 2 \text{ eggs} + \tfrac{1}{2} \text{ tsp baking powder} \longrightarrow 5 \text{ pancakes}$$

Suppose we have 3 cups flour, 10 eggs, and 4 tsp baking powder. How many pancakes can we make? We have enough flour to make:

$$3 \text{ cups flour} \times \frac{5 \text{ pancakes}}{1 \text{ cup flour}} = 15 \text{ pancakes}$$

We have enough eggs to make:

$$10 \text{ eggs} \times \frac{5 \text{ pancakes}}{2 \text{ eggs}} = 25 \text{ pancakes}$$

We have enough baking powder to make:

$$4 \text{ tsp baking powder} \times \frac{5 \text{ pancakes}}{\tfrac{1}{2} \text{ tsp baking powder}} = 40 \text{ pancakes}$$

We have enough flour for 15 pancakes, enough eggs for 25 pancakes, and enough baking powder for 40 pancakes. Consequently, unless we get more ingredients, *we can make only 15 pancakes*. The amount of flour we have *limits* the number of pancakes we can make. If this were a chemical reaction, the flour would be the *limiting reactant*, the reactant that limits the amount of product in a chemical reaction. Notice that the **limiting reactant** is simply the reactant that makes *the least amount of product*. If this were a chemical reaction, 15 pancakes would be the **theoretical yield**, the amount of product that can be made in a chemical reaction based on the amount of limiting reactant.

The term *limiting reagent* is sometimes used in place of limiting reactant.

Limiting reactant

Theoretical yield

15 pancakes   25 pancakes   40 pancakes

▲ If this were a chemical reaction, the flour would be the limiting reactant and 15 pancakes would be the theoretical yield.

The actual yield of a chemical reaction, which must be determined experimentally, often depends in various ways on the reaction conditions.

Let us carry this analogy one step further. Suppose we go on to cook our pancakes. We accidentally burn three of them and one falls on the floor. So even though we had enough flour for 15 pancakes, we finished with only 11 pancakes. If this were a chemical reaction, the 11 pancakes would be our **actual yield**, the amount of product actually produced by a chemical reaction. Finally, our **percent yield**, the percentage of the theoretical yield that was actually attained, is:

$$\text{Percent yield} = \frac{11 \text{ pancakes}}{15 \text{ pancakes}} \times 100\% = 73\%$$

Since four of the pancakes were ruined, we got only 73% of our theoretical yield. In a chemical reaction, the actual yield is almost always less than 100% because at least some of the product does not form or is lost in the process of recovering it (in analogy to some of the pancakes being burned).

To summarize:

- **Limiting reactant (or limiting reagent)**—the reactant that is completely consumed in a chemical reaction.
- **Theoretical yield**—the amount of product that can be made in a chemical reaction based on the amount of limiting reactant.
- **Actual yield**—the amount of product actually produced by a chemical reaction.
- $$\textbf{Percent yield} = \frac{\textbf{Actual yield}}{\textbf{Theoretical yield}} \times \textbf{100\%}$$

Consider the reaction.

$$\text{Ti}(s) + 2\,\text{Cl}_2(g) \longrightarrow \text{TiCl}_4(s)$$

If we begin with 1.8 mol of titanium and 3.2 mol of chlorine, what is the limiting reactant and theoretical yield of TiCl_4 in moles? We begin by sorting the information in the problem according to our standard problem-solving procedure.

GIVEN: 1.8 mol Ti

3.2 mol Cl_2

FIND: limiting reactant

theoretical yield

SOLUTION MAP

As in our pancake analogy, we determine the limiting reactant by calculating how much product can be made from each reactant. The reactant that makes the *least amount of product* is the limiting reactant.

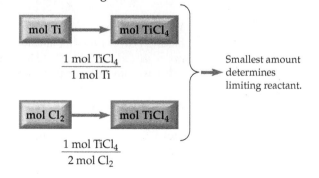

mol Ti → mol TiCl₄

$$\frac{1 \text{ mol TiCl}_4}{1 \text{ mol Ti}}$$

mol Cl₂ → mol TiCl₄

$$\frac{1 \text{ mol TiCl}_4}{2 \text{ mol Cl}_2}$$

Smallest amount determines limiting reactant.

RELATIONSHIPS USED

The conversion factors come from the balanced chemical equation and give the relationships between moles of each of the reactants and moles of product.

$$1 \text{ mol Ti} : 1 \text{ mol TiCl}_4$$

$$2 \text{ mol Cl}_2 : 1 \text{ mol TiCl}_4$$

SOLUTION

$$1.8 \text{ mol Ti} \times \frac{1 \text{ mol TiCl}_4}{1 \text{ mol Ti}} = 1.8 \text{ mol TiCl}_4$$

$$3.2 \text{ mol Cl}_2 \times \frac{1 \text{ mol TiCl}_4}{2 \text{ mol Cl}_2} = 1.6 \text{ mol TiCl}_4$$

Limiting reactant

Least amount of product

In many industrial applications, the more costly reactant or the reactant that is most difficult to remove from the product mixture is chosen to be the limiting reactant.

Since the 3.2 mol of Cl_2 make the least amount of $TiCl_4$, Cl_2 is the limiting reactant. Notice that we began with more moles of Cl_2 than Ti, but since the reaction requires 2 Cl_2 for each Ti, Cl_2 is still the limiting reactant. The theoretical yield is 1.6 mol of $TiCl_4$.

EXAMPLE 4 Limiting Reactant and Theoretical Yield from Initial Moles of Reactants

Consider the reaction:

$$2 \text{ Al}(s) + 3 \text{ Cl}_2(g) \longrightarrow 2 \text{ AlCl}_3(s)$$

If you begin with 0.552 mol of aluminum and 0.887 mol of chlorine, what is the limiting reactant and theoretical yield of $AlCl_3$ in moles?

SORT You are given the number of moles of aluminum and chlorine and asked to find the limiting reactant and theoretical yield of aluminum chloride.	**GIVEN** 0.552 mol Al 0.887 mol Cl_2 **FIND** limiting reactant theoretical yield of $AlCl_3$
STRATEGIZE Draw a solution map that shows how to get from moles of each reactant to moles of $AlCl_3$. The reactant that makes the *least amount of AlCl₃* is the limiting reactant. The conversion factors are the stoichiometric relationships (from the balanced equation).	**SOLUTION MAP** 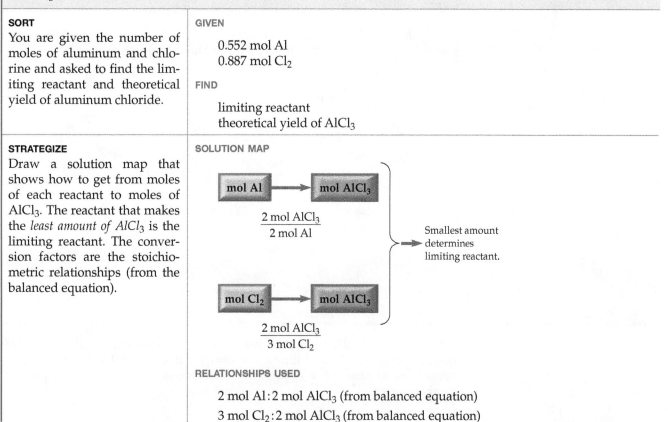 **RELATIONSHIPS USED** 2 mol Al : 2 mol $AlCl_3$ (from balanced equation) 3 mol Cl_2 : 2 mol $AlCl_3$ (from balanced equation)

SOLVE	SOLUTION
Follow the solution map to solve the problem.	$$0.552 \; \text{mol Al} \times \frac{2 \; \text{mol AlCl}_3}{2 \; \text{mol Al}} = 0.552 \; \text{mol AlCl}_3$$ Limiting reactant Least amount of product $$0.887 \; \text{mol Cl}_2 \times \frac{2 \; \text{mol AlCl}_3}{3 \; \text{mol Cl}_2} = 0.591 \; \text{mol AlCl}_3$$ Since the 0.552 mol of Al makes the least amount of $AlCl_3$, Al is the limiting reactant. The theoretical yield is 0.552 mol of $AlCl_3$.
CHECK Are the units correct? Does the answer make physical sense?	The units, mol $AlCl_3$, are correct. The magnitude of the answer seems reasonable because it is of the same order of magnitude as the given number of moles of Al and Cl_2. An answer that is orders of magnitude different would immediately be suspect.

▶ **SKILLBUILDER 4 | Limiting Reactant and Theoretical Yield from Initial Moles of Reactants**

Consider the reaction:

$$2 \, Na(s) + F_2(g) \longrightarrow 2 \, NaF(s)$$

If you begin with 4.8 mol of sodium and 2.6 mol of fluorine, what is the limiting reactant and theoretical yield of NaF in moles?

▶ **FOR MORE PRACTICE** Problems 43, 44, 45, 46, 47, 48, 49, 50.

✔ CONCEPTUAL CHECKPOINT 2

Consider the reaction:

$$N_2(g) + 3 \, H_2(g) \longrightarrow 2 \, NH_3(g)$$

If the flask at left represents the mixture before the reaction, which flask represents the products after the limiting reactant has completely reacted?

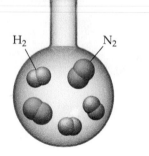

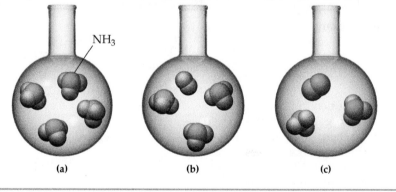

(a)   (b)   (c)

6 Limiting Reactant, Theoretical Yield, and Percent Yield from Initial Masses of Reactants

When working in the laboratory, we normally measure the initial amounts of reactants in grams. To find limiting reactants and theoretical yields from initial masses, we must add two steps to our calculations. Consider, for example, the synthesis reaction:

$$2 \, Na(s) + Cl_2(g) \longrightarrow 2 \, NaCl(s)$$

If we have 53.2 g of Na and 65.8 g of Cl_2, what is the limiting reactant and theoretical yield? We begin by sorting the information in the problem.

GIVEN: 53.2 g Na

65.8 g Cl_2

FIND: limiting reactant

theoretical yield

SOLUTION MAP

Again, we find the limiting reactant by calculating how much product can be made from each reactant. Since we are given the initial amounts in grams, we must first convert to moles. After we convert to moles of product, we convert back to grams of product. The reactant that makes the *least amount of product* is the limiting reactant.

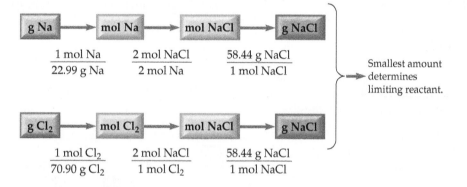

RELATIONSHIPS USED

From the balanced chemical equation, we know:

$$2 \text{ mol Na} : 2 \text{ mol NaCl}$$
$$1 \text{ mol Cl}_2 : 2 \text{ mol NaCl}$$

We also use these molar masses:

$$\text{Molar mass Na} = \frac{22.99 \text{ g Na}}{1 \text{ mol Na}}$$

$$\text{Molar mass Cl}_2 = \frac{70.90 \text{ g Cl}_2}{1 \text{ mol Cl}_2}$$

$$\text{Molar mass NaCl} = \frac{58.44 \text{ g NaCl}}{1 \text{ mol NaCl}}$$

SOLUTION

Beginning with the actual amounts of each reactant, we follow the solution map to calculate how much product can be made from each.

The limiting reactant can also be found by calculating the number of moles of NaCl (rather than grams) that can be made from each reactant. However, since theoretical yields are normally calculated in grams, we take the calculation all the way to grams to determine limiting reactant.

$$53.2 \text{ g Na} \times \frac{1 \text{ mol Na}}{22.99 \text{ g Na}} \times \frac{2 \text{ mol NaCl}}{2 \text{ mol Na}} \times \frac{58.44 \text{ g NaCl}}{1 \text{ mol NaCl}} = 135 \text{ g NaCl}$$

$$65.8 \text{ g Cl}_2 \times \frac{1 \text{ mol Cl}_2}{70.90 \text{ g Cl}_2} \times \frac{2 \text{ mol NaCl}}{1 \text{ mol Cl}_2} \times \frac{58.44 \text{ g NaCl}}{1 \text{ mol NaCl}} = 108 \text{ g NaCl}$$

Limiting
reactant

Least amount
of product

The limiting reactant is not necessarily the reactant with the least mass.

Since Cl_2 makes the least amount of product, it is the limiting reactant. Notice that the limiting reactant is not necessarily the reactant with the least mass. In this case, we had fewer grams of Na than Cl_2, yet Cl_2 was the limiting reactant because it made less NaCl. The theoretical yield is therefore 108 g of NaCl, the amount of product possible based on the limiting reactant.

Now suppose that when the synthesis was carried out, the actual yield of NaCl was 86.4 g. What is the percent yield? The percent yield is:

> The actual yield is always less than the theoretical yield because at least a small amount of product is usually lost or does not form during a reaction.

$$\text{Percent yield} = \frac{\text{Actual yield}}{\text{Theoretical yield}} \times 100\% = \frac{86.4 \text{ g}}{108 \text{ g}} \times 100\% = 80.0\%$$

EXAMPLE 5 Finding Limiting Reactant and Theoretical Yield

Ammonia, NH_3, can be synthesized by the reaction:

$$2\,NO(g) + 5\,H_2(g) \longrightarrow 2\,NH_3(g) + 2\,H_2O(g)$$

What maximum amount of ammonia in grams can be synthesized from 45.8 g of NO and 12.4 g of H_2?

SORT You are given the masses of two reactants and asked to find the maximum mass of ammonia that can be formed. Although this problem does not specifically ask for the limiting reactant, it must be found to determine the theoretical yield, which is the maximum amount of ammonia that can be synthesized.	**GIVEN:** 45.8 g NO, 12.4 g H_2 **FIND:** maximum amount of NH_3 in g (this is the theoretical yield)
STRATEGIZE Find the limiting reactant by calculating how much product can be made from each reactant. The reactant that makes the *least amount of product* is the limiting reactant. The mass of ammonia formed by the limiting reactant is the maximum amount of ammonia that can be synthesized.	**SOLUTION MAP** 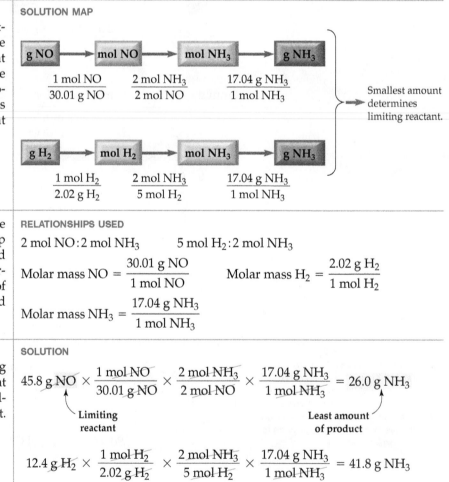
The main conversion factors come from the stoichiometric relationship between moles of each reactant and moles of ammonia. The other conversion factors are the molar masses of nitrogen monoxide, hydrogen gas, and ammonia.	**RELATIONSHIPS USED** 2 mol NO : 2 mol NH_3 5 mol H_2 : 2 mol NH_3 $$\text{Molar mass NO} = \frac{30.01 \text{ g NO}}{1 \text{ mol NO}} \quad \text{Molar mass } H_2 = \frac{2.02 \text{ g } H_2}{1 \text{ mol } H_2}$$ $$\text{Molar mass } NH_3 = \frac{17.04 \text{ g } NH_3}{1 \text{ mol } NH_3}$$
SOLVE Follow the solution map, beginning with the actual amount of each reactant given, to calculate the amount of product that can be made from each reactant.	**SOLUTION** $$45.8 \text{ g NO} \times \frac{1 \text{ mol NO}}{30.01 \text{ g NO}} \times \frac{2 \text{ mol } NH_3}{2 \text{ mol NO}} \times \frac{17.04 \text{ g } NH_3}{1 \text{ mol } NH_3} = 26.0 \text{ g } NH_3$$ Limiting reactant / Least amount of product $$12.4 \text{ g } H_2 \times \frac{1 \text{ mol } H_2}{2.02 \text{ g } H_2} \times \frac{2 \text{ mol } NH_3}{5 \text{ mol } H_2} \times \frac{17.04 \text{ g } NH_3}{1 \text{ mol } NH_3} = 41.8 \text{ g } NH_3$$ There is enough NO to make 26.0 g of NH_3 and enough H_2 to make 41.8 g of NH_3. Therefore, NO is the limiting reactant, and the maximum amount of ammonia that can possibly be made is 26.0 g, which is the theoretical yield.

CHECK Are the units correct? Does the answer make physical sense?	The units of the answer, g NH_3, are correct. The magnitude of the answer seems reasonable because it is of the same order of magnitude as the given masses of NO and H_2. An answer that is orders of magnitude different would immediately be suspect.

▶ **SKILLBUILDER 5 | Finding Limiting Reactant and Theoretical Yield**

Ammonia can also be synthesized by the reaction:

$$3 H_2(g) + N_2(g) \longrightarrow 2 NH_3(g)$$

What maximum amount of ammonia in grams can be synthesized from 25.2 g of N_2 and 8.42 g of H_2?

▶ **SKILLBUILDER PLUS 1**

What maximum amount of ammonia in kilograms can be synthesized from 5.22 kg of H_2 and 31.5 kg of N_2?

▶ **FOR MORE PRACTICE** Problems 55, 56, 57, 58.

EXAMPLE 6 Finding Limiting Reactant, Theoretical Yield, and Percent Yield

Consider the reaction:

$$Cu_2O(s) + C(s) \longrightarrow 2 Cu(s) + CO(g)$$

When 11.5 g of C are allowed to react with 114.5 g of Cu_2O, 87.4 g of Cu are obtained. Find the limiting reactant, theoretical yield, and percent yield.

SORT You are given the mass of the reactants, carbon and copper(I) oxide, as well as the mass of copper formed by the reaction. You are asked to find the limiting reactant, theoretical yield, and percent yield.	GIVEN: 11.5 g C 114.5 g Cu_2O 87.4 g Cu produced FIND: limiting reactant theoretical yield percent yield
STRATEGIZE The solution map shows how to find the mass of Cu formed by the initial masses of Cu_2O and C. The reactant that makes the *least amount of product* is the limiting reactant and determines the theoretical yield.	SOLUTION MAP
The main conversion factors are the stoichiometric relationships between moles of each reactant and moles of copper. The other conversion factors are the molar masses of copper(I) oxide, carbon, and copper.	RELATIONSHIPS USED 1 mol Cu_2O : 2 mol Cu 1 mol C : 2 mol Cu Molar mass Cu_2O = 143.10 g/mol Molar mass C = 12.01 g/mol Molar mass Cu = 63.55 g/mol

SOLVE	SOLUTION
Follow the solution map, beginning with the actual amount of each reactant given, to calculate the amount of product that can be made from each reactant. Since Cu_2O makes the least amount of product, Cu_2O is the limiting reactant. The theoretical yield is then the amount of product made by the limiting reactant. The percent yield is the actual yield (87.4 g Cu) divided by the theoretical yield (101.7 g Cu) multiplied by 100%.	$$11.5 \text{ g C} \times \frac{1 \text{ mol C}}{12.01 \text{ g C}} \times \frac{2 \text{ mol Cu}}{1 \text{ mol C}} \times \frac{63.55 \text{ g Cu}}{1 \text{ mol Cu}} = 122 \text{ g Cu}$$ $$114.5 \text{ g Cu}_2\text{O} \times \frac{1 \text{ mol Cu}_2\text{O}}{143.10 \text{ g Cu}_2\text{O}} \times \frac{2 \text{ mol Cu}}{1 \text{ mol Cu}_2\text{O}} \times \frac{63.55 \text{ g Cu}}{1 \text{ mol Cu}} = 101.7 \text{ g Cu}$$ Limiting reactant Least amount of product Theoretical yield = 101.7 g Cu $$\text{Percent yield} = \frac{\text{Actual yield}}{\text{Theoretical yield}} \times 100\%$$ $$= \frac{87.4 \text{ g}}{101.7 \text{ g}} \times 100\% = 85.9\%$$
CHECK Are the units correct? Does the answer make physical sense?	The theoretical yield has the right units (g Cu). The magnitude of the theoretical yield seems reasonable because it is of the same order of magnitude as the given masses of C and Cu_2O. The theoretical yield is reasonable because it is less than 100%. Any calculated theoretical yield above 100% would be suspect.

▶**SKILLBUILDER 6 | Finding Limiting Reactant, Theoretical Yield, and Percent Yield**

This reaction is used to obtain iron from iron ore:

$$Fe_2O_3(s) + 3\,CO(g) \longrightarrow 2\,Fe(s) + 3\,CO_2(g)$$

The reaction of 185 g of Fe_2O_3 with 95.3 g of CO produces 87.4 g of Fe. Find the limiting reactant, theoretical yield, and percent yield.

▶**FOR MORE PRACTICE**   Example 10; Problems 61, 62, 63, 64, 65, 66.

CONCEPTUAL CHECKPOINT 3

Limiting Reactant and Theoretical Yield

Ammonia can by synthesized by the reaction of nitrogen monoxide and hydrogen gas.

$$2\,NO(g) + 5\,H_2(g) \longrightarrow 2\,NH_3(g) + 2\,H_2O(g)$$

A reaction vessel initially contains 4.0 mol of NO and 15.0 mol of H_2. What is in the reaction vessel once the reaction has occurred to the fullest extent possible?

(a) 2 mol NO; 5 mol H_2; 2 mol NH_3; and 2 mol H_2O

(b) 0 mol NO; 0 mol H_2; 6 mol NH_3; and 6 mol H_2O

(c) 2 mol NO; 0 mol H_2; 4 mol NH_3; and 2 mol H_2O

(d) 0 mol NO; 5 mol H_2; 4 mol NH_3; and 4 mol H_2O

7 Enthalpy: A Measure of the Heat Evolved or Absorbed in a Reaction

Chemical reactions can be *exothermic* (in which case they *emit* thermal energy when they occur) or *endothermic* (in which case they *absorb* thermal energy when they occur). The *amount* of thermal energy

EVERYDAY CHEMISTRY

Bunsen Burners

In the laboratory, we often use Bunsen burners as heat sources. These burners are normally fueled by methane. The balanced equation for methane (CH_4) combustion is:

$$CH_4(g) + 2\,O_2(g) \longrightarrow CO_2(g) + 2\,H_2O(g)$$

Most Bunsen burners have a mechanism to adjust the amount of air (and therefore of oxygen) that is mixed with the methane. If you light the burner with the air completely closed off, you get a yellow, smoky flame that is not very hot. As you increase the amount of air going into the burner, the flame becomes bluer, less smoky, and hotter. When you reach the optimum adjustment, the flame has a sharp, inner blue triangle, no smoke, and is hot enough to melt glass easily. Continuing to increase the air beyond this point causes the flame to become cooler again and may actually extinguish it.

CAN YOU ANSWER THIS? *Can you use the concepts from this chapter to explain the changes in the Bunsen burner as the air intake is adjusted?*

Richard Megna/Fundamental Photographs.

| (a) No air | (b) Small amount of air | (c) Optimum | (d) Too much air |

▲ Bunsen burner at various stages of air intake adjustment.

---

emitted or absorbed by a chemical reaction, under conditions of constant pressure (which are common for most everyday reactions), can be quantified with a function called **enthalpy**. Specifically, we define a quantity called the **enthalpy of reaction** (ΔH_{rxn}) as the amount of thermal energy (or heat) that flows when a reaction occurs at constant pressure.

SIGN OF ΔH_{rxn}

The *sign* of ΔH_{rxn} (positive or negative) depends on the *direction* in which thermal energy flows when the reaction occurs. If thermal energy flows out of the reaction and into the surroundings (as in an exothermic reaction), then ΔH_{rxn} is negative. For example, we can specify the enthalpy of reaction for the combustion of CH_4, the main component in natural gas, as:

$$CH_4(g) + 2\,O_2(g) \longrightarrow CO_2(g) + 2\,H_2O(g) \qquad \Delta H_{rxn} = -802.3\ kJ$$

This reaction is exothermic and therefore has a negative enthalpy of reaction. The magnitude of ΔH_{rxn} tells us that 802.3 kJ of heat are emitted when 1 mol of CH_4 reacts with 2 mol of O_2.

If, by contrast, thermal energy flows into the reaction and out of the surroundings (as in an endothermic reaction), then ΔH_{rxn} is positive. For example, we specify the enthalpy of reaction for the reaction between nitrogen and oxygen gas to form nitrogen monoxide as:

$$N_2(g) + O_2(g) \longrightarrow 2\,NO(g) \qquad \Delta H_{rxn} = +182.6\ kJ$$

451

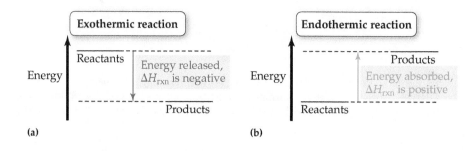

► FIGURE 3 **Exothermic and endothermic reactions** (a) In an exothermic reaction, energy is released into the surroundings. (b) In an endothermic reaction, energy is absorbed from the surroundings.

This reaction is endothermic and therefore has a positive enthalpy of reaction. When 1 mol of N_2 reacts with 1 mol of O_2, 182.6 kJ of heat are absorbed from the surroundings.

You can think of the energy of a chemical system in the same way that you think about the balance in your checking account. Energy flowing *out* of the chemical system is like a withdrawal and carries a negative sign as shown in ▲ Figure 3a. Energy flowing *into* the system is like a deposit and carries a positive sign as shown in Figure 3b.

STOICHIOMETRY OF ΔH_{rxn}

The amount of heat emitted or absorbed when a chemical reaction occurs depends on the *amounts* of reactants that actually react. As we have just seen, we usually specify ΔH_{rxn} in combination with the balanced chemical equation for the reaction. The magnitude of ΔH_{rxn} is for the stoichiometric amounts of reactants and products for the reaction *as written*. For example, the balanced equation and ΔH_{rxn} for the combustion of propane (the fuel used in LP gas) is:

$$C_3H_8(g) + 5\,O_2(g) \longrightarrow 3\,CO_2(g) + 4\,H_2O(g) \qquad \Delta H_{rxn} = -2044 \text{ kJ}$$

This means that when 1 mole of C_3H_8 reacts with 5 moles of O_2 to form 3 moles of CO_2 and 4 moles of H_2O, 2044 kJ of heat are emitted. We can write these relationships in the same way that we express stoichiometric relationships: as ratios between two quantities. For example, for the reactants, we write:

$$1 \text{ mol } C_3H_8 : -2044 \text{ kJ} \quad \text{or} \quad 5 \text{ mol } O_2 : -2044 \text{ kJ}$$

The ratios mean that 2044 kJ of thermal energy are evolved when 1 mole of C_3H_8 and 5 moles of O_2 completely react. These ratios can then be used to construct conversion factors between amounts of reactants or products and the quantity of heat emitted (for exothermic reactions) or absorbed (for endothermic reactions). To find out how much heat is emitted upon the combustion of a certain mass in grams of C_3H_8, we can use the following solution map:

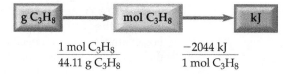

We use the molar mass to convert between grams and moles, and the stoichiometric relationship between moles of C_3H_8 and kJ to convert between moles and kJ, as shown in the following example.

EXAMPLE 7   Stoichiometry Involving ΔH

An LP gas tank in a home barbecue contains 11.8×10^3 g of propane (C_3H_8). Calculate the heat (in kJ) associated with the complete combustion of all of the propane in the tank.

$$C_3H_8(g) + 5\,O_2(g) \longrightarrow 3\,CO_2(g) + 4\,H_2O(g) \qquad \Delta H_{rxn} = -2044 \text{ kJ}$$

SORT

You are given the mass of propane and asked to find the heat evolved (in kJ) in its combustion.

GIVEN: 11.8×10^3 g C_3H_8

FIND: kJ

STRATEGIZE

Start with the given mass of propane and then use its molar mass to find the number of moles. Next, use the stoichiometric relationship between moles of propane and kilojoules of heat to find the heat evolved.

SOLUTION MAP

$$\boxed{\text{g } C_3H_8} \longrightarrow \boxed{\text{mol } C_3H_8} \longrightarrow \boxed{\text{kJ}}$$

$$\frac{1 \text{ mol } C_3H_8}{44.11 \text{ g } C_3H_8} \qquad \frac{-2044 \text{ kJ}}{1 \text{ mol } C_3H_8}$$

RELATIONSHIPS USED

1 mol C_3H_8 : -2044 kJ (from balanced equation)

Molar mass $C_3H_8 = 44.11$ g/mol

SOLVE

Follow the solution map to solve the problem. Begin with 11.8×10^3 g C_3H_8 and multiply by the appropriate conversion factors to arrive at kJ.

SOLUTION

$$11.8 \times 10^3 \text{ g } C_3H_8 \times \frac{1 \text{ mol } C_3H_8}{44.11 \text{ g } C_3H_8} \times \frac{-2044 \text{ kJ}}{1 \text{ mol } C_3H_8} = -5.47 \times 10^5 \text{ kJ}$$

CHECK

Check your answer. Are the units correct? Does the answer make physical sense?

The units, kJ, are correct. The answer is negative, as it should be when heat is evolved by a reaction.

▶**SKILLBUILDER 7** | Stoichiometry Involving ΔH

Ammonia reacts with oxygen according to the equation:

$$4 NH_3(g) + 5 O_2(g) \longrightarrow 4 NO(g) + 6 H_2O \qquad \Delta H_{rxn} = -906 \text{ kJ}$$

Calculate the heat (in kJ) associated with the complete reaction of 155 g of NH_3.

▶**SKILLBUILDER PLUS 2**

What mass of butane in grams is necessary to produce 1.5×10^3 kJ of heat? What mass of CO_2 is produced?

$$C_4H_{10}(g) + \tfrac{13}{2} O_2(g) \longrightarrow 4 CO_2(g) + 5 H_2O(g) \qquad \Delta H_{rxn} = -2658 \text{ kJ}$$

▶**FOR MORE PRACTICE** Example 11; Problems 71, 72, 73, 74, 75, 76.

✓ **CONCEPTUAL CONNECTION 4**

Stoichiometry Involving ΔH

Consider the generic reaction:

$$2A + 3B \longrightarrow 2C \qquad \Delta H_{rxn} = -100 \text{ kJ}$$

If a reaction mixture initially contains 5 mol of A and 6 mol of B, how much heat (in kJ) will be evolved once the reaction has occurred to the greatest extent possible?

(a) 100 kJ

(b) 150 kJ

(c) 200 kJ

(d) 300 kJ

CHAPTER IN REVIEW

CHEMICAL PRINCIPLES

RELEVANCE

Stoichiometry: A balanced chemical equation gives quantitative relationships between the amounts of reactants and products. For example, the reaction $2 H_2 + O_2 \longrightarrow 2 H_2O$ says that 2 mol of H_2 reacts with 1 mol of O_2 to form 2 mol of H_2O. These relationships can be used to calculate quantities such as the amount of product possible with a certain amount of reactant, or the amount of one reactant required to completely react with a certain amount of another reactant. The quantitative relationship between reactants and products in a chemical reaction is called reaction stoichiometry.

Stoichiometry: Reaction stoichiometry is important because we often want to know the numerical relationship between the reactants and products in a chemical reaction. For example, we might want to know how much carbon dioxide, a greenhouse gas, is formed when a certain amount of a particular fossil fuel burns.

Limiting Reactant, Theoretical Yield, and Percent Yield: The limiting reactant in a chemical reaction is the reactant that limits the amount of product that can be made. The theoretical yield in a chemical reaction is the amount of product that can be made based on the amount of the limiting reactant. The actual yield in a chemical reaction is the amount of product actually produced. The percent yield in a chemical reaction is the actual yield divided by theoretical yield times 100%.

Limiting Reactant, Theoretical Yield, and Percent Yield: Calculations of limiting reactant, theoretical yield, and percent yield are central to chemistry because they allow for quantitative understanding of chemical reactions. Just as you need to know relationships between ingredients to follow a recipe, so you must know relationships between reactants and products to carry out a chemical reaction. The percent yield in a chemical reaction is often used as a measure of the success of the reaction. Imagine following a recipe and making only 1% of the final product—your cooking would be a failure. Similarly, low percent yields in chemical reactions are usually considered poor, and high percent yields are considered good.

Enthalpy of Reaction: The amount of heat released or absorbed by a chemical reaction under conditions of constant pressure, is the enthalpy of reaction (ΔH_{rxn}).

Enthalpy of Reaction: The enthalpy of reaction describes the relationship between the amount of reactant that undergoes reaction and the amount of thermal energy produced. This is important, for example, in determining quantities such as the amount of fuel needed to produce a given amount of energy.

CHEMICAL SKILLS

EXAMPLES

Mole-to-Mole Conversions (Section 3)

EXAMPLE 8   Mole-to-Mole Conversions

How many moles of sodium oxide can be synthesized from 4.8 mol of sodium? Assume that more than enough oxygen is present. The balanced equation is:

$$4 Na(s) + O_2(g) \longrightarrow 2 Na_2O(s)$$

GIVEN: 4.8 mol Na

FIND: mol Na_2O

SORT
You are given the number of moles of sodium and asked to find the number of moles of sodium oxide formed by the reaction.

STRATEGIZE

Draw a solution map beginning with the number of moles of the given substance and then use the conversion factor from the balanced chemical equation to determine the number of moles of the substance you are trying to find.

SOLVE

Follow the solution map to get to the number of moles of the substance you are trying to find.

CHECK

Are the units correct? Does the answer make physical sense?

SOLUTION MAP

$$\frac{2 \text{ mol Na}_2\text{O}}{4 \text{ mol Na}}$$

RELATIONSHIPS USED

4 mol Na : 2 mol Na$_2$O

SOLUTION

$$4.8 \text{ mol Na} \times \frac{2 \text{ mol Na}_2\text{O}}{4 \text{ mol Na}} = 2.4 \text{ mol Na}_2\text{O}$$

The units of the answer, mol Na$_2$O, are correct. The magnitude of the answer seems reasonable because it is of the same order of magnitude as the given number of moles of Na.

Mass-to-Mass Conversions (Section 4)

EXAMPLE 9   Mass-to-Mass Conversions

How many grams of sodium oxide can be synthesized from 17.4 g of sodium? Assume that more than enough oxygen is present. The balanced equation is:

$$4 \text{ Na}(s) + \text{O}_2(g) \longrightarrow 2 \text{ Na}_2\text{O}(s)$$

SORT

You are given the mass of sodium and asked to find the mass of sodium oxide that forms upon reaction.

GIVEN: 17.4 g Na

FIND: g Na$_2$O

STRATEGIZE

Draw the solution map by beginning with the mass of the given substance. Convert to moles using the molar mass and then convert to moles of the substance you are trying to find, using the conversion factor obtained from the balanced chemical equation. Finally, convert to mass of the substance you are trying to find, using its molar mass.

SOLUTION MAP

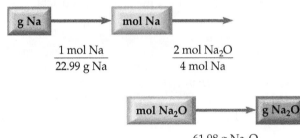

$$\frac{1 \text{ mol Na}}{22.99 \text{ g Na}} \qquad \frac{2 \text{ mol Na}_2\text{O}}{4 \text{ mol Na}}$$

$$\frac{61.98 \text{ g Na}_2\text{O}}{1 \text{ mol Na}_2\text{O}}$$

RELATIONSHIPS USED

4 mol Na : 2 mol Na$_2$O (from balanced equation)

Molar mass Na = 22.99 g/mol

Molar mass Na$_2$O = 61.98 g/mol

SOLVE

Follow the solution map and calculate the answer by beginning with the mass of the given substance and multiplying by the appropriate conversion factors to determine the mass of the substance you are trying to find.

SOLUTION

$$17.4 \text{ g Na} \times \frac{1 \text{ mol Na}}{22.99 \text{ g Na}} \times \frac{2 \text{ mol Na}_2\text{O}}{4 \text{ mol Na}} \times$$

$$\frac{61.98 \text{ g Na}_2\text{O}}{1 \text{ mol Na}_2\text{O}} = 23.5 \text{ g Na}_2\text{O}$$

CHECK

Are the units correct? Does the answer make physical sense?

The units of the answer, g Na$_2$O, are correct. The magnitude of the answer seems reasonable because it is of the same order of magnitude as the given mass of Na.

Limiting Reactant, Theoretical Yield, and Percent Yield (Sections 5, 6)

EXAMPLE 10 Limiting Reactant, Theoretical Yield, and Percent Yield

10.4 g of As reacts with 11.8 g of S to produce 14.2 g of As_2S_3. Find the limiting reactant, theoretical yield, and percent yield for this reaction. The balanced chemical equation is:

$$2\ As(s) + 3\ S(l) \longrightarrow As_2S_3(s)$$

GIVEN: 10.4 g As
11.8 g S
14.2 g As_2S_3

FIND: limiting reactant
theoretical yield
percent yield

SORT

You are given the masses of iron and sulfur as well as the mass of iron(III) sulfide formed by the reaction. You are asked to find the limiting reactant, theoretical yield, and percent yield.

STRATEGIZE

The solution map for limiting-reactant problems shows how to convert from the mass of each of the reactants to mass of the product for each reactant. These are mass-to-mass conversions with the basic outline of

$$\text{Mass} \longrightarrow \text{Moles} \longrightarrow \text{Moles} \longrightarrow \text{Mass}$$

The reactant that forms the least amount of product is the limiting reactant.

The conversion factors you need are the stoichiometric relationships between each of the reactants and the product. You also need the molar masses of each reactant and product.

SOLUTION MAP

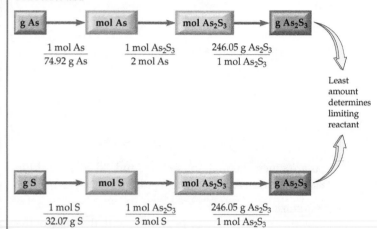

RELATIONSHIPS USED

2 mol As : 1 mol As_2S_3

3 mol S : 1 mol As_2S_3

Molar mass As = 74.92 g/mol

Molar mass S = 32.07 g/mol

Molar mass As_2S_3 = 246.05 g/mol

SOLVE

To calculate the amount of product formed by each reactant, begin with the given amount of each reactant and multiply by the appropriate conversion factors, as shown in the solution map, to arrive at the mass of product for each reactant. The reactant that forms the least amount of product is the limiting reactant.

SOLUTION

$$10.4\ \text{g As} \times \frac{1\ \text{mol As}}{74.92\ \text{g As}} \times \frac{1\ \text{mol As}_2\text{S}_3}{2\ \text{mol As}} \times \frac{246.05\ \text{g As}_2\text{S}_3}{1\ \text{mol As}_2\text{S}_3}$$

Limiting reactant

$$= 17.1\ \text{g As}_2\text{S}_3$$

Least amount of product

$$11.8\ \text{g S} \times \frac{1\ \text{mol S}}{32.07\ \text{g S}} \times \frac{1\ \text{mol As}_2\text{S}_3}{3\ \text{mol S}} \times \frac{246.05\ \text{g As}_2\text{S}_3}{1\ \text{mol As}_2\text{S}_3}$$

$$= 30.2\ \text{g As}_2\text{S}_3$$

The limiting reactant is As.

The theoretical yield is the amount of product formed by the limiting reactant.

The percent yield is the actual yield divided by the theoretical yield times 100%.

The theoretical yield is 17.1 g of As_2S_3.

$$Percent\ yield = \frac{Actual\ yield}{Theoretical\ yield} \times 100\%$$

$$= \frac{14.2\ g}{17.1\ g} \times 100\% = 83.0\%$$

The percent yield is 83.0%.

CHECK

Check your answer. Are the units correct? Does the answer make physical sense?

The theoretical yield has the right units (g As_2S_3). The magnitude of the theoretical yield seems reasonable because it is of the same order of magnitude as the given masses of As and S. The theoretical yield is reasonable because it is less than 100%. Any calculated theoretical yield above 100% would be suspect.

Stoichiometry Involving ΔH (Section 7)

EXAMPLE 11 Stoichiometry Involving ΔH

Calculate the heat evolved (in kJ) upon complete combustion of 25.0 g of methane (CH_4).

$$CH_4(g) + 2\,O_2(g) \longrightarrow CO_2(g) + 2\,H_2O(g)$$

$$\Delta H_{rxn} = -802\ kJ$$

SORT

You are given the mass of methane and asked to find the quantity of heat in kJ emitted upon combustion.

Draw the solution map by beginning with the mass of the given substance. Convert to moles using molar mass and then to kJ using ΔH.

GIVEN: 25 g CH_4

FIND: kJ

SOLUTION MAP

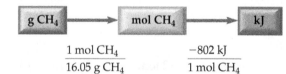

$$\frac{1\ mol\ CH_4}{16.05\ g\ CH_4}$$ $$\frac{-802\ kJ}{1\ mol\ CH_4}$$

RELATIONSHIPS USED

1 mol CH_4 : -802 kJ (from balanced equation)

Molar mass $CH_4 = 16.05$ g/mol

SOLVE

Follow the solution map to solve the problem. Begin with the mass of the given substance and multiply by the appropriate conversion factors to arrive at kJ. A negative answer means that heat is evolved into the surroundings. A positive answer means that heat is absorbed from the surroundings.

SOLUTION

$$25.0\ g\ CH_4 \times \frac{1\ mol\ CH_4}{16.05\ g\ CH_4} \times \frac{-802\ kJ}{1\ mol\ CH_4}$$

$$= -1.25 \times 10^3\ kJ$$

CHECK

Are the units correct? Does the answer make physical sense?

The units, kJ, are correct. The answer is negative, as it should be since heat is evolved by the reaction.

KEY TERMS

actual yield [**Section 5**]
enthalpy [**Section 7**]

enthalpy of reaction
(ΔH_{rxn}) [**Section 7**]

global warming [**Section 1**]
greenhouse gases [**Section 1**]
limiting reactant [**Section 5**]

percent yield [**Section 5**]
stoichiometry [**Section 1**]
theoretical yield [**Section 5**]

EXERCISES

QUESTIONS

1. Why is reaction stoichiometry important? Give some examples.

2. Nitrogen and hydrogen can react to form ammonia.

$$N_2(g) + 3\,H_2(g) \longrightarrow 2\,NH_3(g)$$

   (a) Write ratios showing the relationships between moles of each of the reactants and products in the reaction.

   (b) How many molecules of H_2 are required to completely react with two molecules of N_2?

   (c) How many moles of H_2 are required to completely react with 2 mol of N_2?

3. Write the conversion factor that you would use to convert from moles of Cl_2 to moles of NaCl in the reaction:

$$2\,Na(s) + Cl_2(g) \longrightarrow 2\,NaCl$$

4. What is wrong with this statement in reference to the reaction in the previous problem? "Two grams of Na react with 1 g of Cl_2 to form 2 g of NaCl." Correct the statement to make it true.

5. What is the general form of the solution map for problems in which you are given the mass of a reactant in a chemical reaction and asked to find the mass of the product that can be made from the given amount of reactant?

6. Consider the recipe for making tomato and garlic pasta.

$$2 \text{ cups noodles} + 12 \text{ tomatoes} + 3 \text{ cloves garlic}$$
$$\longrightarrow 4 \text{ servings pasta}$$

   If you have 7 cups of noodles, 27 tomatoes, and 9 cloves of garlic, how many servings of pasta can you make? Which ingredient limits the amount of pasta that it is possible to make?

7. In a chemical reaction, what is the limiting reactant?

8. In a chemical reaction, what is the theoretical yield?

9. In a chemical reaction, what are the actual yield and percent yield?

10. If you are given a chemical equation and specific amounts for each reactant in grams, how would you determine how much product can possibly be made?

11. Consider the generic chemical reaction:

$$A + 2\,B \longrightarrow C + D$$

   Suppose you have 12 g of A and 24 g of B. Which statement is true?

   (a) A will definitely be the limiting reactant.

   (b) B will definitely be the limiting reactant.

   (c) A will be the limiting reactant if its molar mass is less than B.

   (d) A will be the limiting reactant if its molar mass is greater than B.

12. Consider the generic chemical equation:

$$A + B \longrightarrow C$$

   Suppose 25 g of A were allowed to react with 8 g of B. Analysis of the final mixture showed that A was completely used up and 4 g of B remained. What was the limiting reactant?

13. What is the enthalpy of reaction (ΔH_{rxn}). Why is this quantity important?

14. Explain the relationship between the sign of ΔH_{rxn} and whether a reaction is exothermic or endothermic.

PROBLEMS

MOLE-TO-MOLE CONVERSIONS

15. Consider the generic chemical reaction:

$$A + 2\,B \longrightarrow C$$

   How many moles of C are formed upon complete reaction of:

   (a) 2 mol of A

   (b) 2 mol of B

   (c) 3 mol of A

   (d) 3 mol of B

16. Consider the generic chemical reaction:

$$2\,A + 3\,B \longrightarrow 3\,C$$

   How many moles of B are required to completely react with:

   (a) 6 mol of A

   (b) 2 mol of A

   (c) 7 mol of A

   (d) 11 mol of A

17. For the reaction shown, calculate how many moles of NO_2 form when each amount of reactant completely reacts.

$$2\,N_2O_5(g) \longrightarrow 4\,NO_2(g) + O_2(g)$$

(a) 1.3 mol N_2O_5

(b) 5.8 mol N_2O_5

(c) 4.45×10^3 mol N_2O_5

(d) 1.006×10^{-3} mol N_2O_5

18. For the reaction shown, calculate how many moles of NH_3 form when each amount of reactant completely reacts.

$$3\,N_2H_4(l) \longrightarrow 4\,NH_3(g) + N_2(g)$$

(a) 5.3 mol N_2H_4

(b) 2.28 mol N_2H_4

(c) 5.8×10^{-2} mol N_2H_4

(d) 9.76×10^7 mol N_2H_4

19. Dihydrogen monosulfide reacts with sulfur dioxide according to the balanced equation:

$$2\,H_2S(g) + SO_2(g) \longrightarrow 3\,S(s) + 2\,H_2O(g)$$

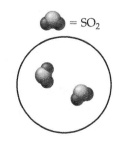

= SO_2

If the above figure represents the amount of SO_2 available to react, which figure best represents the amount of H_2S required to completely react with all of the SO_2?

= H_2S

(a)　　(b)　　(c)

20. Chlorine gas reacts with fluorine gas according to the balanced equation:

$$Cl_2(g) + 3\,F_2(g) \longrightarrow 2\,ClF_3(g)$$

= F_2

If the above figure represents the amount of fluorine available to react, and assuming that there is more than enough chlorine, which figure best represents the amount of chlorine trifluoride that would form upon complete reaction of all of the fluorine?

= ClF_3

(a)　　(b)　　(c)

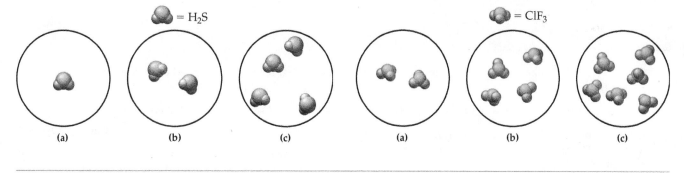

21. For each reaction, calculate how many moles of product form when 1.75 mol of the reactant in color completely reacts. Assume there is more than enough of the other reactant.

(a) $H_2(g) + Cl_2(g) \longrightarrow 2\,HCl(g)$

(b) $2\,H_2(g) + O_2(g) \longrightarrow 2\,H_2O(l)$

(c) $2\,Na(s) + O_2(g) \longrightarrow Na_2O_2(s)$

(d) $2\,S(s) + 3\,O_2(g) \longrightarrow 2\,SO_3(g)$

22. For each reaction, calculate how many moles of the product form when 0.112 mol of the reactant in color completely reacts. Assume there is more than enough of the other reactant.

(a) $2\,Ca(s) + O_2(g) \longrightarrow 2\,CaO(s)$

(b) $4\,Fe(s) + 3\,O_2(g) \longrightarrow 2\,Fe_2O_3(s)$

(c) $4\,K(s) + O_2(g) \longrightarrow 2\,K_2O(s)$

(d) $4\,Al(s) + 3\,O_2(g) \longrightarrow 2\,Al_2O_3(s)$

23. For the reaction shown, calculate how many moles of each product form when the given amount of each reactant completely reacts. Assume there is more than enough of the other reactant.

$$2\,PbS(s) + 3\,O_2(g) \longrightarrow 2\,PbO(s) + 2\,SO_2(g)$$

(a) 2.4 mol PbS

(b) 2.4 mol O_2

(c) 5.3 mol PbS

(d) 5.3 mol O_2

24. For the reaction shown, calculate how many moles of each product form when the given amount of each reactant completely reacts. Assume there is more than enough of the other reactant.

$$C_3H_8(g) + 5\,O_2(g) \longrightarrow 3\,CO_2(g) + 4\,H_2O(g)$$

(a) 4.6 mol C_3H_8

(b) 4.6 mol O_2

(c) 0.0558 mol C_3H_8

(d) 0.0558 mol O_2

25. Consider the balanced equation:

$$2\,N_2H_4(g) + N_2O_4(g) \longrightarrow 3\,N_2(g) + 4\,H_2O(g)$$

Complete the table showing the appropriate number of moles of reactants and products. If the number of moles of a reactant is provided, fill in the required amount of the other reactant, as well as the moles of each product formed. If the number of moles of a product is provided, fill in the required amount of each reactant to make that amount of product, as well as the amount of the other product that is made.

mol N_2H_4	mol N_2O_4	mol N_2	mol H_2O
___	2	___	___
6	___	___	___
___	___	___	8
___	5.5	___	___
3	___	___	___
___	___	12.4	___

26. Consider the balanced equation:

$$SiO_2(s) + 3\,C(s) \longrightarrow SiC(s) + 2\,CO(g)$$

Complete the table showing the appropriate number of moles of reactants and products. If the number of moles of a reactant is provided, fill in the required amount of the other reactant, as well as the moles of each product formed. If the number of moles of a product is provided, fill in the required amount of each reactant to make that amount of product, as well as the amount of the other product that is made.

mol SiO_2	mol C	mol SiC	mol CO
___	6	___	___
3	___	___	___
___	___	___	10
___	9.5	___	___
3.2	___	___	___

27. Consider the unbalanced equation for the combustion of butane:

$$C_4H_{10}(g) + O_2(g) \longrightarrow CO_2(g) + H_2O(g)$$

Balance the equation and determine how many moles of O_2 are required to react completely with 4.9 mol of C_4H_{10}.

28. Consider the unbalanced equation for the neutralization of acetic acid:

$$HC_2H_3O_2(aq) + Ca(OH)_2(aq) \longrightarrow$$
$$H_2O(l) + Ca(C_2H_3O_2)_2(aq)$$

Balance the equation and determine how many moles of $Ca(OH)_2$ are required to completely neutralize 1.07 mol of $HC_2H_3O_2$.

29. Consider the unbalanced equation for the reaction of solid lead with silver nitrate:

$$Pb(s) + AgNO_3(aq) \longrightarrow Pb(NO_3)_2(aq) + Ag(s)$$

(a) Balance the equation.

(b) How many moles of silver nitrate are required to completely react with 9.3 mol of lead?

(c) How many moles of Ag are formed by the complete reaction of 28.4 mol of Pb?

30. Consider the unbalanced equation for the reaction of aluminum with sulfuric acid:

$$Al(s) + H_2SO_4(aq) \longrightarrow Al_2(SO_4)_3(aq) + H_2(g)$$

(a) Balance the equation.

(b) How many moles of H_2SO_4 are required to completely react with 8.3 mol of Al?

(c) How many moles of H_2 are formed by the complete reaction of 0.341 mol of Al?

MASS-TO-MASS CONVERSIONS

31. For the reaction shown, calculate how many grams of oxygen form when each quantity of reactant completely reacts.

$$2 HgO(s) \longrightarrow 2 Hg(l) + O_2(g)$$

(a) 2.13 g HgO

(b) 6.77 g HgO

(c) 1.55 kg HgO

(d) 3.87 mg HgO

32. For the reaction shown, calculate how many grams of oxygen form when each quantity of reactant completely reacts.

$$2 KClO_3(s) \longrightarrow 2 KCl(s) + 3 O_2(g)$$

(a) 2.72 g $KClO_3$

(b) 0.361g $KClO_3$

(c) 83.6 kg $KClO_3$

(d) 22.4 mg $KClO_3$

33. For each of the reactions shown, calculate how many grams of the product form when 2.4 g of the reactant in color completely reacts. Assume there is more than enough of the other reactant.

(a) $2 Na(s) + Cl_2(g) \longrightarrow 2 NaCl(s)$

(b) $CaO(s) + CO_2(g) \longrightarrow CaCO_3(s)$

(c) $2 Mg(s) + O_2(g) \longrightarrow 2 MgO(s)$

(d) $Na_2O(s) + H_2O(l) \longrightarrow 2 NaOH(aq)$

34. For each of the reactions shown, calculate how many grams of the product form when 17.8 g of the reactant in color completely reacts. Assume there is more than enough of the other reactant.

(a) $Ca(s) + Cl_2(g) \longrightarrow CaCl_2(s)$

(b) $2 K(s) + Br_2(l) \longrightarrow 2 KBr(s)$

(c) $4 Cr(s) + 3 O_2(g) \longrightarrow 2 Cr_2O_3(s)$

(d) $2 Sr(s) + O_2(g) \longrightarrow 2 SrO(s)$

35. For the reaction shown, calculate how many grams of each product form when the given amount of each reactant completely reacts to form products. Assume there is more than enough of the other reactant.

$$2 Al(s) + Fe_2O_3(s) \longrightarrow Al_2O_3(s) + 2 Fe(l)$$

(a) 4.7 g Al

(b) 4.7 g Fe_2O_3

36. For the reaction shown, calculate how many grams of each product form when the given amount of each reactant completely reacts to form products. Assume there is more than enough of the other reactant.

$$2 HCl(aq) + Na_2CO_3(aq) \longrightarrow$$
$$2 NaCl(aq) + H_2O(l) + CO_2(g)$$

(a) 10.8 g HCl

(b) 10.8 g Na_2CO_3

37. Consider the balanced equation for the combustion of methane, a component of natural gas:

$$CH_4(g) + 2 O_2(g) \longrightarrow CO_2(g) + 2 H_2O(g)$$

Complete the table with the appropriate masses of reactants and products. If the mass of a reactant is provided, fill in the mass of other reactants required to completely react with the given mass, as well as the mass of each product formed. If the mass of a product is provided, fill in the required masses of each reactant to make that amount of product, as well as the mass of the other product that is formed.

Mass CH_4	Mass O_2	Mass CO_2	Mass H_2O
_____	2.57 g	_____	_____
22.32 g	_____	_____	_____
_____	_____	_____	11.32 g
_____	_____	2.94 g	_____
3.18 kg	_____	_____	_____
_____	_____	2.35×10^3 kg	_____

38. Consider the balanced equation for the combustion of butane, a fuel often used in lighters:

$$2 C_4H_{10}(g) + 13 O_2(g) \longrightarrow 8 CO_2(g) + 10 H_2O(g)$$

Complete the table showing the appropriate masses of reactants and products. If the mass of a reactant is provided, fill in the mass of other reactants required to completely react with the given mass, as well as the mass of each product formed. If the mass of a product is provided, fill in the required masses of each reactant to make that amount of product, as well as the mass of the other product that is formed.

Mass C_4H_{10}	Mass O_2	Mass CO_2	Mass H_2O
_____	1.11 g	_____	_____
5.22 g	_____	_____	_____
_____	_____	10.12 g	_____
_____	_____	_____	9.04 g
232 mg	_____	_____	_____
_____	_____	118 mg	_____

39. For each acid–base reaction, calculate how many grams of acid are necessary to completely react with and neutralize 2.5 g of the base.

    (a) $HCl(aq) + NaOH(aq) \longrightarrow H_2O(l) + NaCl(aq)$

    (b) $2\,HNO_3(aq) + Ca(OH)_2(aq) \longrightarrow$
    $$2\,H_2O(l) + Ca(NO_3)_2(aq)$$

    (c) $H_2SO_4(aq) + 2\,KOH(aq) \longrightarrow$
    $$2\,H_2O(l) + K_2SO_4(aq)$$

40. For each precipitation reaction, calculate how many grams of the first reactant are necessary to completely react with 17.3 g of the second reactant.

    (a) $2\,KI(aq) + Pb(NO_3)_2(aq) \longrightarrow$
    $$PbI_2(s) + 2\,KNO_3(aq)$$

    (b) $Na_2CO_3(aq) + CuCl_2(aq) \longrightarrow$
    $$CuCO_3(s) + 2\,NaCl(aq)$$

    (c) $K_2SO_4(aq) + Sr(NO_3)_2(aq) \longrightarrow$
    $$SrSO_4(s) + 2\,KNO_3(aq)$$

41. Sulfuric acid can dissolve aluminum metal according to the reaction:

    $$2\,Al(s) + 3\,H_2SO_4(aq) \longrightarrow Al_2(SO_4)_3(aq) + 3\,H_2(g)$$

    Suppose you wanted to dissolve an aluminum block with a mass of 22.5 g. What minimum amount of H_2SO_4 in grams would you need? How many grams of H_2 gas would be produced by the complete reaction of the aluminum block?

42. Hydrochloric acid can dissolve solid iron according to the reaction:

    $$Fe(s) + 2\,HCl(aq) \longrightarrow FeCl_2(aq) + H_2(g)$$

    What minimum mass of HCl in grams would dissolve a 2.8-g iron bar on a padlock? How much H_2 would be produced by the complete reaction of the iron bar?

LIMITING REACTANT, THEORETICAL YIELD, AND PERCENT YIELD

43. Consider the generic chemical equation:
    $$2\,A + 4\,B \longrightarrow 3\,C$$
    What is the limiting reactant when each of the initial quantities of A and B is allowed to react?

    (a) 2 mol A; 5 mol B

    (b) 1.8 mol A; 4 mol B

    (c) 3 mol A; 4 mol B

    (d) 22 mol A; 40 mol B

44. Consider the generic chemical equation:
    $$A + 3\,B \longrightarrow C$$
    What is the limiting reactant when each of the initial quantities of A and B is allowed to react?

    (a) 1 mol A; 4 mol B

    (b) 2 mol A; 3 mol B

    (c) 0.5 mol A; 1.6 mol B

    (d) 24 mol A; 75 mol B

45. Determine the theoretical yield of C when each of the initial quantities of A and B is allowed to react in the generic reaction:
    $$A + 2\,B \longrightarrow 3\,C$$

    (a) 1 mol A; 1 mol B

    (b) 2 mol A; 2 mol B

    (c) 1 mol A; 3 mol B

    (d) 32 mol A; 68 mol B

46. Determine the theoretical yield of C when each of the initial quantities of A and B is allowed to react in the generic reaction:
    $$2\,A + 3\,B \longrightarrow 2\,C$$

    (a) 2 mol A; 4 mol B

    (b) 3 mol A; 3 mol B

    (c) 5 mol A; 6 mol B

    (d) 4 mol A; 5 mol B

47. For the reaction shown, find the limiting reactant for each of the initial quantities of reactants.
    $$2\,K(s) + Cl_2(g) \longrightarrow 2\,KCl(s)$$

    (a) 1 mol K; 1 mol Cl_2

    (b) 1.8 mol K; 1 mol Cl_2

    (c) 2.2 mol K; 1 mol Cl_2

    (d) 14.6 mol K; 7.8 mol Cl_2

48. For the reaction shown, find the limiting reactant for each of the initial quantities of reactants.
    $$4\,Cr(s) + 3\,O_2(g) \longrightarrow 2\,Cr_2O_3(s)$$

    (a) 1 mol Cr; 1 mol O_2

    (b) 4 mol Cr; 2.5 mol O_2

    (c) 12 mol Cr; 10 mol O_2

    (d) 14.8 mol Cr; 10.3 mol O_2

49. For the reaction shown, calculate the theoretical yield of product in moles for each of the initial quantities of reactants.

$$2 \, Mn(s) + 3 \, O_2(g) \longrightarrow 2 \, MnO_3(s)$$

(a) 2 mol Mn; 2 mol O_2

(b) 4.8 mol Mn; 8.5 mol O_2

(c) 0.114 mol Mn; 0.161 mol O_2

(d) 27.5 mol Mn; 43.8 mol O_2

50. For the reaction shown, calculate the theoretical yield of the product in moles for each of the initial quantities of reactants.

$$Ti(s) + 2 \, Cl_2(g) \longrightarrow TiCl_4(s)$$

(a) 2 mol Ti; 2 mol Cl_2

(b) 5 mol Ti; 9 mol Cl_2

(c) 0.483 mol Ti; 0.911 mol Cl_2

(d) 12.4 mol Ti; 15.8 mol Cl_2

51. Consider the generic reaction between reactants A and B:

$$3 \, A + 4 \, B \longrightarrow 2 \, C$$

If a reaction vessel initially contains 9 mol A and 8 mol B, how many moles of A, B, and C will be in the reaction vessel once the reactants have reacted as much as possible? (Assume 100% actual yield.)

52. Consider the reaction between reactants S and O_2:

$$2 \, S(s) + 3 \, O_2(g) \longrightarrow 2 \, SO_3(g)$$

If a reaction vessel initially contains 5 mol S and 9 mol O_2, how many moles of S, O_2, and SO_3 will be in the reaction vessel once the reactants have reacted as much as possible? (Assume 100% actual yield.)

53. Consider the reaction:

$$4 \, HCl(g) + O_2(g) \longrightarrow 2 \, H_2O(g) + 2 \, Cl_2(g)$$

Each molecular diagram represents an initial mixture of the reactants. How many molecules of Cl_2 would be formed by complete reaction in each case? (Assume 100% actual yield.)

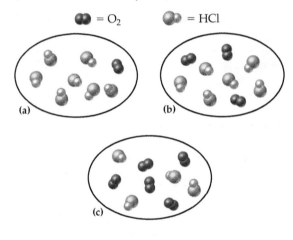

54. Consider the reaction:

$$2 \, CH_3OH(g) + 3 \, O_2(g) \longrightarrow 2 \, CO_2(g) + 4 \, H_2O(g)$$

Each molecular diagram represents an initial mixture of the reactants. How many CO_2 molecules would be formed by complete reaction in each case? (Assume 100% actual yield.)

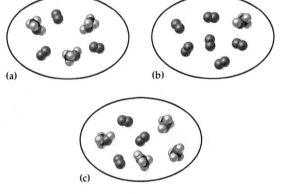

55. For the reaction shown, find the limiting reactant for each of the initial quantities of reactants.

$$2 \, Li(s) + F_2(g) \longrightarrow 2 \, LiF(s)$$

(a) 1.0 g Li; 1.0 g F_2

(b) 10.5 g Li; 37.2 g F_2

(c) 2.85×10^3 g Li; 6.79×10^3 g F_2

56. For the reaction shown, find the limiting reactant for each of the initial quantities of reactants.

$$4 \, Al(s) + 3 \, O_2(g) \longrightarrow 2 \, Al_2O_3(s)$$

(a) 1.0 g Al; 1.0 g O_2

(b) 2.2 g Al; 1.8 g O_2

(c) 0.353 g Al; 0.482 g O_2

57. For the reaction shown, calculate the theoretical yield of the product in grams for each of initial quantities of reactants.

$$2 \, Al(s) + 3 \, Cl_2(g) \longrightarrow 2 \, AlCl_3(s)$$

(a) 1.0 g Al; 1.0 g Cl_2

(b) 5.5 g Al; 19.8 g Cl_2

(c) 0.439 g Al; 2.29 g Cl_2

58. For the reaction shown, calculate the theoretical yield of the product in grams for each of the initial quantities of reactants.

$$Ti(s) + 2 \, F_2(g) \longrightarrow TiF_4(s)$$

(a) 1.0 g Ti; 1.0 g F_2

(b) 4.8 g Ti; 3.2 g F_2

(c) 0.388 g Ti; 0.341 g F_2

59. If the theoretical yield of a reaction is 24.8 g and the actual yield is 18.5 g, what is the percent yield?

60. If the theoretical yield of a reaction is 0.118 g and the actual yield is 0.104 g, what is the percent yield?

61. Consider the reaction between calcium oxide and carbon dioxide:

$$CaO(s) + CO_2(g) \longrightarrow CaCO_3(s)$$

A chemist allows 14.4 g of CaO and 13.8 g of CO_2 to react. When the reaction is finished, the chemist collects 19.4 g of $CaCO_3$. Determine the limiting reactant, theoretical yield, and percent yield for the reaction.

62. Consider the reaction between sulfur trioxide and water:

$$SO_3(g) + H_2O(l) \longrightarrow H_2SO_4(aq)$$

A chemist allows 61.5 g of SO_3 and 11.2 g of H_2O to react. When the reaction is finished, the chemist collects 54.9 g of H_2SO_4. Determine the limiting reactant, theoretical yield, and percent yield for the reaction.

63. Consider the reaction between NiS_2 and O_2:

$$2 \, NiS_2(s) + 5 \, O_2(g) \longrightarrow 2 \, NiO(s) + 4 \, SO_2(g)$$

When 11.2 g of NiS_2 react with 5.43 g of O_2, 4.86 g of NiO are obtained. Determine the limiting reactant, theoretical yield of NiO, and percent yield for the reaction.

64. Consider the reaction between HCl and O_2:

$$4 \, HCl(g) + O_2(g) \longrightarrow 2 \, H_2O(l) + 2 \, Cl_2(g)$$

When 63.1 g of HCl react with 17.2 g of O_2, 49.3 g of Cl_2 are collected. Determine the limiting reactant, theoretical yield of Cl_2, and percent yield for the reaction.

65. Lead ions can be precipitated from solution with NaCl according to the reaction:

$$Pb^{2+}(aq) + 2 \, NaCl(aq) \longrightarrow PbCl_2(s) + 2 \, Na^+(aq)$$

When 135.8 g of NaCl are added to a solution containing 195.7 g of Pb^{2+}, a $PbCl_2$ precipitate forms. The precipitate is filtered and dried and found to have a mass of 252.4 g. Determine the limiting reactant, theoretical yield of $PbCl_2$, and percent yield for the reaction.

66. Magnesium oxide can be produced by heating magnesium metal in the presence of oxygen. The balanced equation for the reaction is:

$$2 \, Mg(s) + O_2(g) \longrightarrow 2 \, MgO(s)$$

When 10.1 g of Mg react with 10.5 g of O_2, 11.9 g of MgO are collected. Determine the limiting reactant, theoretical yield, and percent yield for the reaction.

67. Consider the reaction between TiO_2 and C:

$$TiO_2(s) + 2 \, C(s) \longrightarrow Ti(s) + 2 \, CO(g)$$

A reaction vessel initially contains 10.0 g of each of the reactants. Calculate the masses of TiO_2, C, Ti, and CO that will be in the reaction vessel once the reactants have reacted as much as possible. (Assume 100% yield.)

68. Consider the reaction between N_2H_4 and N_2O_4:

$$2 \, N_2H_4(g) + N_2O_4(g) \longrightarrow 3 \, N_2(g) + 4 \, H_2O(g)$$

A reaction vessel initially contains 27.5 g N_2H_4 and 74.9 g of N_2O_4. Calculate the masses of N_2H_4, N_2O_4, N_2, and H_2O that will be in the reaction vessel once the reactants have reacted as much as possible. (Assume 100% yield.)

ENTHALPY AND STOICHIOMETRY OF ΔH_{rxn}

69. Classify each process as exothermic or endothermic and indicate the sign of ΔH.

(a) butane gas burning in a lighter

(b) the reaction that occurs in the chemical cold packs used to ice athletic injuries

(c) the burning of wax in a candle

70. Classify each process as exothermic or endothermic and indicate the sign of ΔH.

(a) ice melting

(b) a sparkler burning

(c) acetone evaporating from skin

71. Consider the generic reaction:

$$A + 2B \longrightarrow C \qquad \Delta H_{rxn} = -55\ kJ$$

Determine the amount of heat emitted when each amount of reactant completely reacts (assume that there is more than enough of the other reactant):

(a) 1 mol A

(b) 2 mol A

(c) 1 mol B

(d) 2 mol B

72. Consider the generic reaction:

$$2A + 3B \longrightarrow C \qquad \Delta H_{rxn} = -125\ kJ$$

Determine the amount of heat emitted when each amount of reactant completely reacts (assume that there is more than enough of the other reactant):

(a) 2 mol A

(b) 3 mol A

(c) 3 mol B

(d) 5 mol B

73. Consider the equation for the combustion of acetone (C_3H_6O), the main ingredient in nail polish remover.

$$C_3H_6O(l) + 4\ O_2(g) \longrightarrow 3\ CO_2(g) + 3\ H_2O(g)$$
$$\Delta H_{rxn} = -1790\ kJ$$

If a bottle of nail polish remover contains 155 g of acetone, how much heat is released by its complete combustion?

74. The equation for the combustion of CH_4 (the main component of natural gas) is shown below. How much heat is produced by the complete combustion of 237 g of CH_4?

$$CH_4(g) + 2\ O_2(g) \longrightarrow CO_2(g) + 2\ H_2O(g)$$
$$\Delta H_{rxn}^\circ = -802.3\ kJ$$

75. Octane (C_8H_{18}) is a component of gasoline that burns according to the equation:

$$C_8H_{18}(l) + \tfrac{25}{2}\ O_2(g) \longrightarrow 8\ CO_2(g) + 9\ H_2O(g)$$
$$\Delta H_{rxn}^\circ = -5074.1\ kJ$$

What mass of octane (in g) is required to produce 1.55×10^3 kJ of heat?

76. The evaporation of water is endothermic:

$$H_2O(l) \longrightarrow H_2O(g) \qquad \Delta H_{rxn}^\circ = +44.01\ kJ$$

What minimum mass of water (in g) has to evaporate to absorb 175 kJ of heat?

CUMULATIVE PROBLEMS

77. Consider the reaction:

$$2\ N_2(g) + 5\ O_2(g) + 2\ H_2O(g) \longrightarrow 4\ HNO_3(g)$$

If a reaction mixture contains 28 g of N_2, 150 g of O_2, and 36 g of H_2O, what is the limiting reactant? (Try to do this problem in your head without any written calculations.)

78. Consider the reaction:

$$2\ CO(g) + O_2(g) \longrightarrow 2\ CO_2(g)$$

If a reaction mixture contains 28 g of CO and 32 g of O_2, what is the limiting reactant? (Try to do this problem in your head without any written calculations.)

79. A solution contains an unknown mass of dissolved barium ions. When sodium sulfate is added to the solution, a white precipitate forms. The precipitate is filtered and dried and found to have a mass of 258 mg. What mass of barium was in the original solution? (Assume that all of the barium was precipitated out of solution by the reaction.)

80. A solution contains an unknown mass of dissolved silver ions. When potassium chloride is added to the solution, a white precipitate forms. The precipitate is filtered and dried and found to have a mass of 212 mg. What mass of silver was in the original solution? (Assume that all of the silver was precipitated out of solution by the reaction.)

81. Sodium bicarbonate is often used as an antacid to neutralize excess hydrochloric acid in an upset stomach. How much hydrochloric acid in grams can be neutralized by 3.5 g of sodium bicarbonate? (*Hint:* Begin by writing a balanced equation for the reaction between aqueous sodium bicarbonate and aqueous hydrochloric acid.)

82. Toilet bowl cleaners often contain hydrochloric acid to dissolve the calcium carbonate deposits that accumulate within a toilet bowl. How much calcium carbonate in grams can be dissolved by 5.8 g of HCl? (*Hint:* Begin by writing a balanced equation for the reaction between hydrochloric acid and calcium carbonate.)

83. The combustion of gasoline produces carbon dioxide and water. Assume gasoline to be pure octane (C_8H_{18}) and calculate how many kilograms of carbon dioxide are added to the atmosphere per 1.0 kg of octane burned. (*Hint:* Begin by writing a balanced equation for the combustion reaction.)

84. Many home barbecues are fueled with propane gas (C_3H_8.) How much carbon dioxide in kilograms is produced upon the complete combustion of 18.9 L of propane (approximate contents of one 5-gal tank)? Assume that the density of the liquid propane in the tank is 0.621 g/mL. (*Hint:* Begin by writing a balanced equation for the combustion reaction.)

85. A hard water solution contains 4.8 g of calcium chloride. How much sodium phosphate in grams should be added to the solution to completely precipitate all of the calcium?

86. Magnesium ions can be precipitated from seawater by the addition of sodium hydroxide. How much sodium hydroxide in grams must be added to a sample of seawater to completely precipitate the 88.4 mg of magnesium present?

87. Hydrogen gas can be prepared in the laboratory by a single-displacement reaction in which solid zinc reacts with hydrochloric acid. How much zinc in grams is required to make 14.5 g of hydrogen gas through this reaction?

88. Sodium peroxide (Na_2O_2) reacts with water to form sodium hydroxide and oxygen gas. Write a balanced equation for the reaction and determine how much oxygen in grams is formed by the complete reaction of 35.23 g of Na_2O_2.

89. Ammonium nitrate reacts explosively upon heating to form nitrogen gas, oxygen gas, and gaseous water. Write a balanced equation for this reaction and determine how much oxygen in grams is produced by the complete reaction of 1.00 kg of ammonium nitrate.

90. Pure oxygen gas can be prepared in the laboratory by the decomposition of solid potassium chlorate to form solid potassium chloride and oxygen gas. How much oxygen gas in grams can be prepared from 45.8 g of potassium chlorate?

91. Aspirin can be made in the laboratory by reacting acetic anhydride ($C_4H_6O_3$) with salicylic acid ($C_7H_6O_3$) to form aspirin ($C_9H_8O_4$) and acetic acid ($C_2H_4O_2$). The balanced equation is:

$$C_4H_6O_3 + C_7H_6O_3 \longrightarrow C_9H_8O_4 + C_2H_4O_2$$

In a laboratory synthesis, a student begins with 5.00 mL of acetic anhydride (density = 1.08 g/mL) and 2.08 g of salicylic acid. Once the reaction is complete, the student collects 2.01 g of aspirin. Determine the limiting reactant, theoretical yield of aspirin, and percent yield for the reaction.

92. The combustion of liquid ethanol (C_2H_5OH) produces carbon dioxide and water. After 3.8 mL of ethanol (density = 0.789 g/mL) is allowed to burn in the presence of 12.5 g of oxygen gas, 3.10 mL of water (density = 1.00 g/mL) is collected. Determine the limiting reactant, theoretical yield of H_2O, and percent yield for the reaction. (*Hint:* Write a balanced equation for the combustion of ethanol.)

93. Urea (CH_4N_2O), a common fertilizer, can be synthesized by the reaction of ammonia (NH_3) with carbon dioxide:

$$2\,NH_3(aq) + CO_2(aq) \longrightarrow CH_4N_2O(aq) + H_2O(l)$$

An industrial synthesis of urea obtains 87.5 kg of urea upon reaction of 68.2 kg of ammonia with 105 kg of carbon dioxide. Determine the limiting reactant, theoretical yield of urea, and percent yield for the reaction.

94. Silicon, which occurs in nature as SiO_2, is the material from which most computer chips are made. If SiO_2 is heated until it melts into a liquid, it reacts with solid carbon to form liquid silicon and carbon monoxide gas. In an industrial preparation of silicon, 52.8 kg of SiO_2 reacts with 25.8 kg of carbon to produce 22.4 kg of silicon. Determine the limiting reactant, theoretical yield, and percent yield for the reaction.

95. The ingestion of lead from food, water, or other environmental sources can cause lead poisoning, a serious condition that affects the central nervous system, causing symptoms such as distractibility, lethargy, and loss of motor function. Lead poisoning is treated with chelating agents, substances that bind to lead and allow it to be eliminated in the urine. A modern chelating agent used for this purpose is succimer ($C_4H_6O_4S_2$). Suppose you are trying to determine the appropriate dose for succimer treatment of lead poisoning. Assume that a patient's blood lead levels are 0.550 mg/L, that total blood volume is 5.0 L, and that 1 mol of succimer binds 1 mol of lead. What minimum mass of succimer in milligrams is needed to bind all of the lead in this patient's bloodstream?

96. An emergency breathing apparatus placed in mines or caves works via the chemical reaction:

$$4\,KO_2(s) + 2\,CO_2(g) \longrightarrow 2\,K_2CO_3(s) + 3\,O_2(g)$$

If the oxygen supply becomes limited or if the air becomes poisoned, a worker can use the apparatus to breathe while exiting the mine. Notice that the reaction produces O_2, which can be breathed, and absorbs CO_2, a product of respiration. What minimum amount of KO_2 is required for the apparatus to produce enough oxygen to allow the user 15 minutes to exit the mine in an emergency? Assume that an adult consumes approximately 4.4 g of oxygen in 15 minutes of normal breathing.

97. The propane fuel (C_3H_8) used in gas barbecues burns according to the equation:

$$C_3H_8(g) + 5\,O_2(g) \longrightarrow 3\,CO_2(g) + 4\,H_2O(g)$$
$$\Delta H^\circ_{rxn} = -2044\ \text{kJ}$$

If a pork roast must absorb 1.6×10^3 kJ to fully cook, and if only 10% of the heat produced by the barbecue is actually absorbed by the roast, what mass of CO_2 is emitted into the atmosphere during the grilling of the pork roast?

98. Charcoal is primarily carbon. Determine the mass of CO_2 produced by burning enough carbon to produce 5.00×10^2 kJ of heat.

$$C(s) + O_2(g) \longrightarrow CO_2(g) \qquad \Delta H^\circ_{rxn} = -393.5\ \text{kJ}$$

HIGHLIGHT PROBLEMS

99. A loud classroom demonstration involves igniting a hydrogen-filled balloon. The hydrogen within the balloon reacts explosively with oxygen in the air to form water.

$$2\,H_2(g) + O_2(g) \longrightarrow 2\,H_2O(g)$$

If the balloon is filled with a mixture of hydrogen and oxygen, the explosion is even louder than if the balloon is filled with only hydrogen; the intensity of the explosion depends on the relative amounts of oxygen and hydrogen within the balloon. Consider the molecular views representing different amounts of hydrogen and oxygen in four different balloons. Based on the balanced chemical equation, which balloon will make the loudest explosion?

(a)

(b)

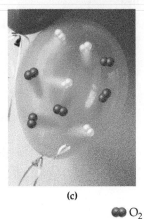

(c)

(d)

$\bullet\!\bullet\,O_2$ $\omega\,H_2$

Getty Images.

100. A hydrochloric acid solution will neutralize a sodium hydroxide solution. Consider the molecular views showing one beaker of HCl and four beakers of NaOH. Which NaOH beaker will just neutralize the HCl beaker? Begin by writing a balanced chemical equation for the neutralization reaction.

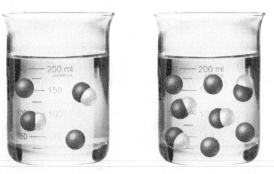

(a)   (b)

(c)   (d)

Katrina Leigh/Shutterstock.

101. As we have seen, scientists have grown progressively more worried about the potential for global warming caused by increasing atmospheric carbon dioxide levels. The world burns the fossil fuel equivalent of approximately 9.0×10^{12} kg of petroleum per year. Assume that all of this petroleum is in the form of octane (C_8H_{18}) and calculate how much CO_2 in kilograms is produced by world fossil fuel combustion per year. (*Hint:* Begin by writing a balanced equation for the combustion of octane.) If the atmosphere currently contains approximately 3.0×10^{15} kg of CO_2, how long will it take for the world's fossil fuel combustion to double the amount of atmospheric carbon dioxide?

102. Lakes that have been acidified by acid rain can be neutralized by the addition of limestone ($CaCO_3$). How much limestone in kilograms would be required to completely neutralize a 5.2×10^9-L lake containing 5.0×10^{-3} g of H_2SO_4 per liter?

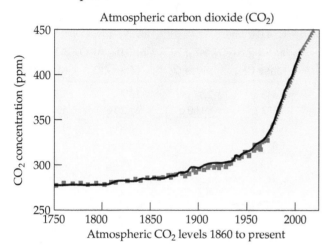

Atmospheric carbon dioxide (CO_2)

Atmospheric CO_2 levels 1860 to present

►ANSWERS TO SKILLBUILDER EXERCISES

Skillbuilder 1	49.2 mol H_2O	**Skillbuilder Plus 1**	29.4 kg NH_3
Skillbuilder 2	6.88 g HCl	**Skillbuilder 6**	Limiting reactant is CO; theoretical yield = 127 g Fe; percent yield = 68.8%
Skillbuilder 3	4.0×10^3 kg H_2SO_4		
Skillbuilder 4	Limiting reactant is Na; theoretical yield is 4.8 mol of NaF	**Skillbuilder 7**	-2.06×10^3 kJ
		Skillbuilder Plus 2	33 g C_4H_{10} necessary; 99 g CO_2 produced
Skillbuilder 5	30.7 g NH_3		

►ANSWERS TO CONCEPTUAL CHECKPOINTS

(a) Since the reaction requires 2 O_2 molecules to react with 1 CH_4 molecule, and since there are 4 O_2 molecules available to react, then 2 CH_4 molecules are required for complete reaction.

2(c) Hydrogen is the limiting reactant. The reaction mixture contains 3 H_2 molecules; therefore 2 NH_3 molecules will form when the reactants have reacted as completely as possible. Nitrogen is in excess, and there is one leftover nitrogen molecule.

3(d) NO is the limiting reagent. The reaction mixture initially contains 4 mol NO; therefore 10 moles of H_2 will be consumed, leaving 5 mol H_2 unreacted. The products will be 4 mol NH_3 and 4 mol H_2O.

4(c) B is the limiting reactant. If 4 mol B react, then 200 kJ of heat is produced.

ANSWERS TO ODD-NUMBERED EXERCISES

QUESTIONS

1. Reaction stoichiometry is very important to chemistry. It gives us a numerical relationship between the reactants and products that allows chemists to plan and carry out chemical reactions to obtain products in the desired quantities.

    For example, how much CO_2 is produced when a given amount of C_8H_{10} is burned?

    How much $H_2(g)$ is produced when a given amount of water decomposes?

3. 1 mol $Cl_2 \equiv$ 2 mol NaCl

5. mass A $\longrightarrow$ moles A $\longrightarrow$ moles B $\longrightarrow$

    mass B (A = reactant, B = product)

7. The limiting reactant is the reactant that limits the amount of product in a chemical reaction.

9. The actual yield is the amount of product actually produced by a chemical reaction. The percent yield is the percentage of the theoretical yield that was actually attained.

11. d

13. The enthalpy of reaction is the total amount of heat generated or absorbed by a particular chemical reaction. The quantity is important because it quantifies the change in heat for the chemical reaction. It is useful for determining the necessary starting conditions and predicting the outcome of various reactions.

PROBLEMS

15. **a.** 2 mol C   **b.** 1 mol C

    c. 3 mol C   **d.** 1.5 mol C

17. **a.** 2.6 mol NO_2 **b.** 11.6 mol NO_2

    c. 8.90×10^3 mol NO_2 **d.** 2.012×10^{-3} mol NO_2

19. c

21. **a.** 3.50 mol HCl   **b.** 3.50 mol H_2O

    c. 0.875 mol Na_2O_2 **d.** 1.17 mol SO_3

23. **a.** 2.4 mol PbO(s), 2.4 mol $SO_2(g)$

    b. 1.6 mol PbO(s), 1.6 mol $SO_2(g)$

    c. 5.3 mol PbO(s), 5.3 mol $SO_2(g)$

    d. 3.5 mol PbO(s), 3.5 mol $SO_2(g)$

25.

mol N_2H_4	mol N_2O_4	mol N_2	mol H_2O
4	2	6	8
6	3	9	12
4	2	6	8
11	5.5	16.5	22
3	1.5	4.5	6
8.26	4.13	12.4	16.5

27. $2 C_4H_{10}(g) + 13 O_2(g) \longrightarrow$

    $8 CO_2(g) + 10 H_2O(g)$; 32 mol O_2

29. **a.** Pb(s) + 2 $AgNO_3(aq) \longrightarrow Pb(NO_3)_2(aq)$ + 2 Ag(s)

    b. 19 mol $AgNO_3$ **c.** 56.8 mol Ag

31. **a.** 0.157 g O_2 **b.** 0.500 g O_2

    c. 114 g O_2 **d.** 2.86×10^{-4} g O_2

33. **a.** 4.0 g NaCl   **b.** 4.3 g $CaCO_3$

    c. 4.0 g MgO   **d.** 3.1 g NaOH

35. **a.** 8.9 g Al_2O_3, 9.7 g Fe   **b.** 3.0 g Al_2O_3, 3.3 g Fe

37.

Mass CH_4	Mass O_2	Mass CO_2	Mass H_2O
0.645 g	2.57 g	1.77 g	1.45 g
22.32 g	89.00 g	61.20 g	50.09 g
5.044 g	20.11 g	13.83 g	11.32 g
1.07 g	4.28 g	2.94 g	2.41 g
3.18 kg	12.7 kg	8.72 kg	7.14 kg
8.57×10^2 kg	3.42×10^3 kg	2.35×10^3 kg	1.92×10^3 kg

39. **a.** 2.3 g HCl   **b.** 4.3 g HNO_3

    c. 2.2 g H_2SO_4

41. 123 g H_2SO_4, 2.53 g H_2

43. **a.** 2 mol A   **b.** 1.8 mol A

    c. 4 mol B   **d.** 40 mol B

45. **a.** 1.5 mol C   **b.** 3 mol C

    c. 3 mol C   **d.** 96 mol C

47. **a.** 1 mol K   **b.** 1.8 mol K

    c. 1 mol Cl_2 **d.** 14.6 mol K

49. **a.** 1.3 mol MnO_3 **b.** 4.8 mol MnO_3

    c. 0.107 mol MnO_3 **d.** 27.5 mol MnO_3

51. 3 mol A, 0 mol B, 4 mol C

53. **a.** 2 Cl_2 **b.** 3 Cl_2

    c. 2 Cl_2

55. **a.** 1.0 g F_2 **b.** 10.5 g Li

    c. 6.79×10^3 g F_2

57. **a.** 1.3 g $AlCl_3$ **b.** 24.8 g $AlCl_3$

    c. 2.17 g $AlCl_3$

59. 74.6%

61. CaO; 25.7 g $CaCO_3$; 75.5%

63. O_2; 5.07 g NiO; 95.9%

65. Pb^{2+}; 262.7 g $PbCl_2$; 96.09%

67. TiO_2: 0 g, C: 7.0 g, Ti: 5.99 g, CO: 7.00 g

69. **a.** exothermic, $-\Delta H$ **b.** endothermic, $+\Delta H$

    c. exothermic, $-\Delta H$

71. **a.** 55 kJ   **b.** 110 kJ

   c. 28 kJ   **d.** 55 kJ

73. 4.78×10^3 kJ

75. 34.9 g C_8H_{18}

77. N_2

79. 0.152 g Ba^{2+}

81. 1.5 g HCl

83. 3.1 kg CO_2

85. 4.7 g Na_3PO_4

87. 469 g Zn

89. 2 $NH_4NO_3(s) \longrightarrow$

   $2 N_2(g) + O_2(g) + 4 H_2O(l)$; 2.00×10^2 g O_2

91. salicylic acid ($C_7H_6O_3$); 2.71 g $C_9H_8O_4$; 74.1%

93. NH_3; 120 kg (CH_4N_2O); 72.9%

95. 2.4 mg $C_4H_6O_4S_2$

97. 1.0×10^3 g CO_2

99. b; the loudest explosion will occur when the ratio is 2 hydrogen to 1 oxygen, for that is the ratio that occurs in water.

101. 2.8×10^{13} kg CO_2 per year; 1.1×10^2 years

Solutions

From Chapter 13 of *Introductory Chemistry*, Fourth Edition, Nivaldo J. Tro. Copyright © 2011 by Pearson Education, Inc. Published by Pearson Prentice Hall. All rights reserved.

Solutions

"The goal of science is to make sense of the diversity of nature."

JOHN BARROW (B. 1952)

1   Tragedy in Cameroon

▲ Cameroon is in West Africa.

◄ Late in the summer of 1986, carbon dioxide bubbled out of Lake Nyos and flowed into the adjacent valley. The carbon dioxide came from the bottom of the lake, where it was held in solution by the pressure of the water above it. When the layers in the lake were disturbed, the carbon dioxide came out of solution due to the decrease in pressure—with lethal consequences.

On August 22, 1986, most people living near Lake Nyos in Cameroon, West Africa, began their day in an ordinary way. Unfortunately, the day ended in tragedy. On that evening, a large cloud of carbon dioxide gas, burped up from the depths of Lake Nyos, killed more than 1700 people and about 3000 head of cattle. Survivors tell of smelling rotten eggs, feeling a warm sensation, and then losing consciousness. Two years before that, a similar tragedy had occurred in Lake Monoun, just 60 miles away, killing 37 people. Today, scientists have taken steps to prevent these lakes from burping again.

Lake Nyos is a water-filled volcanic crater. Some 50 miles beneath the surface of the lake, molten volcanic rock (magma) produces carbon dioxide gas that seeps into the lake through the volcano's plumbing system. The carbon dioxide then mixes with the lake water. However, as we will see later in this chapter, the concentration of a gas (such as carbon dioxide) that can build up in water increases with increasing pressure. The great pressure at the bottom of the deep lake therefore allows the concentration of carbon dioxide to become very high (just as the pressure in a soda can allows the concentration of carbon dioxide in soda to be very high). Over time, the carbon dioxide and water mixture at the bottom of the lake became so concentrated that—either because of the high concentration itself or because of some other natural trigger, such as a landslide—some gaseous carbon dioxide escaped. The rising bubbles disrupted the stratified layers of lake water, causing the highly concentrated carbon dioxide and water mixture at the bottom of the lake to rise, which lowered the pressure on it. The drop in pressure on the mixture released

475

more carbon dioxide bubbles just as the drop in pressure upon opening a soda can releases carbon dioxide bubbles. This in turn caused more churning and more carbon dioxide release. Since carbon dioxide is more dense than air, once freed from the lake, it traveled down the sides of the volcano and into the nearby valley, displacing air and asphyxiating many of the local residents.

In efforts to prevent these events from occurring again—by 2001, carbon dioxide concentrations had already returned to dangerously high levels—scientists built a piping system to slowly vent carbon dioxide from the lake bottom. Since 2001, this system has gradually been releasing the carbon dioxide into the atmosphere, preventing a repeat of the tragedy.

▶ Engineers watch as the carbon dioxide vented from the bottom of Lake Nyos creates a geyser. The controlled release of carbon dioxide from the lake bed is designed to prevent future catastrophes like the one that killed more than 1700 people in 1986.

University of Savoie.

2 Solutions: Homogeneous Mixtures

The carbon dioxide and water mixture at the bottom of Lake Nyos is an example of a **solution**, a homogeneous mixture of two or more substances. Solutions are common—most of the liquids and gases that we encounter every day are actually solutions. When most people think of a solution, they think of a solid dissolved in water. The ocean, for example, is a solution of salt and other solids dissolved in water. Blood plasma (blood that has had blood cells removed from it) is a solution of several solids (as well as some gases) dissolved in water. In addition to these, many other kinds of solutions exist. A solution may be composed of a gas and a liquid (like the carbon dioxide and water of Lake Nyos), a liquid and another liquid, a solid and a gas, or other combinations (see Table 1).

Aqueous comes from the Latin word aqua, meaning "water."

The most common solutions, however, are those containing a solid, a liquid, or a gas and water. These are *aqueous solutions*—they are critical to life and are the

TABLE 1 Common Types of Solutions

Solution Phase	Solute Phase	Solvent Phase	Example
gaseous solutions	gas	gas	air (mainly oxygen and nitrogen)
liquid solutions	gas	liquid	soda water (CO_2 and water)
	liquid	liquid	vodka (ethanol and water)
	solid	liquid	seawater (salt and water)
solid solutions	solid	solid	brass (copper and zinc) and other alloys

In a solid/liquid solution, the liquid is usually considered the solvent, regardless of the relative proportions of the components.

main focus of this chapter. Common examples of aqueous solutions include sugar water and salt water, both solutions of solids and water. Similarly, ethyl alcohol—the alcohol in alcoholic beverages—readily mixes with water to form a solution of a liquid with water, and we have already seen an example of a gas-and-water solution in Lake Nyos.

A solution has at least two components. The majority component is usually called the **solvent**, and the minority component is called the **solute**. In our carbon-dioxide-and-water solution, carbon dioxide is the solute and water is the solvent. In a salt-and-water solution, salt is the solute and water is the solvent. Because water is so abundant on Earth, it is a common solvent. However, other solvents are often used in the laboratory, in industry, and even in the home, especially to form solutions with nonpolar solutes. For example, you may use paint thinner, a nonpolar solvent, to remove grease from a dirty bicycle chain or from ball bearings. The paint thinner dissolves (or forms a solution with) the grease, removing it from the metal.

In general, polar solvents dissolve polar or ionic solutes, and nonpolar solvents dissolve nonpolar solutes. This tendency is described by the rule *like dissolves like*. Thus, similar kinds of solvents dissolve similar kinds of solutes. Table 2 lists some common polar and nonpolar laboratory solvents.

TABLE 2 Common Laboratory Solvents

Common Polar Solvents	Common Nonpolar Solvents
water (H_2O)	hexane (C_6H_{12})
acetone (CH_3COCH_3)	diethyl ether ($CH_3CH_2OCH_2CH_3$)
methyl alcohol (CH_3OH)	toluene (C_7H_8)

CONCEPTUAL CHECKPOINT 1

Which compound would you expect to be *least* soluble in water?

(a) CCl_4 **(b)** CH_3Cl **(c)** H_2S **(d)** KF

3 Solutions of Solids Dissolved in Water: How to Make Rock Candy

We have already seen several examples of solutions of a solid dissolved in water. The ocean, for example, is a solution of salt and other solids dissolved in water. A sweetened cup of coffee is a solution of sugar and other solids dissolved in water. Blood plasma is a solution of several solids (and some gases) dissolved in water. Not all solids, however, dissolve in water. We already know that nonpolar solids—such as lard and shortening—do not dissolve in water. Solids such as calcium carbonate and sand do not dissolve either.

When a solid is put into water, there is competition between the attractive forces that hold the solid together (the solute–solute interactions) and the attractive forces occurring between the water molecules and the particles that compose the solid (the solvent–solute interactions). For example, when sodium chloride is put into water, there is competition between the mutual attraction of Na^+ cations and Cl^- anions and the attraction of Na^+ and Cl^- to water molecules as shown in the margin. For sodium ions, the attraction is between the positive charge of the sodium ion and the negative side of water's dipole moment as shown in

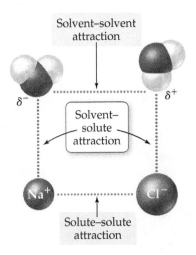

◀ When NaCl is put into water, the attraction between water molecules and Na^+ and Cl^- ions (solvent–solute attraction) overcomes the attraction between Na^+ and Cl^- ions (solute–solute attraction).

477

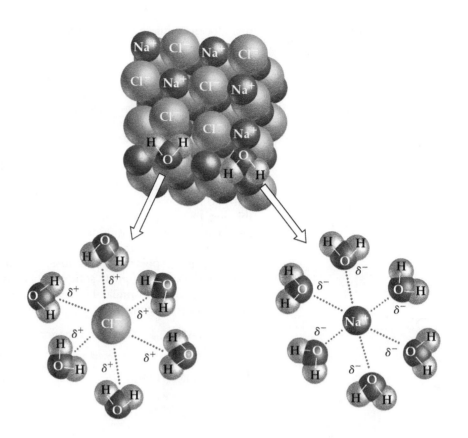

▶ FIGURE 1 **How a solid dissolves in water** The positive ends of the water dipoles are attracted to the negatively charged Cl^- ions, and the negative ends of the water dipoles are attracted to the positively charged Na^+ ions. The water molecules surround the ions of NaCl and disperse them in the solution.

▲ Figure 1. For chloride ions, the attraction is between the negative charge of the chloride ion and the positive side of water's dipole moment. In the case of NaCl, the attraction to water wins, and sodium chloride dissolves (▼ Figure 2). However, in the case of calcium carbonate ($CaCO_3$), the attraction between Ca^{2+} ions and CO_3^{2-} ions wins and calcium carbonate does not dissolve in water.

SOLUBILITY AND SATURATION

The **solubility** of a compound is defined as the amount of the compound, usually in grams, that dissolves in a certain amount of liquid. For example, the solubility of sodium chloride in water at 25 °C is 36 g NaCl per 100 g water, while the solubility

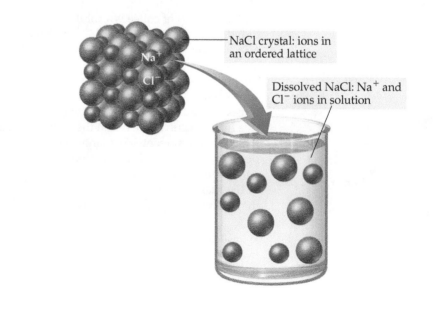

NaCl crystal: ions in an ordered lattice

Dissolved NaCl: Na^+ and Cl^- ions in solution

▶ FIGURE 2 **A sodium chloride solution** In a solution of NaCl, the Na^+ and Cl^- ions are dispersed in the water.

of calcium carbonate in water is close to zero. A solution that contains 36 g of NaCl per 100 g water is a *saturated* sodium chloride solution. A **saturated solution** holds the maximum amount of solute under the solution conditions. If additional solute is added to a saturated solution, it will not dissolve. An **unsaturated solution** is holding less than the maximum amount of solute. If additional solute is added to an unsaturated solution, it will dissolve. A **supersaturated solution** is one holding more than the normal maximum amount of solute. The solute will normally *precipitate* from (or come out of) a supersaturated solution. As the carbon dioxide and water solution rose from the bottom of Lake Nyos, for example, it became supersaturated because of the drop in pressure. The excess gas came out of the solution and rose to the surface of the lake, where it was emitted into the surrounding air.

> Supersaturated solutions can form under special circumstances, such as the sudden release in pressure that occurs in a soda can when it is opened.

▶ A supersaturated solution holds more than the normal maximum amount of solute. In some cases, such as the sodium acetate solution pictured here, a supersaturated solution may be temporarily stable. Any disturbance however, such as dropping in a small piece of solid sodium acetate **(a)**, will cause the solid to come out of solution **(b, c)**.

(a)   (b)   (c)

Richard Megna/Fundamental Photographs.

The solubility rules give us a qualitative description of the solubility of ionic solids. Molecular solids may also be soluble in water depending on whether the solid is polar. Table sugar ($C_{12}H_{22}O_{11}$), for example, is polar and soluble in water. Nonpolar solids, such as lard and vegetable shortening, are usually insoluble in water.

ELECTROLYTE SOLUTIONS: DISSOLVED IONIC SOLIDS

> NaCl forms a strong electrolyte solution.

A sugar solution (containing a molecular solid) and a salt solution (containing an ionic solid) are very different, as shown in ▼ Figure 3. In a salt solution the dissolved particles are ions, while in a sugar solution the dissolved particles are molecules. The ions in the salt solution are mobile charged particles and can therefore conduct electricity. A solution containing a solute that dissociates into ions is called an **electrolyte solution**. The sugar solution contains dissolved sugar molecules and cannot conduct electricity; it is a **nonelectrolyte solution**. In general, soluble ionic solids form electrolyte solutions, while soluble molecular solids form nonelectrolyte solutions.

Dissolved ions (NaCl)   Dissolved molecules (sugar)

Electrolyte solution   Nonelectrolyte solution

▶ FIGURE 3 **Electrolyte and nonelectrolyte solutions** Electrolyte solutions contain dissolved ions (charged particles) and therefore conduct electricity. Nonelectrolyte solutions contain dissolved molecules (neutral particles) and so do not conduct electricity.

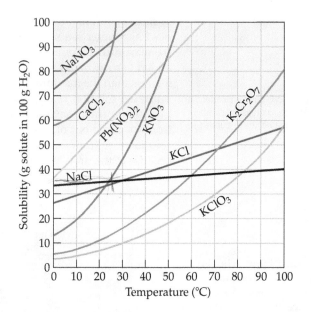

HOW SOLUBILITY VARIES WITH TEMPERATURE

Have you ever noticed how much easier it is to dissolve sugar in hot tea than in cold tea? The solubility of solids in water can be highly dependent on temperature. In general, the solubility of *solids* in water increases with increasing temperature (▲ Figure 4). For example, the solubility of potassium nitrate (KNO_3) at 20 °C is about 30 g KNO_3 per 100 g of water. However, at 50 °C, the solubility rises to 88 g KNO_3 per 100 g of water. A common way to purify a solid is a technique called **recrystallization**. Recrystallization involves putting the solid into water (or some other solvent) at an elevated temperature. Enough solid is added to the solvent to create a saturated solution at the elevated temperature. As the solution cools, the solubility decreases, causing some of the solid to precipitate from solution. If the solution cools slowly, the solid will form crystals as it comes out. The crystalline structure tends to reject impurities, resulting in a purer solid.

ROCK CANDY

Recrystallization can be used to make rock candy. To make rock candy, prepare a saturated sucrose (table sugar) solution at an elevated temperature. Dangle a string in the solution, and leave it to cool and stand for several days. As the solution cools, it becomes supersaturated and sugar crystals grow on the string. After several days, beautiful and sweet crystals, or "rocks," of sugar cover the string, ready to be admired and eaten.

▲ Rock candy is composed of sugar crystals that form through recrystallization.

4 Solutions of Gases in Water: How Soda Pop Gets Its Fizz

The water at the bottom of Lake Nyos and a can of soda pop are both examples of solutions in which a gas (carbon dioxide) is dissolved in a liquid (water). Most liquids exposed to air contain some dissolved gases. Lake water and seawater, for example, contain dissolved oxygen necessary for the survival of fish. Our blood contains dissolved nitrogen, oxygen, and carbon dioxide. Even tap water contains dissolved atmospheric gases.

You can see the dissolved gases in ordinary tap water by heating it on a stove. Before the water reaches its boiling point, you will see small bubbles develop in the water. These bubbles are dissolved air (mostly nitrogen and oxygen) coming out of solution. Once the water boils, the bubbling becomes more vigorous—these larger bubbles are composed of water vapor. The dissolved air comes out of solution upon heating because—unlike solids, whose solubility *increases* with increasing temperature—the solubility of gases in water *decreases* with increasing temperature. As the temperature of the water rises, the solubility of the dissolved nitrogen and oxygen decreases and these gases come out of solution, forming small bubbles around the bottom of the pot.

The decrease in the solubility of gases with increasing temperature is the reason that warm soda pop bubbles more than cold soda pop and also the reason that warm soda goes flat faster than cold soda. The carbon dioxide comes out of solution faster (bubbles more) at room temperature than at lower temperature because it is less soluble at room temperature.

The solubility of gases also depends on pressure. The higher the pressure above a liquid, the more soluble the gas is in the liquid (▼ Figure 5), a relationship known as **Henry's law**.

Cold soda pop: carbon dioxide more likely to stay in solution

Warm soda pop: carbon dioxide more likely to bubble out of solution

▲ Warm soda pop fizzes more than cold soda pop because the solubility of the dissolved carbon dioxide decreases with increasing temperature.

▶ FIGURE 5 **Pressure and solubility** The higher the pressure above a liquid, the more soluble the gas is in the liquid.

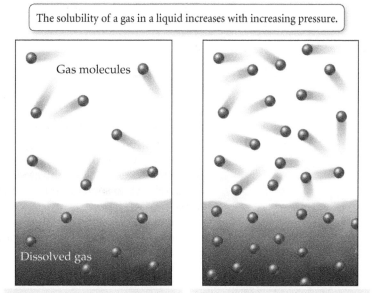

The solubility of a gas in a liquid increases with increasing pressure.

Gas molecules

Dissolved gas

Gas at low pressure over a liquid

Gas at high pressure over a liquid

In a can of soda pop and at the bottom of Lake Nyos, carbon dioxide is maintained in solution by high pressure. In soda pop, the pressure is provided by a large amount of carbon dioxide gas that is pumped into the can before sealing it. When the can is opened, the pressure is released and the solubility of carbon dioxide decreases, resulting in bubbling (▼ Figure 6). The bubbles are formed by the carbon dioxide gas as it escapes. In Lake Nyos, the pressure is provided by the mass of the lake

▶ FIGURE 6 **Pop! Fizz!** A can of soda pop is pressurized with carbon dioxide. When the can is opened, the pressure is released, lowering the solubility of carbon dioxide in the solution and causing it to come out of solution as bubbles.

CO_2 under pressure

CO_2 dissolved in solution

CO_2 pressure released

CO_2 bubbles out of solution

water itself pushing down on the carbon-dioxide–rich water at the bottom of the lake. When the stratification (or layering) of the lake is disturbed, the pressure on the carbon dioxide solution is lowered and the solubility of carbon dioxide decreases, resulting in the release of excess carbon dioxide gas.

✓ CONCEPTUAL CHECKPOINT 2

A solution is saturated in both nitrogen gas (N_2) and potassium chloride (KCl) at 75 °C. What happens when the solution is cooled to room temperature?

(a) Some nitrogen gas bubbles out of solution.

(b) Some potassium chloride precipitates out of solution.

(c) Both (a) and (c).

(d) Nothing happens.

5 Specifying Solution Concentration: Mass Percent

As we have seen, the amount of solute in a solution is an important property of the solution. For example, the amount of carbon dioxide in the water at the bottom of Lake Nyos is an important predictor of when the deadly event may repeat itself. A **dilute solution** is one containing small amounts of solute relative to solvent. If the water at the bottom of Lake Nyos were a dilute carbon dioxide solution, it would pose little threat. A **concentrated solution** is one containing large amounts of solute relative to solvent. If the carbon dioxide in the water at the bottom of Lake Nyos becomes concentrated (through the continual feeding of carbon dioxide from magma into the lake), it becomes a large threat. A common way to report solution concentration is *mass percent*.

MASS PERCENT

Also in common use are *parts per million* (ppm), the number of grams of solute per 1 million g of solution, and *parts per billion* (ppb), the number of grams of solute per 1 billion g of solution.

Note that the denominator is the mass of *solution*, not the mass of solvent.

Mass percent is the number of grams of solute per 100 g of solution. So a solution with a concentration of 14% by mass, for example, contains 14 g of solute per 100 g of solution. To calculate mass percent, simply divide the mass of the solute by the mass of the solution (solute *and* solvent) and multiply by 100%.

$$\text{Mass percent} = \frac{\text{Mass solute}}{\text{Mass solute} + \text{Mass solvent}} \times 100\%$$

Suppose you wanted to calculate the mass percent of NaCl in a solution containing 15.3 g of NaCl and 155.0 g of water. Begin by sorting the information in the problem statement.

GIVEN: 15.3 g NaCl

155.0 g H_2O

FIND: mass percent

SOLUTION

To solve this problem, substitute the correct values into the mass percent equation just presented.

$$\text{Mass percent} = \frac{\text{Mass solute}}{\text{Mass solute} + \text{Mass solvent}} \times 100\%$$

$$= \frac{15.3\,\text{g}}{15.3\,\text{g} + 155.0\,\text{g}} \times 100\%$$

$$= \frac{15.3\,\text{g}}{170.3\,\text{g}} \times 100\%$$

$$= 8.98\%$$

The solution is 8.98% NaCl by mass.

EXAMPLE 1 Calculating Mass Percent

Calculate the mass percent of a solution containing 27.5 g of ethanol (C_2H_6O) and 175 mL of H_2O. (Assume that the density of water is 1.00 g/mL.)

Begin by setting up the problem. You are given the mass of ethanol and the volume of water and asked to find the mass percent of the solution.	**GIVEN:** $27.5\,g\ C_2H_6O$ $175\,mL\ H_2O$ $d_{H_2O} = \dfrac{1.00\,g}{mL}$ **FIND:** mass percent

To find the mass percent, substitute into the equation for mass percent. You need the mass of ethanol and the mass of water. Obtain the mass of water from the volume of water by using the density as a conversion factor.	**SOLUTION** $\text{Mass percent} = \dfrac{\text{Mass solute}}{\text{Mass solute} + \text{Mass solvent}} \times 100\%$ $\text{Mass } H_2O = 175\ \text{mL } H_2O \times \dfrac{1.00\,g}{\text{mL}} = 175\,g$
Finally, substitute the correct quantities into the equation and calculate the mass percent.	$\text{Mass percent} = \dfrac{\text{Mass solute}}{\text{Mass solute} + \text{Mass solvent}} \times 100\%$ $= \dfrac{27.5\,g}{27.5\,g + 175\,g}$ $= \dfrac{27.5\,g}{202.5\,g} \times 100\%$ $= 13.6\%$

▶**SKILLBUILDER 1 | Calculating Mass Percent**

Calculate the mass percent of a sucrose solution containing 11.3 g of sucrose and 412.1 mL of water. (Assume that the density of water is 1.00 g/mL.)

▶**FOR MORE PRACTICE** Example 11; Problems 41, 42, 43, 44, 45, 46.

USING MASS PERCENT IN CALCULATIONS

We can use the mass percent of a solution as a conversion factor between mass of the solute and mass of the solution. The key to using mass percent in this way is to write it as a fraction.

$$\text{Mass percent} = \frac{g\ \text{solute}}{100\,g\ \text{solution}}$$

A solution containing 3.5% sodium chloride, for example, has the following conversion factor.

$$\frac{3.5\,g\ NaCl}{100\,g\ \text{solution}} \qquad \text{converts g solution} \longrightarrow g\ NaCl$$

This conversion factor converts from grams of solution to grams of NaCl. If you want to go the other way, simply invert the conversion factor.

$$\frac{100\,g\ \text{solution}}{3.5\,g\ NaCl} \qquad \text{converts g NaCl} \longrightarrow g\ \text{solution}$$

For example, to use mass percent as a conversion factor, consider a water sample from the bottom of Lake Nyos containing 8.5% carbon dioxide by mass. We can determine how much carbon dioxide in grams is contained in 28.6 L of the water solution. (Assume that the density of the solution is 1.03 g/mL.) We begin by sorting the information in the problem statement.

GIVEN: 8.5% CO_2 by mass

28.6 L solution

$$d = \frac{1.03 \text{ g}}{\text{mL}}$$

FIND: g CO_2

SOLUTION MAP

We strategize by drawing a solution map that begins with L solution and shows the conversion to mL solution and then to g solution using the density. Then we proceed from g solution to g CO_2, using the mass percent (expressed as a fraction) as a conversion factor.

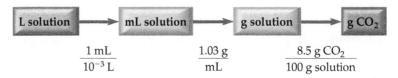

RELATIONSHIPS USED

$$\frac{8.5 \text{ g } CO_2}{100 \text{ g solution}} \text{ (given mass percent, written as a fraction)}$$

$$\frac{1.03 \text{ g}}{\text{mL}} \text{ (given density of the solution)}$$

$$1 \text{ mL} = 10^{-3} \text{ L}$$

SOLUTION

We follow the solution map to calculate the answer.

$$28.6 \text{ L solution} \times \frac{1 \text{ mL}}{10^{-3} \text{ L}} \times \frac{1.03 \text{ g}}{\text{mL}} \times \frac{8.5 \text{ g } CO_2}{100 \text{ g solution}} = 2.5 \times 10^3 \text{ g } CO_2$$

In this example, we used mass percent to convert from a given amount of *solution* to the amount of *solute* present in the solution. In Example 2, we use mass percent to convert from a given amount of *solute* to the amount of *solution* containing that solute.

EXAMPLE 2   Using Mass Percent in Calculations

A soft drink contains 11.5% sucrose ($C_{12}H_{22}O_{11}$) by mass. What volume of the soft drink solution in milliliters contains 85.2 g of sucrose? (Assume a density of 1.04 g/mL.)

SORT	
You are given the concentration of sucrose in a soft drink and a mass of sucrose. You are asked to find the volume of the soft drink that contains the given mass of sucrose.	GIVEN: 11.5% $C_{12}H_{22}O_{11}$ by mass 85.2 g $C_{12}H_{22}O_{11}$ $d = \dfrac{1.04 \text{ g}}{\text{mL}}$ FIND: mL solution (soft drink)

STRATEGIZE	
Draw a solution map to convert from g solute ($C_{12}H_{22}O_{11}$) to g solution using the mass percent in fractional form as the conversion factor. Convert to mL using the density.	SOLUTION MAP 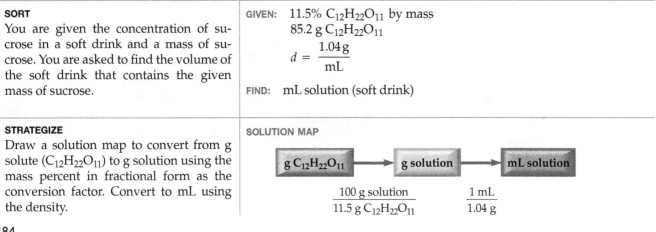

RELATIONSHIPS USED

$$\frac{11.5\,\text{g}\,C_{12}H_{22}O_{11}}{100\,\text{g solution}}\ \text{(given mass percent, written as a fraction)}$$

$$\frac{1.04\,\text{g}}{\text{mL}}\ \text{(given density of solution)}$$

SOLVE Follow the solution map to solve the problem.	**SOLUTION** $$85.2\ \text{g}\ \cancel{C_{12}H_{22}O_{11}} \times \frac{100\ \text{g solution}}{11.5\ \text{g}\ \cancel{C_{12}H_{22}O_{11}}} \times \frac{1\ \text{mL}}{1.04\ \text{g}} = 712\ \text{mL solution}$$
CHECK Check your answer. Are the units correct? Does the answer make physical sense?	The units (mL solution) are correct. The magnitude of the answer makes sense because each 100 mL of solution contains 11.5 g sucrose; therefore 712 mL should contain a bit more than 77 g, which is close to the given amount of 85.2 g.

▶**SKILLBUILDER 2 | Using Mass Percent in Calculations**

How much sucrose ($C_{12}H_{22}O_{11}$) in grams is contained in 355 mL (12 oz) of the soft drink in Example 2?

▶**FOR MORE PRACTICE**   Example 12; Problems 47, 48, 49, 50, 51, 52.

6   Specifying Solution Concentration: Molarity

Note that molarity is abbreviated with a capital M.

A second way to express solution concentration is **molarity** (M), defined as the number of moles of solute per liter of solution. We calculate the molarity of a solution as follows:

$$\textbf{Molarity (M)} = \frac{\text{Moles solute}}{\text{Liters solution}}$$

Note that molarity is moles of solute per liter of *solution*, not per liter of solvent. To make a solution of a specified molarity, you usually put the solute into a flask and then add water to the desired volume of solution. For example, to make 1.00 L of a 1.00 M NaCl solution, you add 1.00 mol of NaCl to a flask and then add water to make 1.00 L of solution (◀ Figure 7). You *do not* combine 1.00 mol of NaCl with 1.00 L of water because that would result in a total volume exceeding 1.00 L and therefore a molarity of less than 1.00 M.

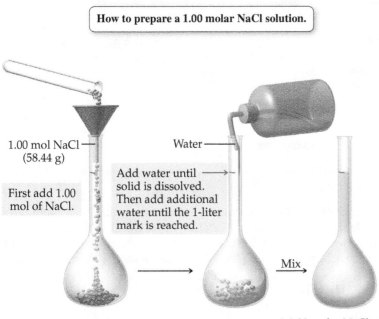

How to prepare a 1.00 molar NaCl solution.

1.00 mol NaCl (58.44 g)

First add 1.00 mol of NaCl.

Water

Add water until solid is dissolved. Then add additional water until the 1-liter mark is reached.

Mix

A 1.00 molar NaCl solution

◀ FIGURE 7   **Making a solution of specific molarity**   To make 1.00 L of a 1.00 M NaCl solution, you add 1.00 mol (58.44 g) of sodium chloride to a flask and then dilute to 1.00 L of total volume.   Question: What would happen if you added 1 L of water to 1 mol of sodium chloride? Would the resulting solution be 1 M?

CHEMISTRY IN THE ENVIRONMENT

The Dirty Dozen

A number of potentially harmful chemicals—such as DDT, dioxin, and polychlorinated biphenyls (PCBs)—can make their way into our water sources from industrial dumping, atmospheric emissions, agriculture, and household dumping. Since crops, livestock, and fish all rely on water, they too can accumulate these chemicals from water. Human consumption of food or water contaminated with these chemicals leads to a number of diseases and adverse health effects such as increased cancer risk, liver damage, or central nervous system damage. Governments around the world have joined forces to ban a number of these chemicals—called persistent organic pollutants or POPs—from production. The original treaty targeted 12 such substances called the dirty dozen (Table 3).

A difficult problem posed by these chemicals is their persistence. Once they get into the environment, they stay there for a long time. A second problem is their tendency to undergo *bioamplification*. Because these chemicals are nonpolar, they are stored and concentrated in the fatty tissues of the organisms that consume them. As larger organisms eat smaller ones that have consumed the chemical, the larger organisms consume even more of the stored chemicals. The result is an increase in the concentrations of these chemicals as they move up the food chain. Under the treaty, nearly all intentional production of these chemicals is banned. In the United States, the presence of these contaminants in water

TABLE 3   The Dirty Dozen

1. aldrin (insecticide)
2. chlordane (insecticide by-product)
3. DDT (insecticide)
4. dieldrin (insecticide)
5. dioxin (industrial by-product)
6. eldrin (insecticide)
7. furan (industrial by-product)
8. heptachlor (insecticide)
9. hexachlorobenzene (fungicide, industrial by-product)
10. mirex (insecticide, fire retardant)
11. polychlorinated biphenyls (PCBs) (electrical insulators)
12. toxaphene (insecticide)

supplies is monitored under supervision of the Environmental Protection Agency (EPA). The EPA has set limits, called maximum contaminant levels (MCLs), for each of the dirty dozen in food and drinking water. Some MCLs for selected compounds in water supplies are listed in Table 4.

TABLE 4   EPA Maximum Contaminant Level (MCL) for Several "Dirty Dozen" Chemicals

chlordane	0.002 mg/L
dioxin	0.00000003 mg/L
heptachlor	0.0004 mg/L
hexachlorobenzene	0.001 mg/L

Notice the units that the EPA uses to express the concentration of the contaminants: milligrams per liter. This unit is a conversion factor between liters of water consumed and the mass in milligrams of the pollutant. According to the EPA, as long as the contaminant concentrations are below these levels, the water is safe to drink.

CAN YOU ANSWER THIS? *Using what you know about conversion factors, calculate how much of each of the chemicals in Table 4 (at their MCL) would be present in 715 L of water, the approximate amount of water consumed by an adult in one year.*

▲ Potentially dangerous chemicals can leak into the environment and contaminate water and food supplies.

Don B. Stevenson/Alamy.

To calculate molarity, divide the number of moles of the solute by the volume of the solution (solute *and* solvent) in liters. For example, to calculate the molarity of a sucrose ($C_{12}H_{22}O_{11}$) solution made with 1.58 mol of sucrose diluted to a total volume of 5.0 L of solution, we begin by sorting the information in the problem statement.

GIVEN: 1.58 mol $C_{12}H_{22}O_{11}$

5.0 L solution

FIND: molarity (M)

SOLUTION

We substitute the correct values into the equation for molarity and calculate the answer.

$$\text{Molarity (M)} = \frac{\text{Moles solute}}{\text{Liters solution}}$$

$$= \frac{1.58 \text{ mol } C_{12}H_{22}O_{11}}{5.0 \text{ L solution}}$$

$$= 0.32 \text{ M}$$

EXAMPLE 3   Calculating Molarity

Calculate the molarity of a solution made by putting 15.5 g NaCl into a beaker and adding water to make 1.50 L of NaCl solution.

You are given the mass of sodium chloride (the solute) and the volume of solution. You are asked to find the molarity of the solution.	GIVEN: 15.5 g NaCl 1.50 L solution FIND: molarity (M)
To calculate molarity, substitute the correct values into the equation and calculate the answer. You must first convert the amount of NaCl from grams to moles using the molar mass of NaCl.	SOLUTION $$\text{mol NaCl} = 15.5 \text{ g NaCl} \times \frac{1 \text{ mol NaCl}}{58.44 \text{ g NaCl}} = 0.2652 \text{ mol NaCl}$$ $$\text{Molarity (M)} = \frac{\text{Moles solute}}{\text{Liters solution}}$$ $$= \frac{0.2652 \text{ mol NaCl}}{1.50 \text{ L solution}}$$ $$= 0.177 \text{ M}$$

▶SKILLBUILDER 3 | Calculating Molarity

Calculate the molarity of a solution made by putting 55.8 g of $NaNO_3$ into a beaker and diluting to 2.50 L.

▶FOR MORE PRACTICE   Example 13; Problems 59, 60, 61, 62, 63, 64.

USING MOLARITY IN CALCULATIONS

We can use the molarity of a solution as a conversion factor between moles of the solute and liters of the solution. For example, a 0.500 M NaCl solution contains 0.500 mol NaCl for every liter of solution.

$$\frac{0.500 \text{ mol NaCl}}{\text{L solution}} \qquad \text{converts L solution} \longrightarrow \text{mol NaCl}$$

This conversion factor converts from liters of solution to moles of NaCl. If you want to go the other way, simply invert the conversion factor.

$$\frac{\text{L solution}}{0.500 \text{ mol NaCl}} \qquad \text{converts mol NaCl} \longrightarrow \text{L solution}$$

For example, to determine how many grams of sucrose ($C_{12}H_{22}O_{11}$) are contained in 1.72 L of 0.758 M sucrose solution, begin by sorting the information in the problem statement.

GIVEN: 0.758 M $C_{12}H_{22}O_{11}$

1.72 L solution

FIND: g $C_{12}H_{22}O_{11}$

SOLUTION MAP

We strategize by drawing a solution map that begins with L solution and shows the conversion to moles of sucrose using the molarity, and then the conversion to mass of sucrose using the molar mass.

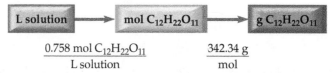

$$\dfrac{0.758 \text{ mol } C_{12}H_{22}O_{11}}{L \text{ solution}} \qquad \dfrac{342.34 \text{ g}}{mol}$$

RELATIONSHIPS USED

$\dfrac{0.758 \text{ mol } C_{12}H_{22}O_{11}}{L \text{ solution}}$ (given molarity of solution, written out as a fraction)

$1 \text{ mol } C_{12}H_{22}O_{11} = 342.34 \text{ g}$ (molar mass of sucrose)

SOLUTION

We then follow the solution map to calculate the answer.

$$1.72 \text{ L solution} \times \dfrac{0.758 \text{ mol } C_{12}H_{22}O_{11}}{L \text{ solution}}$$

$$\times \dfrac{342.34 \text{ g } C_{12}H_{22}O_{11}}{mol \text{ } C_{12}H_{22}O_{11}} = 446 \text{ g } C_{12}H_{22}O_{11}$$

In this example, we used molarity to convert from a given amount of *solution* to the amount of *solute* in that solution. In the example that follows, we use molarity to convert from a given amount of *solute* to the amount of *solution* containing that solute.

EXAMPLE 4 Using Molarity in Calculations

How many liters of a 0.114 M NaOH solution contains 1.24 mol of NaOH?

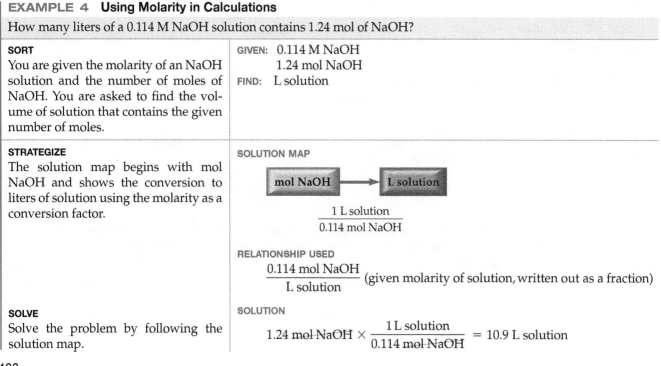

SORT You are given the molarity of an NaOH solution and the number of moles of NaOH. You are asked to find the volume of solution that contains the given number of moles.	GIVEN: 0.114 M NaOH 1.24 mol NaOH FIND: L solution

STRATEGIZE
The solution map begins with mol NaOH and shows the conversion to liters of solution using the molarity as a conversion factor.

SOLUTION MAP

mol NaOH ⟶ L solution

$$\dfrac{1 \text{ L solution}}{0.114 \text{ mol NaOH}}$$

RELATIONSHIP USED

$\dfrac{0.114 \text{ mol NaOH}}{L \text{ solution}}$ (given molarity of solution, written out as a fraction)

SOLVE
Solve the problem by following the solution map.

SOLUTION

$$1.24 \text{ mol NaOH} \times \dfrac{1 \text{ L solution}}{0.114 \text{ mol NaOH}} = 10.9 \text{ L solution}$$

CHECK

Check your answer. Are the units correct? Does the answer make physical sense?

The units (L solution) are correct. The magnitude of the answer makes sense because each L of solution contains a little more than 0.10 moles; therefore about 10 L contains a little more than 1 mole.

▶**SKILLBUILDER 4 | Using Molarity in Calculations**

How much of a 0.225 M KCl solution contains 55.8 g of KCl?

▶**FOR MORE PRACTICE**   Example 14; Problems 65, 66, 67, 68, 69, 70.

ION CONCENTRATIONS

When an ionic compound dissolves in solution, some of the cations and anions may pair up, so that the actual concentrations of the ions are lower than what you would expect if you assume complete dissociation occurred.

The reported concentration of a solution containing a *molecular* compound usually reflects the concentration of the solute as it actually exists in solution. For example, a 1.0 M glucose ($C_6H_{12}O_6$) solution indicates that the solution contains 1.0 mol of $C_6H_{12}O_6$ per liter of solution. However, the reported concentration of solution containing an *ionic* compound reflects the concentration of the solute *before it is dissolved in solution*. For example, a 1.0 M $CaCl_2$ solution contains 1.0 mol of Ca^{2+} per liter and 2.0 mol of Cl^- per liter. The concentration of the individual ions present in a solution containing an ionic compound can usually be approximated from the overall concentration as shown by the following example.

EXAMPLE 5   Ion Concentration

Determine the molar concentrations of Na^+ and PO_4^{3-} in a 1.50 M Na_3PO_4 solution.

You are given the concentration of an ionic solution and asked to find the concentrations of the component ions.	GIVEN: 1.50 M Na_3PO_4 FIND: molarity (M) of Na^+ and PO_4^{3-}
A formula unit of Na_3PO_4 contains 3 Na^+ ions (as indicated by the subscript), so the concentration of Na^+ is three times the concentration of Na_3PO_4. Since the same formula unit contains one PO_4^{3-} ion, the concentration of PO_4^{3-} is equal to the concentration of Na_3PO_4.	SOLUTION molarity of Na^+ = 3(1.50 M) = 4.50 M molarity of PO_4^{3-} = 1.50 M

▶**SKILLBUILDER 5 | Ion Concentration**

Determine the molar concentrations of Ca^{2+} and Cl^- in a 0.75 M $CaCl_2$ solution.

▶**FOR MORE PRACTICE**   Problems 77, 78, 79, 80.

✓ CONCEPTUAL CHECKPOINT 3

A solution is 0.15 M in K_2SO_4. What is the concentration of K^+ in solution?

(a) 0.075 M   (b) 0.15 M   (c) 0.30 M   (d) 0.45 M

7   Solution Dilution

When diluting acids, always add the concentrated acid to the water. *Never add water to concentrated acid solutions.*

To save space in laboratory storerooms, solutions are often stored in concentrated forms called **stock solutions**. For example, hydrochloric acid is typically stored as a 12 M stock solution. However, many lab procedures call for much less concentrated hydrochloric acid solutions, so chemists must dilute the stock solution to the required concentration. This is normally done by diluting a certain amount of the stock solution with water. How do we determine how much of the stock solution to use? The easiest way to solve these problems is to use the dilution equation:

$$M_1 V_1 = M_2 V_2$$

where M_1 and V_1 are the molarity and volume of the initial concentrated solution and M_2 and V_2 are the molarity and volume of the final diluted solution. This equation works because the molarity multiplied by the volume gives the number of moles of solute ($M \times V = \text{mol}$), which is the same in both solutions. For example, suppose a laboratory procedure calls for 5.00 L of a 1.50 M KCl solution. How should we prepare this solution from a 12.0 M stock solution? We begin by sorting the information in the problem statement.

The equation $M_1 V_1 = M_2 V_2$ applies only to solution dilution, NOT to stoichiometry.

GIVEN: $M_1 = 12.0$ M

$M_2 = 1.50$ M

$V_2 = 5.00$ L

FIND: V_1

SOLUTION
We solve the solution dilution equation for V_1 (the volume of the stock solution required for the dilution) and then substitute in the correct values to calculate it.

$$M_1 V_1 = M_2 V_2$$

$$V_1 = \frac{M_2 V_2}{M_1}$$

$$= \frac{1.50 \frac{\text{mol}}{\text{L}} \times 5.00 \text{ L}}{12.0 \frac{\text{mol}}{\text{L}}}$$

$$= 0.625 \text{ L}$$

We can therefore make the solution by diluting 0.625 L of the stock solution to a total volume of 5.00 L (V_2). The resulting solution will be 1.50 M in KCl (▶ Figure 8).

EXAMPLE 6 Solution Dilution

To what volume should you dilute 0.100 L of a 15 M NaOH solution to obtain a 1.0 M NaOH solution?

You are given the initial volume and concentration of an NaOH solution and a final concentration. You are asked to find the volume required to dilute the initial solution to the given final concentration.	GIVEN: $V_1 = 0.100$ L $M_1 = 15$ M $M_2 = 1.0$ M FIND: V_2
Solve the solution dilution equation for V_2 (the volume of the final solution) and substitute the required quantities to calculate V_2. You can make the solution by diluting 0.100 L of the stock solution to a total volume of 1.5 L (V_2). The resulting solution has a concentration of 1.0 M.	SOLUTION $M_1 V_1 = M_2 V_2$ $V_2 = \dfrac{M_1 V_1}{M_2}$ $= \dfrac{15 \frac{\text{mol}}{\text{L}} \times 0.100 \text{ L}}{1.0 \frac{\text{mol}}{\text{L}}}$ $= 1.5 \text{ L}$

▶**SKILLBUILDER 6 | Solution Dilution**

How much 6.0 M $NaNO_3$ solution should you use to make 0.585 L of a 1.2 M $NaNO_3$ solution?

▶**FOR MORE PRACTICE**   Example 15; Problems 81, 82, 83, 84, 85, 86, 87, 88.

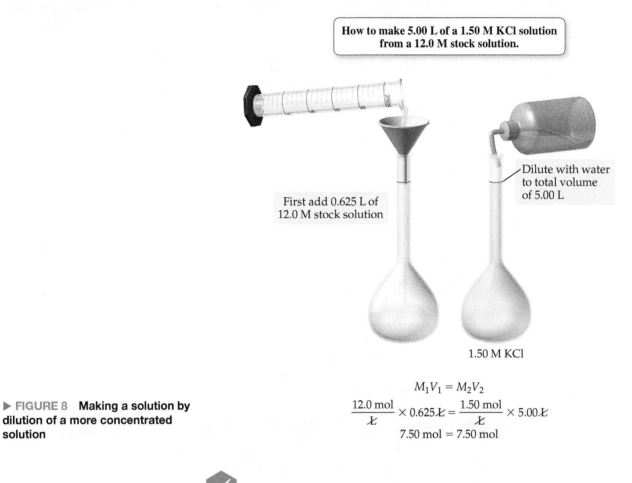

How to make 5.00 L of a 1.50 M KCl solution from a 12.0 M stock solution.

First add 0.625 L of 12.0 M stock solution

Dilute with water to total volume of 5.00 L

1.50 M KCl

▶ **FIGURE 8** **Making a solution by dilution of a more concentrated solution**

$$M_1V_1 = M_2V_2$$

$$\frac{12.0 \text{ mol}}{\cancel{L}} \times 0.625\,\cancel{L} = \frac{1.50 \text{ mol}}{\cancel{L}} \times 5.00\,\cancel{L}$$

$$7.50 \text{ mol} = 7.50 \text{ mol}$$

✓ **CONCEPTUAL CHECKPOINT 4**

If 25 g of salt are dissolved in 251 g of water, what is the mass of the resulting solution?

(a) 276 g   **(b)** 251 g   **(c)** 226 g

8   Solution Stoichiometry

Many chemical reactions take place in aqueous solutions. Precipitation reactions, neutralization reactions, and gas evolution reactions, for example, all occur in aqueous solutions. We use the coefficients in chemical equations as conversion factors between moles of reactants and moles of products in stoichiometric calculations. These conversion factors are often used to determine, for example, the amount of product obtained in a chemical reaction based on a given amount of reactant or the amount of one reactant needed to completely react with a given amount of another reactant. The general solution map for these kinds of calculations is:

Moles A ⟶ Moles B

where A and B are two different substances involved in the reaction and the conversion factor between them comes from the stoichiometric coefficients in the balanced chemical equation.

In reactions involving aqueous reactant and products, it is often convenient to specify the amount of reactants or products in terms of their volume and concentration. We can use the volume and concentration to calculate the number of moles of reactants or products, and then use the stoichiometric coefficients to convert to other quantities in the reaction. The general solution map for these kinds of calculations is:

where the conversions between volume and moles are achieved using the molarities of the solutions. For example, consider the reaction for the neutralization of sulfuric acid.

$$H_2SO_4(aq) + 2\ NaOH(aq) \longrightarrow Na_2SO_4(aq) + 2\ H_2O(l)$$

How much 0.125 M NaOH solution do we need to completely neutralize 0.225 L of 0.175 M H_2SO_4 solution? Begin by sorting the information in the problem statement.

GIVEN: 0.225 L H_2SO_4 solution
0.175 M H_2SO_4
0.125 M NaOH

FIND: L NaOH solution

SOLUTION MAP
We strategize by drawing a solution map, which is similar to those for other stoichiometric problems. We first use the volume and molarity of H_2SO_4 solution to get mol H_2SO_4. Then we use the stoichiometric coefficients from the equation to convert mol H_2SO_4 to mol NaOH. Finally, we use the molarity of NaOH to get to L NaOH solution.

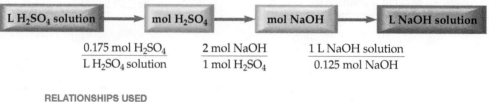

RELATIONSHIPS USED

$$M(H_2SO_4) = \frac{0.175\ mol\ H_2SO_4}{L\ H_2SO_4\ solution} \quad \text{(given molarity of } H_2SO_4 \text{ solution, written out as a fraction)}$$

$$M(NaOH) = \frac{0.125\ mol\ NaOH}{L\ NaOH\ solution} \quad \text{(given molarity of NaOH solution, written out as a fraction)}$$

1 mol H_2SO_4 : 2 mol NaOH (stoichiometric relationship between H_2SO_4 and NaOH, from balanced chemical equation)

SOLUTION
To solve the problem, we follow the solution map and calculate the answer.

$$0.225\ L\ \cancel{H_2SO_4\ solution} \times \frac{0.175\ \cancel{mol\ H_2SO_4}}{L\ \cancel{H_2SO_4\ solution}} \times \frac{2\ \cancel{mol\ NaOH}}{1\ \cancel{mol\ H_2SO_4}}$$

$$\times \frac{1\ L\ NaOH\ solution}{0.125\ \cancel{mol\ NaOH}} = 0.630\ L\ NaOH\ solution$$

It will take 0.630 L of the NaOH solution to completely neutralize the H_2SO_4.

EXAMPLE 7 Solution Stoichiometry

Consider the precipitation reaction:

$$2 \text{ KI}(aq) + \text{Pb(NO}_3)_2(aq) \longrightarrow \text{PbI}_2(s) + 2 \text{ KNO}_3(aq)$$

How much 0.115 M KI solution in liters will completely precipitate the Pb^{2+} in 0.104 L of 0.225 M $\text{Pb(NO}_3)_2$ solution?

SORT You are given the concentration of a reactant, KI, in a chemical reaction. You are also given the volume and concentration of a second reactant, $\text{Pb(NO}_3)_2$. You are asked to find the volume of the first reactant that completely reacts with the given amount of the second.	**GIVEN:** 0.115 M KI 0.104 L $\text{Pb(NO}_3)_2$ solution 0.225 M $\text{Pb(NO}_3)_2$ **FIND:** L KI solution

STRATEGIZE

The solution map for this problem is similar to the solution maps for other stoichiometric problems. First use the volume and molarity of $\text{Pb(NO}_3)_2$ solution to get mol $\text{Pb(NO}_3)_2$ Then use the stoichiometric coefficients from the equation to convert mol $\text{Pb(NO}_3)_2$ to mol KI. Finally, use mol KI to find L KI solution.

SOLUTION MAP

L $\text{Pb(NO}_3)_2$ solution $\longrightarrow$ mol $\text{Pb(NO}_3)_2$ $\longrightarrow$ mol KI $\longrightarrow$ L KI solution

$$\frac{0.225 \text{ mol Pb(NO}_3)_2}{\text{L Pb(NO}_3)_2 \text{ solution}} \qquad \frac{2 \text{ mol KI}}{1 \text{ mol Pb(NO}_3)_2} \qquad \frac{1 \text{ L KI solution}}{0.115 \text{ mol KI}}$$

RELATIONSHIPS USED

$$\text{M KI} = \frac{0.115 \text{ mol KI}}{\text{L KI solution}} \text{ (given molarity of KI solution, written out as a fraction)}$$

$$\text{M Pb(NO}_3)_2 = \frac{0.225 \text{ mol Pb(NO}_3)_2}{\text{L Pb(NO}_3)_2 \text{ solution}} \text{ (given molarity of Pb(NO}_3)_2 \text{ solution,}$$
$$\text{written out as a fraction)}$$

$$2 \text{ mol KI} \equiv 1 \text{ mol Pb(NO}_3)_2 \text{ (stoichiometric relationship between KI}$$
$$\text{and Pb(NO}_3)_2, \text{ from balanced chemical equation)}$$

SOLVE

Follow the solution map to solve the problem. Begin with volume of $\text{Pb(NO}_3)_2$ solution and cancel units to arrive at volume of KI solution.

SOLUTION

$$0.104 \text{ L Pb(NO}_3)_2 \text{ solution} \times \frac{0.225 \text{ mol Pb(NO}_3)_2}{\text{L Pb(NO}_3)_2 \text{ solution}} \times \frac{2 \text{ mol KI}}{\text{mol Pb(NO}_3)}$$

$$\times \frac{\text{L KI solution}}{0.115 \text{ mol KI}} = 0.407 \text{ L KI solution}$$

CHECK

Check your answer. Are the units correct? Does the answer make physical sense?

The units (L KI solution) are correct. The magnitude of the answer makes sense because the lead nitrate solution is about twice as concentrated as the potassium iodide solution and 2 mol of potassium iodide are required to react with 1 mol of lead(II) nitrate. Therefore we would expect the volume of the potassium solution required to completely react with a given volume of the $\text{Pb(NO}_3)_2$ solution to be about four times as much.

▶**SKILLBUILDER 7** | Solution Stoichiometry

How many milliliters of 0.112 M Na_2CO_3 will completely react with 27.2 mL of 0.135 M HNO_3 according to the reaction?

$$2 \text{ HNO}_3(aq) + \text{Na}_2\text{CO}_3(aq) \longrightarrow \text{H}_2\text{O}(l) + \text{CO}_2(g) + 2 \text{ NaNO}_3(aq)$$

▶**SKILLBUILDER PLUS 1**

A 25.0-mL sample of HNO_3 solution requires 35.7 mL of 0.108 M Na_2CO_3 to completely react with all of the HNO_3 in the solution. What is the concentration of the HNO_3 solution?

▶**FOR MORE PRACTICE** Example 16; Problems 89, 90, 91, 92.

9 Freezing Point Depression and Boiling Point Elevation: Making Water Freeze Colder and Boil Hotter

Dennis McDonald/PhotoEdit.

▲ Sprinkling salt on icy roads lowers the freezing point of water, so the ice melts even if the temperature is below 0 °C.

Have you ever wondered why salt is added to ice in an ice-cream maker? Or why salt is scattered on icy roads in cold climates? Salt actually lowers the melting point of ice. A salt-and-water solution will remain a liquid even below 0 °C. By adding salt to ice in the ice-cream maker, you form a mixture of ice, salt, and water that can reach a temperature of about −10 °C, cold enough to freeze the cream. On the road, the salt allows the ice to melt, even if the ambient temperature is below freezing.

Adding a nonvolatile solute—one that does not readily evaporate—to a liquid extends the temperature range over which the liquid remains a liquid. The solution has a lower melting point and a higher boiling point than the pure liquid; these effects are called **freezing point depression** and **boiling point elevation**. Freezing point depression and boiling point elevation depend only on the number of solute particles *in solution*, not on the type of solute particles. Properties such as these—which depend on the number of dissolved solute particles and not on the type of solute particles—are called **colligative properties**.

FREEZING POINT DEPRESSION

The freezing point of a solution containing a nonvolatile solute is lower than the freezing point of the pure solvent. For example, antifreeze, added to engine coolant to prevent it from freezing in cold climates, is an aqueous solution of ethylene glycol ($C_2H_6O_2$). The ethylene glycol lowers the freezing point of the aqueous solution. The more concentrated the solution is, the lower the freezing point becomes. For freezing point depression and boiling point elevation, the concentration of the solution is usually expressed in **molality (*m*)**, the number of moles of solute per kilogram of solvent.

Note that molality is abbreviated with a lowercase *m*, while molarity is abbreviated with a capital M.

$$\text{Molality } (m) = \frac{\text{Moles solute}}{\text{Kilograms slovent}}$$

Notice that molality is defined with respect to kilograms of *solvent*, not kilograms of *solution*.

EXAMPLE 8 Calculating Molality

Calculate the molality of a solution containing 17.2 g of ethylene glycol ($C_2H_6O_2$) dissolved in 0.500 kg of water.

You are given the mass of ethylene glycol in grams and the mass of the solvent in kilograms. You are asked to find the molality of the resulting solution.	GIVEN: 17.2 g $C_2H_6O_2$ 0.500 kg H_2O FIND: molality (*m*)
To calculate molality, substitute the correct values into the equation and calculate the answer. You must first convert the amount of $C_2H_6O_2$ from grams to moles using the molar mass of $C_2H_6O_2$.	SOLUTION 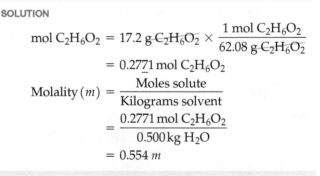

$$\text{mol } C_2H_6O_2 = 17.2 \text{ g } C_2H_6O_2 \times \frac{1 \text{ mol } C_2H_6O_2}{62.08 \text{ g } C_2H_6O_2}$$
$$= 0.2771 \text{ mol } C_2H_6O_2$$
$$\text{Molality } (m) = \frac{\text{Moles solute}}{\text{Kilograms solvent}}$$
$$= \frac{0.2771 \text{ mol } C_2H_6O_2}{0.500 \text{ kg } H_2O}$$
$$= 0.554 \ m$$

▶SKILLBUILDER 8 | Calculating Molality

Calculate the molality (*m*) of a sucrose ($C_{12}H_{22}O_{11}$) solution containing 50.4 g sucrose and 0.332 kg of water.

▶FOR MORE PRACTICE   Example 17; Problems 97, 98, 99, 100.

jane/Istockphoto.com.

▲ Ethylene glycol is the chief component of antifreeze, which keeps engine coolant from freezing in winter or boiling over in summer.

The equations for freezing point depression and boiling point elevation given in this section apply only to nonelectrolyte solutions.

Different solvents have different values of K_f.

CONCEPTUAL CHECKPOINT 5

A laboratory procedure calls for a 2.0 molal aqueous solution. A student accidentally makes a 2.0 molar solution. The solution made by the student is:

(a) too concentrated

(b) too dilute

(c) just right

(d) it depends on the molar mass of the solute

With an understanding of molality, we can now quantify freezing point depression. The amount that the freezing point of a solution is lowered by a particular amount of solute is given by the following equation.

The freezing point depression of a solution

$$\Delta T_f = m \times K_f$$

where

- ΔT_f is the change in temperature of the freezing point in °C (from the freezing point of the pure solvent).
- m is the molality of the solution in $\dfrac{\text{mol solute}}{\text{kg solvent}}$.
- K_f is the freezing point depression constant for the solvent.

For water:

$$K_f = 1.86 \, \frac{\text{°C kg solvent}}{\text{mol solute}}$$

Calculating the freezing point of a solution involves substituting into the given equation, as the following example demonstrates.

EXAMPLE 9   Freezing Point Depression

Calculate the freezing point of a 1.7 m ethylene glycol solution.

You are given the molality of an aqueous solution and asked to find the freezing point depression. You will need the freezing point depression equation provided in this section.	GIVEN: 1.7 m solution FIND: ΔT_f
To solve this problem, simply substitute the values into the equation for freezing point depression and calculate ΔT_f.	SOLUTION $\Delta T_f = m \times K_f$ $= 1.7 \, \dfrac{\text{mol solute}}{\text{kg solvent}} \times 1.86 \, \dfrac{\text{°C kg solvent}}{\text{mol solute}}$ $= 3.2 \, \text{°C}$
The actual freezing point will be the freezing point of pure water (0.00 °C) − ΔT_f.	Freezing point = 0.00 °C − 3.2 °C $= -3.2 \, \text{°C}$

▶ SKILLBUILDER 9 | Freezing Point Depression

Calculate the freezing point of a 2.6 m sucrose solution.

▶ FOR MORE PRACTICE   Example 18; Problems 101, 102.

EVERYDAY CHEMISTRY

Antifreeze in Frogs

On the outside, wood frogs (*Rana sylvatica*) look like most other frogs. They are a few inches long and have characteristic greenish-brown skin. However, wood frogs survive cold winters in a remarkable way—they partially freeze. In the frozen state, the frog has no heartbeat, no blood circulation, no breathing, and no brain activity. Within 1 to 2 hours of thawing, however, these vital functions return, and the frog hops off to find food. How is this possible?

Most cold-blooded animals cannot survive freezing temperatures because the water within their cells freezes. When water freezes, it expands, irreversibly damaging cells. When the wood frog hibernates for the winter, however, it secretes large amounts of glucose into its blood and into the interior of its cells. When the temperature drops below freezing, extracellular bodily fluids, such as those in the abdominal cavity, freeze solid. Fluids within the frogs' cells, however, remain liquid because the high glucose concentration lowers their freezing point. In other words, the concentrated glucose solution within the cells acts as antifreeze, preventing the water within from freezing and allowing the frog to survive.

Masonjar /Shutterstock.

▲ The wood frog survives cold winters by partially freezing. The fluids in frog cells are protected by a high concentration of glucose that acts as antifreeze, lowering their freezing point so the intercellular fluids remain liquid to temperatures as low as −8 °C.

CAN YOU ANSWER THIS? *The wood frog can survive at body temperatures as low as −8.0 °C. Calculate the molality of a glucose solution ($C_6H_{12}O_6$) required to lower the freezing point of water to −8.0 °C.*

BOILING POINT ELEVATION

The boiling point of a solution containing a nonvolatile solute is higher than the boiling point of the pure solvent. In automobiles, antifreeze not only prevents the freezing of coolant within engine blocks in cold climates, but it also prevents the boiling of engine coolant in hot climates. The amount that the boiling point is raised for solutions is given by the following equation.

The boiling point elevation of a solution:

$$\Delta T_b = m \times K_b$$

where

- ΔT_b is change in temperature of the boiling point in °C (from the boiling point of the pure solvent).
- m is the molality of the solution in $\dfrac{\text{mol solute}}{\text{kg solvent}}$.
- K_b is the boiling point elevation constant for the solvent.

For water:

$$K_b = 0.512 \, \frac{\text{°C kg solvent}}{\text{mol solute}}$$

Different solvents have different values of K_b

The boiling point of solutions is calculated by substituting into the preceding equation as the following example demonstrates.

EXAMPLE 10 Boiling Point Elevation

Calculate the boiling point of a 1.7 m ethylene glycol solution.

You are given the molality of an aqueous solution and asked to find the boiling point.	**GIVEN:** 1.7 m solution **FIND:** boiling point
To solve this problem, simply substitute the values into the equation for boiling point elevation and calculate ΔT_b.	**SOLUTION** $\Delta T_b = m \times K_b$ $= 1.7 \dfrac{\text{mol solute}}{\text{kg solvent}} \times 0.512 \dfrac{\text{°C kg solvent}}{\text{mol solute}}$ $= 0.87\,°C$
The actual boiling point of the solution will be the boiling point of pure water (100.00 °C) plus ΔT_b.	Boiling point $= 100.00\,°C + 0.87\,°C$ $= 100.87\,°C$

▶**SKILLBUILDER 10 | Boiling Point Elevation**

Calculate the boiling point of a 3.5 m glucose solution.

▶**FOR MORE PRACTICE** Problems 103, 104, 105, 106.

CONCEPTUAL CHECKPOINT 6

Which solution has the highest boiling point?

(a) 0.50 M $C_{12}H_{22}O_{11}$ **(b)** 0.50 M $C_6H_{12}O_6$ **(c)** 0.50 M $C_2H_6O_2$

(d) All of these solutions will have the same boiling point.

10 Osmosis: Why Drinking Salt Water Causes Dehydration

Humans adrift at sea are surrounded by water, yet drinking that water would only accelerate their dehydration. Why? Salt water causes dehydration because of **osmosis**, the flow of solvent from a less concentrated solution to a more concentrated solution. Solutions containing a high concentration of solute draw solvent from solutions containing a lower concentration of solute. In other words, aqueous solutions with high concentrations of solute, such as seawater, are actually *thirsty solutions*— they draw water away from other, less concentrated solutions, including those in the human body (◀ Figure 9).

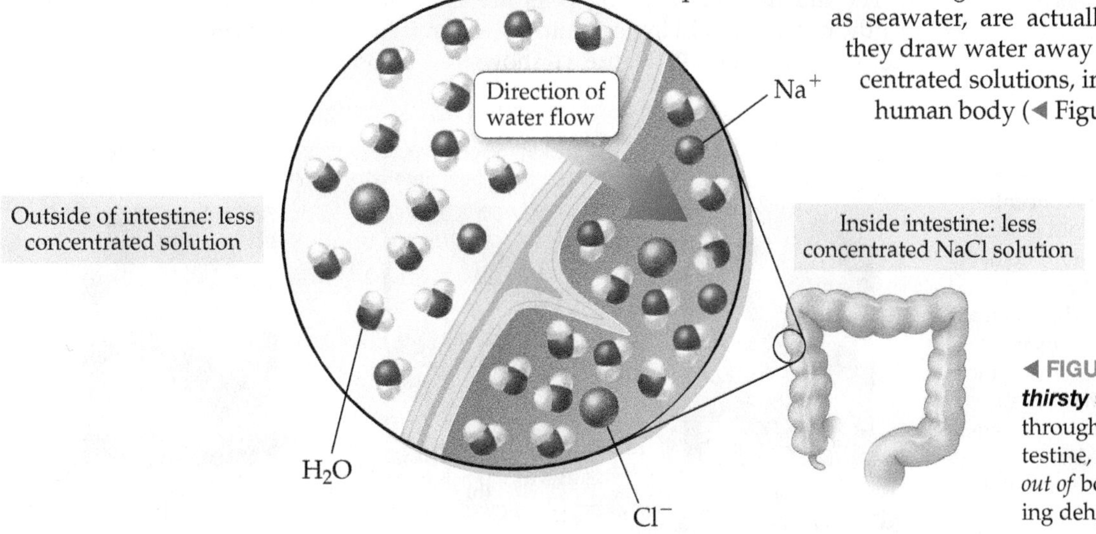

Direction of water flow

Na$^+$

Outside of intestine: less concentrated solution

Inside intestine: less concentrated NaCl solution

H_2O

Cl$^-$

◀ **FIGURE 9 Seawater is a *thirsty* solution** As it flows through the stomach and intestine, seawater draws water *out of* bodily tissues, promoting dehydration.

497

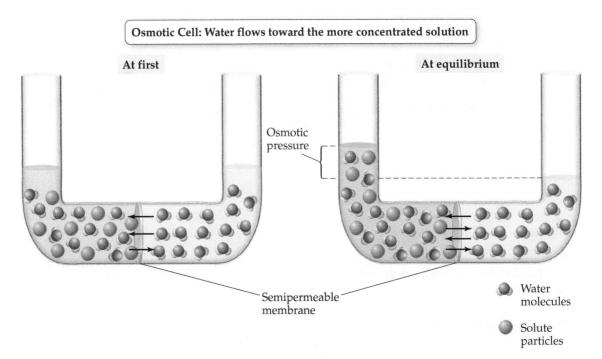

Osmotic Cell: Water flows toward the more concentrated solution

At first — At equilibrium

Osmotic pressure

Semipermeable membrane

Water molecules

Solute particles

▲ FIGURE 10 **An osmosis cell** In an osmosis cell, water flows through a semipermeable membrane from a less concentrated solution into a more concentrated solution. As a result, fluid rises in one side of the tube until the weight of the excess fluid creates enough pressure to stop the flow. This pressure is the osmotic pressure of the solution.

▲ Figure 10 shows an osmosis cell. The left side of the cell contains a concentrated saltwater solution, and the right side of the cell contains pure water. A **semipermeable membrane**—a membrane that allows some substances to pass through but not others—separates the two halves of the cell. Through osmosis, water flows from the pure-water side of the cell through the semipermeable membrane into the saltwater side. Over time, the water level on the left side of the cell rises while the water level on the right side of the cell falls. This continues until the pressure created by the weight of the water on the left side is enough to stop the osmotic flow. The pressure required to stop the osmotic flow is the **osmotic pressure** of the solution. Osmotic pressure—like freezing point depression and boiling point elevation—is a colligative property; it depends only on the concentration of the solute particles, not on the type of solute. The more concentrated the solution, the greater its osmotic pressure.

The **membranes** of living cells act as semipermeable membranes. Consequently, if you put a living cell into seawater, it loses water through osmosis and becomes dehydrated. ▼ Figure 11 shows red blood cells in solutions of various

▶ FIGURE 11 **Red blood cells in solutions of different concentration** (a) When the solute concentration of the surrounding fluid is equal to that within the cell, there is no net osmotic flow, and the red blood cell exhibits its typical shape. (b) When a cell is placed in pure water, osmotic flow of water into the cell causes it to swell up. Eventually it may burst. (c) When a cell is placed in a concentrated solution, osmosis draws water out of the cell, distorting its normal shape.

Normal red blood cell

Red blood cell in pure water: water flows into cell

Red blood cell in concentrated solution: water flows out of cell

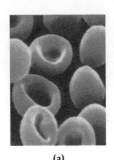

(a)

(b)

(c)

Sam Singer/Pearson Education.

CHEMISTRY AND HEALTH

Solutions in Medicine

Doctors and others working in health fields often administer solutions to patients. The osmotic pressure of these solutions is controlled for the desired effect on the patient. Solutions having osmotic pressures less than that of bodily fluids are called *hypoosmotic*. These solutions tend to pump water into cells. When a human cell is placed in a hypoosmotic solution—such as pure water—water enters the cell, sometimes causing it to burst (Figure 11b). Solutions having osmotic pressures greater than that of bodily fluids are called *hyperosmotic*. These solutions tend to take water out of cells and tissues. When a human cell is placed in a hyperosmotic solution, it typically shrivels as it loses water to the surrounding solution (Figure 11c).

Intravenous solutions—those that are administered directly into a patient's veins—must have osmotic pressure equal to that of bodily fluids. These solutions are called *isoosmotic*. When a patient is given an IV in a hospital, the majority of the fluid is usually an isoosmotic saline solution—a solution containing 0.9 g NaCl per 100 mL of solution. In medicine and in other health-related fields, solution concentrations are often reported in units that indicate the mass of the solute in a given volume of solution. Also common is *percent mass to volume*—which is the mass of the solute in grams divided by volume of the solution in milliliters times 100%. In these units, the concentration of an isoosmotic saline solution is 0.9% mass/volume.

CAN YOU ANSWER THIS? *An isoosmotic sucrose ($C_{12}H_{22}O_{11}$) solution has a concentration of 0.30 M. Calculate its concentration in percent mass to volume.*

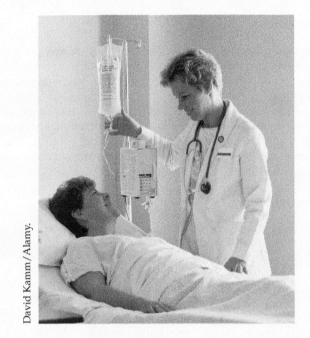

David Kamm / Alamy.

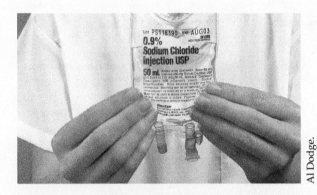

Al Dodge.

▲ Intravenous fluids consist mostly of isoosmotic saline solutions with an osmotic pressure equal to that of bodily fluids. Question: Why would it be dangerous to administer intravenous fluids that do not have an osmotic pressure comparable to that of bodily fluids?

concentrations. The cells in Figure 11a, immersed in a solution with the same solute concentration as the cell interior, have the normal red blood cell shape. The cells in Figure 11b, in pure water, are swollen. Because the solute concentration within the cells is higher than that of the surrounding fluid, osmosis has pulled water across the membrane *into* the cells. The cells in Figure 11c, in a solution more concentrated than the cell interior, are starting to shrivel as osmosis draws water *out of* the cells. Similarly, if you drink seawater, the seawater actually draws water out of your body as it passes through your stomach and intestines. All of that extra water in your intestine promotes dehydration of bodily tissues and diarrhea. Consequently, seawater should never be consumed.

CHAPTER IN REVIEW

CHEMICAL PRINCIPLES

RELEVANCE

Solutions: A solution is a homogeneous mixture with two or more components. The solvent is the majority component, and the solute is the minority component. Water is the solvent in aqueous solutions.

Solutions: Solutions are all around us—most of the fluids that we encounter every day are solutions. Common solutions include seawater (solid and liquid), soda pop (gas and liquid), alcoholic spirits such as vodka (liquid and liquid), air (gas and gas), and blood (solid, gas, and liquid).

Solid-and-Liquid Solutions: The solubility—the amount of solute that dissolves in a certain amount of solvent—of solids in liquids increases with increasing temperature. Recrystallization involves dissolving a solid into hot solvent to saturation and then allowing it to cool. As the solution cools, it becomes supersaturated and the solid crystallizes.

Solid-and-Liquid Solutions: Solutions of solids dissolved in liquids, such as seawater, coffee, and sugar water, are important both in chemistry and in everyday life. Recrystallization is used extensively in the laboratory to purify solids.

Gas-and-Liquid Solutions: The solubility of gases in liquids decreases with increasing temperature but increases with increasing pressure.

Gas-and-Liquid Solutions: The temperature and pressure dependence of gas solubility is the reason that soda pop fizzes when opened and the reason that warm soda goes flat.

Solution Concentration: Solution concentration is used to specify how much of the solute is present in a given amount of solution. Three common ways to express solution concentration are mass percent, molarity, and molality.

Solution Concentration: Solution concentration is useful in converting between amounts of solute and solution. Mass percent and molarity are the most common concentration units. Molality is used to quantify colligative properties such as freezing point depression and boiling point elevation.

$$\text{Mass percent} = \frac{\text{Mass solute}}{\text{Mass solute } + \text{ Mass solvent}} \times 100\%$$

$$\text{Molarity (M)} = \frac{\text{Moles solute}}{\text{Liters solution}}$$

Molality

$$\text{Molarity } (m) = \frac{\text{Moles solute}}{\text{Kilograms solvent}}$$

Solution Dilution: Solution dilution problems are most conveniently solved using the following equation:

$$M_1V_1 = M_2V_2$$

Solution Dilution: Since many solutions are stored in concentrated form, it is often necessary to dilute them to a desired concentration.

Freezing Point Depression and Boiling Point Elevation: A nonvolatile solute will extend the liquid temperature range of a solution relative to the pure solvent. The freezing point of a solution is lower than the freezing point of the pure solvent, and the boiling point of a solution is higher than the boiling point of the pure solvent. These relationships are quantified by the following equations.

Freezing Point Depression and Boiling Point Elevation: Salt is often added to ice in ice-cream makers and is used to melt ice on roads in frigid weather. The salt lowers the freezing point of water, allowing the cream within the ice-cream maker to freeze and the ice on icy roads to melt. Antifreeze is used in the cooling systems of cars both to lower the freezing point of the coolant in winter and to raise its boiling point in summer.

Freezing point depression:
$$\Delta T_f = m \times K_f$$
Boiling point elevation:
$$\Delta T_b = m \times K_b$$

Osmosis: Osmosis is the flow of water from a low-concentration solution to a high-concentration solution through a semipermeable membrane.

Osmosis: Osmosis is the reason drinking seawater causes dehydration. As seawater goes through the stomach and intestines, it draws water away from the body through osmosis, resulting in diarrhea and dehydration. To avoid damage to body tissues, transfused fluids must always be isoosmotic with body fluids. Most transfused fluids consist in whole or part of 0.9% mass/volume saline solution.

CHEMICAL SKILLS

EXAMPLES

Calculating Mass Percent (Section 5)

You are given the mass of the solute and the solvent and asked to find the concentration of the solution in mass percent.

To calculate mass percent concentration, divide the mass of the solute by the mass of the solution (solute and solvent) and multiply by 100%.

EXAMPLE 11 Calculating Mass Percent

Find the mass percent concentration of a solution containing 19 g of solute and 158 g of solvent.

GIVEN: 19 g solute
158 g solvent

FIND: mass percent

SOLUTION

$$\text{Mass percent} = \frac{\text{mass solute}}{\text{mass solute} + \text{mass solvent}} \times 100\%$$

$$\text{Mass percent} = \frac{19\,g}{19\,g + 158\,g} \times 100\%$$

$$\text{Mass percent} = \frac{19\,g}{177\,g} \times 100\%$$

$$= 11\%$$

Using Mass Percent in Calculations (Section 5)

SORT
You are given the volume of a potassium chloride solution and its mass percent concentration. You are asked to find the mass of potassium chloride.

STRATEGIZE
Draw a solution map. Begin with the given volume of the solution in L and convert to mL. Then use the density to find the mass of the solution. Finally, use the mass percent to get to the mass of potassium chloride.

EXAMPLE 12 Using Mass Percent in Calculations

How much KCl in grams is in 0.337 L of a 5.80 % mass percent KCl solution? (Assume that the density of the solution is 1.05 g/mL.)

GIVEN: 5.80% KCl by mass
0.337 L solution

$$d = \frac{1.05\,g}{mL}$$

FIND: g KCl

SOLUTION MAP

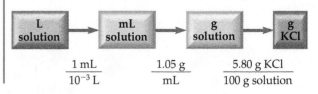

RELATIONSHIPS USED

$$\frac{5.80 \text{ g KCl}}{100 \text{ g solution}} \text{ (given mass percent, written as a fraction)}$$

$$\frac{1.05 \text{ g}}{\text{mL}} \text{ (given density)}$$

$$1 \text{ mL} = 10^{-3} \text{ L (Table 2.2)}$$

SOLVE

Follow your solution map to calculate the answer.

SOLUTION

$$0.337 \text{ L solution} \times \frac{1 \text{ mL}}{10^{-3} \text{ L}} \times \frac{1.05 \text{ g}}{\text{mL}} \times \frac{5.80 \text{ g KCl}}{100 \text{ g solution}}$$
$$= 20.5 \text{ g KCl}$$

CHECK

Check your answer. Are the units correct? Does the answer make physical sense?

The units (g KCl) are correct. The magnitude of the answer makes sense because 0.337 L is a bit more than 300 g of solution. Each 100 g of solution contains about 6 g KCl, Therefore the answer should be a bit more than 18 g.

Calculating Molarity (Section 6)

You are given the number of moles of potassium chloride and the volume of solution. You are asked to find the molarity.

EXAMPLE 13 Calculating Molarity

Calculate the molarity of a KCl solution containing 0.22 mol of KCl in 0.455 L of solution.

GIVEN: 0.22 mol KCl
0.455 L solution

FIND: molarity (M)

To calculate molarity, divide the number of moles of solute by the volume of the solution in liters.

SOLUTION

$$\text{Molarity (M)} = \frac{0.22 \text{ mol KCl}}{0.455 \text{ L solution}}$$
$$= 0.48 \text{ M}$$

Using Molarity in Calculations (Section 6)

EXAMPLE 14 Using Molarity in Calculations

How much KCl in grams is contained in 0.488 L of 1.25 M KCl solution?

GIVEN: 1.25 M KCl
0.488 L solution

FIND: g KCl

SORT

You are given the volume and molarity of a potassium chloride solution and asked to find the mass of potassium chloride contained in the solution.

STRATEGIZE

Draw a solution map beginning with liters of solution and converting to moles of solute using the molarity as a conversion factor. Then convert to grams using the molar mass.

SOLUTION MAP

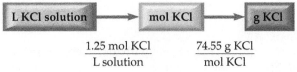

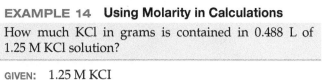

$$\frac{1.25 \text{ mol KCl}}{\text{L solution}} \text{ (given molarity, written as a fraction)}$$

$$1 \text{ mol} = 74.55 \text{ g (molar mass KCl)}$$

SOLVE

Follow your solution map to compute the answer.

SOLUTION

$$0.488 \text{ L solution} \times \frac{1.25 \text{ mol KCl}}{\text{L solution}} \times \frac{74.55 \text{ g KCl}}{\text{mol KCl}}$$

$$= 45.5 \text{ g KCl}$$

CHECK

Check your answer. Are the units correct? Does the answer make physical sense?

The units (g KCl) are correct. The magnitude of the answer makes sense because if each liter of solution contains 1.25 mol, then the given amount of solution (which is about 0.5 L) should contain a bit more than 0.5 mol, which would have a mass that is bit more than about 37 g.

Solution Dilution (Section 7)

EXAMPLE 15 Solution Dilution

How much of an 8.0 M HCl solution should be used to make 0.400 L of a 2.7 M HCl solution?

You are given the initial molarity and final molarity of a solution as well as the final volume. You are asked to find the initial volume.

GIVEN: $M_1 = 8.0 \text{ M}$

$M_2 = 2.7 \text{ M}$

$V_2 = 0.400 \text{ L}$

FIND: V_1

Most solution dilution problems will use equation $M_1V_1 = M_2V_2$.

Solve the equation for the quantity you are trying to find (in this case, V_1) and then substitute in the correct values to calculate it.

SOLUTION

$$M_1V_1 = M_2V_2$$

$$V_1 = \frac{M_2V_2}{M_1}$$

$$= \frac{2.7 \frac{\text{mol}}{\text{L}} \times 0.400 \text{ L}}{8.0 \frac{\text{mol}}{\text{L}}}$$

$$= 0.14 \text{ L}$$

Solution Stoichiometry (Section 8)

EXAMPLE 16 Solution Stoichiometry

Consider the reaction:

$$\text{HCl}(aq) + \text{NaOH}(aq) \longrightarrow \text{NaCl}(aq) + \text{H}_2\text{O}(l)$$

How much 0.113 M NaOH solution will completely neutralize 1.25 L of 0.228 M HCl solution?

SORT

You are given the volume and concentration of a hydrochloric acid solution as well as the concentration of a sodium hydroxide solution with which it reacts. You are asked to find the volume of the sodium hydroxide solution that will completely react with the hydrochloric acid.

GIVEN: 1.25 L HCl solution

0.228 M HCl

0.113 M NaOH

FIND: L NaOH solution

STRATEGIZE

Draw a solution map. Use the volume and molarity of HCl to get to mol HCl. Then use the stoichiometric coefficients to convert to mole NaOH. Finally, convert back to volume of NaOH using the molarity of NaOH.

SOLUTION MAP

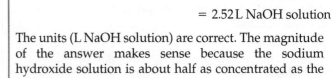

$$\frac{0.228 \text{ mol HCl}}{\text{L HCl solution}} \quad \frac{1 \text{ mol NaOH}}{1 \text{ mol HCl}} \quad \frac{1 \text{ L NaOH solution}}{0.113 \text{ mol NaOH}}$$

RELATIONSHIPS USED

$$M (\text{HCl}) = \frac{0.228 \text{ mol HCl}}{\text{L HCl solution}}$$ (given concentration of HCl solution, written as a fraction)

$$M (\text{NaOH}) = \frac{0.113 \text{ mol NaOH}}{\text{L NaOH solution}}$$ (given concentration of NaOH solution, written as a fraction)

1 mol HCl:1 mol NaOH (stoichiometric relationship between HCl and NaOH, from balanced equation)

SOLVE

Follow the solution map to calculate the answer.

SOLUTION

$$1.25 \text{ L HCl solution} \times \frac{0.228 \text{ mol HCl}}{\text{L HCl solution}}$$

$$\times \frac{1 \text{ mol NaOH}}{1 \text{ mol HCl}} \times \frac{\text{L NaOH solution}}{0.113 \text{ mol NaOH}}$$

$$= 2.52 \text{ L NaOH solution}$$

CHECK

Check your answer. Are the units correct? Does the answer make physical sense?

The units (L NaOH solution) are correct. The magnitude of the answer makes sense because the sodium hydroxide solution is about half as concentrated as the hydrochloric acid. Since the reaction stoichiometry is 1:1, the volume of the sodium hydroxide solution should therefore be about twice the volume of the hydrochloric acid.

Calculating Molality (Section 9)

You are given the number of moles of sucrose and the mass of water into which it is dissolved. You are asked to find the molality of the resulting solution.

EXAMPLE 17 Calculating Molality

Calculate the molality of a solution containing 0.183 mol of sucrose dissolved in 1.10 kg of water.

GIVEN: 0.183 mol of sucrose
1.10 kg H_2O

FIND: molality (*m*)

SOLUTION

Substitute the correct values into the definition of molality and calculate the answer. If any of the quantities are not in the correct units, convert them into the correct units before substituting into the equation.

$$\text{Molality} (m) = \frac{\text{Moles solute}}{\text{Kilograms solvent}}$$

$$\text{Molality} (m) = \frac{0.183 \text{ mol sucrose}}{1.10 \text{ kg } H_2O}$$

$$= 0.166 \ m$$

Freezing Point Depression and Boiling Point Elevation (Section 9)

You are given the molality of the solution and asked to find its freezing point.

To find ΔT_f or ΔT_b, simply substitute the values into the equation and calculate the answer.

The freezing point will be the freezing point of pure water $(0.00\,°\text{C}) - \Delta T_f$.

EXAMPLE 18   Freezing Point Depression and Boiling Point Elevation

Calculate the freezing point of a 2.5 m aqueous sucrose solution.

GIVEN: 2.5 m solution

FIND: ΔT_f

SOLUTION

$$\Delta T_f = m \times K_f$$

$$= 2.5\,\frac{\text{mol solute}}{\text{kg solvent}} \times 1.86\,\frac{°\text{C kg solvent}}{\text{mol solute}}$$

$$= 4.7\,°\text{C}$$

$$\text{Freezing point} = 0.00\,°\text{C} - 4.7\,°\text{C}$$

$$= -4.7\,°\text{C}$$

KEY TERMS

boiling point elevation **[Section 9]**
colligative properties **[Section 9]**
concentrated solution **[Section 5]**
dilute solution **[Section 5]**
electrolyte solution **[Section 3]**

freezing point depression **[Section 9]**
Henry's law **[Section 4]**
mass percent **[Section 5]**
molality (m) **[Section 9]**
molarity (M) **[Section 6]**
nonelectrolyte solution **[Section 3]**
osmosis **[Section 10]**

osmotic pressure **[Section 10]**
recrystallization **[Section 3]**
saturated solution **[Section 3]**
semipermeable membrane **[Section 10]**
solubility **[Section 3]**
solute **[Section 2]**
solution **[Section 2]**

solvent **[Section 2]**
stock solution **[Section 7]**
supersaturated solution **[Section 3]**
unsaturated solution **[Section 3]**

EXERCISES

QUESTIONS

1. What is a solution? List some examples.
2. What is an aqueous solution?
3. In a solution, what is the solvent? What is the solute? List some examples.
4. Explain what "like dissolves like" means.
5. What is solubility?
6. Describe what happens when additional solute is added to:
   (a) a saturated solution
   (b) an unsaturated solution
   (c) a supersaturated solution
7. Explain the difference between a strong electrolyte solution and a nonelectrolyte solution. What kinds of solutes form strong electrolyte solutions?
8. How does gas solubility depend on temperature?
9. Explain recrystallization.
10. How is rock candy made?
11. When you heat water on a stove, bubbles form on the bottom of the pot *before* the water boils. What are these bubbles? Why do they form?

12. Explain why warm soda pop goes flat faster than cold soda pop.
13. How does gas solubility depend on pressure? How does this relationship explain why a can of soda pop fizzes when opened.
14. What is the difference between a dilute solution and a concentrated solution?
15. Define the concentration units mass percent and molarity.
16. What is a stock solution?
17. How does the presence of a nonvolatile solute affect the boiling point and melting point of a solution relative to the boiling point and melting point of the pure solvent?
18. What are colligative properties?
19. Define molality.
20. What is osmosis?

21. Two shipwreck survivors were rescued from a life raft. One had drunk seawater while the other had not. The one who had drunk the seawater was more severely dehydrated than the one who did not. Explain.

22. Why are intravenous fluids always isoosmotic saline solutions? What would happen if pure water were administered intravenously?

PROBLEMS

SOLUTIONS

23. Determine whether or not each mixture is a solution.
    (a) sand and water mixture
    (b) oil and water mixture
    (c) salt and water mixture
    (d) sterling silver cup

24. Determine whether or not each mixture is a solution.
    (a) air
    (b) carbon dioxide and water mixture
    (c) a blueberry muffin
    (d) a brass buckle

25. Identify the solute and solvent in each solution.
    (a) salt water
    (b) sugar water
    (c) soda water

26. Identify the solute and solvent in each solution.
    (a) 80-proof vodka (40% ethyl alcohol)
    (b) oxygenated water
    (c) antifreeze (ethylene glycol and water)

27. Pick an appropriate solvent from Table 2 to dissolve:
    (a) motor oil (nonpolar)
    (b) sugar (polar)
    (c) lard (nonpolar)
    (d) potassium chloride (ionic)

28. Pick an appropriate solvent from Table 2 to dissolve:
    (a) glucose (polar)
    (b) salt (ionic)
    (c) vegetable oil (nonpolar)
    (d) sodium nitrate (ionic)

SOLIDS DISSOLVED IN WATER

29. What are the dissolved particles in a solution containing an ionic solute? What is the name for this kind of solution?

30. What are the dissolved particles in a solution containing a molecular solute? What is the name for this kind of solution?

31. A solution contains 35 g of NaCl per 100 g of water at 25 °C. Is the solution unsaturated, saturated, or supersaturated? (See Figure 4.)

32. A solution contains 28 g of KNO_3 per 100 g of water at 25 °C. Is the solution unsaturated, saturated, or supersaturated? (See Figure 4.)

33. A KNO_3 solution containing 45 g of KNO_3 per 100 g of water is cooled from 40 °C to 0 °C. What happens during cooling? (See Figure 4.)

34. A KCl solution containing 42 g of KCl per 100 g of water is cooled from 60 °C to 0 °C. What happens during cooling? (See Figure 4.)

35. Refer to Figure 4 to determine whether each of the given amounts of solid will completely dissolve in the given amount of water at the indicated temperature.
    (a) 30.0 g $KClO_3$ in 85.0 g of water at 35 °C
    (b) 65.0 g $NaNO_3$ in 125 g of water at 15 °C
    (c) 32.0 g KCl in 70.0 g of water at 82 °C

36. Refer to Figure 4 to determine whether each of the given amounts of solid will completely dissolve in the given amount of water at the indicated temperature.
    (a) 45.0 g $CaCl_2$ in 105 g of water at 5 °C
    (b) 15.0 g $KClO_3$ in 115 g of water at 25 °C
    (c) 50.0 g $Pb(NO_3)_2$ in 95.0 g of water at 10 °C

GASES DISSOLVED IN WATER

37. Some laboratory procedures involving oxygen-sensitive reactants or products call for using preboiled (and then cooled) water. Explain why this is so.

38. A person preparing a fish tank uses preboiled (and then cooled) water to fill it. When the fish is put into the tank, it dies. Explain.

39. Scuba divers breathing air at increased pressure can suffer from nitrogen narcosis—a condition resembling drunkenness—when the partial pressure of nitrogen exceeds about 4 atm. What property of gas/water solutions causes this to happen? How could the diver reverse this effect?

40. Scuba divers breathing air at increased pressure can suffer from oxygen toxicity—too much oxygen in the bloodstream—when the partial pressure of oxygen exceeds about 1.4 atm. What happens to the amount of oxygen in a diver's bloodstream when he or she breathes oxygen at elevated pressures? How can this be reversed?

MASS PERCENT

41. Calculate the concentration of each solution in mass percent.

(a) 41.2 g $C_{12}H_{22}O_{11}$ in 498 g H_2O

(b) 178 mg $C_6H_{12}O_6$ in 4.91 g H_2O

(c) 7.55 g NaCl in 155 g H_2O

42. Calculate the concentration of each solution in mass percent.

(a) 132 g KCl in 598 g H_2O

(b) 22.3 mg KNO_3 in 2.84 g H_2O

(c) 8.72 g C_2H_6O in 76.1 g H_2O

43. A soft drink contains 42 g of sugar in 311 g of H_2O. What is the concentration of sugar in the soft drink in mass percent?

44. A soft drink contains 32 mg of sodium in 309 g of H_2O. What is the concentration of sodium in the soft drink in mass percent?

45. Complete the table:

Mass Solute	Mass Solvent	Mass Solution	Mass Percent
15.5 g	238.1 g	———	———
22.8 g	———	———	12.0%
———	183.3 g	212.1 g	———
———	315.2 g	———	15.3%

46. Complete the table:

Mass Solute	Mass Solvent	Mass Solution	Mass Percent
2.55 g	25.0 g	———	———
———	45.8 g	———	3.8%
1.38 g	———	27.2 g	———
23.7 g	———	———	5.8%

47. Ocean water contains 3.5% NaCl by mass. How much salt can be obtained from 254 g of seawater?

48. A saline solution contains 1.1% NaCl by mass. How much NaCl is present in 96.3 g of this solution?

49. Determine the amount of sucrose in each solution.

(a) 48 g of a solution containing 3.7% sucrose by mass

(b) 103 mg of a solution containing 10.2% sucrose by mass

(c) 3.2 kg of a solution containing 14.3% sucrose by mass

50. Determine the amount of potassium chloride in each solution.

(a) 19.7 g of a solution containing 1.08% KCl by mass

(b) 23.2 kg of a solution containing 18.7% KCl by mass

(c) 38 mg of a solution containing 12% KCl by mass

51. Determine the mass (in g) of each NaCl solution that contains 1.5 g of NaCl.

(a) 0.058% NaCl by mass

(b) 1.46% NaCl by mass

(c) 8.44% NaCl by mass

52. Determine the mass (in g) of each sucrose solution that contains 12 g of sucrose.

(a) 4.1% sucrose by mass

(b) 3.2% sucrose by mass

(c) 12.5% sucrose by mass

53. $AgNO_3$ solutions are often used to plate silver onto other metals. What is the maximum amount of silver in grams that can be plated out of 4.8 L of an $AgNO_3$ solution containing 3.4% Ag by mass? (Assume that the density of the solution is 1.01 g/mL.)

54. A dioxin-contaminated water source contains 0.085% dioxin by mass. How much dioxin is present in 2.5 L of this water? (Assume that the density of the solution is 1.01 g/mL.)

55. Ocean water contains 3.5% NaCl by mass. What mass of ocean water in grams contains 45.8 g of NaCl?

56. A hard water sample contains 0.0085% Ca by mass (in the form of Ca^{2+} ions). What mass of water in grams contains 1.2 g of Ca? (1.2 g of Ca is the recommended daily allowance of calcium for 19- to 24-year-olds.)

57. Lead is a toxic metal that affects the central nervous system. A Pb-contaminated water sample contains 0.0011% Pb by mass. What volume of the water in milliliters contains 115 mg of Pb? (Assume that the density of the solution is 1.0 g/mL.)

58. Benzene is a carcinogenic (cancer-causing) compound. A benzene-contaminated water sample contains 0.000037% benzene by mass. What volume of the water in liters contains 175 mg of benzene? (Assume that the density of the solution is 1.0 g/mL.)

MOLARITY

59. Calculate the molarity of each solution.
    (a) 0.127 mol of sucrose in 655 mL of solution
    (b) 0.205 mol of KNO_3 in 0.875 L of solution
    (c) 1.1 mol of KCl in 2.7 L of solution

60. Calculate the molarity of each solution.
    (a) 1.54 mol of LiCl in 22.2 L of solution
    (b) 0.101 mol of $LiNO_3$ in 6.4 L of solution
    (c) 0.0323 mol of glucose in 76.2 mL of solution

61. Calculate the molarity of each solution.
    (a) 22.6 g of $C_{12}H_{22}O_{11}$ in 0.442 L of solution
    (b) 42.6 g of NaCl in 1.58 L of solution
    (c) 315 mg of $C_6H_{12}O_6$ in 58.2 mL of solution

62. Calculate the molarity of each solution.
    (a) 33.2 g of KCl in 0.895 L of solution
    (b) 61.3 g of C_2H_6O in 3.4 L of solution
    (c) 38.2 mg of KI in 112 mL of solution

63. A 205-mL sample of ocean water contains 6.8 g of NaCl. What is the molarity of the solution with respect to NaCl?

64. A 355-mL can of soda pop contains 41 g of sucrose ($C_{12}H_{22}O_{11}$). What is the molarity of the solution with respect to sucrose?

65. How many moles of NaCl are contained in each solution?
    (a) 1.5 L of a 1.2 M NaCl solution
    (b) 0.448 L of a 0.85 M NaCl solution
    (c) 144 mL of a 1.65 M NaCl solution

66. How many moles of sucrose are contained in each solution?
    (a) 3.4 L of a 0.100 M sucrose solution
    (b) 0.952 L of a 1.88 M sucrose solution
    (c) 21.5 mL of a 0.528 M sucrose solution

67. What volume of each solution contains 0.15 mol of KCl?
    (a) 0.255 M KCl
    (b) 1.8 M KCl
    (c) 0.995 M KCl

68. What volume of each solution contains 0.325 mol of NaI?
    (a) 0.152 M NaI
    (b) 0.982 M NaI
    (c) 1.76 M NaI

69. Complete the table:

Solute	Solute Mass	Mol Solute	Volume Solution	Molarity
KNO_3	22.5 g	_____	125.0 mL	_____
$NaHCO_3$	_____	_____	250.0 mL	0.100 M
$C_{12}H_{22}O_{11}$	55.38 g	_____	_____	0.150 M

70. Complete the table:

Solute	Solute Mass	Mol Solute	Volume Solution	Molarity
$MgSO_4$	0.588 g	_____	25.0 mL	_____
$NaOH$	_____	_____	100.0 mL	1.75 M
CH_3OH	12.5 g	_____	_____	0.500 M

71. Calculate the mass of NaCl in a 35-mL sample of a 1.3 M NaCl solution.

72. Calculate the mass of glucose ($C_6H_{12}O_6$) in a 105-mL sample of a 1.02 M glucose solution.

73. A chemist wants to make 2.5 L of a 0.100 M KCl solution. How much KCl in grams should the chemist use?

74. A laboratory procedure calls for making 500.0 mL of a 1.4 M KNO_3 solution. How much KNO_3 in grams is needed?

75. How many liters of a 0.500 M sucrose ($C_{12}H_{22}O_{11}$) solution contain 1.5 kg of sucrose?

76. What volume of a 0.35 M $Mg(NO_3)_2$ solution contains 87 g of $Mg(NO_3)_2$?

77. Determine the concentration of Cl^- in each aqueous solution. (Assume complete dissociation of each compound.)

(a) 0.15 M NaCl

(b) 0.15 M $CuCl_2$

(c) 0.15 M $AlCl_3$

78. Determine the concentration of NO_3^- in each aqueous solution. (Assume complete dissociation of each compound.)

(a) 0.10 M KNO_3

(b) 0.10 M $Ca(NO_3)_2$

(c) 0.10 M $Cr(NO_3)_3$

79. Determine the concentration of the cation and anion in each aqueous solution. (Assume complete dissociation of each compound.)

(a) 0.12 M Na_2SO_4

(b) 0.25 M K_2CO_3

(c) 0.11 M RbBr

80. Determine the concentration of the cation and anion in each aqueous solution. (Assume complete dissociation of each compound.)

(a) 0.20 M $SrSO_4$

(b) 0.15 M $Cr_2(SO_4)_3$

(c) 0.12 M SrI_2

SOLUTION DILUTION

81. A 122-mL sample of a 1.2 M sucrose solution is diluted to 500.0 mL. What is the molarity of the diluted solution?

82. A 3.5-L sample of a 5.8 M NaCl solution is diluted to 55 L. What is the molarity of the diluted solution?

83. Describe how you would make 2.5 L of a 0.100 M KCl solution from a 5.5 M stock KCl solution.

84. Describe how you would make 500.0 mL of a 0.200 M NaOH solution from a 15.0 M stock NaOH solution.

85. To what volume should you dilute 25 mL of a 12 M stock HCl solution to obtain a 0.500 M HCl solution?

86. To what volume should you dilute 75 mL of a 10.0 M H_2SO_4 solution to obtain a 1.75 M H_2SO_4 solution?

87. How much of a 12.0 M HNO_3 solution should you use to make 850.0 mL of a 0.250 M HNO_3 solution?

88. How much of a 5.0 M sucrose solution should you use to make 85.0 mL of a 0.040 M solution?

SOLUTION STOICHIOMETRY

89. Determine the volume of 0.150 M NaOH solution required to neutralize each sample of hydrochloric acid. The neutralization reaction is:

$$NaOH(aq) + HCl(aq) \longrightarrow H_2O(l) + NaCl(aq)$$

(a) 25 mL of a 0.150 M HCl solution

(b) 55 mL of a 0.055 M HCl solution

(c) 175 mL of a 0.885 M HCl solution

90. Determine the volume of 0.225 M KOH solution required to neutralize each sample of sulfuric acid. The neutralization reaction is:

$$H_2SO_4(aq) + 2\,KOH(aq) \longrightarrow$$
$$K_2SO_4(aq) + 2\,H_2O(l)$$

(a) 45 mL of 0.225 M H_2SO_4

(b) 185 mL of 0.125 M H_2SO_4

(c) 75 mL of 0.100 M H_2SO_4

91. Consider the reaction:

$$2\,K_3PO_4(aq) + 3\,NiCl_2(aq) \longrightarrow$$
$$Ni_3(PO_4)_2(s) + 6\,KCl(aq)$$

What volume of 0.225 M K_3PO_4 solution is necessary to completely react with 134 mL of 0.0112 M $NiCl_2$?

92. Consider the reaction:

$$K_2S(aq) + Co(NO_3)_2(aq) \longrightarrow 2\,KNO_3(aq) + CoS(s)$$

What volume of 0.225 M K_2S solution is required to completely react with 175 mL of 0.115 M $Co(NO_3)_2$?

93. A 10.0-mL sample of an unknown H_3PO_4 solution requires 112 mL of 0.100 M KOH to completely react with the H_3PO_4. What was the concentration of the unknown H_3PO_4 solution?

$$H_3PO_4(aq) + 3\,KOH(aq) \longrightarrow 3\,H_2O(l) + K_3PO_4(aq)$$

94. A 25.0-mL sample of an unknown $HClO_4$ solution requires 45.3 mL of 0.101 M NaOH for complete neutralization. What was the concentration of the unknown $HClO_4$ solution? The neutralization reaction is:

$$HClO_4(aq) + NaOH(aq) \longrightarrow H_2O(l) + NaClO_4(aq)$$

95. What is the minimum amount of 6.0 M H_2SO_4 necessary to produce 15.0 g of $H_2(g)$ according to the reaction:

$$2\,Al(s) + 3\,H_2SO_4(aq) \longrightarrow Al_2(SO_4)_3(aq) + 3\,H_2(g)$$

96. What is the molarity of $ZnCl_2(aq)$ that forms when 15.0 g of zinc completely reacts with $CuCl_2(aq)$ according to the following reaction? (Assume a final volume of 175 mL.)

$$Zn(s) + CuCl_2(aq) \longrightarrow ZnCl_2 + Cu(s)$$

MOLALITY, FREEZING POINT DEPRESSION, AND BOILING POINT ELEVATION

97. Calculate the molality of each solution.

(a) 0.25 mol solute; 0.250 kg solvent

(b) 0.882 mol solute; 0.225 kg solvent

(c) 0.012 mol solute; 23.1 g solvent

98. Calculate the molality of each solution.

(a) 0.455 mol solute; 1.97 kg solvent

(b) 0.559 mol solute; 1.44 kg solvent

(c) 0.119 mol solute; 488 g solvent

99. Calculate the molality of a solution containing 12.5 g of ethylene glycol ($C_2H_6O_2$) dissolved in 135 g of water.

100. Calculate the molality of a solution containing 257 g glucose ($C_6H_{12}O_6$) dissolved in 1.62 L of water. (Assume a density of 1.00 g/mL for water.)

101. Calculate the freezing point of a water solution at each concentration.

(a) 0.85 m

(b) 1.45 m

(c) 4.8 m

(d) 2.35 m

102. Calculate the freezing point of a water solution at each concentration.

(a) 0.100 m

(b) 0.469 m

(c) 1.44 m

(d) 5.89 m

103. Calculate the boiling point of a water solution at each concentration.

(a) 0.118 m

(b) 1.94 m

(c) 3.88 m

(d) 2.16 m

104. Calculate the boiling point of a water solution at each concentration.

(a) 0.225 m

(b) 2.58 m

(c) 4.33 m

(d) 6.77 m

105. A glucose solution contains 55.8 g of glucose ($C_6H_{12}O_6$) in 455 g of water. Calculate the freezing point and boiling point of the solution. (Assume a density of 1.00 g/mL for water.)

106. An ethylene glycol solution contains 21.2 g of ethylene glycol ($C_2H_6O_2$) in 85.4 mL of water. Calculate the freezing point and boiling point of the solution. (Assume a density of 1.00 g/mL for water.)

CUMULATIVE PROBLEMS

107. An NaCl solution is made using 133 g of NaCl and diluting to a total solution volume of 1.00 L. Calculate the molarity and mass percent of the solution. (Assume a density of 1.08 g/mL for the solution.)

108. A KNO$_3$ solution is made using 88.4 g of KNO$_3$ and diluting to a total solution volume of 1.50 L. Calculate the molarity and mass percent of the solution. (Assume a density of 1.05 g/mL for the solution.)

109. A 125-mL sample of an 8.5 M NaCl solution is diluted to 2.5 L. What volume of the diluted solution contains 10.8 g of NaCl?

110. A 45.8-mL sample of a 5.8 M KNO$_3$ solution is diluted to 1.00 L. What volume of the diluted solution contains 15.0 g of KNO$_3$?

111. To what final volume should you dilute 50.0 mL of a 5.00 M KI solution so that 25.0 mL of the diluted solution contains 3.25 g of KI?

112. To what volume should you dilute 125 mL of an 8.00 M CuCl$_2$ solution so that 50.0 mL of the diluted solution contains 5.9 g CuCl$_2$?

113. What is the molarity of an aqueous solution that is 5.88% NaCl by mass? (Assume a density of 1.02 g/mL for the solution.)

114. What is the molarity of an aqueous solution that is 6.75% glucose ($C_6H_{12}O_6$) by mass? (Assume a density of 1.03 g/mL for the solution.)

115. Consider the reaction:

$2\,Al(s) + 3\,H_2SO_4(aq) \longrightarrow Al_2(SO_4)_3(aq) + 3\,H_2(g)$

What minimum volume of 4.0 M H$_2$SO$_4$ is required to produce 15.0 L of H$_2$ at STP?

116. Consider the reaction:

$Mg(s) + 2\,HCl(aq) \longrightarrow MgCl_2(aq) + H_2(g)$

What minimum amount of 1.85 M HCl is necessary to produce 28.5 L of H$_2$ at STP?

117. How much of a 1.25 M sodium chloride solution in milliliters is required to completely precipitate all of the silver in 25.0 mL of a 0.45 M silver nitrate solution?

118. How much of a 1.50 M sodium sulfate solution in milliliters is required to completely precipitate all of the barium in 150.0 mL of a 0.250 M barium nitrate solution?

119. Nitric acid is usually purchased in concentrated form with a 70.3% HNO$_3$ concentration by mass and a density of 1.41 g/mL. How much of the concentrated stock solution in milliliters should you use to make 2.5 L of 0.500 M HNO$_3$?

120. Hydrochloric acid is usually purchased in concentrated form with a 37.0% HCl concentration by mass and a density of 1.20 g/mL. How much of the concentrated stock solution in milliliters should you use to make 2.5 L of 0.500 M HCl?

121. An ethylene glycol solution is made using 58.5 g of ethylene glycol ($C_2H_6O_2$) and diluting to a total volume of 500.0 mL. Calculate the freezing point and boiling point of the solution. (Assume a density of 1.09 g/mL for the solution.)

122. A sucrose solution is made using 144 g of sucrose ($C_{12}H_{22}O_{11}$) and diluting to a total volume of 1.00 L. Calculate the freezing point and boiling point of the solution. (Assume a density of 1.06 g/mL for the final solution.)

123. A 250.0-mL sample of a 5.00 M glucose ($C_6H_{12}O_6$) solution is diluted to 1.40 L. What are the freezing and boiling points of the final solution? (Assume a density of 1.06 g/mL for the final solution.)

124. A 135-mL sample of a 10.0 M ethylene glycol ($C_2H_6O_2$) solution is diluted to 1.50 L. What are the freezing and boiling points of the final solution? (Assume a density of 1.05 g/mL for the final solution.)

125. An aqueous solution containing 17.5 g of an unknown molecular (nonelectrolyte) compound in 100.0 g of water has a freezing point of −1.8 °C. Calculate the molar mass of the unknown compound.

126. An aqueous solution containing 35.9 g of an unknown molecular (nonelectrolyte) compound in 150.0 g of water has a freezing point of −1.3 °C. Calculate the molar mass of the unknown compound.

127. What is the boiling point of an aqueous solution that freezes at −6.7 °C?

128. What is the freezing point of an aqueous solution that boils at 102.1 °C?

129. A 125-g sample contains only glucose ($C_6H_{12}O_6$) and sucrose ($C_{12}H_{22}O_{11}$). When the sample is added to 0.500 kg of pure water, the resulting solution has a freezing point of −1.75 °C. What were the masses of glucose and sucrose in the original sample?

130. A 13.03-g sample contains only ethylene glycol ($C_2H_6O_2$) and propylene glycol ($C_3H_8O_2$). When the sample is added to 100.0 g of pure water, the resulting solution has a freezing point of −3.50 °C. What was the percent composition of ethylene glycol and propylene glycol in the original sample?

HIGHLIGHT PROBLEMS

131. Consider the molecular views of osmosis cells. For each cell, determine the direction of water flow.

(a)

(c)

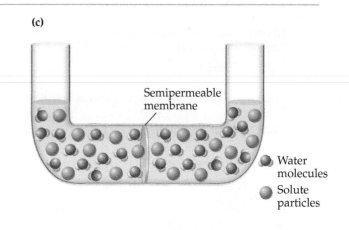

(b)

132. What is wrong with this molecular view of a sodium chloride solution? What would make the picture correct?

133. The Safe Drinking Water Act (SDWA) sets a limit for mercury—a toxin to the central nervous system—at 0.002 mg/L. Water suppliers must periodically test their water to ensure that mercury levels do not exceed 0.002 mg/L. Suppose water became contaminated with mercury at twice the legal limit (0.004 mg/L). How much of this water would have to be consumed to ingest 0.100 g of mercury?

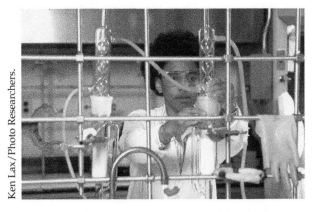

Ken Lax/Photo Researchers.

134. Water softeners often replace calcium ions in hard water with sodium ions. Since sodium compounds are soluble, the presence of sodium ions in water does not result in the white, scaly residues caused by calcium ions. However, calcium is more beneficial to human health than sodium. Calcium is a necessary part of the human diet, while high levels of sodium intake are linked to increases in blood pressure. The Food and Drug Administration (FDA) recommends that adults ingest less than 2.4 g of sodium per day. How many liters of softened water, containing a sodium concentration of 0.050% sodium by mass, have to be consumed to exceed the FDA recommendation? (Assume a density of 1.0 g/mL for water.)

◄ Drinking water must be tested for the presence of various pollutants, including mercury compounds that can damage the nervous system.

►ANSWERS TO SKILLBUILDER EXCERISES

Skillbuilder 1	2.67%	**Skillbuilder 7**	16.4 mL
Skillbuilder 2	42.5 g sucrose	**Skillbuilder Plus 1**	0.308 M
Skillbuilder 3	0.263 M	**Skillbuilder 8**	0.443 m
Skillbuilder 4	3.33 L	**Skillbuilder 9**	−4.8 °C
Skillbuilder 5	0.75 M Ca^{2+} and 1.5 M Cl^-	**Skillbuilder 10**	101.8 °C
Skillbuilder 6	0.12 L		

►ANSWERS TO CONCEPTUAL CHECKPOINTS

1 (a) CH_3Cl and H_2S are both polar compounds, and KF is ionic. All three would therefore interact more strongly with water molecules (which are polar) than CCl_4, which is nonpolar.

2 (b) Some potassium chloride precipitates out of solution. The solubility of most solids decreases with decreasing temperature. However, the solubility of gases increases with decreasing temperature. Therefore, the nitrogen becomes more soluble and will not bubble out of solution.

3 (c) The solution is 0.30 M in K^+ because the compound K_2SO_4 forms two moles of K^+ in solution for each mole of K_2SO_4 that dissolves.

4 (a) The mass of a solution is equal to the mass of the solute plus the mass of the solvent. Although the solute seems to disappear, it does not, and its mass becomes part of the mass of the solution, in accordance with the law of conservation of mass.

5 (a) A 2.0 m solution would be made by adding 2 mol of solute to 1 kg of solvent. 1 kg of water has a volume of 1 L, but because of the dissolved solute, the final solution would have a volume of slightly *more than* 1 L. A 2.0 M solution, by contrast, would consist of 2 mol of solute in a solution of *exactly* 1 L. Therefore, a 2 M aqueous solution would be slightly more concentrated than a 2 m solution.

6 (d) Since boiling point elevation depends only on the *concentration* of the dissolved particles, and not on the *kind* of dissolved particles, all of these solutions have the same boiling point.

ANSWERS TO ODD-NUMBERED EXERCISES

QUESTIONS

1. A solution is a homogeneous mixture of two or more substances. Some examples are air, seawater, soda water, and brass.

3. In a solution, the solvent is the majority component of the mixture, and the solute is the minority component. For example, in a seawater solution, the water is the solvent, and the salt content is the solute.

5. Solubility is the amount of the compound, usually in grams, that will dissolve in a specified amount of solvent.

7. In solutions with solids, soluble ionic solids form strong electrolyte solutions, while soluble molecular solids form nonelectrolyte solutions. Strong electrolyte solutions are solutions containing solutes that dissociate into ions, for example, $BaCl_2$ and $NaOH$.

9. Recrystallization is a common way to purify a solid. In recrystallization, enough solid is put into high-temperature water until a saturated solution is created. Then the solution cools slowly, and crystals result from the solution. The crystalline structure tends to reject impurities, resulting in a purer solid.

11. The bubbles formed on the bottom of a pot of heated water (before boiling) are dissolved air coming out of the solution. These gases come out of solution because the solubility of the dissolved nitrogen and oxygen decreases as the temperature of the water rises.

13. The solubility of gases increases with increasing pressure. When a soda can is opened, the pressure is lowered, decreasing the solubility of carbon dioxide. This causes bubbles of carbon dioxide to come out of the solution.

15. Mass percent is the number of grams of solute per 100 grams of solution. Molarity is defined as the number of moles of solute per liter of solution.

17. The boiling point of a solution containing a nonvolatile solute is higher than the boiling point of the pure solvent. The melting point of the solution, however, is lower.

19. Molality is a common unit of concentration of a solution expressed as number of moles of solute per kilogram of solvent.

21. Water tends to move from lower concentrations to higher concentrations, and when the salt water is being passed through the human body, the salt content draws the water out of the body, causing dehydration.

PROBLEMS

23. c and d are solutions

25. **a.** solute: salt, solvent: water

 b. solute: sugar, solvent: water

 c. solute: CO_2, solvent: water

27. **a.** hexane   **b.** water

 c. ethyl ether   **d.** water

29. ions, strong electrolyte solution

31. unsaturated

33. recrystallization

35. **a.** no

 b. yes

 c. yes

37. At room temperature water contains some dissolved oxygen gas; however, the boiling of the water will remove dissolved gases.

39. Under higher pressure, the gas (nitrogen) will be more easily dissolved in the blood. To reverse this process, the diver should ascend to relieve the pressure.

41. **a.** 7.64%

 b. 3.50%

 c. 4.64%

43. 12%

45.

Mass Solute	Mass Solvent	Mass Solution	Mass%
15.5	238.1	253.6	6.11%
22.8	167.2	190.0	12.0%
28.8	183.3	212.1	13.6%
56.9	315.2	372.1	15.3%

47. 8.9 g NaCl

49. **a.** 1.8 g   **b.** 10.5 mg

 c. 0.46 kg

51. **a.** 2.6 kg   **b.** 1.0×10^2 g

 c. 18 g

53. 1.6×10^2 g

55. 1.3×10^3 g

57. 11 L

59. **a.** 0.194 M   **b.** 0.234 M

 c. 0.41 M

61. **a.** 0.149 M   **b.** 0.461 M

 c. 3.00×10^{-2} M

63. 0.57 M

65. **a.** 1.8 mol   **b.** 0.38 mol

 c. 0.238 mol

67. **a.** 0.59 L   **b.** 0.083 L

 c. 0.15 L

69.

Solute	Mass Solute	Mol Solute	Volume Solution	Molarity
KNO_3	22.5 g	<u>0.223</u>	125 mL	<u>1.78 M</u>
$NaHCO_3$	<u>2.10 g</u>	<u>0.0250</u>	250.0 mL	0.100 M
$C_{12}H_{22}O_{11}$	55.38 g	<u>0.162</u>	<u>1.08 L</u>	0.150 M

71. 2.7 g

73. 19 g

75. 8.8 L

77. **a.** 0.15 M **b.** 0.30 M
 c. 0.45 M

79. **a.** 0.24 M Na^+, 0.12 M SO_4^{2-}
 b. 0.50 M K^+, 0.25 M CO_3^{2-}
 c. 0.11 M Rb^+, 0.11 M Br^-

81. 0.29 M

83. Dilute 0.045 L of the stock solution to 2.5 L.

85. 6.0×10^2 mL

87. 17.7 mL

89. **a.** 0.025 L **b.** 0.020 L
 c. 1.03 L

91. 4.45 mL

93. 0.373 M

95. 1.2 L

97. **a.** 1.0 m **b.** 3.92 m
 c. 0.52 m

99. 1.49 m

101. **a.** −1.6 °C **b.** −2.70 °C
 c. −8.9 °C **d.** −4.37 °C

103. **a.** 100.060 °C **b.** 100.993 °C
 c. 101.99 °C **d.** 101.11 °C

105. −1.27 °C, 100.348 °C

107. 2.28 M, 12.3%

109. 0.43 L

111. 319 mL

113. 1.03 M

115. 0.17 L

117. 9.0 mL

119. 8.0×10^2 mL

121. −3.60 °C, 100.992 °C

123. −1.86 °C, 100.508 °C

125. 1.8×10^2 g/mol

127. 101.8 °C

129. 39.8 g glucose, 85.2 g sucrose

131. **a.** Water will flow from left to right.
 b. Water will flow from right to left.
 c. Water won't flow between the two.

133. 3×10^4 L